Reactions Under Plasma Conditions

VOLUME II

REACTIONS UNDER PLASMA CONDITIONS

EDITED BY

M. VENUGOPALAN
Western Illinois University

VOLUME II

WILEY–INTERSCIENCE

a Division of John Wiley & Sons, Inc.
New York · London · Sydney · Toronto

CHEMISTRY

Library of Congress Catalog Card Number: 78-132857

ISBN 0 471 90611 5

Printed in the United States of America

10 9 8 7 6 5 4 3 2 1

Contributors to Volume II

H. F. CALCOTE, AeroChem Research Laboratories, Inc., O. P. Box 12, Princeton, New Jersey.

W. C. GARDINER, JR., The University of Texas at Austin, Department of Chemistry, Austin, Texas.

G. V. KARACHEVTSEV, Institut Khimicheskoi Fiziki, Akademiya Nauk SSSR, Vorobjevskoje Shausse 2B, Moskwa V-334, U.S.S.R.

G. LEHNER, Institut für Plasmaphysik, 8046 Garching bei München, Germany.

W. J. MILLER, AeroChem Research Laboratories, Inc., P. O. Box 12, Princeton, New Jersey.

L. POLAK, Institut Neftekhimicheskogo Sinteza, Akademiya Nauk SSSR, Lenin Prospect 29, B-71, Moskwa, U.S.S.R.

M. M. SHAHIN, Research and Engineering Sciences Division, Xerox Corporation, Rochester, New York.

C. S. STOKES, Research Institute of Temple University, 4150 Henry Avenue, Philadelphia, Pennsylvania.

V. L. TAL'ROSE, Institut Khimicheskoi Fiziki, Akademiya Nauk SSSR, Vorobjevskoje Shausse 2B, Moskwa V-334, U.S.S.R.

M. VENUGOPALAN, Western Illinois University, Department of Chemistry, Macomb, Illinois.

F. VURSEL, Institut Neftekhimicheskogo Sinteza, Akademiya Nauk SSSR, Lenin Prospect 29, B-71, Moskwa, U.S.S.R.

Editor's Note

In the framework of cosmology, the engineering and technological utility of the plasma or ionized state of matter began with the origin of the universe. For mankind, however, it has been a comparatively recent field of study. Thanks largely to the pioneering experiments of many twentieth-century scientists, many aspects of the exotic nature of the plasma state have at long last been revealed. The study of plasmas has since developed with such amazing rapidity that there already exist several books on plasma physics. However, the interest in plasma chemistry and plasma chemical technology has developed only much more recently and only a beginning has been made in the production of chemicals using plasmas. This is evidenced by the limited number of publications that have appeared until recently in this field and by the very few books that have been published.

However, there has never been an attempt to correlate in any single book or under one title the bulk of information currently available on both the physics and chemistry of plasmas, together with the necessary theoretical and experimental background. The need for such a book is justified as the barriers between physics and chemistry are being narrowed each day, and as we face groups of scientists interested in both the chemistry and physics of the plasma state. The fundamental physical theories and properties of the plasma state, the types of reactions that can be achieved in such a medium, and the practical methods that can be applied for their investigation are of great interest to them. It is for these plasma scientists and their students that the present book on reactions under plasma conditions is designed.

This book is intended to give a survey of the reactions under plasma conditions and is presented in two volumes.

Volume 1 includes a general discussion of the plasma state of matter and the fundamental definitions and relationships pertinent to it (Chapters 1 and 2); thermodynamic properties of the equilibrium and nonequilibrium states of plasmas (Chapter 3), and transport properties of plasmas (Chapter 4);

experimental methods of plasma production, together with the necessary theoretical background (Chapters 5 and 6); and theories and practices of the various techniques useful in plasma analysis, such as spectroscopic (Chapter 7), microwave, and laser techniques (Chapter 8), the electric probe methods (Chapter 9), and ion mass-spectrometry (Chapter 10).

Volume 2 begins with an introduction to plasma chemistry (Chapter 11) and includes detailed discussions of the elementary reactions (Chapter 12) and of the principles of nonequilibrium reaction kinetics (Chapter 13) in plasmas; surveys of chemical reactions investigated in electrical discharges (Chapter 14), in plasma jets (Chapter 15), and a discussion of plasma chemical processing (Chapter 16); reviews of the recent investigations of reactions in flame plasmas (Chapter 17), in shock-wave generated plasmas (Chapter 18), and in plasmas obtained by irradiation with electromagnetic rediations and by bombardment with high-energy particles (Chapter 19); and finally, a discussion of the *nuclear* reactions in fully ionized plasmas at high temperatures (Chapter 20).

In both volumes, wherever it was found necessary, adequate descriptions of work on natural plasmas have been included, although the main emphasis has been on the studies of laboratory plasmas.

In view of the wide range of topics covered in a multi-author survey such as this book, some overlapping of the subject matter was inevitable. Although I have made every effort to minimize such overlapping of material from chapter to chapter, this could be considered an advantage in many chapters, since it even serves to widen the basis of understanding.

The book was planned in the fall of 1967, when I was on the staff of the Royal Military College of Canada, Kingston, Ontario. In fact, work on the book began early in 1968 and many of the chapters were prepared as recently as March 1969. Except for some minor additions and later revisions, these chapters were finalized in July 1969. Unfortunatley, the preparation of the remaining chapters and thus the completion of the book took a much longer time than anticipated. Therefore, some of the very latest developments may be missing from certain chapters. Nevertheless, it is hoped that the book will serve as a source of coordinated information for plasma scientists of the present and the future as well.

I am very fortunate in having scientists from many countries agree to cooperate in the preparation of the text and contribute substantially to the book. I wish to thank these contributors and, particularly those authors whose advice has been most helpful in the organization of the book. Indeed, the book in its present form owes much to the many suggestions, which I solicited and readily received, from several scientists, especially some of its contributors, Dr. H. W. Drawin, Professor L. Polak, and Dr. M. M. Shahin. To them and to those contributors who prepared their chapters within a short period, I am very much indebted.

Financial assistance from the Defence Research Board of Canada during the early stages and from the Research Council of Western Illinois University during the final stages in the preparation of the manuscript is gratefully acknowledged.

I also express my gratitude to Mrs. Debra Smith for undertaking the greater part of the secretarial work and typing of some of the manuscripts, to Mrs. R. Boucher for secretarial help rendered during preliminary work in connection with the book, to Miss Barbara Kleist for extensive help with the proof-reading and with the preparation of the author and subject indexes, and to the Wiley–Interscience staff of Dr. T. P. Hoffman for their patience and very helpful cooperation. Furthermore, I am grateful to my wife for translating one of the chapters from French into English, and for assisting with correspondence in many foreign languages.

Finally, it would be unforgivable on my part not to recognize and place on record the understanding and cooperation all the authors have received from their families and friends which, to a certain degree, have also contributed to the final publication of this book.

M. VENUGOPALAN

Macomb, Illinois
June 1970

Contents of Volume II

Reactions Under Plasma Conditions

VOLUME II

CHAPTER ELEVEN

Plasma Chemistry—An Introduction

M. VENUGOPALAN

I. INTRODUCTION

Although the nineteenth century was relatively active in plasma chemistry, using electric arcs for high-temperature solid state reactions (1), material preparation (2), and gaseous syntheses of endothermic molecules (3), it is only recently that numerous laboratories have directed a concerted effort to understanding the advantages of plasmas for chemical and nuclear reactions. This impetus was due to the realization that the early work was largely empirical in nature and was accomplished with little knowledge of the nature and temperatures of plasmas. The types of species produced and their relative abundance in plasmas are no doubt determined by the conditions that exist within the plasma. On the other hand, the increased scientific understanding of the nature of plasmas built up during this century and the development of new techniques for plasma experimentation following World War II have made advanced chemical and nuclear research with plasmas possible in a controlled fashion. The recent interest in plasma chemistry stems from the possibility of producing adequate quantities of known species in plasmas and their usefulness in studying reaction kinetics and molecular and nuclear syntheses.

The chief purpose of this introductory chapter is to call attention to the unique possibilities for studying the reactions of species which are available in plasmas and to the problems which must be resolved in plasma chemistry. Whereas a considerable amount of work in plasma chemistry involves the use of the so-called low-temperature $(T < 10^5 \,^\circ\text{K})$ plasma for molecular or chemical synthesis, high-temperature $(T > 10^7 \,^\circ\text{K})$ plasma is interesting in its own right. The latter finds application in achieving nuclear synthesis, that is, the synthesis of heavier nuclei from lighter ones. We shall therefore also be concerned in this chapter with this aspect of plasma chemistry.

II. DEFINITIONS AND PRINCIPLES

Plasma chemistry is concerned with reactions occurring in plasmas, whose properties have already been discussed in the first few chapters of this book. The title also includes reactions between plasma particles and those comprising the material constituting the containing walls of the reactor and electrodes, if any. Since ions and electrons are common species and even neutral particles have great kinetic energy in a plasma, plasma chemistry is quite different from ordinary chemistry. Atoms in highly excited states may react to give compounds which are unlikely to be formed in conventional chemical reactions.

Since plasma temperatures often lie just above those at which chemical bonds can exist, the term "plasma chemistry" may in a sense be a misnomer. This situation has led to a variety of definitions (4) such as "chemistry that utilizes the high temperature and high energies produced in plasmas in reactions at lower temperatures, or where the high rates of heat transfer available from plasmas are used to effect a chemical or physical change," "the application of the temperatures and energies which can be achieved in plasmas to chemical problems" and "the reactions which can occur best at the very high temperatures which can be most conveniently generated using thermal plasmas." Unfortunately, some of these definitions do not include under the title "plasma chemistry" a large number of chemical reactions occurring in low-pressure glow discharges in which the atoms, though active, are near room temperature, nor do they include nuclear reactions that may be achieved in high-temperature plasmas.

It has been the practice for some time to classify plasmas into three main categories: plasmas in complete thermodynamic equilibrium (CTE plasmas), plasmas in local thermodynamic equilibrium (LTE plasmas), and plasmas in nonlocal thermodynamic equilibrium (non-LTE plasmas). Most laboratory plasmas, except those used for thermonuclear fusion experiments, belong to the two latter categories. Figure 1 shows typical plasmas characterized by their densities and energies. It does not, however, show transient plasmas generated by shock waves, exploding wires, and electrical resistance heating techniques at very high pressures, nor does it indicate the regions of plasmas maintained by nuclear fragmentation. Plasmas generated by electron and photon beams, which are indicated in Fig. 1, belong to the non-LTE category.

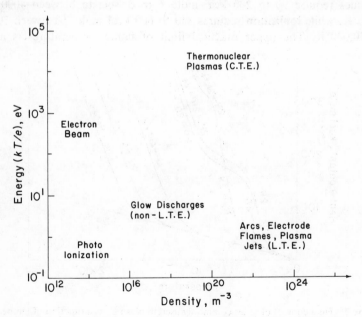

Figure 1 Typical plasmas characterized by their energies and densities.

In chemical literature it is not unusual to find LTE plasmas referred to as thermal or "hot" plasmas and non-LTE plasmas referred to·as nonthermal or "cold" plasmas. A knowledge of the degree of thermal equilibrium in plasmas is important for any serious plasma chemistry research program.

Usually, in plasma chemistry literature one distinguishes between "low"-temperature and "high"-temperature chemistry of plasmas. A distinctive point of difference often cited is the accompanying nonpropagating electromagnetic field, which may be present as the agency supplying the energy needed to maintain the plasma or as the means of providing a confining wall, such as a magnetic field. In this chapter and in the chapters which follow we consider low-temperature plasma chemistry to include the reactions in plasmas with temperatures below 10^5 °K, that is, energies less than 10 eV per particle. High-temperature plasma chemistry is then concerned with reactions in plasmas at temperatures much greater than 10^5 °K. To be more specific, nuclear reactions in plasmas are discussed under the latter topic.

Often the major reason for using a plasma will be to achieve high temperatures in a chemical reaction, not as a reactant in the reaction itself. For this reason we shall examine the relation between energy and temperature for gases commonly used in plasmas and briefly refer to plasma heat-transfer literature. The dependence of energy on temperature (at equilibrium, 1 atm) is shown in Fig. 2 for some monatomic and diatomic gases. The diatomic molecules require 90 to 200 kcal mole^{-1} to dissociate between 4000 and 10,000°K, while ionization requires 340 to 600 kcal mole^{-1} between 10,000 and 30,000°K. The upper practical limit of flame temperatures is about

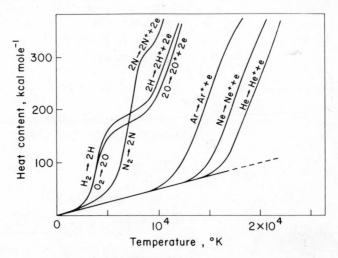

Figure 2   Heat content of gases commonly used in plasmas as a function of temperature at 1 atm pressure. [After T. B. Reed (4).]

3500°K, where molecules begin to dissociate, while the lower limit of plasma temperatures is about 10,000°K, since only at these temperatures is there enough ionization to carry the current that maintains the plasma. Most laboratory plasmas are heated electrically and, therefore, their temperatures will lie above the bottom end of the ionization curve, or above 10,000°K for the diatomic gases, but may be as low as 5000°K for some metal vapors.

Figure 2 also illustrates an important economic fact about the use of plasmas. In any process operated below 1000°K an air-fuel flame ($\sim$2000°K) or an oxygen-fuel flame ($\sim$3000°K) will have a high percentage of its energy available for the process. However, for a reaction occurring at 2500°K, for instance, only one sixth of the energy contained in an oxygen flame is available, and the rest must either be wasted or recovered in expensive heat exchangers. On the other hand, a plasma flame composed of atomic nitrogen at 10,000°K would have more than 90% of its energy available above 2500°K. This high energy efficiency may more than offset the economic advantage that combustion energy has over electrical energy; certainly this advantage will increase as electrical energy gets cheaper while fossil energy gets more expensive.

Heat transfer from plasmas depends on gaseous convection, electron transfer, and radiation. Plasma jets and electric arcs impinging on solid surfaces can produce very high heat-transfer rates. The heat-transfer intensity has been measured or estimated for a number of plasma devices, and the interested reader may find a summary of the results in the articles by Emmons (5) and Reed (4). Such information is sometimes useful to the plasma chemist, since it indicates temperature and enthalpy profiles and reaction times in plasma flows.

In principle, for both reactions within the bulk plasma and reactions of the plasma with the confining material walls, we shall be concerned with two distinct processes: (a) destruction of existing bonds, leading to creation of simpler molecules or free radicals and (b) formation of new bonds, resulting in the synthesis of bigger molecules.

Chemical bonds simply represent electron distributions between positively charged nuclei making up the cores of the atomic population of the molecule, mutually adjusted to yield maximum binding. These electron distributions will exhibit varying topologies for different molecules. Therefore, the nature of the agency supplying the energy needed to maintain the plasma will determine to some degree the efficiency with which particular bonds are broken or, conversely, the ease with which certain bonds can be created. A complication which must be accepted is that in any given type of reactor in which plasma reactions occur, there will usually be many different species which are simultaneously inducing the formation as well as destruction of bonds. Hence the net yield will be determined by the outcome of this competition.

Chemical synthesis which involves rearrangement of electron distributions to form new bonds (molecules) may frequently be achieved more efficiently in glow discharges at low pressures. However, sometimes a high yield can be obtained in spark discharges, and for particular chemical reactions the arc discharge may be most suitable. Again, the electromagnetic radiation quanttum (photon) may be the best means of achieving certain types of chemical or molecular syntheses.

Nuclear synthesis, on the other hand, involves the synthesis of heavier nuclei from lighter and simpler constituents by "fusion" reactions. The process is analogous to chemical synthesis of molecules from atoms or lighter molecules, and as in some chemical synthesis there is considerable interest in the energy release attending the reaction. However, nuclear synthesis can be achieved only at temperatures as high as 10^8–10^9 °K and therefore very high-temperature plasmas are required.

Although there is no strict isomorphism between molecular reactions and nuclear reactions, they are both describable in similar terms. The nucleus can be described in terms which very much resemble the description given an atom or molecule. That is, nuclear properties have been found to be almost completely explicable on the basis of the existence of a central field which localizes the neutrons and protons much the same as the nuclear electrical positive charge constrains and orders the motions of the surrounding electrons of atoms and molecules. Just as in atoms, in which there is a tendency to form shells of electrons, there is in the nucleus a similar tendency to form shells of both protons and neutrons. The problem of determining the kinetics of the nuclear reactions, like the chemical problem, is solved if the cross-section is found as a function of the relative velocities of the reactant particles. It must however be noted that chemical reactions correspond to energies per individual particle synthesis of the order of 1 eV and their cross-sections are of the order of 10^{-16} cm². In contrast nuclear reactions correspond to energies in the MeV range, and their cross-sections are of the order of 10^{-24} cm² only, with fusion collisions having still somewhat lower cross-sections.

III. LOW-TEMPERATURE PLASMA CHEMISTRY

A. General Observations

The particles present in a low-temperature plasma—electrons, ions, and neutrals—do not necessarily have the same temperature. A characteristic trend is that such differences become pronounced with decreasing pressure. Conversely, with high pressures the temperatures of the plasma particles tend to equilibrate.

Working temperatures ordinarily vary from near room temperatures to 10^4 °K for the heavy particles, atoms, and ions. For the electron component the temperatures range from those descriptive of the heavy particles to upwards of 10^5 °K and more. (Pressures can run from vacuum values to hundreds of atmospheres.) Therefore, equilibration will lead to a considerable lowering of the electron temperature. If electrons are the means by which a certain reaction occurs, an increase in pressure can produce a deleterious effect on the net reaction yield. In other words, the effect of increasing pressure will lead to a greater frequency of energy exchange between the electrons, ions, and neutral species, and will tend to adjust the electron temperature closer to that of the heavy particles. The degree of cooling for electrons will be far greater than the heating of the heavy particles, since there will be, in a low-temperature plasma, a great excess of low-temperature neutrals and ions compared to electrons, and since each neutral molecule and ion may be capable of absorbing much more energy for a given temperature rise than the electrons. Thus with increasing pressure there will be an associated decrease in electron energy. If the electron temperature is greatly reduced, only few electrons will have the required energy of activation to carry out the formation of the required bonds, and the yield will thereby be diminished.

Increasing the system pressure may also tend to decrease the number concentration of electrons—this trend is readily understood when the kinetics of electron generation is defined. Ionization occurs when an electron colliding inelastically with a neutral species, drives out an electron, suffering at the same time a reduction of its own energy equal to the amount given to the ejected electron. The nonradiative reverse process, which predominantly accounts for electron-ion recombination, is that in which two electrons collide in the neighborhood of an ion. The electron with the reduced energy is simultaneously captured into the bound state of the neutral molecule. The latter is a three-body process, whereas ionization is a two-body process; the rates of both processes are proportional to the product of the number densities of the particles taking part in each. If the number densities of the particles taking part in each were to be scaled up, it is clear that the recombination rate would increase more rapidly than the ionization rate—hence the observation that the number concentration of electrons tends to reduce at the higher pressures.

Unfortunately, only a partial knowledge of the somewhat complicated pattern of low-temperature plasma chemistry is accessible to us. In addition to the component of plasma electrons, other species do not maintain good thermal contact with their associates. Molecules in excited vibrational levels, metastable electronic levels, and certain ionic species can, in special circumstances, be quite indifferent to environmental changes or, at times, excessively sensitive to such disturbances.

Compared to conventional chemistry, the characteristic departure which plasma chemistry shows is oversimplified when categorized as a failure of the equilibrium. If two plasma states are superposed one on the other, the deviation from equilibrium will be altered in exceedingly complicated ways. Reaction rates do not run proportional to particle densities alone—this is simply the failure of Guldberg and Waage's mass action law. One should therefore anticipate that the concentration ratios of reactants and products in electrical discharges might differ very much from the values obtained in purely thermal reactors. This is not always the case. For example, in the oxidation of CO to CO_2 in an electrical discharge at low-current densities the concentration ratios obtained at room temperature can be shown to correspond to the ratios of reactants and products obtained in a purely thermal reactor at 3000 °K.

It has long been recognized that in electrical discharges the essential chemical nature of each type of molecule can be changed. For example, the normally inert noble gases can become quite active chemically. The reason for this is that if an electron, in colliding with a neutral, can throw a bound electron into a normally unpopulated shell, the latter can then be free to form chemical bonds with other atoms, that is, it is no longer compelled to exist in such a strongly localized bound state. It is therefore not too suprising that noble gases such as helium and argon readily oxidize in an electrical discharge. They can also be made to combine with a number of other elements and with each other. The compounds thus formed are not stable in the gaseous form and will decompose in the absence of the discharge. However, they can enter into the kinetics of some other reactions in the discharge, functioning very importantly as does a catalyst.

On the other hand, in atoms with nearly filled shells electron collisions may move electrons from deep-lying levels to populate the top vacant levels and thus, temporarily, create the appearance of chemical inertness.

All these considerations reaffirm the fact that one must examine plasma reactions individually to discover the relevant and significant principles which govern the kinetics of the process. Different modes of plasma generation alter relative populations of various plasma species in characteristically different ways, forcing one to conclude that different plasma types have the status of distinctly unique elements.

Before discussing the reactions that may occur in the bulk plasma and plasma chemical processing in general, we shall briefly refer to the reactions between plasma particles and electrode or wall materials of the plasma reactor.

B. Reactions with the Electrode and Wall Materials

1. *Cathode Interactions.* When positively charged ions moving down the electrical-field gradient collide with the cathode surface atoms, combinations of dissimilar atoms may occur. For example, a bombarding ion with adequate energy and small enough cross-section can penetrate the lattice of atoms forming the cathode solid surface and lodge internally, thus forming an alloy. Barriers of the order of 10 eV must be surmounted to push atoms from a favored position to another metastable position in the lattice (interstitial position). It is therefore difficult to effect such a change under normal arc conditions. However, adequate energies are available at the reduced pressures operating in the glow, spark, or high intensity arc to effect the alloying of cathode element and normally metastable ingredients such as helium, argon, and neon.

Instead of simple penetration, the impacting ion after penetration may drive one of the native cathode ions from its preferred position to an interstitial position. If there is sufficient energy, the penetrating ion may produce additional dislocations before coming to rest. A following ion may then succeed in dislodging some of the dislocated native ions which can subsequently splash out of the parent lattice or knock out one of the surface atoms. The new lattice alloy, formed by the latter process of "sputtering," is one in which there are dislocated native ions and normal vacancies (Frenkel defects). Foreign bombardment ions can terminate also by occupying vacant lattice positions.

If the cathode originally has an oxide layer on the surface, the bombardment of ions may cause a reduction of the oxygen in some of the oxide groups with subsequent oxidation of some of the deeper-lying lattice ions. This effect is one of broadening the oxidation zone of the indigenous ions.

Under certain conditions positive ion bombardments may cause undesirable results. For example, bombardment by hydrogen ions with energies characteristic of cosmic radiation damages photovoltaic cells by dislocating both the boron and silicon of which it is made of. (Similar damaging effects can be produced by α-particles.) On the other hand, where the cathode lattice already possesses dislocations and is subjected to ionic bombardment with energies insufficient to cause penetration, bombardment may result in annealing. In this process dislocations are made to disappear by the mechanism of vibrational shaking of the lattice through collisions taking place at the surface.

The phenomenon of impacting ions removing surface atoms of the cathode reminds one of the chemical etching process. In the latter process a reagent coming into contact with the surface of a solid removes atoms by chemical combination. For example, a radical of the reagent unites with an atom of the solid lattice. Removal of the combined group then leads to characteristic etch patterns on the surface. In ionic bombardment, however, removal of surface atoms can take place where conditions are favorable for interior atoms to be ejected toward the surface layers. Since the original energy for the removal comes from the input to the lattice by ion bombardment, the etch pattern will tend to attack the domains of relatively close-packed atoms and leave relatively undisturbed the so-called defect domains. Chemical etching, on the other hand, tends to avoid the close-packed atomic domains, concentrating on the region of defect sites. In some respects ionic bombardment is complementary to chemical etching in that the surface atoms become excited in collisions and thus more active than they ordinarily would be. Conventional chemical combination is therefore sometimes enhanced. In addition, during collisions at the surface, instead of causing appreciable interior damage to the cathode lattice, the surface can yield electrons which go into the electron constituent of the bulk plasma. In this way the reactions in the bulk plasma are influenced by the reactions going on at the cathode.

The ions coming into the surface of the cathode may react with each other as a result of the collision with the surface. The process resembles three-body ion-electron recombination. Incoming ions can also give up their excess energy to the surface lattice, neutralize charge, and combine with each other (surface recombination).

Finally, we note that occurrences at the cathode are extremely sensitive to the presence of adsorbed foreign atoms. Depending on the nature of the adsorption, plasma ions can succeed in driving these adsorption particles into the underlying lattice, thus forming an alloy of the two substances. Where the adsorbed atoms enter into a normal chemical combination with the solid lattice, the ion collisions also act to provide the needed energy of activation. The ability of the ions to liberate electrons at the cathode surface is also strongly influenced by the presence of surface adsorbed impurities. It may, however, be noted that the adsorbed atoms do not enter so readily into these phenomena because they are not normally bound intimately with the underlying lattice atoms.

2. *Anode Reactions.* Since the anode is at a potential positive with respect to all other surface in the plasma reactor and also with respect to the bulk plasma, it will attract negatively charged particles such as electrons, negatively charged free radicals, and molecules.

Electron bombardment of the anode surface can lead to disruption of the molecules normally resident there. With the flow of electrons into the anode lattice, condensation heat (work function of the electrons) is released to the anode along with other energy forms. Thus decomposition of a given compound can result both from electron bombardment and from thermal collisions with heavy particles. (The same can also be said for phenomena occurring at the cathode and in the bulk plasma.)

Usually there will be only a slight influx of heavy negative ions at the anode. Therefore the surface may be worked by the high thermal level of energy, and loosely bound atoms are disposed to volatilize and leave the parent lattice.

The use of anode electron bombardment (cathode ray furnace) to remove impurities from solids is found in extractive metallurgy. This application has already found considerable use in a special form where the cathode is made to permit continuous movement over the anode surface. The cathode traverses the anode at a speed adjusted to the depth of the material that is to be refined and to the current densities employed. In some respects the method is similar to chemical etching in that the zones likely to be attacked are those characterized as defect domains. Ordinarily the defect regions consist of cohesional bonds that are considerably weakened and therefore yield readily to thermal and electronic excitation.

The anode (and also the cathode) can function as a catalyst for reactions occuring with low yield in the bulk plasma. For example, the yield of ozone in a glow discharge is increased considerably by using aluminum electrodes. On the other hand, the anode (and cathode) can supply a contaminant to the bulk plasma which can influence the reactions occurring therein by either accelerating or retarding their rates. An interesting property of such contaminants is their ability to deactivate, that is, remove energy residing in the excited states of the various constituents of the plasma. A molecule of the same species as that activated is, in general, very inefficient for deactivation. For example, the deactivation of vibrational modes of CO_2 by CO_2 requires about 10^5 collisions whereas H_2O molecules will deactivate CO_2 with only 100 collisions. Again, H_2O molecule is much more capable of deactivating the nitrogen oxides than the latter species themselves formed by a complicated and slowly equilibrated series of reactions in air plasmas. For N_2O, the H_2O molecule is capable of deactivating the vibrational levels about a hundred times more effectively than N_2O itself. However, where the H_2O molecule possesses a large amount of energy it can also activate the vibrational modes of the aforementioned molecules.

Anode impurities can also influence the activation or deactivation of rotational levels. (The cross-sections for activation or deactivation of rotational levels are of the same magnitude as the gas-kinetic cross-sections.) For example, ordinarily the rotational temperatures excited in the OH bands in an electrical discharge far exceed the gas translational and vibrational temperature. The addition of small amounts of helium impurity nullifies this excess temperature. A somewhat similar phenomenon sometimes occurs in discharges in hydrogen.

Silicon polymerization reactions can be induced on an anode surface by interaction with incident electrons. The energies required for the reactions, analyzed as free-radical polymerization of the molecules adsorbed on the anode surface, are readily available in the fall regions of glow discharges at low pressures.

3. Wall Reactions. The walls of a plasma reactor maintained by electrical power are by no means inactive during a discharge. The concentration of ions and electrons will be high in the main discharge path but low near the walls. Therefore there will be a tendency for the ions and electrons to diffuse toward the walls. As earlier noted, both the ions and electrons will diffuse together (ambipolar diffusion). Since the electrons are usually at the higher temperature and have somewhat longer mean free paths, they will tend to lead the diffusion and make the walls negative with respect to the plasma. When the walls acquire a negative charge the ions follow and the two then tend to form a two-dimensional plasma on the wall surface. The recombination of ions and electrons is facilitated because of the restriction of freedom of motion. Since the recombination rate is much higher than the corresponding ambipolar diffusion rate out of the bulk plasma, the limiting process for the loss of ions and electrons from the plasma will be that governed by the magnitude of ambipolar diffusion.

In addition to the simultaneous diffusion of ions and electrons, there is diffusion of any ingredient which has a high concentration in the region of the electrical discharge and a low concentration in the neighborhood of the walls. For example, in the dissociation of H_2 by an electrical discharge the production of H atoms is subject to loss due to the diffusion of the H atoms toward the walls. When H atoms reach the walls they find an environment able to absorb the energy released by recombination. Hence the recombination rate will be quite rapid, particularly on cold metallic surfaces.

Since it is essential for recombination that an associated deactivation take place simultaneously, it is clear that there will be an influence on the process depending on the nature of the wall material. Experiments of various investigators have had rather limited success in providing a clear picture of just what is involved. Glass, if it is clean, does not contribute appreciably to recombination. However, if it is dirty, wall recombination does occur, often with very large rates. With any arrangement of wall materials and electrodes it is usually found that the presence of water vapor has a great effect on the rate of recombination. The direction of the effect may change, however, depending on the nature of the wall element on which the water vapor is free to absorb. In addition, the presence of water vapor in the bulk plasma also has an effect on the dissociation taking place in the regions far removed from the walls. Water has been reported as assisting the generation of the H radical, but conclusions are subject to the review of contaminants.

C. Reactions in the Bulk Plasma

As mentioned earlier, both free radicals and ions may be produced in the bulk plasma. The particular importance of free radicals is due to their intense chemical activity and the very high energy yields associated with their combination. As with the free radicals which have relatively long lifetimes, it is possible to prepare ions which exist for comparatively long times and which frequently play important roles in connection with certain chemical reactions. Table 1 lists the ions produced in a number of gases and vapors in

TABLE 1

Ions produced by electron-induced reactions in plasmas[a]

Plasma	Ions
H_2	H^+, H_2^+
He	He^+, He_2^+
O_2	O^+, O^-, O^{2+}, O_2^{2+}
N_2	N^+, N_2^+
Cl_2	Cl^-, Cl_2^-
Br_2	Br^-, Br_2^-
I_2	I^+, I^-, I_2^-
CO	C^+, O^+, O^-, CO^+
C_2H_2	$C_2H_2^+$, CH^+, C_2^+, C_2H^+
C_6H_6	$C_6H_6^+$, $C_6H_5^+$, $C_6H_4^+$, $C_6H_3^+$, $C_6H_2^+$, C_6H^+, C_6^+
	$C_5H_3^+$, $C_5H_2^+$, C_5H^+, C_5^+
	$C_4H_4^+$, $C_4H_3^+$, $C_4H_2^+$, C_4H^+, C_4^+
	$C_3H_3^+$, $C_3H_2^+$, C_3H^+, C_3^+
	$C_2H_4^+$, $C_2H_3^+$, $C_2H_2^+$, C_2H^+, C_2H^+, C_2^+
	CH_3^+, CH_2^+, CH^+, C^+
	H_2^+, H^+
	$C_6H_6^{2+}$, $C_6H_5^{2+}$, $C_6H_3^{2+}$
	C_4H^{2+}

[a] Data presented here are meant to be illustrative rather than all inclusive.

the plasma state. The higher hydrocarbons produce an extremely complicated array of ions; for example see the ions in benzene vapor subjected to a glow, corona, or spark discharge at reduced pressures. Hydrocarbon impurities in a discharge being examined for a specific reaction may therefore interfere in kinetic investigations by entering into complexes with the main component of the plasma and also in the role of an ion catalyst.

Examples of ionic reactions with various hydrocarbons are given in Table 2. Their classification and discussions are outside the scope of this chapter.

Many of the reactions referred to above have also been observed in plasmas generated by nonelectrical methods, for example combustion flame plasmas and plasmas obtained on irradiation of a gas with the electromagnetic radiation quantum (photon).

As evidence of the greatly altered chemistry, Table 3 shows some reactions of the so-called inert or noble gases.

TABLE 2
Examples of ionic reactions in Hydrocarbon plasmas

Plasma	Reaction
Methane	$CH_3^+ + CH_4 \rightarrow C_2H_3^+ + 2H_2$
Ethane	$C_2H_3^+ + C_2H_6 \rightarrow C_2H_5^+ + C_2H_4$
Ethylene	$C_2H_3^+ + C_2H_4 \rightarrow C_2H_5^+ + C_2H_2$
	$C_2H_4^+ + C_2H_4 \rightarrow C_3H_5^+ + CH_3$
Acetylene	$C_2H_2^+ + C_2H_2 \rightarrow C_4H_3^+ + H$
	$C_2H_2^+ + C_2H_2 \rightarrow C_4H_2^+ + H_2$
	$C_2^+ + C_2H_2 \rightarrow C_4H_2^+$
	$CH^+ + C_2H_2 \rightarrow C_3H_2^+ + H$
	$CH^+ + C_2H_2 \rightarrow C_3H^+ + 2H$
	$CH^+ + C_2H_2 \rightarrow C_3H_3^+$
Cyclopropane	$C_3H_6^+ + C_3H_6 \rightarrow C_3H_7 + C_3H_5$
	$C_3H_5^+ + C_3H_6 \rightarrow C_4H_7 + C_2H_4$

TABLE 3
Some reactions of Noble gases in plasma state

Plasma	Reactions
He	$He + e \rightarrow He^* + e$
	$He^* + He \rightarrow He_2^+ + e$
	$He^+ + 2He \rightarrow He_2^+ + He$
Ne—H$_2$	$e + Ne \rightarrow Ne^+ + 2e$
	$Ne^+ + H_2 \rightarrow NeH^+ + H$
Ne—He	$He + He + Ne^+ \rightarrow HeNe^+ + He$
Ar—HCl	$e + Ar \rightarrow Ar^* + e$
	$Ar^* + Ar + Ar \rightarrow Ar_2^* + Ar$
	$e + Ar \rightarrow Ar^+ + 2e$
	$Ar^+ + HCl \rightarrow ArH^+ + Cl$
	$Ar + HCl^+ \rightarrow ArH^+ + Cl$
Kr—H$_2$	$e + Kr \rightarrow Kr^+ + 2e$
	$Kr^+ + H_2 \rightarrow KrH^+ + H$

The complication of reactions given in Table 1 through 3 emphasizes again the complexity of the chemistry of low-temperature plasmas.

Investigations of elementary chemical processes in low-temperature plasmas have been the subject of extensive studies for several years. The main object of these investigations has been to obtain a set of kinetic constants which make it possible to derive equations for space and time functions of particle concentrations (6). The number of elementary reaction types encountered in plasma is great, and it is not intended to give here a full account of the present state of the field which is the subject of another chapter in this book (see Chapter 12). Broadly speaking, all elementary reactions occurring in low-temperature plasma may be classified roughly as belonging to two types. (*a*) Neutral particle reactions associated with some kind of vibrational energy transfer. These include the main part of purely chemical reactions, such as dissociation and exchange reactions. (*b*) Electronic excitation, ionization, and reactions involving electrons, ions, and excited particles. The parts played by the two types of reactions will, certainly, be different depending upon the plasma production and the nature of the medium. At present a considerable number of methods for experimental investigation of elementary processes are available. However, the information obtained is considerably less than that required for overall kinetics due both to experimental and theoretical difficulties. Consequently, sometimes determination is made of parameters that can be measured, rather than of those that need to be measured.

Nevertheless, studies of atom and free radical chemistry, which may be said to have commenced in detail with the first experiments on dissociation of the simpler molecules by electrical discharges, have proceeded at a moderate pace throughout this century. An extensive review on the subject was first prepared thirty years ago by Glockler and Lind (7). More recently several reviews (8–10) have appeared. The work of Steacie (11) treats the use of electric discharges primarily for studying organic and free radical reactions, while the reviews of Kana'an and Margrave (9) and Massey (12) summarize the use of electrical discharges for homogeneous and heterogeneous reactions. Books have been published on the much studied chemistry of atoms of nitrogen (13), oxygen (14), and hydrogen (14). Although gaseous atoms of most elements should be very reactive, in many cases there has been little work on species other than N, O, H, and C. These studies have provided us with a great number of rate constants for atomic and free radical reactions near room temperature. However, data on rate constants at higher temperatures have mainly been obtained by shock-tube studies or by an adiabatic compression method.

Although the formation of ions in flames and in gases subjected to electrical discharges or exposed to high-energy radiation has been recognized for over sixty years, studies of interactions between ions and atoms or molecules in plasmas began only with the development of special techniques for the mass spectrometer as the major tool in analyzing such reactions. In fact, the first experimental determinations of ion-molecule reaction rates were made in 1952 by Tal'rose and Lyubimova (15). This was closely followed by many others, and several papers on the topic have been published during the last two decades. In 1966 a symposium on ion-molecule reactions in the gas phase was held under the sponsorship of the American Chemical Society and the proceedings have since been published (16). Much of the interest of this symposium centered on the effects of the kinetic energy of the reacting ion on the reaction cross-section. The list of ion-molecule reactions is impressive at this time; there are easily several hundred. Detailed discussions of many ion-molecule reactions occurring in laboratory plasmas are given in later chapters.

Excited species play an important and sometimes decisive role in plasmas. The properties, kinetics, and diagnosis of plasma are to a considerable degree determined by the concentration of excited atoms, and their distribution in space and time. Direct experiments provide information on transition from the ground state only. It is the transitions between excited states that are most important for low-temperature plasma, since these determine the rate of stepwise ionization. These problems and the problems connected with radiative transfer have been discussed in Chapter 12.

Somewhat more tractable is the technology dealing with chemical syntheses in the bulk plasma. Nitric oxide, ammonia, and sulfur monoxide represent the earliest of the important achievements in molecular synthesis using plasma reactors. While not all the reactions are thoroughly understood, the overall transformations, for example

$$N_2^+ + e + O_2 \rightarrow N_2^+ O_2 + e \rightarrow 2NO$$

in the case of NO, are sufficiently clear at the present time. The multiplicity of transformations of hydrocarbons in the plasma provides a strong evidence of the potential usefulness of a plasma reactor in effecting modifications in naturally occurring chemicals to forms more suitable for specific uses. Some plasma reactions with hydrocarbons are listed in Table 4. It must be remembered that any reaction in a plasma is sensitive to the energies of the electrons, ions, and neutrals, and also to the degree of excitation of the various particles present. Therefore, variation of electrode geometry, wall geometry, heat extraction, conditions of introduction of the working medium, level of impurities, type of impurities, radiation losses, applied voltage, wave form of the voltage, current density, and pressure, all influence the type of reaction which will take place.

D. Plasma Chemical Processing

The application of low-temperature plasmas to chemical processing and studies of the kinetic and thermodynamic aspects thereof are attracting ever increasing attention (17,18). A few chemical systems have been studied in depth using thermal (LTE) plasmas. These include acetylene manufacture, nitrogen fixation, and, to a lesser extent, fluorocarbon reactions. Some studies have also been reported for a variety of inorganic materials (19). More

TABLE 4
Plasma reactions with Hydrocarbons[a]

Process	Reactions	Reactor
Hydrogenation	$C + 2H_2 \rightarrow CH_4$	Carbon arc
	$2C + 3H_2 \rightarrow C_2H_6$	Carbon arc
	$C_2H_2 + H_2 \rightarrow$ Gasoline products	hf and spark discharges
	$C_2H_2 + H_2 + Ar \rightarrow C_2H_4, C_2H_2, H_2,$ 1,3-butadiene	Shock wave reactor
Cracking	$4CH_4 + 3O_2 \rightarrow 2C_2H_2 + 6H_2O$	Arc discharge
	$C_2H_6 \rightarrow C_2H_2 + 2H_2$	Arc discharge
	Amylene $\rightarrow C, H_2, CH_4, C_2H_6, C_2H_4, C_2H_2$	Spark discharge
	Amylene $\rightarrow C_2H_2$, allylene, vinylacetylene, diacetylene, liquid olefins, paraffins	Corona discharge
	Trimethylene $\rightarrow C$, diamylene, tetraisoamylene, nonaisoamylene	Corona discharge
	$C_2H_4 + Ar \rightarrow H_2 + C_2H_2, CH_4,$ 1,3-butadiene	Shock wave reactor
	Benzene $\rightarrow C, C_2H_2, H_2$	Metal spark
	$\rightarrow$ Resins, C_2H_2, H_2	hf discharge
	$\rightarrow H_2$, liquid hydrocarbons	Carbon arc
	$\rightarrow C_2H_2, C_2H_4, C$	Metal arc
	$\rightarrow C_2H_2, C_2H_6, CH_4, C, H_2$	Explosive arc
	$\rightarrow C, H_2, CH_4, C_2H_2$	Carbon spark
	$\rightarrow C$, phenylacetylene, diphenyl anthracene, diacetylene	High pressure, high voltage arc
	$\rightarrow C_{28}H_{36}, CH_4, C_2H_4, C_{28}H_{34}, C_2H_2, C_{48}H_{46}, C_{12}H_{14}, H_2, C_{28}H_{24}$	Corona
	$\rightarrow (C_6H_6)_n, C_{24}H_{26}, (C_{24}H_{26})$ isomer, benzene polymers	Dark discharge
	$\rightarrow C, H_2, C_2$, diphenyl, diphenylene isomers	Electrodeless discharge
	$\rightarrow C_2H_2, C_2H_4, H_2$, paraffins, diphenyl, diphenylbenzene	Brush discharge
Reaction with N_2	$2CH_4 + N_2 \rightarrow 2HCN + 3H_2$	High pressure arc
	$C_2H_2 + N_2 \rightarrow 2HCN$	Arc discharge
	$2C + H_2 + N_2 \rightarrow 2HCN$	Glow discharge
	$NH_3 + CH_4 \rightarrow HCN + 3H_2$	hf discharge

[a] Reactions listed here are meant to be illustrative rather than all inclusive.

recently, there has been some renewed interest in the field of electrical discharge polymerizations (20). A realistic appraisal of the associated economic
and engineering problems in plasma chemical processing may be found for
those chemical systems studied in detail in the book edited by Baddour and
Timmins (18).

One of the main trends in the development of present-day plasma chemical
processing is an increasing use of more intense operating conditions: higher
temperatures, velocities, reduced residence times of reagents in the reaction
zone, and so on. A knowledge of the physical and chemical kinetics of
processes in plasmas forms an important part of any plasma chemical
processing program. In the temperature range (10^3–5×10^4 °K) now used in
plasma chemical processing, deviations from the classical description of
chemical processes due to the nonequilibrium and relaxation characteristics
of systems, collective effects and specific features of elementary events are
important.

1. Reaction Sequence and Apparatus. The main components of any
apparatus used in low-temperature plasma chemistry are power supplies and
feeding devices for any form of reactant materials. In plasma chemical
synthesis the apparatus also includes quenching units, since gradual cooling
of the labile intermediates present in the plasma usually does not yield the
most interesting or valuable products and may allow the system to revert to
original reactants. A general scheme of the apparatus assembly and the
functions of each unit are shown in Fig. 3. A three-stage sequence is often
followed: plasma generation, post-generator injection, quenching.

a. PLASMA GENERATION.   The first stage in the overall process involves the
generation of the plasma state.

Nonthermal low-pressure (non-LTE) plasmas are generated usually using
dc or ac discharges with electrodes, rf and microwave discharges, and modified electron beam methods. Various methods of generation have been reviewed elsewhere (9,10,14,21–24)

Thermal (LTE) plasmas are generated using a variety of high intensity
electric arcs, sometimes with added jet devices, and using induction heating of
gases in a radiofrequency field. A review by Reed (4) summarizes the various
techniques critically.

There are many commercial plasma generators that serve to couple
electric energy into the gas stream efficiently. Available temperatures in the
plasma formed are in the range 2×10^3 to 3×10^4 °K—this is, of course,
a function of the power input, composition of the inlet gas, and design of the
generator.

b. FLOW-PATTERNS.   Two usable flow-pattern options are obvious in Fig. 3—
pregenerator mixing and postgenerator injection. Different mixing patterns
adopt to different reaction systems.

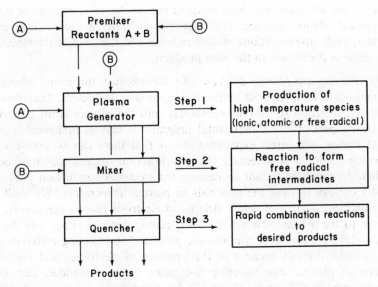

Figure 3 Apparatus assembly for plasma chemical processing, indicating the functions of each unit.

(1) *Pregenerator Mixing.* In premixing reagents upstream of the plasma generator, the problems of intermixing a cold reagent stream with a hot plasma are eliminated. Also, exposure of all reagent species to plasma temperatures is assured. Premixed feeds are not applicable, however, for systems in which heated reactants would corrode exposed generator electrodes. Neither is premixing applicable for systems wherein solid or liquid feeds would foul or short-circuit generator operation. Premixing, for some systems, may impede yield optimization at minimum power consumption, which could be achieved by only partial exposure of the reactants to the plasma arc.

(2) *Postgenerator Injection.* Figure 3 also shows this flow pattern, where the reagent stream *A* is sent to the generator, which produces a highly reactive plasma stream. The other reagent *B* is intermixed with this plasma downstream, to induce *A–B* combination reactions. Where the particular application precludes feeding any reactants through the generator, an inert gas can substitute as an enthalpy carrier. The reactant streams are then intermixed downstream with the inert gas plasma to induce high-temperature reactions.

Introduction of a cold reactant stream obviously chills the plasma. The extent of cooling is a function of the heat capacity of the reactants and the ratio of flow rates. If the mixing is achieved and sufficient enthalpy is carried from the plasma generator, high temperature can be sustained in the multi-component plasma mixture. High specific enthalpy in the mixing region supports high concentrations of free radicals and the reactive intermediates that serve as precursors to the final products.

(3) *Feeding and Mixing Devices.* To the chemist the prime interest in plasmas lies in what happens to material exposed to the plasma. Therefore the successful injection of various substances into the plasma is an important practical aspect of any experimental program. It may at first seem to be a trivial matter, but direct experience shows that there can be considerable difficulties, since it is necessary that the injection of cold materials occur gradually enough so as not to destroy the electrical conduction path, but rapidly enough to raise the materials to plasma temperature. We shall not describe these devices in detail. Briefly, in electrode plasma generators, jets normal to the plasma flow are used for feeding material either into the arc region (25) or beyond the arc into the plasma (26). Injecting materials into arcs is more difficult because of the presence of electrodes and the small volume of plasma. For injecting hot gases, hollow cathodes, and more recently porous (27) and volatile (28,29) anodes, have been used. When feeding fine powders into a plasma the powder is usually first mixed with a carrier gas. A great variety of commercial devices such as electrically shaking sieves, vibrating tubes and tracks, and fluidized bed systems are also available for feeding a variety of powders. Reed (4) describes a water-cooled probe comprising three concentric tubes for dropping powder into induction heated plasmas. The feeding of liquids has recently been accomplished by using ultrasonic atomizers (30).

(4) *Low-Pressure Discharge Flows.* In low-pressure discharge flows, such as the Wood-Bonhoeffer fast flow systems (14) used for kinetic experiments at near-room temperatures, postgenerator injection is used (as shown in Fig. 3) for studying atom-atom, atom-radical, radical-radical, and atom-, ion- or radical-molecule reactions. Besides the limitations of the system itself (31), a complicating factor in postgenerator injection is the often experienced problem of back diffusion.

c. QUENCHING.   Since gradual cooling of the labile intermediates present in the mixed plasma usually does not yield the most interesting or valuable products and may allow the system to revert to original reactants, a quenching step is necessary.

(1) *Quenching Techniques for Thermal (LTE) Plasmas.* Several techniques have been recommended for quenching at rates from 10^5 to 10^8 °K sec^{-1}: homogeneous cooling (adiabatic expansion), contact with solids or liquids, either fixed or moving, cold gas entrainment, chemical cooling, and so on.

Unfortunately, there has been no comparative study of a number of methods used in one chemical system to give an idea of relative effectiveness of these methods.

The use of adiabatic expansion was suggested by Marynowski et al. (32). The cooling is produced by expansion through a Laval nozzle, turbine blades being used to remove the excess kinetic energy of the molecules. The technique is capable of achieving quenching rates of 10^7 $^\circ$K sec^{-1} or times the order of 10^{-4} sec.

Another technique involves cooling the hot gases by contact with cold walls using probes similar to those employed in injecting material into plasmas. Plooster and Reed (33) report on the use of a probe for withdrawing and quenching the equilibrium mixture of hydrogen and hydrocarbons in a carbon tube furnace at 3000 $^\circ$K. They found that both 24 and 28 gauge tubing gave poorer acetylene quenching than 26 gauge tubing (0.025 cm id). From the flows observed in such a probe and assuming that the gas ceases to react after traversing ten probe diameters, they calculated a quenching time of $\sim 2 \times 10^{-5}$ sec or a quench rate of $\sim 10^8$ $^\circ$K sec^{-1}. Baddour and Blanchet (34) used 0.12–0.32 cm inside diameter tubes and found that quenching occurred in a few milliseconds. Timmins and Amman (35) studied analytically the quench history to be expected in a 0.13 cm diameter probe using a numerical analysis of two-dimensional heat transfer in laminar flow involving a heat transfer coefficient and taking into consideration chemical reaction during cooling of the nitrogen-oxygen system. They found the average rate of decay to be 3.5×10^7 $^\circ$K sec^{-1} during the first 100 μsec. Such probes can be made much more effective with a sonic orifice at the entry and would then give some cooling by adiabatic expansion as well as contact with cold walls. One advantage of such a probe is that it can be used to sample reaction volumes at various points after mixing to determine the effectiveness of mixing and the degree of reaction at each point. A disadvantage is that it only collects relatively small samples.

Other variations of cold wall quenching include passing the gas through larger water-cooled tubes or over cold fingers where one might expect lower quench rates owing to larger boundary layers associated with the lower veclocities. Leutner (36) reports that use of a water-cooled funnel decreased conversion of carbon vapor to C_2N_2. Freeman and Skrivan (37) studied decomposition rates of methane and ammonia in such a system and found cooling times of about 1 msec. Skrivan and von Jaskowsky (38) have established some cooling-rate correlations for heat transfer from plasma to the cold tube wall.

Quenching can also be accomplished on moving solids using fluidized beds. This has been investigated at Battelle Institute (39) for depositing solids continuously in chemical deposition. When the quench process produces solids, such an approach is required. Otherwise the solids formed would soon plug up the small diameter probes. Even in large quenching cross-sections, the conditions will change rapidly as deposits build up. Moving droplets of liquid in plasma jets have been quenched at rates greater than 10^6 °K sec^{-1} by impingment on water-cooled copper in order to stabilize the metastable intermetallic compounds (40).

A very attractive quench for industrial processes and also useful in the laboratory is a liquid spray. Anderson and Case (41) describe a water spray to quench the products in acetylene synthesis. Their kinetic analysis shows that acetylene decomposition is not severe in 1 msec, but would reach about 25% decomposition in 10 msec. Since they observe little or no decomposition, this type of quench may stop the reaction in less than 1 msec. Similar quenches are used commercially for acetylene production (25). There is no truly inert liquid for practical use, so that the quench liquid may take part in the reaction. For instance, a spray of liquid oxygen was used in production of ozone by Stokes and Streng (42). A variation of liquid quenching may be seen in submerged arcs and sparks (43,44) in liquid gases.

Goldberg and Oxley (45) fired an argon plasma jet directly into a bed of fluidized alumina. A substantial argon flow, separate from the plasma-forming flow, was required to achieve fluidization. As already described, the heat transfer to solid particles and gas which were observed to be entrained into the jet resulted in a high quenching rate.

Another technique uses the principle of cold gas entrainment. At plasma temperatures the density of the plasma gas is very low relative to that of a cold ambient-gas environment. Issuing a plasma into such an environment creates a rapid, efficient entrainment of the ambient gas, resulting in a high quenching rate with an accompanying high rate of dilution of the plasma stream by the entrained species. Grey and Jacobs (46) have evaluated the quenching rate effected by room-temperature helium entraining into an argon plasma jet.

Finally, an important factor in quenching endothermic compounds may be the chemical reaction itself. Anderson and Case (41) take this " self-quenching " or " chemical cooling " into account in their iterated calculations of methane decomposition to acetylene.

(2)   *Quenching Techniques for Nonthermal Low-Pressure Plasmas.*   Whereas it is rarely possible to isolate radicals or ions in plasmas at near atmospheric pressure by quenching, with low-pressure plasmas it is feasible to manipulate ions (47) and to trap radicals by freezing them out on cold surfaces. Sometimes polymerization of the radicals may occur. Complete isolation of radicals can be achieved by using refrigerants with temperatures very close to the absolute zero or more simply by co-condensing the species with a large

excess of an inert gas to form a rigid matrix at liquid hydrogen or helium temperature.

2. *Kinetics and Thermodynamics.* Some very thorough thermodynamic and kinetic analyses have been made for the carbon-hydrogen, carbon-hydrogen-nitrogen, and nitrogen-oxygen systems (17,18).

The thermodynamic stability relationships at high temperatures are conveniently studied using diagrams in which the free energy change, ΔG, is plotted against temperature, T. The equilibrium constant, K, can be read directly using a "fan" of lines passing through the origin, since

$$\Delta G = -RT \ln K = \Delta H - T\Delta S$$

It can be seen from Fig. 4 that for the oxygen-ozone reaction $K = 10^{-4}$ at 300°K and that K increases slowly with temperature. In Fig. 4 the left intercept gives the value of ΔH, since $\Delta H = \Delta G$ at 0°K, and the slope of the reaction line is $-\Delta S$. Increasing the temperature increases the degree of reaction only for endothermic reactions ($\Delta H > 0$) and only to a practical degree ($K > 10^{-3}$) if ΔH is not too large or if ΔS is large and positive.

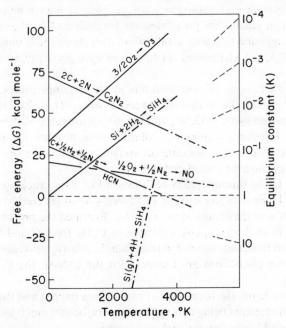

Figure 4 Stability diagram for plasma reactions showing free energy versus temperature, with isostability (equal K) lines indicated. Reactions proceed as written for negative values of ΔG. Reactions from nonstandard states shown as dotted lines. [Adapted from T. B. Reed (4).]

However, one must be careful to use appropriate standard states in using such a diagram to predict high temperature equilibrium and the results to be expected on quenching. For example, consider the reaction of carbon and hydrogen to form acetylene (Fig. 5):

$$2C(s) + H_2 \rightarrow C_2H_2 \qquad [1]$$

For $1500°K < T < 2500°K$, C_2H_2 is easily the most stable of all hydro-carbons and radicals, and this line represents quite well the equilibrium that was found experimentally by Plooster and Reed (33). However, at 3000°K hydrogen dissociates appreciably and at 4000°K carbon boils so that above 4000°K the reaction follows the solid line shown in Fig. 5 for the reaction

$$2C(g) + 2H \rightarrow C_2H_2 \qquad [2]$$

One can see that the temperature, at which C_2H_2 formation is optimum, will be between 3000° and 4000°K. For $3000°K < T < 4000°K$, a large variety of free radicals take on transient stability.

Plooster and Reed (33) obtained yields greater than those which could be predicted from the thermodynamic data in experiments in which equilibrium mixtures of carbon and hydrogen were sampled at high temperatures. To explain the high yields they postulated the formation of C_2H as a precursor radical and suggested that such a radical on quenching could unite with H to form more C_2H_2. Calculations on this basis gave good agreement with the experiment.

Detailed calculations of compositions at these temperatures have been made, notably for the carbon-hydrogen system (34,48,49), the carbon-hydrogen-nitrogen system (32,50), and the nitrogen-oxygen system (35). Such calculations, however, require the solution of a number of simultaneous equations and thermodynamic data on known and unknown species, so that at present they must be considered tentative.

According to the thermodynamics shown in Fig. 5 the cracking of methane to acetylene, being a strong entropy producer, should proceed to completion below 2000°K and the results agree with this. Provided the precursor radicals are included in the calculations, synthesis of C_2H_2 from C and H gives the yields expected from the thermodynamic data. Similarly, yields commensurate with qualitative predictions are observed for the C-N-H, the C-N, and the N-O systems.

On the other hand, the formation of ozone from oxygen and the formation of silane from elements being entropy consumers, benefit much less from high temperature and hence the low yields obtained.

Thus the results mentioned show that simple thermodynamic data form a useful basis for predicting to some degree the success of a plasma reaction. However, if equilibrium existed at all temperatures it would be impossible to

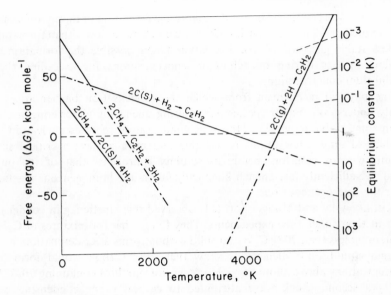

Figure 5 Stability diagram for carbon-hydrogen system illustrating condensation barrier. Dotted lines indicate metastable reaction kinetically favored by condensation barrier. [Adapted from T. B. Reed (4).]

quench in products formed at the high temperatures. This suggests that equilibrium may be established in reaction times of a millisecond at high temperatures, but that during the shorter quenching times and at lower temperatures it is not.

It is important to understand the kinetics of reactions during the quenching process if equilibrium is established only at plasma temperatures and not during the quenching. Detailed kinetic calculations have therefore been made on the reactions occurring during quenching for the C-H (41) and the N-O systems (35), of course making use of several assumptions. Although such calculations are very instructive, quench results do not critically test the various assumptions, and the data used is usually extrapolated to several thousand degrees above where it was taken. At the present stage of work it appears that, whatever the mechanisms occurring during quenching, yields in homogeneous reactions are at least commensurate with what one would expect from thermodynamic equilibrium compositions at the reaction temperatures, but for heterogeneous reactions they are often lower or higher than expected. Some reasons for these deviations are examined here.

The assumption of equilibrium can give results very different from those calculated from thermodynamic compositions for two reasons. (a) The *vaporization barrier* or the difficulty of volatilizing condensed phases in a plasma. (*b*) The *condensation barrier*, that is, the formation of thermodynamic-ally favored condensation species occurring much more slowly than formation of less stable gaseous species. The latter makes possible the formation of gaseous species during quenching in concentrations far exceeding their equilibrium concentrations.

The physical mechanism from which the condensation barrier arises is easily understood. Vapor species must during quenching either condense or form some stable molecules. However, condensation requires nucleation. A nucleus of only a few atoms is unstable and must achieve a critical size, requiring many collisions before its stability approaches that of the bulk solid. A sufficiently fast quench kinetically favors the homogeneous reaction over the heterogeneous one.

Kistiakowsky and Mangelsdorf (51) observed this kinetic lag in condensa-tion in their shock-tube experiments. They found that for mixtures of C_2H_2 containing less than 70% C_2H_2 no solid carbon forms after detonation, even though equilibrium calculations show that solid carbon would form for concentrations above about 55%. However, for mixtures containing $70–72\%$ C_2H_2 a second shock wave attributed to carbon vapor condensing was observed to follow a short time after the primary reaction between O_2 and C_2H_2. The authors concluded that the success of the industrial synthesis of acetylene in methane rich oxygen-methane flames indicates that the de-composition reaction has an induction period and that the duration of the period has a strong negative temperature coefficient.

The condensation barrier mechanism is illustrated graphically for the C–H system in Fig. 5. At about $1000°K$ methane becomes unstable with respect to the elements in the heterogeneous reaction

$$2CH_4 \rightarrow 2C(s) + 4H_2 \tag{3}$$

and under equilibrium conditions solid carbon forms. At high velocities, however, there is no time for carbon to nucleate and CH_4 breaks down to C_2H_2 along the homogeneous reaction route [4] instead:

$$2CH_4 \rightarrow C_2H_2 + 3H_2 \tag{4}$$

At very high temperatures a quench of a mixture of carbon vapor and atomic hydrogen should follow the homogeneous reaction route [2] down to $4000°K$ and then follow the heterogeneous reaction [1]. With sufficiently fast quench rates, however, the reaction can follow the metastable dotted line of reaction [2] in Fig. 5. Other metastable reaction lines have been shown in Fig. 4.

Reaction [2] represents condensation of elemental vapor with a gas to form a molecule, endothermic with respect to the solid element. This appears to be a general type of reaction which can be used to synthesize endothermic molecules of many elements, especially silicon and boron. The fact that more such reactions and molecules are not known at the present time is due to the difficulty of obtaining elemental vapor. Since this barrier relies on the lag in formation of condensation nuclei, it is also necessary to make sure no nuclei are present. Since the mechanism requires as few collisions as possible during quenching, it is necessary to use extreme quench rates.

As an example, a modification of the Huels process has been used to synthesize silane and silane derivatives by heating a rod of ferrosilicon in a plasma of hydrogen and methane. Although it can be seen from Fig. 4 that silane has very little thermodynamic stability at any temperature (and other silane derivatives will behave similarly) the product contained 2.7% SiH_4 and its derivatives, and the walls of the reaction chamber were coated with organic silicon products. In this case thermodynamic considerations would give a wrong answer.

Although in its early stages chemistry has concentrated on finding less expensive routes to known compounds, it seems that an equally fruitful search would be for new simple molecules which could be quenched from plasmas, relying on the condensation barrier to force elemental vapors to form new compounds.

E. Summation and Suggestions for Future Work

Looking back over the development of low-temperature plasma chemistry during the post-1950s, it can easily be concluded that although a wide variety of chemical systems have been studied using different plasma-generation techniques, the current knowledge of plasma-reaction paths is quite tenuous because of the uncertainties in plasma characterization, thermochemical data, and reaction kinetics. Under high-pressure, high-temperature conditions one would like to invoke thermochemical equilibrium. While strong arguments lie in favor of this assumption, the direct determination of the chemical composition of a multicomponent, high-pressure, high-temperature plasma has yet to be made. The question of whether additional new species will be found weakens the present analyses. Because of the lack of complete kinetic data, the postulations of reaction path in quench or in other nonequilibrium steps must often be the result of uncertain exploration from conventional-temperature reaction studies.

In view of these observations, it is clear that considerable importance must be attached to fundamental studies directed towards plasma characterization. The important questions to be answered are: What are the prevalent species in the plasma? Is the plasma composition in local thermodynamic equilibrium? What are the temperature and pressure limits for which equilibrium is satisfied?

An understanding of the reaction path in plasma reactions requires a knowledge of the plasma composition. The current knowledge concerning the chemical behavior of species in the plasma is very deficient. Fundamental studies are needed to elucidate the simultaneous interactions of electrons and ions present in electric fields with neutral molecular, free-radical, and atomic species of varying chemical composition. As a first step in this understanding, the studies that seek to identify directly the species present in the plasma can be expected to be most helpful. Although descriptions of the pure-gas plasmas, such as Ar, N_2, He, H_2, are rather well known under a variety of conditions, little has been done to explore the composition of some of the mixed-gas plasmas such as N_2-O_2, O_2-H_2, N_2-F_2, and C-F_2—interesting chemical systems on their own. Spectroscopic identification and quantification of the plasma composition would be one approach. However, one must be cautioned not to ignore species that happen not to emit or absorb in the frequency range under observation in both emission and absorption studies. Another valuable approach would be to determine plasma composition quantitatively by direct sampling of the plasma, through a carefully designed entrance cone, and expansion into a mass spectrograph. Other methods of plasma diagnostics may also provide valuable information. The limited studies hitherto performed indicate the difficulties encountered in this field.

In the production of species in the plasma and in quenching a plasma mixture, reaction-rate data are required to follow the reaction sequence completely. In considering some reaction systems that quench plasma mixtures to liquid-nitrogen temperatures, a range of 10^3 to 10^4 °K may be traversed. At present, kinetic data are available over this range for only a very few chemical systems. Some shock tube studies are contributing important data for the high-temperature range where a dearth of kinetic data now exists. At higher energy conditions, ionic species also become important, and hence the kinetics of ionic reactions needs to be established.

The temperature range available for plasma chemistry studies exceeds the range over which thermochemical properties of the chemical species are well known and fully substantiated. It is quite possible that carefully designed plasma experiments themselves can contribute data in this area. A number of shock tube studies are extending into the high-temperature range and providing heat-of-formation, heat-of-reaction, and equilibrium data. Progress will come in refinement to the thermochemical values of existing data for known species and in the discovery and inclusion of new species with their proper thermochemical data. Further, the temperature range over which these properties are known may be extended upward.

It is clear from the present trend in plasma chemistry research that chemical synthesis using plasmas will continue to be a major area of exploitation in the future. No doubt future studies will include new synthesis routes, involving either untried reagent feeds, production of previously unknown compounds, or the use of new plasma generation techniques. It is to be hoped that these laboratory studies will surely aid the development of plasma chemical processes of commercial significance.

IV. HIGH-TEMPERATURE PLASMA CHEMISTRY

A. General Remarks

At high temperatures $(T > 10^8 \, {}^\circ\text{K})$ only a very small fraction of the particles in the entire plasma remain neutral and the gas is said to be fully ionized. In such a gas the motions of the individual particles are governed by much simpler laws because there are only two kinds of particles, positively and negatively charged, and the complicated reactions between electrons and atomic structures, usually described by wave mechanical equations, are absent. Short-range atomic forces are now replaced by long-range electrostatic repulsion and attraction. Conditions can therefore be relatively simple, if the plasma consists essentially of the nuclei and electrons of the gas. In plasmas of gases of the lightest elements it is probable that all the electrons are removed from the atom so that a gas mixture consisting only of electrons and bare nuclei is obtained. A nuclear "fusion" can occur when two atomic nuclei approach very close to each other at velocities at least large enough to overcome their mutual electrostatic repulsion, that is, the "Coulomb barrier." In what follows we shall examine the cross-sections for some fusion reactions in fully ionized plasmas.

B. Nuclear Fusion Reactions

Consider a fully ionized gas containing n_A nuclei of one kind per cm^3 and n_B of another. There will, of course, be a concentration $Z_A n_A + Z_B n_B$ of electrons if Z_A, Z_B are the atomic numbers of the elements, but apart from their function in preserving charge neutrality their presence will be ignored, that is, it is assumed that the electrons play no part in the nuclear reactions resulting from impacts between the nuclei. If nuclei of type A move through the concentration n_B of type B with velocity v, each impinging particle produces, on the average, $v/\lambda = v n_B \sigma$ nuclear reactions per second. Here λ is the appropriate mean free path and σ the nuclear cross section for a particular reaction. Thus if n_A nuclei of type A are moving about at random among the others, also moving about at random, the total number of nuclear reactions per $\text{cm}^3 \, \text{sec}^{-1}$ (the reaction rate, r) is:

$$r = n_A n_B \langle \sigma v \rangle \qquad [\text{I}]$$

where v is the relative velocity of the two colliding particles and $\langle \sigma v \rangle$ denotes the value of σv averaged over the velocity distribution. In a gas consisting of only one type of nucleus, of total density $n(n_A = n_B = \frac{1}{2}n)$ the reaction rate is:

$$r = \frac{1}{2} n^2 \langle \sigma v \rangle \qquad \text{[II]}$$

It must be noted that all collisions between like particles contribute to the reaction rate.

Let us now consider some numerical estimates of the values of σ and the relative energy ε of the colliding nuclei for reactions between light nuclei such as hydrogen and its isotopes:

Reaction	σ_{max}, cm^2	ϵ_{max}, MeV
$D + D \rightarrow He^3 + N + 3.25$ Mev	0.09×10^{-24}	1
$D + D \rightarrow T + P + 4.03$ MeV	0.08×10^{-24}	1
$D + T \rightarrow He^4 + N + 17.58$ MeV	5.0×10^{-24}	0.1
$D + He^3 \rightarrow He^4 + P + 18.34$ MeV	0.8×10^{-24}	0.45
$T + T \rightarrow He^4 + 2N + 11.3$ MeV	0.1×10^{-24}	1

In the listed reactions, N is the neutron, P for the proton (H^1), D for the deuteron (the nucleus H^2), and T for the tritium nucleus H^3. The comparatively large cross-section for the D–T reaction at a low relative energy suggests that it is the most favorable reaction. If tritium produced in the D–D reaction can be prevented from escaping from the ionized gas, the D–T reaction is then possible. If the He^3 produced can also be contained, the total energy available from the D–D reaction and its secondary products is about 21 MeV. However, the rate of energy release is determined by the small cross section for D–D collisions and the total energy released in one reaction is distributed between charged and uncharged particles (neutrons). In principle, the heavy reaction products carry the smaller fraction of the energy. For example, in the D–D reaction the charged particles receive two thirds of the released energy (~ 2 MeV), and in the D–T reaction about one fifth (~ 3.6 MeV). Thus, although this latter process gives a net gain of energy in charged particles of ~ 4 MeV per reaction, main interest in the reaction arises from its high probability at low impact energies (~ 100 keV).

Values of σ can be measured by firing beams of single energy particles (deuterons of known energy in the present case) at solid targets. The value of $\langle \sigma v \rangle$ is calculated from the energy distribution of the particles (usually Maxwellian) and the energy variation of σ. The values of $\langle \sigma v \rangle$, that is, the reaction probability, for the D + D, D + T, D + He^3, and T + T reactions are shown in Fig. 6 as functions of temperature and energy. It can be seen that

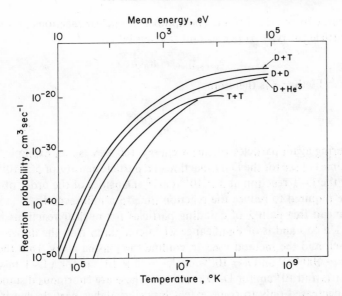

Figure 6 Reaction probabilities for some nuclear reactions between light elements, as functions of mean energy and temperature. [Adapted from W. B. Thompson, *Proc. Phys. Soc.* (*London*), **B70**, 1(1957).]

at mean particle energies below 100 keV, the number of nuclear reactions per second in a mixture of tritium and deuterium is several orders of magnitude greater than in any of the other gas mixtures.

In any nuclear fusion experiment several factors govern the reaction rate. We shall consider below the effects of the particle density n, and the mean free path λ of the particles and their mean lifetimes, τ, that is, the average total path traversed and time taken by one particle before it undergoes a nuclear reaction.

Consider $n \simeq 10^{12}$ particles cm^{-3}, a typical value for ordinary gas discharges. With this value of n, the D–D reaction produces a power of 10^{-5} W cm^{-3} whereas the D–T reaction (equal concentrations) produces 2×10^{-3} W cm^{-3}, both at mean energies of 100 keV. It is clear that appreciable power densities can be obtained only using higher values of n. However, if the value of n is made too high the pressure exerted by the hot gas becomes so enormous that no reactor could hold it in; for example, if $n \simeq 10^{20}$ and $\langle \varepsilon \rangle \simeq 100$ keV, $p \simeq 10^7$ atm. Thus, it is not advantageous to use high densities and lower temperatures because the product σv, and hence the reaction rate, is the most sensitive factor, and falls rapidly with decreasing temperature.

The reaction lifetime must not be long compared with the time taken for a particle to diffuse to the reactor walls. Otherwise many of the particles will lose their original kinetic energy as heat to the walls without producing any fresh energy by nuclear fusion. The number of nuclear reactions produced by each particle (of type A) per second is given by

$$r_{\text{per particle}} = n_B \langle \sigma v \rangle$$

The mean lifetime τ is therefore

$$\tau = \frac{1}{r} = \frac{1}{n_B} \langle \sigma v \rangle$$

Considering again particles of mean energy 100 keV as an example, the reaction time is 1 sec for the D–D reaction at a particle density of 5×10^{16} cm^{-3} and for the D–T reaction at 3×10^{15} cm^{-3}. Densities of the order of 10^{18} or 10^{19} are required to reduce the reaction time to a millisecond.

The mean free path λ of colliding particles for nuclear reactions is given by $\lambda = 1/n \langle \sigma \rangle$ and is of significance when compared with the dimensions of the vessel, and the method used to confine the plasma away from the walls. For $\langle \varepsilon \rangle = 100$ keV and $n = 10^{16}$ cm^{-3}, $\lambda = 5 \times 10^7$ cm for a D–T mixture of equal parts and 10^9 cm for D–D reactions. These are enormous distances and can be decreased only to some extent by using higher particle densities and temperatures. It must be noted that the reaction products are usually released with appreciably greater energy (several MeV); the probability of the products undergoing a second nuclear reaction is relatively small and the problem of containing the products so that they restore some of the energy directly to the plasma is formidable. For example, a deuteron of energy 100 keV spirals with a radius of 1 cm in magnetic field of 60,000 oersted; on an average, it must perform 10^7–10^8 gyrations before it produces a nuclear reaction. A particle such as He, emitted with an energy of 3.6 MeV would have to be subjected to a magnetic field of 700,000 oersted to perform gyrations of radius 1 cm.

Whereas the production of sufficient energy in plasmas for fusion reactions is an important part of any nuclear synthesis program, the problem of confining the energy within the plasma is equally important. It must be remembered that energy can be easily lost from a hot plasma in various ways and one must deal with a number of problems for confining a hot plasma. Several laboratory devices have been built in attempts to tackle the problem of confinement. A discussion of these devices may be found in a later chapter dealing fully with nuclear fusion plasmas (see Chapter 20).

V. CONCLUDING REMARKS

In the preceding sections of this chapter we have outlined the foundations of plasma chemistry and the scope of problems this greatly altered chemistry presents. Although the impression gained from these discussions may be that plasma chemistry is still in its infancy, investigations of reactions obtained in plasma states merit detailed consideration. The remaining chapters in this book are largely devoted to detailed expositions of these investigations and to emphasize the unique potentiality of the plasma reactor, which is promising indeed.

REFERENCES

1. H. Moissan, *Le Four Electrique*. Paris: Steinheil, 1897.
2. R. Hare, *Trans. Am. Phil. Soc.*, **7**, 53(1840). See also W. E. Kuhn, ed. *Arcs in Inert Atmospheres and Vacuum*. New York: Wiley, 1956, p. 1.
3. H. A. Curtis, *Fixed Nitrogen*. New York: Chem. Catalog. Co., 1932, Chapter 4.
4. T. B. Reed, "Chemical Uses of Induction Plasmas." In *The Application of Plasmas to Chemical Processing*, edited by R. F. Baddour and R. S. Timmins. Cambridge, Mass.: M.I.T. Press, 1967, p. 26. "Plasmas for High Temperature Chemistry." In *Advances in High Temperature Chemistry*, Vol. 1, p. 259, edited by L. Eyring. New York: Academic Press, 1967.
5. H. W. Emmons, "Recent Developments in Plasma Heat Transfer." In *Modern Developments in Heat Transfer*, edited by W. Ibele. New York: Academic Press, 1963, p. 401.
6. V. N. Kondratiev, E. E. Nikitin, and V. L. Tal'rose, *Pure Appl. Chem.*, **13**, 367(1966).
7. G. Glockler and S. C. Lind, *The Electrochemistry of Gases and Other Dielectrics*. New York: Wiley, 1939.
8. W. L. Jolly, H. B. Jonassen, and A. Weissberger, "The Use of Electric Discharges in Chemical Synthesis." In *Techniques of Inorganic Chemistry*, Vol. 1, edited by A. Weissberger. New York: Interscience, 1963.
9. A. S. Kana'an and J. L. Margrave, *Advan. Inorg. Chem. Radiochem.*, **6**, 143(1964).
10. F. K. McTaggart, *Plasma Chemistry in Electrical Discharges*. Amsterdam:Elsevier, 1967.
11. E. W. R. Steacie, *Atomic and Free Radical Reactions*. 2nd ed. New York: Reinhold, 1954.
12. A. G. Massey, *J. Chem. Educ.*, **40**, 311(1963).
13. A. N. Wright and C. A. Winkler, *Active Nitrogen*. New York: Academic Press, 1968.
14. M. Venugopalan and R. A. Jones, *Chemistry of Dissociated Water Vapor and Related Systems*. New York: Interscience, 1968.
15. V. L. Tal'rose and A. K. Lyubimova, *Dokl. Akad. Nauk SSSR*, **86**, 909(1952).
16. *Ion-Molecule Reactions in the Gas Phase*, *Advan. Chem. Series*, **58** (1966), Am. Chem. Soc., Washington, D.C., 1966.
17. L. S. Polak, ed., *Kinetika i Termodinamika Khimicheskikh Reaktsii v Nizkotemperaturnoi Plazme* [*Kinetics and Thermodynamics of Chemical Reactions in Low-Temperature Plasma*]. Moscow: Nauka, 1965 (in Russian).
18. R. F. Baddour and R. S. Timmins, eds., *The Application of Plasmas to Chemical Processing*. Cambridge, Mass.: M.I.T. Press, 1967.
19. W. M. Goldberger, "Trends in High Temperature Chemical Processing." *Chem. Eng.*, March 14, 1966, p. 173, and March 28, 1966, p. 125; *High Temperature Chemistry– Current and Future Problems*. Publication 14570. National Academy of Sciences National Research Council, Washington, D.C., 1967.

20. *Symposium on Chemical Reactions in Electrical Discharges.* 153rd National Meeting of the American Chemical Society. Miami, April 1967.

21. A. M. Bass and H. P. Broida, *Stabilization of Free Radicals at Low Temperatures.* Natl. Bur. Stds. (U.S.) Monograph 12, (1960).

22. C. Roddy and B. Green, *Electron. World*, 65, 29(1961).

23. R. Mavrodineanu and H. Boiteux, *Flame Spectroscopy.* New York: Wiley, 1965, p. 50.

24. R. F. Baddour and P. H. Dundas, "Chemical Reactions in a Microwave Discharge." In *The Application of Plasmas to Chemical Processing*, edited by R. F. Baddour and R. S. Timmins. Cambridge, Mass.: M.I.T. Press, 1967, p. 87.

25. H. Gladisch, *Hydrocarbon Process. Petrol. Refiner*, 41, 159(1962).

26. C. S. Stokes, W. W. Knipe, and L. A. Streng, *J. Electrochem. Soc.*, 107, 35(1960).

27. S. Korman, *Intern. Sci. Technol.*, No. 30, 90(1964).

28. J. O. Gibson and R. Weidman, *Chem. Eng. Progr.*, 59(9), 53(1963).

29. J. D. Holmgren, J. O. Gibson, and C. Sheer, *J. Electrochem. Soc.*, 111, 362(1964).

30. C. D. West and D. N. Hume, *Anal. Chem.*, 36, 415(1964).

31. See ref. 14, pp. 423–425.

32. C. W. Marynowski, R. C. Phillips, J. R. Phillips, and N. K. Hiester, *Ind. Eng. Chem. Fundamentals*, 1, 52(1962). See also R. M. Fristrom, G. Grunfelder, and S. Farin, *J. Phys. Chem.*, 64, 1386(1960).

33. M. N. Plooster and T. B. Reed, *J. Chem. Phys.*, 31, 66(1959).

34. R. F. Baddour and J. L. Blanchet, *Ind. Eng. Chem., Process Design Develop.*, 3, 258 (1964).

35. R. S. Timmins and P. R. Amman, "Nitrogen Fixation." In *The Application of Plasmas to Chemical Processing*, edited by R. F. Baddour and R. S. Timmins. Cambridge, Mass.: M.I.T. Press, 1967, p. 99.

36. H. W. Leutner, *Ind. Eng. Chem., Process Design Develop.*, 1, 166(1962).

37. M. P. Freeman and J. F. Skrivan, *A.I.Ch.E.J.*, 8, 450(1962).

38. J. F. Skrivan and W. von Jaskowsky, *Ind. Eng. Chem., Process Design Develop.*, 4, 371(1965).

39. Battelle Institute, *Chem. Eng. News*, 42, 44(1964).

40. M. Moss, D. L. Smith, and R. A. Lefver, *Appl. Phys. Letters*, 5, 120(1964).

41. J. E. Anderson and L. K. Case, *Ind. Eng. Chem., Process Design Develop.*, 1, 161(1962).

42. C. S. Stokes and L. A. Streng, *Ind. Eng. Chem., Prod. Res. Develop.*, 4, 36(1965).

43. F. Fischer and G. Iliovici, *Chem. Ber.*, 42, 527(1909).

44. H. Kautsky and H. Kautsky, Jr., *Chem. Ber.*, 89, 571(1956).

45. W. M. Goldberger and J. H. Oxley, *A.I.Ch.E.J.*, 9, 778(1963).

46. J. Grey and P. F. Jacobs, *A.I.A.A.J.*, 2, 433(1964).

47. S. Singer, N. Kim, A. Merkl, and M. Farber, *J. Phys. Chem.*, 69, 779(1965).

48. R. F. Baddour and B. R. Bronfin, *Ind. Eng. Chem., Process Design Develop.*, 4, 162(1965).

49. J. T. Clarke, "Reaction of Graphite and Hydrogen Above 2000°K." In *The Application of Plasmas to Chemical Processing*, edited by R. F. Baddour and R. S. Timmins. Cambridge, Mass.: M.I.T. Press, 1967, p.132.

50. B. R. Bronfin, M. P. Freeman, V. N. DiStefano, and R. N. Hazlett, "Thermo-Chemical Equilibrium in the Carbon-Hydrogen-Nitrogen System at Very High Temperatures." *15th Chem. Inst. Can. Chem. Eng. Conf.* Quebec: Université de Laval, October 1965.

51. G. B. Kistiakowsky and P. C. Mangelsdorf, *J. Chem. Phys.*, 25, 516(1956).

CHAPTER TWELVE

Elementary Reactions in
Low-Temperature Plasma

V. L. TAL'ROSE and G. V. KARACHEVTSEV

I. GENERAL KINETIC PROBLEMS IN PLASMA REACTIONS

The concentrations of species constituting plasma (electrons, ions, atoms, and molecules) and distribution functions over kinetic energy and over discrete excitation levels are considered characteristic of the plasma state at a given time and point in space. When the plasma is in thermodynamic equilibrium, its state will be unambiguously determined from a macroscopic parameter—the temperature—and from the elemental composition of plasma by means of thermodynamic constants. In the absence of thermodynamic equilibrium, the state of plasma will be established from the effects both of external parameters, which may not consist of temperature only, and of internal parameters, namely the rate constants of elementary reactions yielding and destroying plasma particles. The methods for calculating the state of nonequilibrium plasma (1) are more restricted than those for equilibrium plasma (2,3). Our present knowledge of kinetic constants is insufficient for quantitative calculation of the expected chemical and even ionization effects in real complex nonequilibrium systems. However, semiquantitative and even qualitative kinetic data may frequently appear to be of practical interest permitting one to find possible approaches to either producing desired changes in the plasma properties by chemical methods or creating optimal conditions for chemical synthesis in plasma.

The types of elementary processes in plasma conversions are numerous. Their relative importance markedly differs with the technique of plasma production, its elementary composition and the conditions of its existence. For instance, the rate of ionization in strong shock waves at a sufficiently high electron concentration is determined by that of kinetic energy transfer to electrons in elastic collisions of type $A + e = A + e$ or $A^+ + e = A^+ + e$. In the case of plasma produced by ionizing irradiation of a cold gas, ionization will be ensured by a group of fast electrons with an energy imparted by emission, whereas collisions of electrons with heavy particles will decrease the kinetic energies of electrons to those inducing no ionization. The properties of photo-ionized plasma best represented by the ionosphere of earth and other planets are interesting. In this case the photo-ionization rate will be a function of photo-ionization cross-sections for neutral components. The rate of ionization in gas-discharge plasma is determined by the macroscopic electric field and by the kinetic constants of elastic and inelastic collisions between electrons and neutral or charged plasma species. There is no possibility of discussing in this review all the elementary reactions of interest for non-equilibrium plasma. For instance, elastic scattering, photo-excitation and photo-ionization will be left aside. Attention will be given to inelastic collisions of electrons with neutrals, collisions of charged species and those between neutrals. All or certain of these elementary reactions play an important part in the kinetics of formation of charged and neutral species, in the majority of plasma types and in a number of cases mere allowance for these or a part of these reactions permits describing the kinetics of conversions in plasma. Naturally, detailed discussion of elementary reactions is impossible; hence only most typical and simple examples will be considered. The choice of these examples reflects the scientific interests of the authors.

Let us consider first certain well-known general kinetic problems, choosing the dissociative attachment of an electron to a molecule in a ground state

$$e + HBr = H + Br^- \qquad [1]$$

as an example of a bimolecular reaction. The ionization cross-section σ depending on the kinetic energy E of electrons and on the molecule characteristics will be illustrative of the type [1] elementary reaction. When a beam of monoenergetic electrons of an energy E and an intensity of I_e particles per second passes through a gas of density n reactants per cm^3, equality

$$W_i = \sigma n l I_e, \qquad [2]$$

will give the complete number of neutral ions W_i formed per second over length l, under condition $I_e \gg W_i$. The effective cross-section dimensionality is cm^2 particle^{-1}. Equation [2] was taken as basis for many experimental methods of σ determination. Usually in practice, in thermal ionization, gas discharge, passage of ionizing radiation through a thick gas target, the electrons in plasma will not be monoenergetic. In this case Z, the number of elementary reactions of type [1] per unit volume in unit time, will be described by the law of mass action

$$Z = \frac{dn_{(e)}}{dt} = k n n_e \qquad [3]$$

where n_e is the concentration of molecules or electrons, n is the concentration of molecules, n_e is the concentration of electrons, k is the rate constant for an elementary reaction and is independent both of n and of n_e

$$k = \iint v\sigma(v)\, f_1(v_1)\, f_2(v_2)\, d\bar{v}_1\, d\bar{v}_2 \qquad [4]$$

Here $\bar{v}_1$ is the velocity of molecules; $\bar{v}_2$ is the velocity of electrons; $f_2(v_1)$ is the distribution function over molecular velocities; $f_2(v_2)$ is the distribution function over electron velocities; $v = |\bar{v}_1 - \bar{v}_2|$. Let the distribution functions normalized to unity ($\int f\, dv = 1$) be Maxwellian at the same temperature T:

$$f_1(v_1) = \left(\frac{m}{2\pi kT}\right)^{3/2} \exp\left(\frac{-mv_1^2}{2kT}\right) \qquad [5]$$

and

$$f_2(v_2) = \left(\frac{m_e}{2\pi kT}\right)^{3/2} \exp\left(\frac{-m_e v_2^2}{2kT}\right) \qquad [6]$$

Transformation of velocities in laboratory coordinates $\bar{v}_1$ and $\bar{v}_2$ to the relative velocity $\bar{v}$ and to that of the mass center $\bar{V}$, will be expressed as

$$\bar{v} = \bar{v}_1 - \bar{v}_2$$

and

$$\bar{V} = \frac{m\bar{v}_1 + m_e\bar{v}_2}{m + m_e}$$

With this transformation $d\bar{v}_1\, d\bar{v}_2 = d\bar{V}\, d\bar{v}$ and

$$\frac{1}{2}m\bar{v}_1^2 + \frac{1}{2}m_e\bar{v}_2^2 = \frac{1}{2}\mu\bar{v}^2 + \frac{1}{2}(m + m_e)\bar{V}^2 \qquad \text{where } \mu = \frac{mm_e}{m + m_e}$$

Substituting [5] and [6] into [4] and passing to the center of mass system, we obtain

$$k = \left(\frac{\mu}{2\pi kT}\right)^{3/2} \int v\sigma(v) \exp\left(-\frac{\mu v^2}{2kT}\right) dv \qquad [7]$$

When the distribution of colliding particles over velocities is isotropic, it is convenient to use spherical coordinates in the velocity space. Then $d\bar{v} = 4\pi v^2\, dv$ and, consequently,

$$k = \left[\frac{8}{\mu\pi(kT)^3}\right]^{1/2} \int_0^\infty \sigma(\varepsilon)\varepsilon \exp\left(-\frac{\varepsilon}{kT}\right) d\varepsilon \qquad [8]$$

where $\varepsilon = \frac{1}{2}\mu v^2$ is the kinetic energy of colliding particles in the mass center system. When electrons collide with atoms and molecules, the reduced mass μ is to a good accuracy equal to that of the electron m_e, owing to the great differences in masses of the colliding species. Consequently energy ε is approximately equal to the kinetic energy of electrons in the laboratory system of coordinates. It will be noted that eq. [8] remains valid, when the temperature of the electron gas exceeds that of the gas containing neutral molecules, a case often met with in real plasma. It is only necessary to replace μ by m_e, and T by T_e (T_e is the temperature of the electron gas). If the plasma contains two or several groups of heavy species with various T values, as for instance in ion-molecular collisions, and if the temperature of the ionic gas differs from that of the neutral molecules gas, eqs. [7] and [8] cannot be used for calculation of reaction rate constants. In this case, as the masses of ions and neutral molecules are relatively close, the relative velocity will be essentially dependent both upon that of ions and that of neutral molecules. Consequently, for a general case the expression obtained by substituting relevant distribution functions from [4] for the two-temperature plasma will be more complex, compared to expressions [7] and [8].

When the velocities of reactants in plasma are virtually equal as, for example, in gas ionization by a beam of monoenergetic electrons, eq. [2] will be transformed to [3] by simple substitution of $k = \sigma v$.

It will be shown later for dissociative attachment that in certain cases the dependence of the cross-section on kinetic energy has the shape of a narrow resonance peak. In this case only a small range of energies near the peak maximum ε_0 contributes to integral [8]. When all integrand functions over this narrow ε range, except $\sigma\varepsilon$, do not change considerably and can be put outside the integral sign in the form of constant $\varepsilon_0 \exp(-\varepsilon_0/kT)$ eq. [8] may be rewritten as

$$ k = \left[\frac{8}{\pi\mu(kT)^3} \right]^{1/2} \varepsilon_0 \exp\left(-\frac{\varepsilon_0}{kT} \right) \int_0^\infty \sigma(\varepsilon)\, d\varepsilon \qquad [9] $$

The conditions for possible replacement of expression [8] by [9] are $\varepsilon_0 > \Delta\varepsilon$ and $kT > \Delta\varepsilon$, where $\Delta\varepsilon$ is the effective width of the resonance peak. Strictly speaking, the distribution functions will be Maxwellian only for equilibrium systems. The difference of distribution functions from Maxwellian ones may be accounted for both by external action on the plasma system, such as that of the electric field on electrons in electric discharge plasma, and by action of nonequilibrium reactions in plasma.

Let us deal first with nonequilibrium electron distribution functions obtained without allowance for the effect of reactions. These, distribution functions same as the Maxwellian ones, may be used for calculation of reaction rate constants only when the rate of the reaction disturbing the function is small, for instance, with low concentrations of molecules λ reacting with electrons.

If the effects of inelastic collisions are neglected and only losses of electron energies by elastic collisions are taken into account, and the mean free path of electrons is assumed to be independent of v, the velocity distribution function for electrons in gas at a strong external electric field will follow the Druyvesteyn expression [4]

$$ f(v) = 4\pi A v^2 \exp\left(-\frac{3m_e v^4}{4mF^2\lambda^2} \right)\left(1 + \bar{F}\bar{v}\, \frac{3m_e v}{mF^2\lambda} \right) \qquad [10] $$

where

$$ \bar{F} = \frac{e\bar{E}}{m_e}; \qquad A = \frac{(3m_e/4mF^2\lambda^2)^{3/4}}{\pi F^{3/4}} $$

e is the electron charge, $\bar{E}$ is the vector of the external electric field strength. The relation $\int f(v)\ dv = 1$ will be valid for the distribution function. The condition for the validity of expression [10] is $eE\lambda > 3kT(m/m_e)^{1/2}$. Besides, it is assumed for this expression that the number of electrons in the gas is so small, that their collisions, as well as those of electrons with ions can be neglected. The expression describes only a stationary state at which the energy taken up by the free electron is compensated on the average by its losses through collision with a gas molecule. If, as suggested, all collisions with molecules are only elastic, then the losses and income of energy in a stationary state will be small compared to the mean energy. Yet, as the direction of electron motion changes considerably upon collision, the distribution function will be almost independent of this direction, even though it differs considerably from the Maxwellian one. Comparison shows that the number of electrons of a higher than mean energy is considerably less than for Maxwellian distribution at the same mean energy. The true distribution of velocities is very sensitive to the law of interaction between electrons and molecules (see Refs. 5–8). For instance if the interaction forces vary as the reciprocal of the fifth power of distance, then according to the classical scattering theory $\lambda \sim v$, the distribution function will also appear to be Maxwellian, but the temperature will be considerably higher than that of gas molecules. For real gases the function $\lambda(v)$ is of a complex nature and the distribution function for electron velocities will be calculated numerically. A case of relatively low electron energies such that those of molecules cannot be neglected was discussed in Ref. 9. The most recently calculated distribution functions for kinetic energies of electrons in gases C_2H_4, N_2 and Ar at different E/p values (E is the electric field strength in V cm^{-1}, p is the gas pressure) may be seen in Fig. 1 taken from Ref. 10. In the given case the normalization condition is $\int_0^\infty f(\varepsilon, E/p)d\varepsilon = 1$. As a rule, in experiments on attachment of electrons in gases, when the distribution of electrons over energies is described by functions shown in Fig. 1, use is made not of the attachment constant k, but of the attachment coefficient $\alpha(E/p)$ which represents the probability of capture per cm of the path passed by the electron in the direction of the electric field, at a 1 torr pressure of the electron-capturing gas. The values $\alpha(E/p)$, $w(E/p)$: the velocity of electron drift in the electric field, and $f(\varepsilon, E/p)$ are related as

$$\alpha\left(\frac{E}{p}\right) w\left(\frac{E}{p}\right) = N_0\left(\frac{2}{m_e}\right)^{1/2} \int_0^\infty \varepsilon^{1/2}\sigma(\varepsilon)f\left(\varepsilon, \frac{E}{p}\right)\, d\varepsilon \qquad [11]$$

where N_0 is the number of molecules taking up the electrons at a pressure of 1 torr. The relation between the coefficient $\alpha(E/p)$ and the rate constant $k(E/p)$ for the given distribution function $f(\varepsilon, E/p)$ is

$$\alpha\left(\frac{E}{p}\right) w\left(\frac{E}{p}\right) = N_0\, k\left(\frac{E}{p}\right)$$

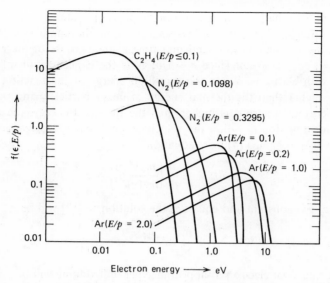

Figure 1   Electron distribution functions over kinetic energy in gases at different values of E/p (10).

Data on the velocity of electron drift in an electric field at various E/p may be found, for example, in Ref. 6 and in the recent papers (11–13). As mentioned above, deviation from Maxwellian distribution is due not only to external action, but also to the reaction as such. When the attachment coefficient or the rate constant taken as an example are calculated from experimental results, making use of eq. [4], there must be certainly that the electron distribution function $f(\varepsilon, E/p)$ is not distributed by dissociative attachment taking up electrons within a certain energy range. In this connection a small amount of the species reacting with electrons is added to the main compound in order that the electron-distribution function be controlled by the latter compound. At a relatively high concentration of electron-capturing gas molecules the electron-distribution function and thus the value k obtained from [4] will depend on the concentrations of reactants. Then calculation of the reaction rate would require knowledge of the cross-section $\sigma(v)$ and of the electron-energy distribution function obtained from the Boltzmann equation. Let us consider a simple calculation of this type. Let the cross-section for electron disappearance be $\sigma(v) \sim 1/v$ for kinetic energies higher than ε_t, the threshold energy, and let electrons of high energy be admitted from outside. These electrons would lose their energy by elastic collisions with molecules until they begin reacting or until their kinetic energy becomes less than ε_t. It will be assumed that the gas is uniform and motionless and that the electric and magnetic fields are absent. Let $\alpha d\bar{v}$ be the number of externally admitted electrons per unit volume and unit time within the range of velocities v, $v + dv$ and $\beta f_e \, d\bar{v}$ the number of electrons disappearing per unit volume and unit time at the expense of the reaction. Here $\beta = N\sigma v = $ constant since $\sigma \sim 1/v$; N is the concentration of species reacting with electrons. When the threshold energy of the reaction is considerably higher than the thermal energy of heavy particles, and the mean initial energy of electrons is higher than the threshold energy, the electron distribution function f_e within the velocity range from v_t (corresponding to ε_t to ∞ will be obtained (4) from equation

$$\alpha - \beta f_e + \frac{1}{v^2} \frac{d}{dv} \left\{ \frac{m_e v^4}{m\lambda(v)} f_e \right\} = 0 \qquad [12]$$

When $\lambda(v)/v$ is constant and equals τ, the solution to [12] will be

$$f_e = v^{m\tau\beta/m_e - 3} \int_v^\infty \alpha \frac{m\tau}{m_e} v^{2 - m\tau\beta/m_e} \, dv, \quad v_t < v < \infty \qquad [13]$$

Thus the rate $\mathscr{L}$ of electron disappearance per unit volume will be

$$\mathscr{L} = \int_{v_t}^\infty \beta f_e \, d\bar{v} = 4\pi \int_{v_t}^\infty \beta f_e v^2 \, dv \qquad [14]$$

where f_e is taken from eq. [13]. The overall rate of electron formation per unit volume is $4\pi \int_0^\infty \alpha v^2 \, dv$. For a general case the rate of electron formation and that of their entering into the reaction may differ, as a part of the electrons may be slowed down to energies lower than the threshold energy without engaging in the reaction. When the kinetic energies of electrons are lower than the threshold energy, the electrons may disappear by other reactions which will not be considered here for simplicity. The stationary electron distribution function f'_e may be found from eq. [13] without allowing for the reaction, at electron velocities higher than v_t, taking $f_e = f'_e$ and $\beta = 0$

$$f'_e = v^{-3} \int_v^\infty \alpha \frac{m}{m_e} v^2 \, dv \qquad v_t < v < \infty \qquad [15]$$

The rate of electron disappearance calculated by means of this distribution function will be

$$\mathscr{L}' = 4\pi \int \beta f'_e v^2 \, dv \qquad [16]$$

It will be clear from general considerations that at relatively low values of constant β showing the reaction effectivity $\mathscr{L}'$ and $\mathscr{L}$ will be equal due to weak disturbance of the distribution function by the reaction. Let us consider a simple example, when $\alpha = c \, \delta(v_0 - v)$ and the integrals in [14] and [16] are readily calculated. We obtain

$$\frac{\mathscr{L}}{\mathscr{L}'} = \frac{v_0^{\gamma\beta} - v_t^{\gamma\beta}}{\gamma\beta v_0 (\ln v_0 - \ln v)} \tag{17}$$

where $\gamma = m\tau/m_e$.

It will be seen that

$$\lim_{\gamma\beta \to 0} \frac{\mathscr{L}}{\mathscr{L}'} = 1$$

and

$$\frac{\mathscr{L}}{\mathscr{L}'} = \frac{1}{\gamma\beta(\ln v_0 - \ln v_i)}$$

at $\gamma\beta \gg 1$. Thus, at low β ($\beta \ll 1/\gamma$) we actually have $\mathscr{L} \simeq \mathscr{L}'$ and at $\beta \gg 1/\gamma$ $\mathscr{L} < \mathscr{L}'$. At the same time $\mathscr{L}' \to \infty$ as $\beta \to \infty$ though it is evident that the number of electrons entering into the reaction cannot exceed that of their formation. For the given example the number of electrons appearing per unit volume in unit time is $4\pi a v_0^2$ and $\mathscr{L}$ tends to this value with increasing β.

The authors are not cognizant of papers dealing with the retardation of heavy particles and their reaction. However, useful information in this respect may be found in papers on the so-called chemistry of hot atoms. For instance, kinetic studies were carried out on the retardation of monoenergetic deuterium atoms obtained by photodissociation of deuterium halide molecules and on their reaction with hydrogen molecules (14). Such an analysis of experimental results for different kinetic energies permits obtaining information on the reaction cross-section as a function of the relative kinetic energy of colliding species.

Disturbance of the Maxwellian function by chemical reactions occurring at high temperatures ($kT \geqslant E_0$, E_0 is the reaction activation energy) was studied by means of a computer (15). It was found that dissociation of molecules in excess inert monoatomic gas may disturb the distribution function to such an extent that the temperature becomes of no consequence for molecules.

Transition to the final state by a number of consecutive step-wise excitations is sometimes and not quite correctly considered as an elementary reaction. However, in some specific cases this may be justified because under certain conditions the rates of such reactions may obey the law of mass action, that is, the reaction rate is proportional to concentrations of relevant particles with a proportionality coefficient independent of their concentration. This coefficient will then be the effective rate constant. The concentrations of reactants in the kinetic equations will represent overall concentrations in the ground and excited states.

For instance, dissociation of diatomic molecules

$$AB + M \rightarrow A + B + M$$

recombination of atoms by three-body collisions

$$A + B + M \rightarrow AB + M$$

ionization of molecules, atoms, and ions by electron impact

$$e + C = C^+ + 2e$$

three body recombination of electrons on ions upon collisions with electrons, atoms or molecules

$$X^+ + e + M = X + M$$

may occur in plasma by stepwise processes. The starting point for kinetic analysis of all stepwise processes is the system of kinetic equations for population of the X_m, m^{-th} energy level of a diatomic system AB (for molecular dissociation or recombination of atoms) or of an excited atom (for stepwise ionization or recombination). Let us consider as an example the relatively well-studied dissociation of diatomic molecules (16). The distribution of molecules can be considered to be equilibrium, Maxwellian, for most dissociation reactions in non-equilibrium systems of interest. This is accounted for by the fact that several gas-kinetic collisions per molecule are sufficient for attaining equilibrium over kinetic energies, vibrational excitation particularly at a moderate kinetic temperature of neutral particles in plasma, requires considerably longer times. These times become comparable only at temperatures higher than 10^4 °K. For instance, a study of the Maxwellization of a nonequilibrium argon-methane mixture by the Monte-Carlo computing method has shown that when methane at a temperature of 3×10^2 °K is heated by argon at a temperature of 10^4 °K, the concentration of the gases being equal (10^{18} cm^{-3}), the time for attaining the Maxwell distribution in a uniform mixture will be 10^{-8} sec. Equilibrium over rotational degrees of freedom in molecular gases at high temperatures will be attained approximately within the same time as for translational degrees of freedom. The kinetic equations for the population of energy levels may be written as

$$\frac{dX_m}{dt} = -\sum k_{m \rightarrow n} X_m + \sum k'_{n \rightarrow m} X_m \qquad [18]$$

These equations involve rate constants for elementary reactions (transitions between m and n states) that are calculated from relevant cross-sections with an equilibrium velocity distribution function of the colliding molecules. Analysis of dissociation would require the addition of terms describing transition of the molecule from a bound to a dissociated state. The rate constants involved in [18] may be calculated theoretically only within the accuracy of certain constants obtained from experimental kinetic results. This is true even for a simple case when dissociation of diatomic molecules occurs in excess inert monatomic gas at relatively low temperatures (adiabatic collisions). Distribution over excitation levels calculated using eq. [18] will be close to the equilibrium Boltzmann distribution with a temperature equal to the kinetic temperature only for $kT < \hbar\omega$, where ω is the frequency of the first vibrational quantum of the molecule. Under this condition the dissociation rate will be characterized by the equilibrium rate constant

$$k^* = A \exp\left(-\frac{\mathscr{D}}{kT}\right) \qquad [19]$$

Here A is a coefficient that remains almost unchanged over the given temperature range, so that it is usually considered as constant and is determined from experimental results; $\mathscr{D}$ is the dissociation energy for a diatomic molecule. Thus, at $kT < \hbar\omega$ the dissociation rate for AB molecules is obtained from equation

$$\frac{d[AB]}{dt} = -k_1^*[AB]^2 \qquad [20]$$

when dissociation occurs in pure diatomic gas, and from equation

$$\frac{d[AB]}{dt} = -k_2^*[AB][C] \qquad [21]$$

for dissociation of a small amount of diatomic gas added to the inert gas. Here k_1^* and k_2^* are relevant "equilibrium" constants described by [19]; $[AB]$ is the total concentration of molecules in the ground and excited states; $[C]$ is the concentration of inert gas atoms. It will be shown later that the rate of energy conversion from translational to vibrational at temperatures of interest for plasma is proportional to $\exp(-BT^{-1/3})$, where B is a certain positive constant. The rate of "irrevocable" loss of vibrational energy is proportional to the dissociation rate constant [19], as dissociation results in ejection of the vibrationally excited molecule from the system. As the temperature rises the irrevocable losses of energy in the vibrational excited system start being in excess over energy income from the translational degrees of freedom. This means that vibrational distribution can be no more described by the equilibrium distribution function with a temperature equal to translational temperature. Consequently, at high temperatures, use can no more be made of the equilibrium rate constant [19]. It may be said, from general considerations that at high temperatures the real dissociation rate must be lower than that calculated with an equilibrium rate constant, since thermal stepwise dissociation from high vibrational levels in the energy range $\sim kT$ near the dissociation limit leads to a decrease in population of the latter compared to the equilibrium population at the vibrational temperature equal to that for translational-rotational motion of molecules. In a general case the nonequilibrium distribution function for vibrational levels is different from the Boltzmann distribution. However, with molecular gases permitting fast exchange by vibrational excitation, the nonequilibrium distribution function may be of an almost Boltzmann kind, but the temperature T_v will be lower than that for translational motion. When the translational temperature of neutrals usually representing the main fraction of low-temperature plasma, is sufficiently low, the time of vibrational energy relaxation $\tau_v = 1/k_v$ will be short compared to the effective time of dissociation τ_d. At times longer than τ_v dissociation can be described by simple kinetic equations of type [20] or [21] involving rate constants $k_d = 1/\tau_d$ called equilibrium rate constants. This is true even for nonequilibrium distribution mentioned previously. Theoretical calculation of these constants is based on relevant simplification of general equations of type [18]. Equilibrium rate constants for stepwise dissociation k_d and recombination k_{rec} follow the equilibrium relation

$$\frac{k_d}{k_{rec}} = k_{eq} \qquad [22]$$

where k_{eq} is the equilibrium constant estimated from thermodynamic data (19,20). Equation [22] is naturally valid for equilibrium rate constants and for constants of direct and back reactions occurring by one step. The same simple relation will be observed when the reaction involves the formation of an intermediate complex, provided it succeeds in attaining local thermodynamic equilibrium. This path is characteristic of certain bimolecular, in particular ion-molecular reactions. The relation between reaction constants permits finding the back-reaction constant from that known for the direct reaction and vice versa. As to the relation between reaction rates and the equilibrium constant for ionization and recombination proceeding through nonequilibrium intermediate states, this would require specific investigation in certain cases. For instance, the combined impact-radiative nature of electron motion along bound states toward higher bond energy in optically transparent gas has not much in common with its inverse motion during ionization in the same gas, since radiative transitions in transparent gas are always irreversibly directed along the emission of light. Thus, the relation between ionization and recombination rate constants cannot be expressed by the ionization equilibrium constant. When only impact reactions are responsible for the diffusional motion of the electron over energy levels, the relation between constants of direct and back reactions will be approximately equal to the ionization equilibrium constant, provided the time of bound-bound transition is short compared with those of ionization and recombination (20).

As the temperature rises, it becomes impossible to differentiate vibrational relaxation and dissociation. In this case dissociation kinetics cannot be described making use of the rate constant and one has to revert to system [18]. Vibrational relaxation starts affecting dissociation (21) when

$$k_d \sim \left(\frac{\mathscr{D}}{kT}\right)^2 k_v \qquad [23]$$

For oxygen, for example, this would correspond to 5000 °K. Only few numerical kinetic calculations of dissociation at high temperatures were reported. A model of a cutoff harmonic oscillator with equidistant energy levels and one-quantum transitions was used for simultaneous description of vibrational relaxation and thermal dissociation of a small amount of O_2 molecules added to Ar (22). The system of balanced equations was solved by a computer for an O_2 molecule with 26 levels. The kinetic equations for dissociation in this case are:

$$\frac{dX_0}{dt} = k_{10}X_1 - k_{01}X_0$$

$$\frac{dX_1}{dt} = k_{21}X_2 - k_{10}X_1 - k_{12}X_1 + k_{01}X_0$$

. . . .

$$\frac{dX_n}{dt} = k_{n+1,n}X_{n+1} - k_{n,n-1}X_n - k_{n,n+1}X_n + k_{n-1,n}X_{n-1} \qquad [24]$$

. . . .

$$\frac{1}{2}\frac{dX_d}{dt} = k_{l,d}X_l - k_{d,l}X_d^2$$

Here X_0, $X_1 \ldots X_l$ are the populations of vibrational levels, $X_d/2$ the number of dissociated molecules, k the relevant constants for elementary steps. The difficulties in quantitative calculation of stepwise dissociation and recombination at high temperatures of $T > 10,000$ °K are: the necessity of allowing for the anharmonicity of molecular vibrations, for the nonadiabaticity of collisions and, consequently for multiquantum transitions (moreover theoretical and experimental information on the efficiency of nonadiabatic vibrational excitation is very scarce), and for disturbance of the Maxwellian distribution by vibrational relaxation and dissociation that are very fast at high temperatures. The vibrational relaxation and dissociation of diatomic molecules will be treated in more detail in sections X and XI.

II. ELECTRON IMPACT FORMATION OF POSITIVE IONS

An electron may form a positive ion by collision with an atom or a molecule, provided its initial kinetic energy is in excess of the threshold one determined by conservation of energy and momentum. As the electron mass m_e is small compared to that of the atom M, the electron threshold energy upon its collision with a quiescent atom

$$\varepsilon_t = \frac{M + m_e}{M} I \qquad [25]$$

will be virtually equal to the ionization potential I of minimal energy required for detachment of an electron from an atom or a molecule. A simple example of electron impact ionization is

$$e + H = H^+ + 2e \qquad [26]$$

The ionization probability is characterized by the cross-section σ dependent upon the kinetic energy of electrons ε and upon internal characteristics of atoms and molecules. The cross-section smoothly increases from zero and attains a maximum at an energy of $3I$ to $5I$. With further increase in kinetic energy the ionization cross-section slowly decreases. Approximate calculation of σ was carried out for a number of molecules; however, strict quantum-mechanical calculation was not made even for reaction [26]. For instance, there is no theoretical explanation for the behavior of the ionization cross-section near the threshold (23), which is of interest for calculation of the rate of thermal electron-impact ionization. The following theoretical expression was obtained (24,25) for the near-to-threshold behavior of the atomic ionization cross-section

$$\sigma(\varepsilon) = \sigma_0(\varepsilon - 1)^n \qquad [27]$$

where σ_0 is a coefficient independent of ε and numerically equal to σ at $\varepsilon = I + 1\text{eV}$, n is the ionization multiplicity, the number of reappearing free electrons. According to [27] the cross-section for single ionization must increase linearly with electron energy. On the other hand more strict calculation of [26] yields non-linear solutions near to threshold functions for single ionization. This is in agreement with experimental data (27) for ionization of helium atoms by electrons with small scatter of kinetic energy. The monoenergeticity of electrons in these experiments was ensured by an electrostatic energy selector. Experiments with helium have shown that the cross-section for single ionization is proportional to $(\varepsilon - I)^{1.127}$ up to energies by 2 eV higher than the threshold, whereas at those from 2 to 12 eV higher the dependence is linear. The available theories are insufficient for estimation of the electron energy range where the theoretical and experimental dependencies would coincide.

The dependence of the cross-section of [26] on electron energy also appeared to be complex (28). The energy resolution in measurements was ≤ 0.06 eV. Up to energies of ~ 0.4 eV beyond the threshold the ionization cross-section is a complex nonlinear function of the electron energy. Its shape tends to the power law $(\varepsilon - I)^{1.13 \pm 0.03}$. (A higher power index is observed above the threshold up to energies by 0.05 eV in excess of the threshold one. However, it is not clear to what extent this must be allowed for, taking into account the instrument resolving power.) Above 0.4 eV and almost up to 3 eV the experimental data obey the linear function. The slope of the linear part of the curve shows good agreement with the results obtained in other work, but disagrees with theory. Intersection of the linear part with the energy axis is 0.032 eV in excess of the ionization threshold. In general the experimental data available seem to show to a good precision that up to energies of approximately 1–2 eV over the threshold the ionization cross-section may be considered linear, and for practical calculation, within the 1 eV range it may be approximated by [27] at $n = 1$. Estimation of the error caused by use of a simplified dependence will be made at the end of this section.

When the formation of excited ions is possible at energies close to the threshold value the dependence of cross-section on electron energy (ionization curve) will be represented by rectilinear sections. The bending points will correspond to thresholds for the appearance of excited ions (25).

A number of approximate and semiempirical expressions are used now for calculation of the absolute ionization cross-sections over wide energy ranges (29,30). Classical calculation yielded a convenient analytical expression for the cross-section of electron repelling σ_k from the Kth shell consisting of n equivalent electrons (31):

$$\sigma_k = \left(n \, \frac{6.56 \times 10^{-14}}{I_k^2} \right) \frac{1}{X} \left(\frac{X-1}{X+1} \right)^{3/2} \left\{ 1 + \frac{2}{3} \left(1 - \frac{1}{2X} \right) \ln \left[2.7 + (X-1)^{1/2} \right] \right\}$$

$$[28]$$

Here I_k is the ionization potential in eV for the given shell and $X = \varepsilon/I_i$. At $X = 3.7$ the σ_k value is maximum, and

$$\sigma_k = n \, \frac{1.4 \times 10^{-14}}{I_k^2}$$

The total cross-section for ionization of an atom or a molecule will be equal to the sum of σ_k over all atomic and molecular shells. It will be noted that the greatest contribution to the total cross-section is that from the outer shell, but contribution from inner shells is also considerable for alkali and earth-alkali atoms (32). Comparison of experimental cross-section with those calculated making use of [28] shows good agreement in many cases (31,32). The semiempirical expression

$$\sigma = \left(N \frac{\varphi}{I^2} \right) \frac{X-1}{X^2} \ln (fX)$$ [29]

is often used for calculating the cross-section for the outer shell. Here N is the number of electrons in the outer shell, and φ and f are universal constants for all atoms. Yet better agreement is attained by selecting φ and f values for every atom. The f parameter permits shifting the cross-section maximum relative to the ionization threshold. For instance, at $f = 1.25$ the value X_m corresponding to a maximum cross-section is 3.7, and at $f = 1$ it is 4.3. At the limit $X \gg 1$ all parameters of [29] may be estimated approximately (the Bethe-Born approximation). However, with low energies the values obtained would be overestimated compared to experimental ones. Better agreement would be obtained by using a modified Born approximation (33,34).

Multicharged positive ions can be formed by collision of electrons of sufficient energy with multi-electron atoms. Multiple ionization by single collision occurs by various mechanisms. For instance, the classical theory treats the formation of doubly charged ions as consecutive collisions of the ionizing electron with two electrons of the atom, or as a single collision of the primary electron with that of the atom, followed by repelling the second electron from the same atom by a fast secondary electron. In the former case the probability of double ionization at a high energy of the primary electron ($X \gg 1$) will be approximately proportional to the square of single ionization probability. As the ionization cross-section decreases with increasing X in the range of kinetic energies, $X \gg 1$, the relation of the doubly charged to singly charged ions yields will also decrease with increasing X. This effect seems to have been observed for the first time (35) for argon ionization by high-energy electrons. Systematic studies on the cross-sections of multiple ionization of inert gases over a wide energy range were reported recently (36–38). While the cross-section of single ionization at a high energy of electrons follows the expression

$$\sigma = \frac{A}{\varepsilon} \ln (B\varepsilon)$$ [30]

that for double ionization of light atoms (36) is best described as

$$\sigma = \frac{C}{\varepsilon}$$ [31]

A, B, and C are constant values. This dependence shows qualitative agreement with the expected relative decrease in the yield of doubly charged ions with increasing energy. Another path for formation of multicharged ions becomes effective for heavy Kr and Xe atoms having many electrons in inner shells. A fast incident electron may repel an electron from the inner-atom shell imparting additionally such excitation to the singly charged ion that loss of additional excitation would occur both by emission of electromagnetic quanta and by spontaneous ionization yielding multicharged ions. The dependence of the cross-section for multiple ionization on electron energy would be approximately the same as for single ionization [30], since eq. [30] will remain valid also for the formation of multicharged ions by ionizing collisions of secondary electrons with those of the same atom (31). In reality different mechanisms contribute to the formation of multicharged ions and this may be seen from the complicated dependence of the multiple ionization cross-section on the kinetic energy of electrons (35,36). Different paths of multicharged-ion formation may sometimes occur close to energy threshold for double ionization. For instance the relevant curve for reaction

$$e + Ca = Ca^{2+} + 3e$$

shows (37) that the Ca^{2+} ions are yielded by three paths: (1) by direct ionization $\sigma \sim (\varepsilon - I_1)^2$; (2) by detachment of one electron from the inner $3p$ orbital with subsequent autoionization of the singly charged ion $\sigma \sim (\varepsilon - I_2)$; (3) through a number of autoionization states, namely the neutral atom becomes excited to energies in excess of that for double ionization, and spontaneously emits electrons. It was mentioned previously that expressions for the cross-section of multiple ionization were obtained from classical mechanics (30). Good agreement with experiment was observed for the most simple case, double ionization. The cross-sections for multiple ionization of other atoms were not calculated.

In addition to electronic degrees of freedom the molecules and molecular ions possess vibrational and rotational ones. Ionization of molecules makes possible an important specific process, the dissociative ionization

$$e + AB = A^+ + B + 2e \qquad [32]$$

When the reaction products are not of a monoatomic nature and are excited to energies in excess of dissociation energies, further decay of fragments is possible.

The entity of relative ion currents and m/e obtained by ionization of an individual compound is called its molecular mass-spectrum. Properly measured ratios of different mass ion currents give those of partial cross-sections for dissociative ionization along various paths.

The fundamental concepts for ionization of atoms remain essentially valid for molecules. It appears that the total cross-section for formation of all positive ions, both molecular and fragmentary, in the ionization of molecules can be approximately described by semiempirical expressions similar to [28] and [29] derived for atom ionization. The total number of outer electrons of all atoms must then be substituted into the expression (39). The main contribution to ionization is usually that from outer, valence electrons of the atoms constituting the molecule. Typical ionization cross-section for molecules in the ground state as a function of electron energy are shown in Fig. 2 taken from (40).

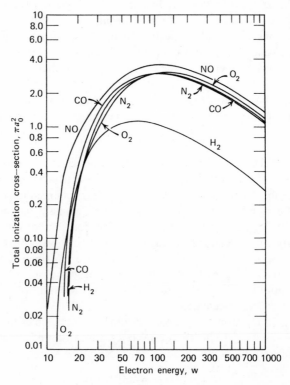

Figure 2   Cross-sections for the total ionization of some molecules as function of kinetic energy of electrons (40).

Consider in more detail the specific features of molecular ionization accounted for by the vibrational degrees of freedom of the molecule and of the molecular ion. Let us begin with diatomic molecules, as the mechanisms of their ionization and dissociative ionization are elucidated. Direct ionization is naturally the simplest. Potential curves for a molecule and an ion in the ground state are shown in Fig. 3. Quantum-mechanical calculation shows that with ionization by fast electrons the probability of formation of an ion

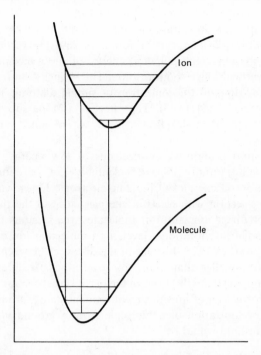

Figure 3   Potential curves of a two-atom molecule and a molecular ion.

in the vibrational state i, when the molecule is in state j, is proportional to the overlapping integral of relevant nuclear wave functions for molecule ψ_i^M and ion ψ_i^I

$$P_{ij} = \int \psi_i^M \psi_j^I \frac{C}{R}$$
[33]

where R is the internuclear distance.

The overlapping integrals are called the Franck-Condon factors. These show that transitions involving no changes in nuclear velocity and in the internuclear separation, in terms of classical mechanics, would be most probable. This is the Franck-Condon principle. When a molecule is in the ground state, most probable, at the position of potential curves in Fig. 3, would be the transition of a molecular ion to the 2nd vibrational level. When a molecule is on the vibrational level 1, the intermolecular distances will mostly correspond to zero velocities of nuclei (turning points): the electron transition, taking considerably less time than that of nuclear vibrations, will

then lead, according to Franck-Condon, to formation, with highest probability, of molecular ions in vibrational states 0 and 5. It will be seen from Fig. 3
that these vibrational states can be found by drawing vertical lines up to
intersect with the curve for potential energy of the molecular ion. This is
often called "vertical" electron transition. The Franck-Condon factor values
for certain transitions in the ionization of simple diatomic molecules were
obtained theoretically (41,42,43). The effect of isotope substitution on the
P_{ij} values was also studied (43). Best accuracy was obtained in experiments on
photo-ionization.

When ionization is induced by electrons of low energy, the transition
probabilities will naturally depend essentially not only on overlapping
integrals, but also on energies of ionizing electrons. Linear variations in the
ionization cross-section with electron energies close to the threshold would
be expected for direct ionization of molecules, the same as for atoms. The
separation of adjacent vibrational levels in a molecular ion does not exceed
several tenths of an eV. For this reason the distances between the ionization
curve bends are smaller than those for transitions to different electronic
levels. Assuming (41) that vibrations in the partial cross-section for ionization,
involving the formation of ions in the vibrational state j, are linear, the total
cross-section for ionization of a molecule from a ground vibrational state
close to the threshold would be

$$\sigma = \sum_{j,\,k} C_k{}^k P_{0j}(\varepsilon - {}^k I_{0j}) \qquad [34]$$

Here ${}^k P_{0j}$ is the Franck-Condon factor for transition of the molecule from
the ground to the jth vibrational level of the ion in the kth state; ${}^k I_{0j}$ is the
energy threshold for excitation of the jth vibrational level of the molecular
ion in the kth state from the ground vibrational level of the molecule; C is the
proportionality coefficient. Summarizing in [34] is made over all indexes
j, k for which the inequality $(\varepsilon - {}^k I_{0j}) > 0$ is valid. Comparison of experimental
curves for electron impact ionization of the O_2, N_2 and CO molecules with
those obtained making use of [34] shows fair agreement within the range of
several eV to the ionization threshold (41). Estimation assumed that $C_k = C$ is
independent of the electronic state of the ion. Consequently, certain deviations from experimental functions may be due to the coarseness of the
assumption.

The assumption of linear variations in the ionization cross-section close to
the threshold was used also in calculating the dependence of the cross-section
for ionization involving molecular ions on the temperature of the gas (41).
This dependence is accounted for by increasing population of the upper
vibrational levels with rising temperature and consequent transitions from
the excited vibrational levels of the molecule to complete ionization. The

molecular ionization cross-section often shows a strong temperature dependence and the shape of the latter is a function of the electron energy. For instance, at an energy of 11 eV the cross-section for a I_2 molecule will increase by 1.5, as the temperature rises from 390 to 490°K. Figure 4 shows the temperature dependences of cross-sections for I_2 ionization at various electron energies. Similar experimental results are available for the more complex CH_3Cl and CH_3I molecules (41). It is evident that allowances for the dependence of the ionization cross-section on vibrational excitation is essential in describing ionization in low-temperature plasma containing, as a rule, high concentrations of vibrationally excited molecules. Theoretical calculation of the ionization cross-section temperature dependence was

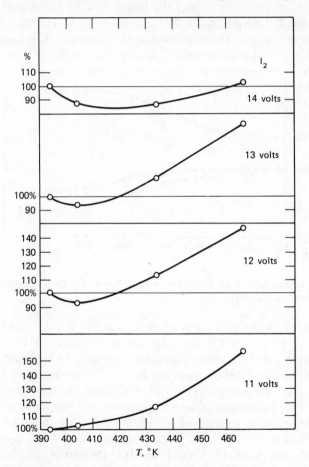

Figure 4 Dependence of the ionization cross-section of I_2 from the electron energies for various temperatures (41).

carried out for Cl_2 and O_2 molecules as well. The expression for ionization cross-section near the threshold at high temperatures of the gas was found to be

$$\sigma = C \sum_{i,j,k} {}^k P_{ij} \frac{\exp(-\hbar\omega_i/kT)}{\sum_i \exp(-\hbar\omega_i/kT)} \qquad [35]$$

Here

$$\frac{\exp(-\hbar\omega_i/kT)}{\sum \exp(-\hbar\omega_i/kT)}$$

is the Boltzmann factor equal to the probability of a molecule occupying the vibrational level i at the gas temperature T. In order to estimate the cross-section at a nonequlibrium $f(\omega_i)$ the latter must be substituted into [35] instead of the Boltzmann factor. The summation in [35] is made within the same limits as for [34]. The calculated cross-sections for Cl_2 ionization are shown in Fig. 5. When the energy of ionizing electrons is 12 eV the ionization

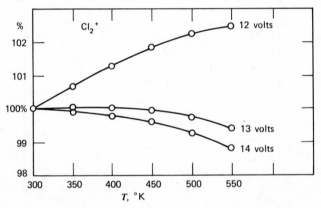

Figure 5 Dependence of the ionization cross-section of Cl_2 from the temperature for various electron energies (41).

cross-section increases with temperature, and at 14 eV it decreases. Only the ground electronic state of Cl_2^+ was taken into account in calculation. It will be noted, however, that the cross-section for ionization of molecules (same as atoms) close to the threshold does not always follow the simple expression [27]. Processes competing with direct ionization, namely ionization by excitation with subsequent autoionization and that by decay of an AB^- complex formed upon collision of an ionizing electron with an AB molecule, may lead to complex variations in the cross-section, depending on electron energies near the threshold. There is no strict theoretical calculation of the threshold dependence of the cross-section for electron impact ionization, and for a general case it is not clear yet which of the ionization processes is predominantly close to the threshold.

The main difficulties in experimental investigations of ionization near the threshold are connected with the necessity of obtaining electron beams with small scatter over kinetic energies. Strongly monoenergetic electrons are needed, in particular, for resolution of the vibrational structure in the ionization curve. It was mentioned previously that the best results obtained in this respect show a scatter of several hundredths of eV. Experimental data for H_2 molecules, showing the validity of a simple model of direct ionization, were reported; however, this is contradicted by recently obtained experimental results (44). It was found in experiments making use of an electron-energy selector that within the range from the ionization threshold to ~ 17.5 eV direct ionization is not predominant and a great number of ions are formed in an indirect way, through excitation of autoionization states. Their lifetimes for the given case seems to be $10^{-7}-10^{-6}$ sec. Consequently, collisions with particles may, in principle, change the probabilities for decay of highly-excited molecular states by various paths, and, consequently, the apparent ionization cross-sections. It was shown in (44) that autoionization processes may contribute essentially to overall ionization of other diatomic molecules as well. In this way the mechanisms of molecular-ionization processes near the threshold cannot be considered to be unambiguous for a general case and the validity of the above expressions based on the assumption of a direct-ionization mechanism, is not strictly warranted. However, indirect-ionization processes were not estimated yet.

Dissociative ionization of diatomic molecules was discussed previously. Theoretical treatment and estimation of its detailed mechanism naturally become considerably more difficult for polyatomic molecules. Vast experimental evidence is available in this field, since molecular mass spectra are, at present, the most reliable means for determination of the structure and analytical identification of polyatomic molecules. Molecular mass spectra are collected in many catalogues, in particular in that referred to in (48).

Without dwelling in detail on molecular mass spectrometry which is described in relevant monographs (49–52) let us only note that a close relation actually exists between the mass spectrum and the structure of a molecule. Dissociative ionization is usually conceived qualitatively as follows. An electronically excited positive ion is formed upon fast electron impact. Its charge may either occupy any site of the molecule with a comparable probability, or, as a result of migration, be fixed at a site with a low ionization potential. At the same time there occurs dissipation of electronic energy over vibrational degrees of freedom, due to multiple intercrossings of potential surfaces. In terms of the "quasi-equilibrium" theory of mass spectra (53,54) decay of the ion, following dissipation, is that of a vibrationally excited polyatomic particle, by analogy with the theory of unimolecular thermal decomposition. This approach provides a natural explanation to the correlation between the mass spectrum and structure: statistical fluctuations of vibrational quanta result in concentration of higher portions of energy at weaker interatomic bonds. Since this would require a time equal to many periods of atomic vibrations, the decay of a polyatomic molecular ion would take a considerably longer time than that of a diatomic ion usually occurring within 10^{-14} to 10^{-13} sec.

Decays of atomic ions over many paths were actually observed to take 10^{-10}–10^{-9} sec (55,56). Still longer times are required for decay of the so-called metastable ions, long known and extensively studied by the molecular mass spectroscopy technique (49). Yet at least a part of these decays might be caused by other reasons as well. It will be of interest to note here that inhibited decay is observed for diatomic species as well (57), for instance when an ion must pass from one electronic term to another by means of a nonadiabatic transition. Slow decays were observed even for diatomic doubly-charged ions (58).

Duration of the decay of excited molecular ions is of great importance in connection with decay competing with stabilization or with a bimolecular reaction upon collisions with neutrals.

Rather satisfactory interpretation of experimental and calculated molecular spectra appeared possible in terms of the quasi-equilibrium theory, by appropriate choice of certain parameters. However, it was found that the electron energy is often not completely converted to vibrational. Thus the mass spectrum will be accounted for by decay of molecular ions from various electronic states and its estimation would be difficult owing to the uncertainity of the energy state and molecular constant values (54).

A method for calculation of the cross-section for formation of fragmentary ions of a diatomic molecule at high electron energies was proposed (55). Let the potential curves for H_2 and for one of the electron states of H_2^+ be those of Fig. 6, taken from (46). The internuclear distance corresponding to a potential energy of the ion equal to that of its dissociation is denoted by r_c; ψ_0 denotes the nuclear wave function of the molecule at its zero vibrational level. The probability that vertical transition will involve an ion energy higher than the dissociation threshold and thus formation of a fragmentary ion is

$$f(<r_c) = \int_0^{r_c} \psi_0^2(r) \, dr$$

The probability for formation of a molecular ion is

$$f(>r_c) = \int_{r_c}^{\infty} \psi_0^2(r) \, dr$$

The relative cross-section for dissociative ionization is equal to the probability ratio for formation of fragmentary and molecular ions: $f(<r_c)/f(>r_c)$.

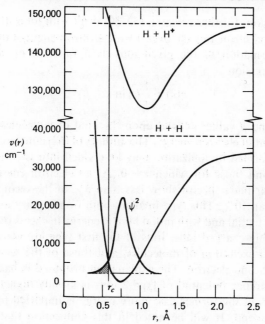

Figure 6   Calculation of mass spectra of H_2 with help of potential curves (46).

The mass spectra of H_2 and D_2 molecules were obtained by this method (45). The ratios $\sigma_{N^+}/\sigma_{N_2^+}$ and $\sigma_{C^+}/\sigma_{CO_2^+}$ for N_2 and CO_2 electron-impact ionization were calculated later (47). More detailed estimation of the ratios of fragmentary to molecular ion beams formed by electron-impact ionization of molecular hydrogen and its isotopes (X = H, D, T) was made making use of the recently obtained potential curves for H_2^+ and H_2 (46). The ratios were calculated for electron energies of 25, 27, 30, 35 and ∞ eV, the ionized molecules being in the ground vibrational states ($v = 0$). The probability of ionization was taken to be directly proportional to electron energy in excess over the ionization threshold. The accuracy was limited by that of obeyance to the Franck-Condon principle. Deviation from experimental results was 5, 16 and 11 percent for hydrogen, deuterium and tritium, respectively. The ratios X^+/X_2^+ for $v = 1, 2, 3$ were calculated for electron energies of 30 eV. The ratios markedly increased with v. These results are of great interest, since neutral particles in plasma may be vibrationally excited.

Let us consider now the ionization of molecules by fast electrons. Decrease in the relative cross-section for hydrogen ionization with increasing electron energy was observed along with that for doubly charged argon ions (35). This fact was explained (34) as being caused by collisions of the ionizing electron with two electrons of the hydrogen molecule to form protons, the same as in the case of argon. Further research (52–59) dealt with ionization of complex molecules by electron impact over a wide electron-energy range. The cross-section for formation of the given ions as a function of electron energy obeys the expression

$$\sigma(\varepsilon) = \frac{1}{\varepsilon}(\alpha \ln \varepsilon - \beta) \qquad [36]$$

where the α and β values depend upon the kind of molecules and ions, but are independent of electron energy. The authors of (62) come to the conclusion that all ions formed by ionization may be divided into two types: those for which $\alpha > 0$ and those for which $\alpha = 0$. At an electron energy of 1000 eV most molecular mass spectra show less than 5% of the second type, and at 400 eV less than 10%. This type involves both fragmentary ions with a high appearance potential and with initial kinetic energy in excess over the thermal one, and doubly charged ions. Ions of the first type are considered (62) to form by single excitation of molecules, and those of the second by double excitation with one electron. The explanation proposed is based on the fact that the appearance potential of type 2 ions is usually higher than that for type 1, that is, in the former case more energy is imparted to the molecule than in the second. It will be noted in this connection that formation of hydrocarbon ions by electron impact (63) may occur by electron detachment and simultaneous excitation or detachment of another electron. The cross-section for this process represents no more than 20% of that for simple detachment of a valence electron. This is approximately equal to the relative intensity of the type 2 ions as reported in (62).

The vast experimental and theoretical information available reveal the various effects of inner molecular excitation on dissociative ionization by electron impact (64–70). In particular, several experimental papers were published on the effect of temperature on dissociative-ionization mass spectra of complex molecules. For these the effect is maximum; owing to the many degrees of freedom they possess, they may store great amounts of internal energy at even low temperatures. The main experimental results obtained for complex molecules at electron energies of ~ 50 eV, are:

1. The intensity of individual mass-spectral lines may change in a different way:
(a) The temperature coefficient for a molecular ion is always negative and increases in absolute value with the number of atoms in a molecule. Here the temperature coefficient is represented by the slope of the curve for the temperature dependence of the ratio of the given ion current to that of inert monatomic gas admitted as standard together with the species investigated.
(b) The temperature coefficients of fragmentary ions may be both positive and negative.

(c) The temperature coefficients of end decomposition products are always positive.

2. The total relative cross-section does not change with temperature or changes only slightly compared to changes of individual mass-spectral lines.

3. The temperature dependence of the given decomposition decreases with increasing activation energy. "Inversion" of the temperature dependence, that is, change of the temperature coefficient sign with electron energy was observed in the mass spectrum of n-heptane at different electron energies (66).

The experimental results can often be explained in terms of the previously mentioned "quasi-stationary" theory of decomposition of excited ions, under the assumption that the excitation energy of a molecular ion is the sum of the internal molecular energy and of that imparted to the ion by electron impact and independent of the excited molecule energy. However, the problem cannot be considered as elucidated, as there is evidence that the imparted energy can depend on that of internal excitation (68). Moreover, it appeared impossible to interpret the temperature effect on photo-ionization mass spectra in terms of the statistical theory (71).

Only scanty reliable information is available on ionization of electronically excited species by electron impact. Yet, as shown by theoretical estimation, at temperatures of $10^4\,°K$ the atoms in plasma close to the thermodynamic equilibrium are ionized by electron impact mostly from higher levels, that is the ionization is stepwise. The same semiempirical expressions as those for ionization from the ground state are used for estimation of ionization cross-sections, taking naturally into account that the ionization potential of an excited atom is less than that for the ground state by the excitation energy value. A semiempirical expression

$$\sigma_n(V) = 1.3na_0^2\left(\frac{V-1}{V+1}\right)^{3/2}\frac{n^3}{V}(\ln V + 4n)$$

for the ionization cross-section for excited hydrogen atoms as a function of the quantum number was obtained in (73). Here a_0 is the Bohr radius, $V = \varepsilon/I_n$, ε is the electron energy, I_n is the ionization potential for an excited hydrogen atom with quantum number n. At $V > 30$ this expression yields values, at any n, coinciding with σ_n calculated to the Born approximation. At $n = 1$ they are in agreement with experimental data for $V = 1$ to 40. Since it follows from theoretical estimation that the cross-section for ionization of electronically excited particles by electron impact is usually higher than that for the ground state, experimental data for the latter may be used for obtaining the lower limit for the rate of ionization in plasma.

Now let us consider reference experimental data on cross-sections for electron-impact ionization of certain ground state atoms and molecules. Detailed discussions of these were made in recent reviews (40,74,75), also containing much reference information, such as cross-sections for ionization of He, Ne, Ar, Kr, Xe, H_2, D_2, N_2, O_2, CO, NO, CO_2, N_2O, and CH_4 from the threshold to 1000 eV (40). Table 1 shows the cross-sections for

TABLE 1

Cross-sections for the ionization of atoms and simple molecules over the energy range from 1 to 1 + 3 eV

Element		Energy range over the cross-section						
He (24.6)	ε,eV	25	25.5	26	26.5	27	27.5	28
	σ, a_0^2	0.006	0.013	0.020	0.027	0.034	0.041	0.048
Ne (21.6)		22	22.5	23	23.5	24	24.5	25
		0.004	0.010	0.017	0.023	0.030	0.036	0.043
Ar (15.8)		16	16.5	17	17.5	18	18.5	19
		0.023	0.076	0.152	0.241	0.334	0.429	0.523
Kr (14.00)		14.5	15	15.5	16	16.5	17	17.5
		0.089	0.182	0.290	0.407	0.528	0.655	0.777
Xe (12.1)		12.5	13	13.5	14	14.5	15	15.5
		0.125	0.291	0.469	0.650	0.844	1.03	1.27
H_2 (15.4)		16	16.5	17	17.5	18	18.5	19
		0.034	0.069	0.105	0.140	0.177	0.213	0.250
D_2 (15.4)		16	16.5	17	17.5	18	18.5	19
		0.039	0.078	0.118	0.157	0.197	0.235	0.272
N_2 (15.6)		16	16.5	17	17.5	18	18.5	19
		0.024	0.053	0.081	0.112	0.147	0.186	0.226
O_2 (12.2)		12.5	13	13.5	14	14.5	15	15.5
		0.012	0.026	0.046	0.061	0.078	0.097	0.112
CO (14.0)		14.5	15	15.5	16	16.5	17	17.5
		0.031	0.058	0.087	0.121	0.158	0.201	0.243
NO (9.3)		9.5	10	10.5	11	11.5	12	12.5
		0.013	0.020	0.035	0.053	0.073	0.105	0.149
CO_2 (13.8)		14.5	15	15.5	16	16.5	17	17.5
		0.063	0.110	0.154	0.198	0.244	0.290	0.333
N_2O (12.7)		14	14.5	15	15.5	16	16.5	17
		0.061	0.137	0.180	0.226	0.270	0.318	0.363
CH_4 (13.0)		13.5	14	14.5	15	15.5	16	16.5
		0.039	0.084	0.148	0.225	0.316	0.410	0.506

ionization of atoms and simple molecules over an energy range from I to $I + 3$ eV. The relevant ionization potential is shown in brackets near the symbol; the electron energy ε is shown in eV. The ionization cross-section at a given electron units of $\pi a_0^2 = 0.880 \times 10^{-16}$ cm^2.

When the electron distribution function is Maxwellian, the rate constant for ionization of ground state atoms and molecules may be obtained from the dependence of ionization cross-sections on electron energies, making use of expression [8]. Calculation becomes simplified at electron temperatures of $kT < I$ characteristic of low-temperature plasma. In this case ionization is induced mostly by electrons of energies close to the threshold one and $\sigma = \sigma_0(\varepsilon - I)$ may be substituted into [8] instead of the precise function $\sigma(\varepsilon)$. Integrating we obtain

$$k = \sigma_0 \, kT \left(\frac{8kT}{\pi m_e}\right)^{1/2} \left(\frac{I}{kT} + 2\right) \qquad [37]$$

The function $\sigma \sim (1 - I/\varepsilon)$ gives the cross-section for atom ionization over a wider energy range than does the linear function. The rate constant for this function obtained from [8] is (69):

$$k = 1.85 bNT^{3/2} \exp\left(-\frac{I}{kT}\right)\left(\frac{I}{kT}\right)^{-2} \qquad [38]$$

Here b is the numerical coefficient characteristic of the given atom; N is the number of equivalent electrons in the outer atomic shell. The b and N values for certain atoms are given in Table 2, taken from (75). Equation [38] is valid for temperatures $T < 2 \times 10^{-4}I$, $(2 \times 10^4 I = 300,000°$ for hydrogen).

Let us estimate now the error in the rate constant that may be caused by substituting a linear function for the complex dependence of the ionization cross-section for reaction [26]. It follows from the results obtained (28) that the exact curve for $\sigma(\varepsilon)$ from the threshold energy I to $I + 3$ eV lies between two parallel lines $\sigma' = 6.3 \times 10^{-18}(\varepsilon - I)$ and $\sigma'' = 6.3 \times 10^{-18}(\varepsilon - I - 0.03)$. The ionization rate constant calculated making use of σ' and σ'', will be higher and lower than the true one, respectively. The relevant ratio of these constants is

$$\frac{k'}{k''} = \exp\left(\frac{0.03}{kT}\right)$$

Thus, in the given case an appreciable difference between the relative and true rate constants will be observed only for very low electron temperatures of no practical interest. At electron temperatures higher than several thousands of degrees linear approximation of the cross-section for $e + H = H^+ + 2e$ as a function of the electron energy gives good agreement of ionization rate constants calculated making use of precise and approximate expressions for $\sigma(\varepsilon)$.

Equations [37] and [38] naturally cannot be used when the ionization curve near the threshold is of a complex shape, as, for instance, that for autoionization of lead (77). Then either the precise experimental function $\sigma(\varepsilon)$ or one accurately approximating it must be substituted into [8].

TABLE 2
Values of b and N for a Number of atoms (75)[a]

Atoms	H	He	Ne	Ar	Kr	Xe	Li	Na	K	Rb	Cs	Ag	N	O	Hg
N	1	2	6	6	6	6	1	1	1	1	1	1	3	4	2
b	0.80	0.70	0.40	0.92	1.08	1.15	0.88	1.23	0.93	0.95	0.88	0.68	0.70	0.44	1.9

[a] Detailed information about ionization of the alkali atoms is given in Ref. (76).

The ionization of positive ions by electron impact becomes increasingly important in connection with the wider temperature range of the plasma investigated. In theory such reactions resemble those occurring in the ionization of neutrals, however the experimental techniques for investigating electron-impact ionization are considerably more complex. Most reliable data are obtained by the mass-spectral method of crossed beams worked out in 1961. The cross-section for reaction

$$e + \text{He}^+ = \text{He}^{2+} + 2e$$

as a function of the electron energy was measured (78). The results obtained were compared with the cross-section for ionization of atomic hydrogen and with theoretical data. Assuming that the ionization cross-section is inversely proportional to the ionization potential square and investigating it as a function of the ratio of electron energies to the ionization potential, the cross-section for He^+ ionization will be close to that for atomic hydrogen at high energies, but it will increase more rapidly in the threshold region. The latter is probably due to "focusing" of slow electrons by the long-range Coulomb field of positive ions. Qualitative estimation seems to suggest that this would increase the ionization cross-section close to the threshold. It will be of interest to note that experimental data on cross-section for electron-impact ionization of atomic ions as a function of energy yield an approximately linear law for Cs^+ ions within the range of some 2 eV from the threshold (79).

The next set of papers describing experiments on collisions between electrons and ions deals with the methods of the ion trap formed by collimation of a dense electron beam in a strong magnetic field. The trap increases the time of ion residence in the electron beam region and, thus, the probability of collisions between electrons and ions (80–83). Ion traps are used now mostly for energy, rather than kinetic measurements, for determining the appearance potentials of various ions. However, the cross-section for

$$e + \text{CO}^+ \, (A^2\Pi_1) = \text{CO}^{2+} + 2e$$

was measured (81). It was found that for He^+ in an ion trap (82) the ionization curve does not coincide with that obtained by the more direct crossed-beam method, and a conclusion was made that true ionization curves cannot be obtained, due to the complexity and uncertainty of the reactions in such traps. Thus the plausibility of their use remains an open question.

Determination of rate constants for ionization of ions in plasma installations became possible recently. It requires accurate knowledge of the plasma temperature and of the electron and ion concentrations. The concentrations of differently charged ions are usually established from the spectral-line intensities. Table 3 lists experimental cross-sections and rate constants for ion

TABLE 3
Experimental cross-sections and rate constants for ion ionization

Ion	Measured value	Experimental condition: n = electron concentration; E = electron energy; kT = electron temperature.	References
He^+	σ; $\sigma_{max}(175\ eV) = 4.9 \times 10^{-18}\ cm^2$	$E = 54.4 - 1000\ eV$	78
Ne^+	σ; $\sigma_{max}(200\ eV) = 3.1 \times 10^{-17}\ cm^2$	$E = 60 - 1000\ eV$	84, 85
N^+	σ; $\sigma_{max}(125\ eV) = 5 \times 10^{-17}\ cm^2$	$E = 20 - 500\ eV$	86
Hg^+	1		
Xe^+	1.4		
Kr^+	1.8		
Ar^+	σ; Relative σ_{max} 0.3	$E = 10 - 500\ eV$	85
Ne^+	0.1		
Hg^{2+}	1.3		
Xe^{2+}	1.5		
Kr^{2+}	0.4		
Ar^{2+}	0.5	$E = 10 - 500\ eV$	87
Li^+	σ; $\sigma_{max}(300\ eV) = 4.5 \times 10^{-18}\ cm^2$	$E = 75 - 800\ eV$	88, 89
Na^+	σ; $\sigma_{max}(300\ eV) = 2.7 \times 10^{-17}\ cm^2$	$E = 20 - 800\ eV$	90
K^+	σ; $\sigma_{max}(100\ eV) = 8.6 \times 10^{-17}\ cm^2$		
Cs^+	$\sigma = (1.0 \pm 0.2)Å^2$	$E = 40\ eV$	79
CO^+	$\sigma = (58 \pm 30)Å^2$	$E = 30\ eV$	81
Ne^+			
Ne^{2+}			
Ne^{3+}		$kT = 10 - 50\ eV$	91
Ne^{4+}	k	$n = 10^{11} - 10^{12}\ cm^{-3}$	
Ne^{5+}			
Ne^{6+}			
C^{4+}	k	$n = 5 \times 10^{15}\ cm^{-3}$, $kT = 190\ eV$	92

ionization. Investigations on reported results on the ionization of positive ions yielded the following conclusions:

1. Reliable experimental data on dependences of absolute values for ionization cross-sections on electron energies are available at present only for singly charged positive ions of alkali metals and certain inert gases mainly in the ground state. These data were obtained by the crossed-beams method. Measurements of cross-sections for ionization of other atomic singly and multicharged ions are hindered due to the presence of ions in various excitation states that are difficult to control.

2. The rate constants for ionization in plasma are unreliable in view of the difficulty in obtaining the Maxwellian distribution function for electrons. The main criterium for the correctness of rate constants still remains the coinci-

dence of experimental data with those calculated making use of semiempirical expressions.

3. It was reported that the lower excited state of helium-like ions in plasma have a great effect on ionization kinetics (92).

III. FORMATION OF NEGATIVE IONS BY COLLISIONS OF ELECTRONS WITH ATOMS AND MOLECULES

When an atom or a molecule possesses electron affinity, it is thermodynamically advantageous for electrons, at low plasma temperatures, to add to neutral particles and form negative ions. Such addition reactions are: (1) radiative capture; (2) dissociative capture; (3) the formation of pairs; (4) nondissociative capture by complex molecules to form excited long-lived ions; (5) capture by three-body collisions.

With atomic ions, the cross-section for radiative capture is usually calculated from the cross-section for photodetachment of electrons from negative ions, making use of a relation obtained in terms of the detailed balance principle (93). In practice it is convenient to use the capture coefficient which is the same as the rate constant for monoenergetic capture

$$\alpha = v\sigma_{capt}$$

The capture coefficient for an s state increases from zero with electron energy, as, for instance, for process $e + H = H^- + hv$. For capture in the p state, as in process $e + O = O^- + hv$ the coefficient is finite at zero and changes but slightly with energy. This fact results in strong temperature dependence in the s state, whereas the capture coefficient for atoms with open p shells is almost independent of temperature. For example, $\alpha \simeq 10^{-15}$ cm^3 sec^{-1} for electron capture by an oxygen atom over an energy range of 0–2 eV, and for atomic hydrogen within 0 to ~ 0.5 eV. α increases from 0 to 2×10^{-16} cm^3 sec^{-1}, and then remains approximately constant at electron energies from 0.5 to 2.5 eV (94). The value of $\alpha \simeq 10^{-14}$ cm^3 sec^{-1} was obtained for electron temperatures of 300 to 500°K by direct observation of the emission spectrum obtained in radiative attachment of electrons to halogen atoms, Cl, Br, and I (95). It will be expected that the α value for these atoms will be the same at higher temperatures as well.

Reliable calculation of α for molecules is difficult owing to lack of information on the distribution over vibrational degrees of freedom in molecules formed by photodetachment of electrons from negative molecular ions. The α value for molecular oxygen at electron temperatures of ~ 3000°K was estimated to be $\sim 10^{-18}$ cm^3 sec^{-1} (95); for oxygen α increases with temperature. The coefficient of radiative attachment for OH is of the same order of magnitude as that for halogen atoms (95). Radiative attachment may also occur for excited species. For instance, it was found that electrons became attached to nitrogen atoms in the metastable excited state ^2D to form a metastable N^- ^1D ion (96). The contribution of N^- ions to formation of continuum spectra of nitrogen and air plasma was discussed (97).

Attachment of electrons to molecular gases may prove to be dissociative. The most detailed theoretical treatment of this phenomenon is to consider it as resonance (98). It may be conceived approximately as attachment of the electron to the molecule, most probable at an electron energy equal to energy of vertical transition between the molecular and the negative ion terms, with subsequent competing reactions of dissociation to a stable negative ion and autoionization. The direct mechanism for dissociative attachment has been estimated theoretically (99). Relevant experimental data are given in reviews (100–103). Analysis of experimental data (103) has shown that the capture cross-section for the resonance maximum $\sigma(\varepsilon_m)$ is strongly dependent on the resonance energy ε_m. The dependence plot shows a bend corresponding to electron energies that induce excitation of neutral molecules. Three groups of molecules will be named: (1) those with the ε_m value lower than the energy ε_N of any electronically excited level of a neutral molecule and with a purely repulsive negative ion in the Franck-Condon region; (2) those for which $\varepsilon_m > \varepsilon_N$; and (3) those with very low $\sigma(\varepsilon_m)$ for which the negative ion term in the Franck-Condon region shows a minimum, so that dissociation may occur only within a very narrow range of interatomic distances. With molecules of group (1) $\sigma(\varepsilon_m) \sim \varepsilon^{-1}$ whereas for group (2) $\sigma(\varepsilon_m)$ decreases much faster with ε_m. In the case of (1) the effect of autoionization on $\sigma(\varepsilon_m)$ is weak and the isotope effect is approximately equal to the square of the inverse ratio for reduced masses of decomposition products. With (2) and particularly (3) the effect of autoionization on $\sigma(\varepsilon_m)$ as well as the isotope effect, are strong. Table 4 lists experimental results on dissociative capture by two and three atom molecules. More detailed information involving polyatomic molecules may be found in Refs. 102 and 103. The Γ_d symbol in Table 4 denotes the resonance peak width at its half-height. The cross-section for dissociative capture as a function of electron energies are tabulated in Ref. 109 for O_2, CO, NO, CO_2, and N_2O molecules. As a rule, dissociative attachment of electrons is endothermal, since the electron affinity of atoms and atomic groups of most chemical elements is lower than the characteristic chemical bond energies. Halide molecules usually prove to be an exception, in particular those of X_2 as such. The rate constant for dissociative attachment of electrons at low temperature of the latter was measured for I_2 molecules from the decrease in electron concentration with time elapsing after the ionizing pulse. The value of $k = 1.8 \times 10^{-10}$ cm^3 sec^{-1} was obtained (118). A higher value was obtained earlier (117). This difference was found (118) to be accoun-

TABLE 4
Experimental data on dissociative capture by two and three atom molecules.

Molecule	Ion	ε_{max}, eV	$\sigma_c\,(\varepsilon_{max})$, cm^2	$\int_0^\infty \sigma(\varepsilon)d\varepsilon$, cm^2 eV	Γ_d, eV	Refs. to Γ_d	Refs. to columns 3, 4, 5
			Group I				
HI	I$^-$	~0.0	2.3×10^{-14}	3.7×10^{-16}			104
DI	I$^-$	~0.0	1.38×10^{-14}	2.6×10^{-16}			104
I$_2$	I$^-$	0.3	3.0×10^{-15}				116, 117
HBr	Br$^-$	0.28	2.7×10^{-16}	7.4×10^{-17}	0.24	104	104
DBr	Br$^-$	0.28	1.87×10^{-16}	5.1×10^{-17}	0.23	104	104
HCl	Cl$^-$	0.81	1.99×10^{-17}	7.4×10^{-18}	0.3	104	104
DCl	Cl$^-$	0.84	1.6×10^{-17}	6.2×10^{-18}	0.28	104	104
N$_2$O	O$^-$	2.2	9.78×10^{-18}	1.05×10^{-18}	1.1	105	109
			Group II				
H$_2$O	H$^-$	6.45	6.94×10^{-18}	6.6×10^{-18}	1.05, 1.0	106, 107	106
D$_2$O	D$^-$	6.5	5.2×10^{-18}	3.9×10^{-18}	0.8	106	106
O$_2$	O$^-$	6.7	1.43×10^{-18}	8.24×10^{-19}	2.0	108	108
					1.9	105	109
					2.1	109	111
CO$_2$	O$^-$	8.03	4.82×10^{-19}	5.3×10^{-19}	1.1	108, 109	108, 112
H$_2$O	H$^-$	8.6	1.3×10^{-18}	2.5×10^{-18}	2.1	106	106
NO	O$^-$	8.6	1.12×10^{-18}	2.68×10^{-18}	2.3	109	109
D$_2$O	D$^-$	8.6	0.6×10^{-18}	0.9×10^{-18}	1.6	106	106
H$_2$	H$^-$	10.1	1.2×10^{-20}	4.84×10^{-20}	3.6	110	110, 111
HD	H$^-$, D$^-$	10.3	0.62×10^{-20}	2.51×10^{-20}	3.2–4.1	110	110
D$_2$	D$^-$	10.6	0.26×10^{-20}	8.8×10^{-21}	3.0	110	110
N$_2$O	O$^-$	11.0	9.2×10^{-19}		3.6	109	109
H$_2$	H$^-$	13.75	2.86×10^{-20}	2.92×10^{-20}	1.2	110	110, 114
HD	H$^-$, D$^-$	13.9	1.56×10^{-20}		1.4	110	110
D$_2$	D$^-$	14.0	1.07×10^{-20}		1.6	110	110
			Group III				
H$_2$	H$^-$	3.75	1.62×10^{-21}				115
HD	H$^-$, D$^-$	3.75	1.0×10^{-22}				115
D$_2$	D$^-$	3.75	8×10^{-24}				115
CO$_2$	O$^-$	4.35	1.6×10^{-19}		0.8	108, 109	108, 109
CO	O$^-$	10.03	2.2×10^{-19}	2.76×10^{-19}	1.4	109	108, 113

ted for by the effect of negative ions on the rate of electron diffusion due to the periodical pulse technique used (117). The resonance width for this reaction measured mass spectrometrically (116) was found to be ~ 0.04 eV (116). Consequently, at electron temperatures of some 0.1 eV the rate constant will decrease with temperature and, at temperatures of interest for electric discharge and certain other plasma it will be less than 1.8×10^{-10} cm^3 sec^{-1}.

Of great importance for plasma is the attachment of electrons to excited species. Dissociative attachment to O_2 at elevated temperatures revealed a considerable decrease in the appearance threshold for O^- ions and an increase in the reaction cross-section with temperature. This is apparently due to appearance of vibrationally excited molecules, since oxygen was heated to 2100°K (119). Thermal excitation by $\sim 1/16$ eV only will shift the threshold by ~ 2 eV. Strong temperature dependence for formation of negative ions in CO_2 was observed (120). The most probable path of formation of primary negative ions in hydrocarbon flames was suggested (121) to be the dissociative attachment of an electron to $C_2H_2O^*$ by reaction

$$e + C_2H_2O^* \rightarrow C_2^- + H_2O$$

Dissociative attachment of electrons to molecules for which the reaction threshold is relatively high may be of great importance in strong electric fields, when the electron temperature is sufficiently high. For instance, it was found (12) that in pure oxygen dissociative attachment of electrons is predominant at $E/p = 3$ V cm^{-1} torr^{-1}, and in air 10 V cm^{-1} torr^{-1}. The attachment coefficients for oxygen and for mixtures of oxygen and nitrogen were measured over wide ranges of pressures and E/p values.

An interesting form of attachment is the nondissociative capture of electrons by complex molecules yielding long-lived negative ions. The long lifetimes of such ions are due to fast distribution of their electronic energy over vibrational degrees of freedom, thus making difficult the back transition necessary for detachment of electrons because of the low statistical factor of the electronic state compared to that of the vibrational state (122). The coefficient for attachment of electrons to SF_6 molecules by this mechanism was found to be 1.24×10^9 cm^{-1} torr^{-1}, and the lifetime of an excited SF_6^- ion relative to ionization was estimated as 25 μ sec (122). The rate of electron capture appeared to be independent of temperature over a range of $298° \leq T \leq 418°$K. This corresponds to a cross-section for electron capture that varies with electron velocity v following the law $\sigma \sim 1/v$. Data on nondissociative capture of electrons by other complex molecules are also given in Ref. 122.

The formation of pairs in the group of reactions considered is of the type

$$e + AB = A^+ + B^- + e$$

The threshold of this reaction is usually high compared to that of dissociative attachment, as the formation of positive ions requires considerable energy. The cross-section for formation of pairs by collisions of electrons with O_2, CO, CO_2, and N_2O molecules may be found in Ref. 123. A marked increase in the cross-section values will be seen to occur from the threshold of some 20 eV up to the maximum value of ~ 30 eV, after which the electron energy slowly decreases. The maximum cross-sections for the previously mentioned molecules are $5 \times 10^{-3} \pi a_0^2$, $2.2 \times 10^{-3} \pi a_0^2$, $1.6 \times 10^{-3} \pi a_0^2$ and $9 \times 10^{-2} \pi a_0^2$, in respectively. Experimental data on pair formation by collisions with electrons of several tens eV with simple and complex molecules are given review (101) and in Ref. 123. Table 5 is an example of cross-sections for

TABLE 5

Cross-sections for formation of negative ions from methane by resonance capture to form pairs.

Ion formed	Maximum cross-section for resonance capture $(\times 10^{19})$, cm^2	Cross-section for pair formation at 90 eV $(\times 10^{19})$ cm^2	Resonance thresholds, eV
H$^-$	2.4	4.4	8.3, 9.5
C$^-$	0.006	4.2	
CH$^-$	0.64	2.7	9.6
CH$_2^-$	2.95	0.8	8.3, 9.3
CH$_3^-$		0.03	

formation of negative ions from methane by resonance capture to form pairs. The width of resonance maxima is of the order of 1 eV.

We have discussed the formation of negative ions by two-body collisions of electrons with atoms and molecules. The importance of three-body collisions that may also yield negative ions increases at relatively high pressures in plasma. The energy released by electron attachment is then imparted to the third body and the ion becomes stabilized. When A and B are atoms, the most simple reactions of negative ion formation will be

$$A + e + B = A^- + B$$

$$A + e + e = A^- + e$$

It is convenient to compare the rates of these reactions with those of back processes involved in decomposition of negative ions by collisions with atoms and electrons. Expressions for the frequency of electron attachment were obtained in terms of the detailed balance principle (124). Analysis of the functions obtained (125) seems to show that the frequency of electron attachment to the atom decreases with temperature. There is no direct experimental information on the attachment of electrons in atomic gases, whereas theoretical calculations are devoted mainly to these gases (126,127). The relevant conclusions may show no agreement with experimental measurements of the coefficient for three-body electron attachment in molecular gases. For instance, when attachment of electrons to molecular oxygen occur by a three-body collision, the attachment rate constants are $(6.8 \pm 0.7) \times 10^{-31}$, $(2.2 \pm 0.2) \times 10^{-31}$, and $(1.1 \pm 0.2) \times 10^{-31}$ cm^6 sec^{-1} at 196, 198, and 358°K, respectively. This disagrees with the dependence for atomic gas. The dependence of the rate constant for attachment in oxygen on the mean kinetic energy of electrons over the range of 0.02 to 1 eV also cannot be explained theoretically, because it is too difficult to take into account the effect of vibrational and rotational levels (129,130). The experimental data for attachment in oxygen at an electron energy of ~ 0.1 eV are reliably described by expression

$$k = 5 \times 10^{-31} \, (T \, \text{eV}) \, \text{cm}^6 \, \text{sec}^{-1} \qquad [39]$$

The experimental rate constants for reactions involving N_2 and He as third body are rather at variance (132). Values ranging over 10^{-30} to 10^{-31} cm^6 sec^{-1} were obtained for nitrogen, and $(2.7 \text{ to } 8) \times 10^{-32}$ cm^6 sec^{-1} for helium. Attachment of electrons to molecular oxygen in mixtures with nitrogen at different electron energies in the electrical field was studied experimentally in (12), and that in mixtures of O_2 with CO_2 and O_2 with H_2O in (133). The data obtained seem to illustrate only the fact known from kinetics that complex species are more effective stabilizers in three-body collisions, compared to simple species. It may be assumed for estimation that the rate constant for attachment to oxygen will approximately obey eq. [39] for complex molecular mixtures as well.

It will be noted that use of the detailed balance principle for a reaction inverse to attachment in the case of collisions between negative oxygen ions and atoms of inert gases at 10 eV and higher energies of colliding partners yields the dependence $k \simeq 10^{-31} \, T^{-1} \, \text{eV}^{-1}$ (134). However, as the internal excitation states of a molecule and of a molecular oxygen ion in the process of electron detachment are unknown, use of the detailed balance principle is unwarranted.

Finally let us enumerate the experimental techniques for measurement of attachment coefficients with reference to those widely used. Most extensive information on cross-sections for reactions involving bimolecular collisions can be obtained for single collisions, by passing a monoenergetic electron beam through a rarefied gas (135). The coefficients for dissociative attachment can also be determined from variations in concentration of electrons appearing by action of some ionizing pulse (the method of degrading plasma) (131,132), or from stationary distribution of electrons and negative ions drifting through the gas under the action of the electric field (12).

IV. EXCITATION AND DISSOCIATION OF MOLECULES AND IONS BY ELECTRON IMPACT

Direct quantum-mechanical calculation of the excitation cross-section is very difficult. Electron-impact excitation was studied most extensively for atomic levels. The calculated results were found to be very sensitive to inevitable simplifications. Direct calculation of inelastic collisions between electrons and alkali metal atoms made in Ref. 136 seems to be the most reliable. Since the result of a quantum-mechanical calculation is markedly dependent on the approximations used, its reliability often does not exceed that of semiempirical calculations. A relatively simple semiempirical method for calculation of the cross-section for atom excitation is that in Ref. 137, or that for transition between optically resolved states (138). In the latter case the cross-section for excitation of an optically resolved state of the atom by electron impact at an arbitrary electron energy E is

$$\sigma_{0n} = \frac{4\pi}{E} (D_x)_{0n}^2 \varphi\left(\frac{E}{\Delta E}\right) \tag{40}$$

where $(D_x)_{0n}$ is the matrix element of the projection of the dipole moment operator, ΔE is the excitation energy, and

$$\varphi(x) = \frac{\ln\left[x - 0.9(x-1)\right]}{x - 0.7}$$

is a universal function independent of the kind of the atom and of the level excited.

The excitation-function maximum for an optically forbidden level usually lies close to the excitation threshold, and the decrease in the cross-section with increasing electron energy is considerably faster than that for the excitation function of resolved states. Many cross-sections for excitation of atomic levels were calculated recently in terms of the Born approximation (139). The theory usually describes inelastic collisions with sufficient accuracy, but with energies several times exceeding that of the threshold.

Variations in the cross-section close to the threshold obey the expression

$$\sigma_{0n} \sim (E - \Delta E_{0n})^{1/2} \tag{41}$$

where E is the energy of the incident electron, ΔE_{0n} is the energy for excitation of state n. It follows that the cross-section for a back reaction, that of de-excitation of the atom by a slow electron is inversely proportional to its velocity. At room temperature it will be 3×10^{-14} cm^2 (140).

In practice the threshold law (41) is valid over a very narrow range. For instance, calculated (141) and experimental (142–144) results on excitation of alkali metal atoms have shown its validity only within the range of electron energies representing less than 10% of the excitation energy. It was found (142,143) that the excitation function for helium, zinc, cadmium, mercury, sodium, and potassium near the threshold is of a resonance structure. This shows that excitation near the threshold may occur not only by a direct mechanism, obeying [40] and [41], but also through formation of a short-lived negative ion.

It is of interest to note that the cross-section for excitation of positive ions near the threshold is not zero and is independent of the electron velocity, as follows both from theory and experiment (145).

Experimental cross-section for excitation of certain levels of alkali metal atoms may be found in Refs. 144 and 146–148. The effective cross-sections for excitation of lithium levels are shown in Table 6.

TABLE 6
Effective cross-sections for excitation of lithium levels

Level	Spectral line measured, Å	E_{ex}, eV	E_{max}, eV	σ_{max} ($\times 10^{18}$), cm^2
2P	6708	1.82	4.9	2220
3P	3233	3.83	7.7	0.26
3	8127	3.38	5.9	40
4	4972	4.35	6.3	16.6
5	4273	4.76	7.3	3.9
6	3985	4.96	7.8	0.9
3	6106	3.88	6.6	115
4	4603	4.55	8.9	23
5	4132	4.85	9.0	6.3
6	3915	5.02	10.0	3.1

Reactions involving atoms and molecules excited to states with high quantum numbers n have attracted attention recently. The cross-section for electron impact excitation of such states were calculated for H atoms (149). For orbital quantum numbers $L = 0$, 1, 2 the cross-section was found to be proportional to $n^{-\alpha}$, where α is 3.07, 3.02, and 2.98, respectively. Table 7 lists the calculated cross-sections in $10^{-4}\ a_0^2$ units at an electron energy of 100 eV. The excitation functions of high long-lived states of inert gases were measured in Ref. 150. They are represented by superposed curves resembling

TABLE 7
Calculated cross-sections for H
atoms, in $10^{-4}a_0^2$ units at an
electron energy of 100 eV

n	$L = 0$	$L = 1$	$L = 2$
3	361	4017	259
4	134	1425	123
5	64.9	676	64.9
6	36.4	375	38.0
7	22.5	231	24.1
8	14.9	152	16.2
9	10.4	106	11.4
10	7.54	76.4	8.33
20	0.926	9.32	1.05
30	0.263	2.76	0.31

in shape the known excitation functions for low-lying optical and metastable atomic states.

Calculation of cross-sections for molecular excitation are even more complex and less reliable than those for atoms. For this reason the relatively scarce results on cross-sections for molecules and molecular ions are of extreme interest. The cross-sections for excitation of molecular nitrogen to the $B^3\Pi_g$; $C^3\Pi_4$, $D^3\Sigma_u^+$, $A^2\Pi_g$ and $B^2\Sigma_u^+$ states, of CO to the $D^3\Pi$, $B^3\Sigma^+$, $A^2\Pi$, $B^1\Sigma^+$ and $B^2\Sigma^+$ states, and of molecular oxygen to the $B^4\Sigma_g^-$ state were measured in Ref. 148. The excitation functions for N_2 and CO are shown in Fig. 7. The excitation functions for the electronic states of N_2^+, CO^+, and O_2^+ attained by collisions of electrons with relevant molecules are shown in Fig. 8 taken from Ref. 148. The maxima of excitation functions for neutrals are seen to be narrower and closer to the threshold than those for molecular ions. The relative intensities of the vibrational state excitation for electronic-vibrational transitions of the type considered are in agreement with the Franck-Condon principle (148). However, it was found (151) that at electron energies less than 100 eV, the population of the first vibrational state $B^2\Sigma_u^+$ of the N_2^+ ion deviates from the value calculated in terms of the Franck-Condon principle, and distribution over rotational levels is not Boltzmanian.

The absolute cross-section for excitation of the 0–0 band of the first negative system $N_2^+[(X^2\Sigma_g^+) \rightarrow (B^2\Sigma_u^+, v = 0) \rightarrow (X^2\Sigma_g^+, v = 0)]$ was measured for collisions of electrons with ions over an energy range of 5–30 eV, making use of the crossed-beams technique (152). It will be of interest to note that a considerable part of the photons recorded arises by collision of electrons

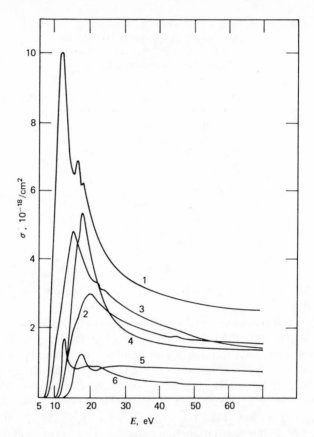

Figure 7 Cross-sections for excitation of N_2 and CO by electron impact. N_2: 1 — $B^3\Pi_g(\sigma \times 0.1)$; 4 — $C^3\Pi_u(\sigma \times 0.2)$; 5 — $D^3\sum_u^+$; CO: 2 — $B^1\sum^+$; 3 — $d^3\Pi$; 6 — $b^3\sum^+$ (144).

with slow ions appearing as a result of charge exchange between ions and molecules of the residual gas. The cross-section was found to change smoothly from 8×10^{-14} to 5×10^{-16} cm^2 over the energy range investigated. The accuracy in determining absolute cross-sections is within a factor of 2. Data are also available on rate constants for electron-impact excitation of ions in discharge, for instance, those for excitation from the ground state 0 VIII of triplet and singlet levels at $n = 2$, $kT = 250 \pm 60$ eV, and electron density $(6.2 \pm 1.5) \times 10^{16}$ cm^{-3}. The rate constant for the transition $1^1S - (2^1S = 2^1P)$ was found to be 3.1×10^{-11} cm^3 sec^{-1}, and that for $1^1S - (2^3S + 2^3P)$ was 1.5×10^{-11} cm^3 sec^{-1}. The experimental rate constants for allowed transitions are in good agreement with those calculated making use of the relatively simple expression

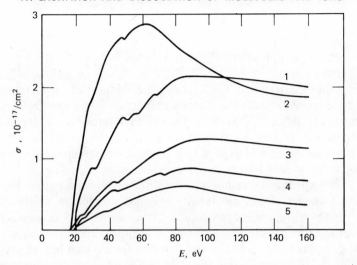

Figure 8   Cross-sections for excitation of the states of N_2^+, CO^+, and O_2^+ by collisions of electrons with molecules. N_2^+: $1 - B_g^2\sum_u^+$; $2 - A^2\Pi_g(\sigma \times 0.5)$; CO^+: $3 - A^2\Pi$; $4 - B^2\sum^+(\sigma \times 10)$; O_2^+: $5 - B^4\sum_g^-$ (144).

$$k = \left(\frac{2\pi}{3m_e kT}\right)^{1/2}\left(\frac{4\pi e^4 f \overline{G} n_e}{E_x}\right)\exp\left(-\frac{E_x}{kT}\right) \qquad [42]$$

Here $\overline{G}$ is the averaged Gaunt factor that was taken as 0.2 according to (155). The oscillator forces f were taken from a monograph (156). Thus, it may be considered that the results of experiments on rate constants for excitation of low-lying discrete levels are in good agreement with theoretical estimation. Detailed investigation of the excitation rates for multicharged neon ions was made (157). Theoretical estimation of excitation (157) made use of the expression for allowed transitions

$$\sigma = \sigma_0 e \frac{\ln 2u}{u} \qquad [43]$$

where $\sigma_0 = f(E_u/E_x)$, E_x is the excitation potential, f is the oscillator force of transition, u is the electron energy. The coefficient 2 is empirical and takes into account the focusing of the incident electron in its collision with an ion. This value was taken for ions of any multiplicity (158). The given expression for the excitation cross-section is confirmed by experimental results on excitation of the levels with $n = 2$ in He^+ (159–161), as well as on excitation of $6s$–$6p$ Ba^+ transitions (162,163). The excitation rate constant for a case obeying Eq. [43] and for Maxwellian distribution may be written as

$$k = \sigma_0 e\left(\frac{8E_x}{\pi m_e}\right)^{1/2}\phi(y) \qquad [44]$$

where

$$\phi(y) = y^{1/2}\left\{\ln 2 \exp(-y) + \int_y^\infty t^{-1} \exp(-t)\,dt\right\} \qquad y = \frac{E_x}{kT_e}$$

and m_e is the electron mass. The f values were obtained by correlating experimental line intensities with the theoretical function [44] and were compared with those calculated in (164–167). Though best agreement in experimental and theoretical data is obtained making use of the results in (167) this cannot be considered as a general rule, as the Coulomb approximation used is inapplicable to ions having equivalent electrons.

Very few experimental results were reported on electron-impact excitation of excited species. These are usually obtained not for the single collision regime but by using optical techniques. Certain elementary processes of this kind occuring in gas-discharge plasma of helium were investigated by the optical-pumping technique. The rate constant for electron impact excitation of 2^3S and 2^3P helium levels from the 2^1S state at an electron energy of $10^4\,°K$ was measured (168). The value obtained appeared to be nine and four times higher than those in Refs. 140 and 169 for an electron energy corresponding to 300°K.

Since experimental measuring of cross-sections for excitation from excited levels is difficult, use had to be made of semiempirical expressions permitting estimation to an order of magnitude only (170).

Inelastic collisions of electrons and molecules resulting in excitation of rotational and vibrational molecular levels become of great importance when the electron energies are low. The theory shows (171) that inelastic collisions on rotational levels of a diatomic molecule possessing identical nuclei induce with greatest probability a two quantum change of the rotation momentum and the cross-section for excitation of rotational levels is

$$\sigma_{j,\,j+2}(E) = \frac{8\pi Q^2}{15}\frac{(j+1)(j+2)}{(2j+1)(2j+3)}\left[1 - \frac{2B(4j+3)}{E}\right]^{1/2} \qquad [45]$$

where E is the energy of the incident electron, B is the rotational constant of the molecule, and Q is its quadrupole moment. The cross-section for electron impact de-excitation on rotational levels obtained from [45], making use of the detailed balance principle, is

$$\sigma_{j,\,j+2}(E) = \frac{8\pi Q^2}{15}\frac{j(j-1)}{(2j-1)(2j+1)}\left[1 + \frac{B(4j-2)}{E}\right]^{1/2} \qquad [46]$$

More detailed calculation of rotational excitation of hydrogen molecules was made in Ref. 172. The expression [45] though simple, may yield sufficiently accurate values of cross-sections for excitation of rotational levels. It was found (173) that the cross-sections obtained making use of [45] are in agreement with the results on electron mobility in molecular nitrogen.

The cross-section for direct vibrational excitation of molecules is considerably smaller than that for rotational states. At an electron energy of 0.63 eV (0.1 eV higher than that for the threshold) the cross-section for electron-impact excitation of the first level of a hydrogen molecule is 10^{-21} cm^2. This coincides in order of magnitude with the result obtained using the Born approximation (175). It was thought until recently that electron-impact vibrational excitation of the ground electronic state is improbable. However, it appeared that there is a very effective mechanism of vibrational excitation through formation of an unstable negative ion with its subsequent decomposition to an electron and a molecule in a vibrationally excited state. This was observed and investigated experimentally for H_2, N_2, CO (176), and CO_2 (177) molecules. For instance, the maximum cross-section for vibrational excitation of nitrogen by electron impact is 3×10^{-16} to 5×10^{-16} cm^2 at electron energies of ~ 2.4 eV. When electrons collide with CO_2 molecules, excitation of asymmetric vibration (001) will be most probable at an energy of 0.9 eV and its cross-section would be 3×10^{-16} cm^2; that for the (002) mode is by an order of magnitude smaller. Six peaks of energy losses connected with symmetric modes (100, 200, etc.) were observed over an energy range of 3 to 4.5 eV with a maximum at 3.8 eV. Experimental data for CO_2 are consistent with the existence of two short-lived negative ion states. Measurement of the angular distribution of scattered electrons shows that at 0.9 eV scattering is of the p wave, and at 3.8 eV of the s wave nature. A double electrostatic analyser producing a monokinetic beam of incident electrons is convenient for analysis of inelastic electron scattering over kinetic energies and angles (177). Theoretical calculations of the vibrational excitation of a molecule by a short-lived negative ion were carried out (178,179). The calculation results depend on knowledge of the short-lived ion characteristics that cannot yet be determined accurately. For this reason the calculated cross-sections show only qualitative agreement with experiment.

The reverse process: transfer of energy from excited molecules to electrons is of great interest for low-temperature plasma. A large amount of vibrationally excited molecules are formed by chemical reactions in flames, transfer of excitation energy will considerably increase the electron energy and this has a great effect on ionization in flames (180,183). Theoretical estimation of vibrational excitation transfer to free electrons, making use of the detailed balance principle (181–184), confirms its great effectivity.

There is no experimental information on the rotational and vibrational excitation of molecular ions by electrons, but a theoretical paper dealing with these processes was published recently (185). It considers the direct non-resonance mechanism of rotational and vibrational excitation of bimolecular-ions in terms of the Born-Coulomb approximation. The cross-section maximum for vibration of H_2^+ and HeH^+ excitation are 1.3×10^{-16} and 7.1×10^{-16} cm^2, respectively. It may be said for a general case that the cross-sections for excitation of molecular ions with different nuclei are considerably larger than those for ions with identical nuclei.

Let us discuss now the electron-impact dissociation of species involving no ionization. Dissociation of molecules by slow electrons is induced mostly by electronic excitation. This is confirmed by experimental results on dissociation of diatomic H_2 and N_2 molecules (186,187). The threshold for H_2 is observed at an electron energy of 8.8 ± 0.2 eV, which corresponds to state $^3\Sigma_u$ attained as a result of exchange interaction between an electron and a molecule. The cross-section maximum for electron-impact dissociation of hydrogen molecules is observed at an electron energy of 16.5 eV and is 9×10^{-17} cm^2. The threshold for N and N_2 formation is 9.6 ± 0.5 eV, which corresponds to process $N_2 \rightarrow N_2^* \rightarrow 2N(^4S)$.

The dissociation of polyatomic molecules was also investigated (186, 188, 189). It will be of interest to note that "super-excited" states with an energy higher than the ionization potential may be formed, with a great probability, at relevant electron energies (190). These states may decay both to neutral and to charged fragments. In this way dissociation may compete with ionization. Table 8 illustrates absolute cross-sections for formation of neutral and

TABLE 8

Absolute cross-sections for the formation of neutral and positively charged fragments by the collision of fast 100 eV electrons with CH$_4$ molecules

Positive ions		Neutral Fragments	
Ion	$\sigma \,(\times 10^{16})$, cm^2	Species	$\sigma \,(\times 10^{16})$, cm^2
H^+	0.04	H	2.4
H_2^+	0.02	H_2	0.8
C^+	0.05	C	—
CH^+	0.14	CH	0.1
CH_2^+	0.28	CH_2	0.2
CH_3^+	1.5	CH_3	1.2
CH_4^+	1.8		—

positively charged fragments by collision of fast 100 eV electrons with methane molecules (188).

Experimental data on dissociation of molecular ions by collisions with electrons became available only recently. Experiments used the crossed beams technique. It was found (191) for collisions of electrons with H_2^+ that over a kinetic energy range $E = 10$–1500 eV the dissociation cross-section is expressed as

$$\sigma = \frac{1}{E}(217 \log E - 184) \qquad [47]$$

Here E is expressed in eV, and σ in πa_0^2. The same authors (192) have studied electron-impact dissociation of N_2^+ and O_2^+ over energy ranges of 10–500 and 15–500 eV, respectively. The maximum cross-section for N_2^+ was found to be $4.3 \ \pi a_0^2$ and that for O_2^+ $4.1 \ \pi a_0^2$, respectively. It will be noted that primary molecular ions were formed by ionization with 150 eV electrons and thus certain ions were in excited electronic states. In this connection the measured cross-sections are averaged over an unknown state distribution function. Since it is natural to believe that the cross-section for dissociation of excited ions exceeds that for ground state ions, the above mentioned values for H_2^+, N_2^+, and O_2^+ may be considered as the upper limit of electron-impact dissociation cross-sections for these ions.

The dissociation of vibrationally excited neutrals and charged species by collisions with electrons was not discussed in scientific literature. The method described in Section II for ionization of vibrationally excited molecules could probably be used for theoretical calculations.

V. FORMATION OF IONS BY COLLISIONS WITH EXCITED AND FAST NEUTRAL SPECIES

Ionization induced by collisions of neutral, excited and unexcited, heavy reactants is of great importance at the initial stage of ion formation in strong shock waves. When the main ionization factor acts no more, most ions start re-combining and convert to excited long-lived species. The same is probably true for ionization in the reaction zone of hydrocarbon flames. The collisions of fast neutrals result in appearance of ionized regions in meteorite tracks.

Let us consider first ionization reactions induced by collisions of long-lived metastable species with atoms and molecules. Their long lifetimes make them convenient for use in measurement of cross-sections and of rate constants for reactions involving excited species.

Table 9 compiled from results given in Ref. 193 lists theoretical and experimental excitation energies and lifetimes, τ, for the emission of certain long-lived metastable states of atoms and simple molecules. The lithium excitation energy is seen to exceed the ionization potential. The long lifetime is accounted for here by the same direction of the three electron spins, so that detachment of one electron results in the appearance of a ^3S lithium-ion

TABLE 9

Theoretical and experimental excitation energies and lifetimes for the emission of long-lived metastable states of atoms and simple molecules (τ_e, experimental; τ_t, theoretical)

Species	H($2^2S_{1/2}$)	He2^3S_1	He2^1S_0	Li($1s\,2s\,2p)^4P_{3/2}$	Ne$^3P_{2,0}$	Ar$^3P_{2,0}$	Hg$^3P_{2,0}$	Hg$^3D_3$	H$_2C^3\Pi_u$	N$_2A^3\Sigma_u^+$	N$_2a^1\Pi_g$	CO$a^3\Pi$
Excitation energy, eV	10.20	19.82	20.61	56	16.62; 16.71	11.55; 11.72	5.43; 4.64	9.05	11.86	6.16	8.54	6.01
τ_e (sec)	$> 2.4 \times 10$	—	—	5.1×10^{-6}	—	—	—	—	—	$>10^{-2}$	1.7×10^{-4}	—
τ_t (sec)	0.12	$\geqslant 1$	—	1.6×10^{-5}	—	—	—	—	—	—	—	—

state which is higher by 6.4 eV than that for the lithium atom $(1s\ 2s\ 2p)^4P$. Consequently the decay is connected with spin interaction and the lifetime of the given state $(\hbar C/e^2)^4$ is longer than that of the state decaying by electrical interaction between electrons. Radiative deactivation of metastable states upon collisions may also be of small effectivity. As shown by experiment and theory (194), the cross-section for reaction

$$He(1^1S) + He(2^1S) = He(1^1S) + He(1^1S)$$

is approximately 2×10^{-20} cm^2. The rate constants for this reaction at various temperatures (194) are shown in Table 10. The two numbers in every

TABLE 10

Rate constant for the reaction
He (1^1S) + He (2^1S) = He (1^1S) + He (1^1S) + $h\nu$
at different temperatures

T, °K	1000	2000	4000	8000	16,000
$k(\times 10^{14})$ cm^3 sec^{-1}	1.3; 1	2; 1.6	2.5; 2	2.9; 2.3	3.1; 2.4

column correspond to two different approximations used and demonstrate the accuracy of the calculations made. Deactivation with conversion of excitation to kinetic energy will probably be even less effective. A high probability of such an inverse conversion of kinetic to internal energy in atomic collisions would be expected only at low internal energies. This suggestion is warranted by theoretical calculations (195) yielding the following expressions for cross-sections for nonresonance atomic reactions occurring at low velocities

$$\sigma \simeq \pi a^2 \exp\left(-\frac{a\,\Delta E}{\hbar v}\right) \qquad [48]$$

Here a is a value of the order of atom size, E is the excitation energy, and v is the relative velocity of reactants. The maximum cross-section (of the order of πa^2) is attained only at relatively high velocities obeying the expression

$$\frac{a|\Delta E|}{\hbar v} \simeq 1$$

which is usually called the Massey criterium. The physical sense of this relation is the equality in times of electron transfer and of interaction between colliding partners.

Collisions between metastable atoms and electrons are more effective. They result in transition of metastable atoms to states of a lower energy, whereas the kinetic electron energy increases. For instance, the cross-section for

$$He(2^1S) + e = He(2^3S) + e + 0.79 \text{ eV}$$

is 3×10^{-14} cm^2 at an electron temperature of 300°K (140). Ionization

$$A^* + B \rightarrow A + B^+ + e \qquad [49]$$

when A is in a metastable state, is called the Penning effect. Theoretical investigation (196) of this reaction for a case of collisions at relatively high velocities v of the colliding partner has shown a weak dependence of the cross-section on the velocities ($\sigma \sim \ln^2 (\text{const}/v)$). However, the conjecture that the trajectory is linear is not fulfilled for collision velocities corresponding to temperatures close to 20°C. The cross-sections for collisions of metastable helium atoms with neutrals were calculated (197) in terms of classical mechanics taking into account the trajectory deflection during motion in potential of the kind $\phi(r) = ar^{-6}$. The expression for such collisions is

$$\sigma = 0.868\pi \left(\frac{12a}{\mu v^2}\right)^{1/3} \qquad [50]$$

where μ is the reduced mass of colliding species. Theoretical values obtained in this way are in good agreement with the experimental cross-sections for Penning reactions. The difference lies only in the coefficient 0.2 to 0.3. Thus equation [50] with an additional factor 0.2 to 0.3 to the part may be considered accurate.

In principle the reaction considered may occur by three mechanisms. The first would be a direct Franck-Condon transition from the potential energy for state ($A^* + B$) to that corresponding to the final ($A + B^+$) state.

The second mechanism would be

$$A^* + B = A + B^*$$

$$B^* = B^+ + e$$

Here the first step is excitation transfer to particle B to form a superexcited state, and the second is the autoionization of this state.

The third mechanism would imply the formation of a colliding complex with subsequent autoionization and decay

$$A^* + B = (AB)^* = A + B^+ + e$$

Experimental evidence is available for all three mechanisms. The first and third were observed in studying the distribution of electrons formed in reaction [49] over kinetic energies (198).

A rather general validity of the Franck-Condon principle has been established (199) by measuring the emission from molecular ions formed in the Penning reaction, by collisions of $He(2^3S)$ with N_2, O_2, and CO. It may be seen from the results obtained that these reactions occur by the first mechanism.

Similar experiments were made in Ref. 200. It will be of interest to note that the third mechanism is obeyed for collisions of metastable helium atoms with molecules having unpaired electrons (O_2, NO) (198). The second mechanism is evidenced by the isotope effect; ionizing collisions of metastable helium atoms with hydrogen isotope molecules show the following relative cross-sections

$$\frac{\sigma_{D_2}}{\sigma_{H_2}} = 1.26 \pm 0.05$$

$$\frac{\sigma_{HD}}{\sigma_{H_2}} = 1.18 \pm 0.05$$

The second mechanism readily explains the isotope effect (201), since auto-ionization and dissociation

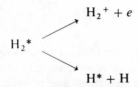

must compete at its second step. The isotope effect was observed (202) in the ionization of deuterated and ordinary hydrocarbon molecules by metastable atoms. It will be noted that both molecular and numerous fragmentary ions are formed upon collisions of metastable atoms with complex molecules. For this reason mass-spectral technique is used for measuring the relative probability of different dissociative ionization paths. Dissociative ionization of methane, ethane, propane, n-butane, ethylene, acetylene, methyl and ethyl alcohols by collisions with excited atoms of inert gases in metastable states was studied (203). An excited molecular ion thus formed seems to decay in the same way as an excited ion of the same energy formed by electron impact, photo-ionization or charge exchange. The collision cross-sections were found to be of the order of 10^{-15} cm^2 and to increase with the sizes of molecules and of inert gas atoms. An important feature of the ionization of polyatomic molecules by metastable inert gas atoms is that the amount of energy imparted to the molecular ion is higher than that taken up by collision with an electron of a kinetic energy equal to the energy for excitation of a metastable atom.

Only one paper on collisions of metastable atoms with vibrationally excited molecules was published (204). The reaction

$$He(2^3S) + N_2 = N_2^+ + He + e$$

was studied over a range of vibrational N_2 temperatures 300–6000°K. No essential change in the reaction cross-section was observed and this is in qualitative agreement with the semiempirical theory (197). It will be noted, however, that vibrational excitation of molecules may cause strong variations in relative probabilities for formation of various fragmentary ions by dissociative ionization induced by metastable atoms.

Of interest would be a comparison of ionization cross-sections for collisions with atoms excited to a metastable level and with those excited to optically allowed levels. When A is in a resonance state before collision, the cross-section for reaction [49] may be obtained theoretically with good accuracy from the experimental cross-section for photo-ionization of B particles at a photon energy equal to the energy for atom A excitation (205, 206). Calculations made use of the impact-parameter method to the approximation of a rectilinear trajectory of relative motion. The expression

$$\sigma = 13.88\left(\frac{\mu\mu_{E_0}}{\hbar v}\right) \qquad [51]$$

was obtained. Here μ and μ_{E_0} are matrix elements for transitions $A \to A^*$ and $B^+ + e$, respectively, and v is the relative velocity of reactants. Expression [51] is more accurate for lower velocities and is valid when the cross-sections obtained by making use of the expression [51] exceed the gas-kinetic values. Cross-sections, σ_1, for ionization of certain molecules by collisions with 2^1P helium atoms at room temperature, calculated by making use of the above expression, (206) are shown in Table 11. It also lists experimental cross-sections, σ_2, for ionization of the same molecules by collisions with metastable

TABLE 11

Calculated cross-sections (σ_1) for ionization of H_2, N_2, and O_2 by collisions with 2^1P helium atoms, and experimental cross-sections (σ_2) for ionization of the same molecules by collisions with metastable helium atoms 2^3S

Molecule	H_2	N_2	O_2
σ_1 ($\times 10^{15}$ cm^2)	2.6	6.9	6.9
σ_2 ($\times 10^{16}$ cm^2)	1–6	3.6–7	14

helium atoms 2^3S. The cross-sections for collisions involving resonance-excited atoms may be seen to be considerably higher than for atoms in a metastable state.

Highly excited states with a high main quantum number are of a specific type. Their lifetimes, as well as the excited particle sizes markedly increase with the main quantum number. The long lifetimes and the large interaction cross-sections permit observing reactions of highly excited atoms, molecules, and ions at low pressures by means of the mass-spectral techniques, (207,208). The cross-sections for ionization of highly excited particles X^{**} by collisions with molecules M were measured at several hundreds °K. The overall reaction is

$$X^{**} + M = X^{+} + M + e \qquad [52]$$

The cross-sections for reaction [52] in units of 10^{-12} cm^2 calculated from ion yields X^{+} are listed in Table 12 for various X and M (209). Out of the

TABLE 12

Cross-sections for ionization of highly excited particles X^{**} by collisions with molecules M, $(X^{**} + M = X^{+} + (M + e))$, in units of 10^{-12} cm^2, calculated from ion yields X^{+}

X \ M	H_2O	NH_3	SO_2	C_2H_5OH	SF_6
He	0.29 ± 0.05	0.15 ± 0.04	0.11 ± 0.05	0.27 ± 0.08	0.76 ± 0.08
Ne	0.78 ± 0.06		0.27 ± 0.07	0.5 ± 0.09	1.4 ± 0.09
Ar	1.2 ± 0.08	0.74 ± 0.07	0.40 ± 0.09	0.8 ± 0.11	1.5 ± 0.11

tabulated pairs negative ions were observed only for reaction

$$A^* + SF_6 = A^{+} + SF_6^{-}$$

Its cross-section calculated from the SF_6^{-} yield appeared to be $(1.7 \pm 0.11) \times 10^{-12}$ cm^2. It will be noted that reaction [52] was not observed when X^{**} collided with H_2, N_2, O_2, N_2O_4, and CH_4 molecules.

An interesting kind of reaction involving highly excited molecules was observed in (207)

$$H_2^{**} + H_2 = H_3^{+} + H + e \qquad [53]$$

and

$$D_2^{**} + D_2 = D_3^{+} + D + e \qquad [54]$$

Ionization occurs here together with transition of a heavy reactant. The cross-sections for reactions [53] and [54] and for electron-impact formation of highly excited D_2^{**} and H_2^{**} ions were not measured. However, the large cross-sections, exceeding the theoretically possible values for ion-molecular reactions

$$D_2^+ + Ar = ArD^+ + D$$

$$CO + D_2^+ = COD^+ + D$$

$$D_2^+ + CO_2 = CO_2D^+ + D$$

warranted the suggestion made by the authors of Ref. 209 that these cross-sections are only apparent, that it is necessary to take into account the reactions of highly excited species, and that at low electron energies loaded secondary ions may be formed to a great extent by reactions of such species, rather than by ion-molecular reactions.

There is yet no quantitative theory for reactions of highly excited species. A good measure for estimating the upper limit for such a reaction would probably be the characteristic cross-section of the electronic shell of a highly excited particle. Relatively close rapprochement of colliding partners would be necessary for reactions involving rearrangement of heavy reactants. The upper limit of such a reaction for highly excited atoms with a high n can be obtained from equation [59] for the cross-section of an ion-molecular reaction under the assumption that at distances between reactants smaller than the radius of the excited electron orbital the highly excited atom "is an ion." Attachment of the outer electron to the approaching particle is possible, in principle. In this case the Coulomb force will be that responsible for rapprochment of colliding partners, as, for instance, in the recombination of ions.

Let us consider now the formation of molecular ions by collisions between excited and unexcited atoms by chemi-ionization and associative ionization. Reactions of this kind were investigated most extensively for inert gases. The appearance potentials for homonuclear and heteronuclear molecular ions in inert gases and their mixtures are listed in Tables 13 and 14 in eV (210,211).

TABLE 13
Appearance potentials for homo-nuclear molecular ions in inert gases

Y_2^+	AP(Y_2^+), eV (210,211)
He_2^+	23.3 ± 0.1
Ne_2^+	20.9 ± 0.2
Ar_2^+	14.7 ± 0.1; 14.710 ± 0.009
Kr_2^+	13.0 ± 0.1; 13.004 ± 0.007
Xe_2^+	11.2 ± 0.1; 11.162 ± 0.005

TABLE 14
Appearance potentials for heteronuclear molecular ions in inert gas mixtures

XY^+	AP(XY^+), eV(211)
HeNe$^+$	23.4 ± 0.1
HeAr$^+$	17.9 ± 0.3
HeKr$^+$	19.9 ± 0.1
NeAr$^+$	16.8 ± 0.1
NeKr$^+$	16.6 ± 0.1
NeXe$^+$	16.0 ± 0.3
ArKr$^+$	14.0 ± 0.1
ArXe$^+$	13.5 ± 0.1
KrXe$^+$	12.2 ± 0.1

When an inert gas atom with a low-ionization potential X^* collides with that with a high-ionization potential, ions may appear by two parallel reactions:

$$X^* + Y \begin{array}{c} \xrightarrow{k_1} XY^+ + e \\ \searrow_{k_2} \\ X + Y^+ + e \end{array}$$

The ratios of k_1/k_2 (210) are shown in Table 15. The absolute rate constant for formation of molecular ions and the eigen lifetimes of excited atoms

TABLE 15
Ratios of rate constants for the reactions $X^* + Y \xrightarrow{k_1} XY^+ + e$, and $X^* + Y \xrightarrow{k_2} X + Y^+ + e$

X	Y	k_1/k_2
He	Ne	1.62
He	Ar	7.8
Ar	Kr	1.7

were measured by the pulse mass-spectral technique worked out by Tal'rose and Frankevich (212). This will be described in short in the section dealing with ion-molecular reactions (see Section VI). It was found by means of the pulse technique that excited atoms with lifetimes of 1.9×10^{-5}, 2.0×10^{-6} and 5.4×10^{-7} sec showing distribution function peaks at 18, 28 and 60–70 eV, respectively, contributed to formation of molecular ions in pure argon.

Detailed investigation of chemi-ionization by the pulse mass-spectral technique was carried out (215). The reactions occurring in the ion source of the mass spectrometer were studied

$$e + Ar \overset{k_i}{=} Ar^+ + e$$

$$e + Ar \overset{k_{ex}}{=} Ar^* + e$$

$$Ar^* \overset{k_2}{=} Ar^+ + e$$

$$Ar^* \overset{k_1 = 1/t}{=} Ar + h\nu$$

The following parameters were obtained for various electron energies:

Electron energy, eV	t, μ sec	$k_2 \times 10^9$ cm^3 sec^{-1}	$k_e/k_i \times 10^2$
18	0.77 ± 0.7	1.7 ± 0.2	3.0 ± 0.6
27.30	0.53 ± 0.3	2.0 ± 0.1	0.55 ± 0.15
65	0.33 ± 0.05	1.3 ± 0.2	0.34 ± 0.4

The high rate constants for chemi-ionization are in good agreement with argon atom cross-sections in the $3p^5 4d$ and $3p^5 5p$ states. The excitation energies of these states coincide with the threshold for Ar_2^+ appearance, within experimental error.

When use is not made of the pulse technique, the ionization rate constant can be obtained only in the $k_2 t$ combination. The results obtained on chemiionization of Ar, Ne, and He (216) are listed in Table 16.

TABLE 16
Values of k_e/k_i and kt for Ar, Ne and He at different electron energies

Gas	Electron energy, eV	$\dfrac{k_e}{k_i}$	$kt(\times 10^{16})$, cm^3
Ar	15	0.055	3.6
	70	0.014	2.7
Ne	20	0.010	11.6
	70	0.0045	11.1
He	22	0.067	0.58

Chemi-ionization in gases other than inert gases was not studied extensively owing to the great complexity of processes leading to ionization. Chem-ionization in a mixture of atomic nitrogen and oxygen with molecular nitrogen was found to occur (217) by reaction

$$N_2^* + NO^* = NO^+ + N_2 + e$$

The excited species were formed in this mixture by three-body recombination of atoms. The overall ionization rate in this system at a pressure of N_2 4 torr and a total concentration $[O] + [N] = 1.2 \times 10^{15}$ cm^3 is expressed as $P = k [N]^3 [O]$, where $k = 4.25 \times 10^{-46}$ cm^9 sec^{-1}. However k is here not an elementary constant, but a combination of several constants and concentrations of reagents involved in deactivation.

It is usually accepted at present (218) that ionization in hydrocarbon flames starts in reaction

$$CH + O = CHO^+ + e \qquad [55]$$

However, it is not quite clear what is the energy state of radicals when they engage in reaction [55]. Recent results (219) show that the radicals may be unexcited. The rate constant for reaction [55] measured for hot hydrocarbon flames is in the order of 10^{-12} cm^3 sec^{-1} (220). The activation energy for ionization in these flames was found to be 19 ± 2 kcal/mole (221).

Ionization in oxygen-hydrocarbon flames is less advantageous thermochemically and the relevant ion concentration is relatively low, in spite of the higher temperature, compared to hydrocarbon flames. Addition of alkali metals considerably increases the electron concentration. It was found (222) that the effective cross-section for ionization of sodium atoms in an oxygen-hydrocarbon flame, obtained from the pre-exponential factor in the expression

$$k = A \exp\left(-\frac{eI}{kT}\right)$$

is unusually high (5000 Å^2). The detailed mechanism of alkali-metal ionization in such flames is not yet elucidated.

When the temperature is high, endothermic associative ionization may also be effective. For instance, it was found from the results of experiments using shock tubes at 9000°K that the rate constant for reaction

$$N + N = N_2^+ + e \qquad [56]$$

was $k \simeq 10^{-14}$ cm^3 sec^{-1}. As the rate constant for reaction [56] is relatively high, it may be that excited nitrogen atoms contribute to the reaction. In air shock waves at temperatures of $\sim 10^4$ °K the main contribution to ionization is that from reaction

$$N + O \rightarrow NO^+ + e$$

The rate constant of this reaction is (224)

$$k = 5 \times 10^{-11} T^{-1/2} \exp\left(\frac{-32500}{T}\right)$$

Initial ionization in atomic gases with relatively low bond energies of molecular-ions is not associative, but occurs as

$$A + B = A^+ + B + e \qquad [57]$$

Recent research on the mechanism of initial ionization in inert gases (225,226) reported that at high temperatures one of the atoms involved in reaction [57] is excited either to the lower metastable or to the resonance level. The separation between these levels in inert gases is less than ~ 0.3 eV. The time of radiative decay of metastable levels is $\sim 10^{-4}$ sec, and that of resonance decay is $\sim 10^{-8}$ sec; however, the cross-section for the taking up of resonance emission is larger, so that under real experimental conditions in shock waves (pressure ~ 1 atm and temperature 5000–9000°K) capture of resonance emission occurs. It is yet impossible to decide at present what is predominant: excitation of metastable states or capture of resonance emission. However it was established that excitation is the limiting step of ionization. Table 17 lists the experimental constants c for various combinations of

TABLE 17
Values of the constant c for various combinations of inert gas atoms

Reaction	c, cm^2 eV^{-1}
Ar + Ar = Ar* + Ar	$1.2 \times 10^{-19} \pm 15\%$
Kr + Kr = Kr* + Kr	$1.4 \times 10^{-19} \pm 15\%$
Xe + Xe = Xe* + Xe	$1.8 \times 10^{-20} \pm 15\%$
Ar + Xe = Xe* + Ar	$1.8 \times 10^{-20} \pm 20\%$

inert gas atoms, obtained under the suggestion that the cross-section of excitation is expressed as $\sigma = c(\varepsilon - \varepsilon_t)$ where ε_t is the threshold excitation energy.

The previous discussion of associative ionization dealt with relative analysis of the kinetic parameters for elementary reactions. However, the mere existence of stable ion-associates, as well as of loaded ions in general, makes it necessary to take them into account in calculating equilibrium reaction as well, for instance the extent of equilibrium ionization in a gas.

Such calculations were made by Tal'rose and Larin (227) for H_2, H_2O and Ar. It appeared that up to temperatures of 3000–5000°K the main positive ions in these systems are loaded ions (H_3^+, H_3O^+ and Ar_2^+). With further increase in temperature the entropy factor becomes more important than the gain in enthalpy due to formation of loaded ions and contribution from the latter becomes small. It was not yet established till the time of these calculations what was the excitation level of Ar^* at which it reacts with Ar to form Ar_2^+ and the $(Ar-Ar)^+$ bond was overestimated. Thus it must be considered that the contribution from loaded ions to thermal ionization of Ar becomes small at temperatures lower than 5000°K.

Ionization by collision of ground state partners is usually studied for single collisions on passage of the fast beam of reactants through a gas target. Full effective cross-sections for electron detachment by fast Na, K, Rb, Cs atoms in H_2, D_2, and O_2 over an energy range of 150 to 2200 eV were determined (228–230). Absolute cross-sections attaining $10^{-17} - 10^{-16}$ cm^2 and the shape of the cross-section dependence on velocity are not consistent with the quasi-adiabatic Massey hypothesis (see eq. [48]). The effective ionization cross-section for $O_2 + N_2 = O_2^+ + N_2 + e$ near the threshold is approximately proportional to the square of the excess ion energy over the ionization potential. Experimental data were treated in terms of the concept about intersection of potential curves for the initial and end states of the colliding species, when the distance between their nuclei becomes smaller. This provides a qualitative explanation for the high cross-sections near the threshold (232). Ionization of helium, neon and molecular nitrogen by collision with fast helium atoms was investigated (233). The ionization cross-sections obtained for He–He and He–Ne collisions are by one to two orders of magnitude smaller than those measured before for N_2-N_2, N_2-O_2, and O_2-O_2 (231). The cross-section for Ne–N_2 is of the same order of magnitude as that for N_2-N_2. The data on elementary ionization reactions in atom-atom collisions are very important for the study of the mechanism of ionization in meteorite tracks. The effective cross-sections for detachment of electrons by typical meteorite atoms, Ca, Mg, Si, Fe, upon collisions with N_2 and O_2 molecules were measured (230). The extreme values for cross-sections as a function of rate are listed in Table 18. The results on Fe atoms (230) are in qualitative agreement with those obtained in experiments on acceleration of microparticles of dust to 15–45 km sec^{-1} with subsequent retardation by thick He, Ne, Ar, Kr, N_2, O_2, CO_2, and air targets (234).

Collisions of neutrals may yield ions also by charge exchange

$$A + B = A^+ + B^- \qquad [58]$$

These reactions are particularly effective on collisions of alkali metal atoms with low ionization potentials with molecules of a high electron affinity. Effective cross-sections for charge exchange between fast atoms, K, Rb, and Cs, and O_2, Cl_2, and Br_2 molecules were studied over an atomic energy range of 150 to 2000 eV. Curves for cross-sections as a function of the charge exchange rate show a maximum (cross-section $\sim 10^{-16}$ cm^2) at $v = 3$ to 4 × 10^6 cm sec^{-1}. In the region corresponding to lower energieselect ron detachment from fast alakli-metal atoms occurs mainly by charge exchange.

The increase in electron concentration in a flame containing alkali-metal atoms A, when halogens X_2 are added to the gas mixture (236), is a convincing argument in favor of the occurrence of reaction [58] at low energies. The electron concentration increase is thought (236) to be connected with reactions

$$A + X = A^+ + X^-$$

and

$$H + X^- = HX + e$$

Finally, let us note also the mechanism of ionization expressed as

$$A + B + C = AB + C^+ + e$$

An example of it would be reaction

$$N + N + Cs = N_2 + Cs^+ + e$$

(237). A specific feature of such reactions is their weak temperature dependence. There is yet no theory for them.

VI. ION-MOLECULE REACTIONS INVOLVING POSITIVE IONS

It became evident in the 1950s, at the start of systematic investigations on ion-molecular reactions in gases (238–241), that these reactions are foremost among those in plasma. They are of particular importance in nonisothermic plasma arising under the action of ionizing radiation (242–244). An ion formed in such a plasma by a primary reaction, for instance by electron impact, succeeds in under-going at least one ion-molecular conversion before recombining with an electron or a negative ion, or before discharge at the wall. The research carried out on ion-molecular reactions resulted in the creation of a specific section of chemical kinetics which is not only of importance for elucidation of plasma-chemical and radiative-chemical reactions, but also opens up new possibilities for development of the theory of elementary reactions in general.

The problems connected with ion-molecular reactions were discussed recently and relevant detailed information may be found in the review by the authors of this chapter (245) and in the Proceedings of the Symposium on Ion-molecular Reactions (246).

The following reactions involve charge transfer and transfer of heavy reactants:

$$A^+ + BC \rightarrow \begin{cases} A + BC^+ \\ A + B^+ + C \\ A + B + C^+ \\ AB^+ + C \\ AC^+ + B \\ AB + C^+ \\ AC + B^+ \end{cases}$$

They may in principle be induced by collisions of slow ions A^+ with molecules BC. The first three reactions are usually called charge transfer (the second and third dissociative charge transfer), the remaining are ion-molecular reactions with transfer of heavy reactants*. The cross-sections for ion-molecular reactions involving transfer of heavy reactants with kinetic energies of ~ 1 eV and lower are, as a rule, large and exceed the gas-kinetic cross-sections for relevant neutrals. The cross-section for collisions of ions and neutrals calculated for nonpolar molecules and taking into account only long-range forces, is expressed as

$$\sigma = \frac{2\pi e}{v} \sqrt{\frac{\alpha}{\mu}} \qquad [59]$$

where α is the polarizability of a neutral particle, e is the ion charge, μ is the reduced mass of colliding partners, and v is the velocity of relative motion. The relevant rate constant will be expressed as

$$k = v\sigma = 2\pi e \sqrt{\frac{\alpha}{\mu}} \qquad [60]$$

that is, the constant is quite independent of the velocity of reactants. It was shown by experiment that eqs. [59] and [60] may actually be used for estimation of the rates of ion-molecular reactions at kinetic energies of 10^{-1} eV and lower, with an accuracy to coefficient 0.3–1. The lower than unity coefficient formally shows that not every collision of an ion with a neutral induces a reaction. A method for theoretical calculation of this coefficient in terms of the statistical theory of reactions was formulated recently (248–250). However, complete theoretical expressions are rather complicated and calculation is usually made by computers.

* Thus both charge transfer and transfer of heavy particles are ion-molecular reactions. Sometimes, and very unsuccessfully from the usage standpoint, only reactions involving heavy particles are called ion-molecular reactions. It would be expedient to consider ion-molecular reactions as a part of a class of neutral-ion reactions, and this class would involve also reactions occurring by collisions of ions with atoms.

The data obtained on angular and energy distribution of the products of certain ion-molecular reactions, as well as on abnormally low effectivities of certain exothermic reactions show the limits of the statistical theory. However the range of the latter application is not established.

The rule for existence of a large cross-section and absence of a noticeable activation barrier at least for one of the possible exothermic paths of ion-molecular reactions was formulated by Tal'rose (239) in a purely empirical way. The information obtained at present for some thousand molecular-reactions has, in general, confirmed this rule; exceptions are rather rare (251).

It will be emphasized that neither the statistical theory nor the physical "pulling" of the ion and molecule towards each other do not imply the absence of activation energy mentioned above and observed in most cases. The long-range ion-dipole forces would explain the "pulling" only, whereas the reaction as such occurs with essential contribution from considerably more strong short-range forces for which the potential surface picture is not clear. Thus, strictly speaking, the absolute rates of ion-molecular reactions remain an experimental fact that has yet received no satisfactory theoretical explanation.

When the cross-section obtained from eq. [59] equals or becomes smaller than the gas-kinetic cross-sections for molecular collisions, eqs. [59] and [60] become senseless for the relevant rates. In this case the reaction may occur by so-called "direct" collisions (252,253), rather than by formation of a relatively long-lived complex with its subsequent decay. The theory of such a mechanism is in its rudimentary stage only (254). Qualitative agreement can be obtained for dependence of the reaction cross-section on kinetic energy, for the isotope effect, and for that of vibrational excitation on the reaction cross-section. However, absolute cross-sections for ion-molecular reactions following the direct mechanism were not calculated. It was found (245) that at kinetic energies of relative motion in the order of 1 eV the cross-sections for various reactions were larger and smaller than those obtained by making use of eq. [59]. Variations in reaction rates were either more or less fast than with eq. [59]. This is usually attributed to different paths of the complex decay depending on internal excitation energy and also to different mechanisms of ion-molecular reactions (transition to the "direct" mechanism). It will be noted that certain ion-molecular reactions may occur by "direct" mechanism (255), without formation of the long lived-complex, even at very low energies of relative motion, such as 0.1 eV. The dependence of the cross-section on kinetic energy E for a reaction between ions and molecules occurring at low energies E and having a low dipole moment (256) is given by

$$\sigma(E) = \frac{\sigma_D(E)}{E} + \sigma_L E^{-1/2} \qquad [61]$$

where σ_D and σ_L do not depend much on energy. The first term of this expression refers to the ion-constant dipole, and the second to ion-induced dipole forces. At high energies the experimental dependence for such reactions deviates from eq. [61], which also seems to be accounted for by transition to the " direct " mechanism.

It was mentioned previously that there are certain exceptions from the general rule of the high rate constants for ion-molecular reactions. To a certain extent reaction

$$O^+ + N_2 = NO^+ + N \qquad [62]$$

may be considered as such an exception. This reaction is of great interest as it is responsible for the concentration of electrons in the ionosphere. Though it is exothermal, its rate constant at thermal energies is considerably lower than those for ordinary exothermic ion-molecular reactions (257,258). The maximum cross-section of this reaction as a function of kinetic energy was found to be 4×10^{-16} cm^2 at an ion energy of 10 eV in the laboratory system of coordinates (259). The behavior of this cross-section with respect to vibrational excitation of N_2 is anomalous. It follows from the statistical theory for ion-molecular reactions (250) and from experimental results on certain cross-sections as a function of the vibrational excitation energy that the cross-section for an exothermic ion-molecular reaction must decrease with increasing vibrational excitation. However, the cross-section for reaction [62] was found to increase (204). Its dependence on the v vibrational quantum number of an N_2 molecule (at vibrational temperatures of 300 to 6000°K) is shown in Table 19.

TABLE 18

Extreme values for the cross-sections of typical meteorite atoms upon collisions with O_2 and N_2 as a function of their velocities

Atom	v, km sec^{-1}	$\sigma(\times 10^{16})$, cm^2	
		O_2	N_2
Ca	65	0.32	0.25
	98	0.75	0.5
Fe	80	0.8	0.25
	100	1.3	0.4
Si	120	0.7	0.5
	143	1	0.85
Mg	125	0.2	0.2
	154	0.3	0.3

TABLE 19

Dependence of the rate constant for the reaction $O^+ + N_2 = NO^+ + N$ on the vibrational quantum number of the N_2 molecule

$k(\times 10^{12})$, cm^3 sec^{-1}	1.5	1.5	50	100	260	370	450
v	0	1	2	3	4	5	6

Let us consider some other experimental results on the effect of vibrational excitation on the effectivity of ion-molecular reactions. It was found (204) that vibrational excitation of N_2 over the 300–6000°K range has no appreciable effect on the overall rate constant for reaction

$$He^+ + N_2 \rightarrow \begin{cases} N_2^+ + He \\ N^+ + N + He \end{cases}$$

however the ratio of secondary ion yields $N^+/(N^+ + N_2^+)$ increases from 0.7 to 0.8. Photo-ionization was used in studying the effect of the excitation energy of molecular ions on the reaction effectivity (260,261). At low kinetic energies the cross-section for reaction

$$H_2^+ + H_2 = H_3^+ + H$$

was found to decrease approximately by a factor of 1.25 with the H_2^+ excitation energy increasing from 0 to 1.25 eV. When the kinetic energy of ions attains about 1 eV the cross-section starts increasing with ion excitation, due to transition to the "direct" mechanism. At low kinetic energies the cross-section for reaction

$$NH_3^+ + NH_3 = NH_4^+ + NH_2$$

decreases with increasing vibrational excitation of NH_3^+ and that for reaction

$$NH_3^+ + H_2O = NH_4^+ + OH$$

remains constant. Though the dependence of cross-sections for ion-molecular reactions on low ion energies qualitatively obeys the statistical theory, quantitative agreement is not satisfactory.

When a molecular ion collides with a neutral at a sufficient kinetic energy, impact dissociation also becomes possible.

The cross-sections for dissociation of slow H_2^+, O_2^+, and NO^+ ions by collisions with neutral atoms and molecules were measured (262). It rapidly increases near the threshold, approximately from 0.01 to 1.0 Å^2 and attains values close to the maximum at relative energies exceeding the threshold only by several eV.

Now let us consider the charge-exchange reactions. The variations in velocity and deviation from the rectilinear trajectory are usually neglected in calculating the charge exchange cross-section. However, charge exchange at low kinetic energies of relative motion, when the ion is captured by the molecule to form a complex, are of interest for molecular species in low-temperature plasma.

It was found (263) that in the case of atomic species resonance charge exchange at a relative velocity $v < 10^5 \mu^{-1/2}$ ($A^+ + B = A + B^+ + \Delta E = 0$ involving equal A and B ionization potentials) occurs mainly by formation of a polarization complex,

$$\frac{10^5}{\mu^{1/2}} < v < \frac{10^6}{\mu^{1/2}}$$

is the intermediate region. At $v > 10^6 \mu^{-1/2}$ the trajectory deflection and the velocity variations may be neglected. The averaged probability of symmetric resonance charge exchange in complex formation (reaction $A^+ + A = A + A^+$) is $\frac{1}{2}$, and thus its cross-section would be given by expression [59] with an additional factor $\frac{1}{2}$ in its right term. When charge exchange of atomic ions is nonresonance ($\Delta E \neq 0$) the maximum cross-section will be attained at a relative motion velocity obeying the Massey criterium. However, if the potential curves for the initial and end systems intersect, the cross-section may become maximum at considerably lower velocities. When charge exchange involves complex molecules, the choice of approximate resonance conditions for exothermic reactions is relatively easy, due to the great number of electronic-vibrational levels. If a complex is then formed, the probability of resonance charge exchange between closely rapproched ion and molecule may be higher than $\frac{1}{2}$, as that for transition from electronic to vibrational energy is great and that for back transition is small (from statistical considerations). The statistical theory for ion-molecular reactions may be used here for charge exchange at low energies. However, correlation between the charge exchange rate constant and the reaction adiabaticity under conditions resembling fortuitous resonance was observed for certain simple three-atom systems (264). In such a case the statistical theory yields overestimated rate constants.

The physical picture of charge exchange becomes evident from the diverse experimental evidence available.

Resonance charge exchange on many molecules was investigated fundamentally (265–270). This research carried out mostly at energies of 10^2–10^3 eV (though certain experiments used several eV only) has revealed the usually ready occurrence of resonance in charge exchange between polyatomic species, though exceptions were observed here as well (271).

On the other hand it was found in our laboratory for strictly non-resonance reactions (272–275) that large charge exchange cross-sections involving molecules may be observed close to the threshold long before attaining the energy range corresponding to the Massey criterium. It may be stated that this is a rule and not an exception here. Relevant curves taken from (272) are shown in Fig. 9. Similar results were obtained for other reactions (276,277).

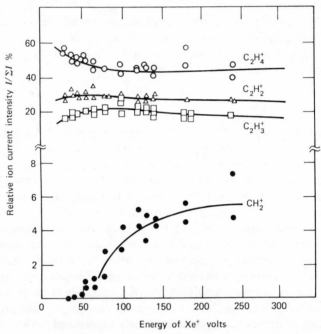

Figure 9   Relative cross-sections for the formation of ions in charge exchange $Xe^+ + C_2H_4$ plotted as a function of kinetic energy of Xe^+ (272).

Such a near-to-threshold behavior of the cross-section is very essential for low-temperature plasma, as it increases considerably the probability of endothermic charge exchange.

Direct investigation of charge exchange, and of other reactions, at maximally low kinetic energies is very important for the application of obtained results to real plasma conditions. It will be noted that relative cross-sections for various paths of charge exchange between Ar^+, Kr^+, Xe^+ ions on CH_4, C_2H_4, C_2H_6 molecules at ion kinetic energies of ~ 0.1 and 300 eV appeared to be close (278,279), though it would be premature to consider it as a rule.

Experimental investigations on elementary ion-molecular reactions use mostly the mass-spectral technique. A relevant detailed review is given in (245). Only methodological research of recent years will be mentioned here: first, that dealing with measurement of the angular distribution of reaction products. This research requires the use of relatively complex experimental techniques, but gives new and valuable information on the reaction mechanisms (255,280). A great amount of information on ion-molecular processes at low kinetic energies may be found in Refs. 204 and 281 and other relevant papers. This information was obtained by means of a new experimental approach which is, in principle, similar to classical techniques for investigation of atoms and radical reactions, namely: molecules reacting with active species are added to a stream of inert gas at different distances from the detector. The pulse technique worked out in our laboratory (212) has found further application (282–284). This technique implies ionization by microsecond pulses in order to obtain conditions maximally close to "thermal" ones. Then after a fixed time τ the secondary and primary ions are repelled by a field pulse. The τ dependence of the ratio of ion currents gives the "thermal" rate constant sought for.

The pulse technique is unique for measuring the cross-sections for reactions of short-lived excited ions, as experiments using a continuous regime give only the product of the rate constant for a bimolecular reaction multiplied by the lifetime of the excited state. Use of the pulse method in studying the reaction

$$(N_2^+)^*(^4\textstyle\sum) + N_2 = N_3 + N$$

permitted obtaining the lifetime of an excited ion, 7.6×10^{-6} sec, and the rate constant, 5.7×10^{-11} cm^3 sec^{-1}.

Our laboratory started using the pulse together with the deviation techniques (286,287) in measuring the initial kinetic energies of secondary ions formed by ion-molecular reactions at thermal energies. It was found, for instance, for reaction $H_2O^+ + D_2 = DH_2O^+ + D + 1.9$ eV that at a 400°K temperature of primary species the kinetic energy of secondary ions will correspond to a temperature of ~ 460°K. It follows that the main part of the reaction heat is taken up by excitation of the internal degrees of freedom of DH_2O^+, and less than 0.1 eV goes to the kinetic energy of secondary products. These results are in agreement with those obtained before for energies of some 0.1 eV and higher (288,289).

The pulse technique was developed upon in Ref. 282. The pulse was shortened to 10^{-8} sec, the electric field being created in the ionization chamber for a fraction of a microsecond; the primary ions take up the necessary energy without considerable displacement, then react with molecules within microseconds, and are ultimately impelled to the analyser. This permits studying reactions of ions with fixed very low energies over a range of several tenths to several eV.

The technique of ion cyclotron resonance starts being used for investigations of ion-molecular reactions (290). It opens up wide possibilities for identification of reactions in complex systems and for studying the energy dependence of rate constants.

Photo-ionization (260,261,291,292) and charge exchange (270,293) are used now for producing primary ions with fixed excitation energy.

Table 20 lists the recently reported experimental rate constants for certain

TABLE 20

Rate constants for simple bimolecular positive ion-molecular reactions. (k_e, experimental; k_t, theoretical, calculated using eq. [60])

Reaction	k_e ($\times 10^9$), cm^3 sec^{-1}	k_t ($\times 10^9$), cm^3 sec^{-1}	References
$He^+ + O_2 = O^+ + O + He$	1.5	1.56	294
$He^+ + N_2 = N^+ + N + He$	1.7 ⎫	1.6	294
$\quad = N_2^+ + He$	1.5 ⎭		
$O^+ + H_2 = OH^+ + H$	2.0	1.56	281
$O^+ + O_2 = O_2^+ + O$	0.04	0.9	281
$H_2^+ + H_2 = H_3^+ + H$	0.59	2.05	283
$N_2^+ + H_2 = N_2H^+ + H$	2.0	1.50	283
$N_2^+ + O = NO^+ + N$	0.25 ⎫	0.56	295
$\quad = O^+ + N_2$	$< 10^{-2}$ ⎭		
$N_2^+ + O_2^+ = O_2^+ + N_2$	0.1	0.76	295
$O_2^+ + N = NO^+ + O$	0.18	0.57	295
$NH_3^+ + NH_3 = NH_4^+ + NH_2$	0.52	1.06	283
$H_2O^+ + H_2O = H_3O^+ + OH$	0.49	1.22	283
$OH^+ + H_2O = H_3O^+ + O$	0.47	0.86	283
$CH_4^+ + CH_4 = CH_5^+ + CH_3$	0.61	1.34	283
$CH_3^+ + CH_4 = C_2H_5^+ + H_2$	0.86	1.35	283

simple bimolecular ion-molecular reactions involving positive ions, as well as theoretical estimations making use of eq. [60].

One of the results of collision between an ion and a neutral may be the conversion of ion vibrational excitation, if any, to translational or rotational energy. Vibrational relaxation is essential under plasma conditions. Experimental evidence on deactivation of vibrational excitation is very scarce. It follows from the statistical theory and the consequent ready formation of an intermediate complex, as mentioned previously, that such deactivation must occur at the same rate as the ion-molecular reaction as such, and that the rate constant will be independent of kinetic energies of relative motion lower than ~ 1 eV. For instance it was shown in terms of the statistical theory (296) that the probability of reaction

$$NO^+(v = 4) + Xe = NO^+ (v = v_k) + Xe$$

occurring by single ion-molecular collision is 0.46, 0.30, 0.17, 0.07, and 0.004

for $v_k = 0$, 1, 2, 3, 4, respectively. This means in particular that the rate of vibrational relaxation of ions must always be higher than that for neutral molecules.

Theoretical calculation using the disturbed wave technique (297) yields relatively low probabilities for deactivation of vibrational excitation by collisions. Table 21 lists the relevant relaxation times in sec at a pressure of 1 atm (297).

TABLE 21

Relaxation times (in sec) at a pressure of 1 atm for the deactivation of vibrational excitation by collisions

T, °K	N_2^+-N_2	O_2^+-O_2	CO^+-CO	H_2O^+-H_2O	CO_2^+-CO_2	CH_4^+-CH_4
300	$7.93(-2)^a$	$5.53(-3)$	$1.49(-2)$	$3.0(-11)$	$1.2(-7)$	$1.7(-7)$
400	$2.89(-2)$	$8.68(-4)$	$6.82(-3)$	$1.0(-10)$	$1.9(-7)$	$1.5(-8)$
600	$7.20(-3)$	$2.70(-4)$	$1.65(-3)$	$4.3(-10)$	$2.3(-7)$	$2.3(-8)$
800	$1.42(-3)$	$1.95(-4)$	$5.33(-4)$	$4.5(-10)$	$3.9(-8)$	
1000	$5.32(-4)$	$4.60(-5)$	$2.21(-4)$		$1.4(-8)$	
1500	$8.82(-5)$	$1.06(-5)$	$2.16(-5)$			
3000	$5.74(-6)$	$5.26(-7)$	$3.31(-6)$			

^{a} Numbers in parentheses denote the exponent of 10.

Unfortunately lack of information on vibrational relaxation of molecular ions containing few atoms does not permit preferential choice between the statistical theory and that based on the disturbed-wave method.

Vibrational deactivation of complex molecular ions of C_4H_8 was studied experimentally (298) by comparison of rate constants for reactions

$$C_4H_8^{*+} \xrightarrow{k_d} C_3H_5^+ + CH_3$$

and

$$C_4H_8^{*+} + Xe \xrightarrow{k_s} C_4H_8^+ + Xe$$

It was found that $k_s/k_d = 1.1 \times 10^{-16}$ cm^3 molecule^{-1}. The ratio is of no great significance, as k_d is unknown and thus k_s cannot be calculated. However, there appears the possibility of correlating deactivation of ions with that of neutrals (298). Deactivation by an inert gas of the C_4H_7 radicals obtained by addition of H atoms to butene-2 was actually studied (299,300). The vibrational excitation energy was found to be 43 kcal mol^{-1} and the excess energy over that for dissociation to propene and methyl was 10 kcal mole^{-1}. The energy for $C_4H_8^{*+}$ excitation is 43 kcal (298) and the excess energy over the dissociation threshold is 10–15 kcal. Thus the butyl radical and butene ion energies are very close, as well as the number of their degrees of freedom. For this reason it could be considered that the rate constants for their unimolecular decomposition will also be approximately similar. The k_s/k_d ratio for deactivation of radicals by krypton is 4×10^{-18} cm^3 $molecule^{-1}$. Consequently the constant for C_4H_8 deactivation by collisions with an inert gas is approximately 25 times higher than that for $C_4H_7^*$.

Termolecular reactions in general, and among them those involving ions, become more probable with increasing pressure. For instance, reactions

$$X^+ + X + X = X_2^+ + X \qquad [63]$$

$$X^+ + y + y = Xy^+ + y \qquad [64]$$

$$X^+ + X + y = X_2^+ + y \qquad [65]$$

$$X^+ + X + y = Xy^+ + X \qquad [66]$$

are probable for mixtures containing neutrals X and Y and X^+ ions. Their mechanisms involve collisions of an ion and a neutral in the field of a third body and the portion of energy imparted to the latter must be such as to leave the first and second bodies in the bound state. In terms of this mechanism the rate constant for eq. [63], when X is an atom (301) is

$$k = 16\left(\frac{\alpha e^2}{M}\right)^{1/2}\left(\frac{\alpha e^2}{kT}\right)^{3/4} \qquad [67]$$

where α is the polarizability and M the mass of atom X. Comparison of experimental and theoretical results shows (301) that best agreement is obtained with

$$k = 42\left(\frac{\alpha e^2}{M}\right)^{1/2}\left(\frac{\alpha e^2}{kT}\right)^{3/4} \qquad [68]$$

When various ions and atoms are involved in the reaction (302) the rate constants will be:

$$k = 42\left(\frac{m}{M}\right)^{1/4}\left(\frac{\alpha_y e^2}{kT}\right)^{3/4}\left(\frac{\alpha_y e^2}{m}\right)^{1/2} \qquad [69]$$

$$k = 42\left(\frac{m}{M}\right)^{1/4}\left(\frac{\alpha e^2}{kT}\right)^{3/4}\left(\frac{\alpha_y e^2}{m}\right)^{1/2} \qquad [70]$$

$$k = 42\left(\frac{m}{M}\right)^{1/4}\left(\frac{\alpha_y e^2}{kT}\right)^{3/4}\left(\frac{\alpha e^2}{M}\right)^{1/2} \qquad [71]$$

for reactions [64] to [66], respectively. Here m is the mass of atom Y (taking $m < M$); α_y is its polarizability. Taking into account possible charge exchange in reaction [63] we obtain (303)

$$k = \frac{3}{4} \pi^{1/2} 2^{1/4} k' \Gamma\left(\frac{3}{2}\right) \left(\frac{\alpha e^2}{kT}\right)^{3/4}$$ [72]

where k' is the exchange rate constant obtained from theoretical or experimental data. Table 22 lists such data for the formation of molecular ions in

TABLE 22

Theoretical and experimental rate constants for termolecular charge exchange reactions leading to the formation of molecular ions in atomic gases

Reaction	k_e ($\times 10^{32}$), cm^6 sec^{-1}	References	k_t ($\times 10^{32}$), cm^6 sec^{-1}	References
$He^+ + He + He = He_2^+ + He$	10.8	304	7.7	303
	6.3	305		
$Ne^+ + Ne + Ne = Ne_2^+ + Ne$	5.8	304	6.2	303
$Ar^+ + Ar + Ar = Ar_2^+ + Ar$	5.7	298		
$Ar^+ + Ar + He = ArHe^+ + Ar$	7.5	306	4.9	303
$Ar^+ + Ar + Ne = ArNe^+ + Ar$	25	306	8.3	303
$Hg^+ + Hg + He = Hg_2^+ + He$	1.7	307	1.5	301

atomic gases. These show good agreement within the coefficient ~ 1.5. The experimental rate constants for the first three reactions that exceed other data by several orders of magnitude (308) are not included in the table, since they were obtained at relatively low pressures in the ion source and the constants obtained at higher pressures seem to be more reliable.

The tabulated rate constants were obtained for temperatures of ions and neutrals of several hundreds °K. The temperature dependence $k \sim T^{-3/4}$ following from the theory shows satisfactory agreement with experiment over this temperature range (309).

The theory for termolecular ion-molecular reactions involving polyatomic species has not been worked out quantitatively, but the direction of possible calculations is qualitatively clear. A two-body collision may yield a relatively long-lived complex. It would stabilize by further collision with a neutral. Its lifetime and the probability of its stabilization may be calculated in terms of the statistical theory. Thus the theory for formation of termolecular associates must be quite similar here to three-body recombination of neutrals (299,300).

The most simple termolecular reaction involving a molecular ion seems to be reaction

$$He_2^+ + He + He = He_3^+ + He$$

The rate constant of this reaction at 76°K is $(1.7 \pm 0.4) \times 10^{-31}$ cm^6 sec^{-1} (310). The He_2^+ and He_3^+ ions are at equilibrium over the temperature range of 135–200°K. The dissociation energy for He_3^+ obtained from the temperature dependence of the rate constant was found to be 0.17 ± 0.003 eV. The rate constant for reaction

$$H^+ + H_2 + H_2 = H_3^+ + H_2$$

appeared to be $(3.2 \pm 1.0) \times 10^{-29}$ cm^6 sec^{-1} at 300°K (311). At a mean kinetic energy of 1 eV the rate constant of reaction

$$CO_2^+ + 2CO_2 = C_2O_4^+ + CO_2$$

is 3×10^{-28} cm^6 sec^{-1} (312).

VII. ION-MOLECULE REACTIONS INVOLVING NEGATIVE IONS

The mechanisms of ion-molecular reactions involving positive and negative ions seem to be very close. The specificity of negative ion reactions can apparently be only thermochemical: the energy of electron bonding in a negative ion is usually considerably lower than that in neutral atoms and molecules and thus, there are less exothermic paths for negative ions. Theoretical study of negative ion-charge exchange was carried out in Ref 313. Ion-molecular reactions with transfer of heavy species have the same limiting cross-sections dependent upon those for complex formation as for positive ions (see eqs. [59] and [61]). The same techniques as for positive ions may be used for experimental investigations of ion-molecular reactions involving negative ions. Experimental rate constants for negative ions were measured mostly in ion sources of mass spectrometers in the presence of an ion-repelling electric field. This technique is known to imply continuous acceleration of ions up to $10^{-1} - 1$ eV, so that it is difficult to refer the obtained reaction rates to relevant energies. The rate constants of ion-molecular reactions

$$D^- + D_2O = OD^- + D_2 \qquad [73]$$

$$O^- + O_2 = O_2^- + O \qquad [74]$$

$$O^- + N_2O = NO^- + NO \qquad [75]$$

$$O^- + N_2O = N_2O^- + O \qquad [76]$$

$$O^- + NO_2 = NO_2^- + O \qquad [77]$$

$$O^- + N_2O = O_2^- + N_2 \qquad [78]$$

were measured as a function of the ion kinetic energy at the reactor output (Table 23). It will be noted that reaction [74] follows the paths both of re-

TABLE 23

Rate constants of several ion-molecule reactions as a function of the ion kinetic energy at the reactor exit

	$k \, (\times 10^{11})$, cm^3 sec^{-1}					
E, eV	Eq. [73]	Eq. [74]	Eq. [75]	Eq. [76]	Eq. [77]	Eq. [78]
2	454	1.7	3.4	0.20	103	1.8
2.5	466	2.3	3.6	0.23	119	2.0
3	463	3.0	3.7	0.24	130	2.0
3.5	468	4.3	3.5	0.27	128	2.1
4	457	5.6	3.7	0.34	130	2.3
4.5	433	6.4	3.6	0.44	122	2.4
5	380	7.6	3.6	0.55	119	2.7
6	364	9.3	3.6	0.74	143	3.3

sonance electron transfer and of rearrangement, the cross-section of the former being three times that of the latter (314) over a kinetic energy range of 2–6 eV.

The pulse technique is also used for studying negative ion reactions in the equipotential region (315,316). Negative ions formed by resonance dissociative attachment show narrow distribution over kinetic energies. This permits one to obtain directly the cross-section for an ion-molecular reaction at an energy corresponding to that of the ion.

Table 24 lists the cross-sections for certain other simple bimolecular reactions and the rate constant for termolecular ion-molecular reactions.

TABLE 24

Cross-sections for some simple bimolecular reactions and rate constants for termolecular ion-molecule reactions

Reaction	$\sigma(\times 10^{16})$, cm^2	k, cm^6 sec^{-1}	References
$O^- + I_2 = OI^- + I$	83		317
$O^- + IBr = OI^- + Br$	5		317
$SO^- + SO_2 = SO_2^- + SO$	312		318
$NO^- + O_2 = O_2^- + NO$	205		319
$O^- + O_2 + O_2 = O_3^- + O_2$		9×10^{-31}	320
$O_2^- + CO_2 + CO_2 = CO_4^- + CO_2$		1.3×10^{-29}	321
$O^- + CO_2 + CO_2 = CO_3^- + CO_2$		8×10^{-29}	321

Data on negative ion reactions involving complex molecules may be found in the reviews (322) and (323).

VIII. DETACHMENT OF ELECTRONS FROM NEGATIVE IONS

At an electron temperature about 1 eV emission in dense plasma will contain a considerable number of photons capable of detaching electrons from negative ions. Photodetachment of electrons is also of interest for calculation of the effectivity of the back reaction, that of radiative electron attachment. The method of crossed ion and photon beams is used for accurate experimental investigations. Quantum-mechanical calculation of the cross-section for photodetachment of C^-, O^-, F^-, Cl^-, B^-, Si^-, and S^- (324) yielded values close to the experimental ones. At photon energies by 1–2 eV in excess over the threshold, the photodetachment cross-section usually is in the order of 10^{-18} cm^2. For instance, for reaction

$$hv + O_2^- = O_2 + e \qquad \sigma_{6200\text{Å}} = 1.1 \times 10^{-18} \text{ cm}^2 \qquad (90)$$

and for reaction

$$hv + O^- = O + e \qquad \sigma_{4000 < \lambda < 6000\text{Å}} = 6.3 \times 10^{-18} \text{ cm}^2 \qquad (90)$$

Decrease in the photodetachment cross-section near the threshold depends on the bound electron momentum. For example, the cross-section for H^- and alkali metal ions is $\sigma \sim E^{3/2}$, where E is the excess photon energy over the threshold, and for O^-, C^-, and other atoms with valency p-shells $\sigma \sim E^{1/2}$ (88,325). The behavior of cross-section for photo-detachment of electrons from negative ions was also estimated (326).

Two-photon photo-detachment, that is, participation of two photons in one elementary step, are possible with intensive photon beams (327,328). Relevant calculations made for I^- show good agreement with experimental results (328).

Another mode of electron detachment from negative ions in plasma may be that by collision with an electron. Regrettably, the information on such reactions is very meagre, and even when available, for instance for high electron energy, where it would be expected to be most reliable, it shows no agreement between experimental and theoretical results (329). Only theoretical results were obtained for energies near the threshold, the most reliable seem to be those in Ref. 330. Experimental data on O^- and H^- over the range of relatively low electron energies that are of interest here, are listed in Tables 25 and 26.

Let us consider now electron detachment by collision of a negative ion X^- with a heavy atom or molecule Y. Two reactions are possible

$$[1] \quad X^- + Y = X + Y + e$$

$$[2] \quad X^- + Y = XY + e$$

TABLE 25
Experimental data on cross-sections for electron detachment from O^- by collisions with electrons of various energies

Electron energy, eV	Cross-section, πa_0^2
7.1	5.55 ± 0.43
12.1	7.00 ± 0.40
17.1	8.32 ± 0.43
22.1	8.69 ± 0.43

TABLE 26
Experimental cross-sections for electron detachment from H^- by collision with electrons of various energies

Electron energy, eV	Cross-section, πa_0^2
8.4	40.5 ± 2.8
13.4	48.8 ± 3.4
18.4	50.0 ± 3.5
24.4	48.0 ± 3.4

Reaction [1] involves intersection of the electronic term with the continuum boundary. It would be plausible to suggest that when the distance R_{min} between a negative ion and a neutral Y on slow collision is smaller than that to the intersection, R_{int} the reaction probability will be unity (331,332). To this approximation, the reaction cross-section

$$\sigma = \pi R_{int}^2 \left[\frac{1 - U(R_{int})}{E} \right] \qquad [79]$$

Here U is the potential for interaction between an ion and a neutral, E is the energy of partners in the inertia center system. Expression [79] shows fair agreement with experimental data obtained for

$$H^- + He = H + He + e \qquad (333) \qquad [80]$$

$$Br^- + He = Br + He + e \qquad (331) \qquad [81]$$

$$I^- + He = I + He + e \qquad (331) \qquad [82]$$

Comparison of theory and experiment requires selection of the R_{int} and $U(R_{int})$ parameters. For example the excitation function for reaction [80] is well described at $R_{int} = 0.9$ Å. The cross-sections for [81] and [82] are given by

$$\sigma = 4.1\text{Å}^2\left[\frac{1 - 180}{E}\,\text{eV}\right]$$

and

$$\sigma = 4\text{Å}^2\left[\frac{1 - 250}{E}\,\text{eV}\right]$$

Electron detachment by collisions $H^- + F$ and $H + F^-$ are described in Ref. 334. The intersection points of relevant terms are calculated. The maximum cross-section for electron detachment in this system is 33.8 Å^2. Data on electron detachment by collisions of molecular species

$$O_2^- + O_2 = O_2 + O_2 + e \qquad\qquad [83]$$

may be found in Ref. 90. At 230°K the rate constant for this reaction is 4×10^{-20} cm^3 sec^{-1}, and the activation energy is close to the O_2 electron affinity.

The type [2] reaction is called associative electron detachment. As it requires rapprochement of reactants to the ordinary intermolecular separations, the cross-section for formation of the polarization complex may be considered as the upper limit for an exothermic reaction at low energies. The experimental rate constants (319) are listed in Table 27.

TABLE 27

Rate constants for associative electron detachment reactions

Reaction	$k \ (\times 10^{10})$, cm^3 sec^{-1}
$O^- + H_2 = H_2O + e + 3.5$ eV	15
$O^- + NO = NO_2 + e + 1.6$ eV	5
$O^- + CO = CO_2 + e + 4$ eV	5
$O^- + O = O_2 + e + 3.6$ eV	3
$O^- + N = NO + e + 5.1$ eV	3
$O_2^- + O = O_3 + e + 0.6$ eV	5
$O_2^- + N = NO_2 + e + 4.1$ eV	5
$OH^- + O = HO_2 + e + 1$ eV	2
$OH^- + N = HNO + e + 2.4$ eV	< 0.1

It was shown by experiments using a drift tube at ion energies from thermal to 0.16 eV that the rate constants for associative attachment reactions $O^- + NO$, $O^- + CO$, $O^- + H_2$, and $O_2^- + CO$ are 2.2×10^{-10}, 6.5×10^{-10}, 7.5×10^{-10}, and $< 10^{-14}$ cm^3 sec^{-1}, respectively (335). Comparison with experimental rate constants for the formation of relevant polarization ion-molecular complexes (60) shows that there are even exothermic processes the effectivity of which is considerably lower than it would follow from the statistical theory.

IX. RECOMBINATION OF CHARGED SPECIES

At low temperatures the ions in dense plasma are usually molecular. In this case dissociative recombination between ions and electrons

$$XY^+ + e \rightleftharpoons (XY)^* = X^* + Y$$

is the main reaction. Theoretical calculation of its cross-section is possible only if the potential curves for various electronic states essential for this reaction are known in detail. To the present time relevant calculations were made for H_2^+ (336), NO^+ (337), O_2^+, N_2^+, and He_2^+ (338). Inaccurate calculation is essentialy due to insufficient knowledge of the potential curves. Theoretical treatment shows that the temperature dependencies of rate constants for dissociative recombination depend on the relative position of these curves. Sometimes the rate constant is markedly dependent on vibrational excitation of ions. For this reason the experimental rate constants for dissociative recombination may appear to differ due to different distribution of molecular ions over vibrational states. The greatest number of rate constants was obtained in experiments on variations in electron density with time in degrading plasma (339). The super high-frequency, optical, and mass-spectrometric diagnostics of plasma were used. Table 28 (339) lists experimental rate constants for dissociative recombination in isothermic plasma at 300°K.

TABLE 28
Experimental rate constants for dissociative recombination in isothermic plasmas, at 300°K

Ion	k ($\times 10^7$), cm^3 sec^{-1}
Ne_2^+	2.0 ± 0.2
N_2^+	2.8 ± 0.3
N_4^+	~ 10
O_2^+	2.0 ± 0.5
NO^+	~ 4
Ar_2^+	7 ± 2
Kr_2^+	~ 12
Xe_2^+	~ 14

As stated previously, the theory gives no general law for the temperature dependence of rate constants. It was found experimentally for He_2^+ (340) and for Ar_2^+ (341) that the dissociative recombination rate constant depends on electron temperature as $k \sim T^{-3/2}$ over the 300–1500 and 300–3000°K ranges, respectively.

The temperature dependence of the rate constant for dissociative recombination of NO^+ (342) was found to change from $T^{-1/2}$ to $T^{-3/2}$ with increasing temperature. An empirical expression for recombination $NO^+ + e$ may be written as

$$\alpha_r = 4.8 \times 10^{-8}(kT)^{-1/2}\left[1 - \exp\left(\frac{-0.27}{kT}\right)\right]$$

where kT is expressed in eV. At 2900°K $\alpha_r = (4 \pm 2) \times 10^{-8}$ cm^3 sec^{-1} (343). The temperature dependence of the rate constant for $NH_3^+ + e$ over the temperature range of 1000–2600°K obeys the law $k \sim T^{-2.2 \pm 0.2}$ (344). At 2150 ± 50°K $k = (9.4 \pm 0.5) \times 10^{-7}$ cm^3 sec^{-1}. The rate constants for recombination of complex ions may be found in (345). The main recombination reaction in a hydrocarbon flame, in the absence of electronegative gases and alkali metal atoms, seems to be $H_3O^+ + e$. Addition of alkali metals results in an effective recombination coefficient by some two orders of magnitude lower, due to conversion of molecular into atomic ions during charge exchange. The effective rate constant for ion recombination in hydrocarbon flames decreases with temperature first rapidly down to a minimum at 2000°K, and then slowly increases. This suggests to the occurrence of several parallel and consecutive reactions. Even in such a relatively simple system as nitrogen, the effective rate constant for recombination of electrons with ions at gas temperatures of 300–735°K and pressures of 0.5–6 torr shows a complex dependence on temperature (346). Over this range k decreases with temperature approximately by an order of magnitude at a pressure of 2 torr and by two orders more at 6 torr. This is probably accounted for by simultaneous existence of N_2^+, N_3^+, and N_4^+ in the system. The chemical effects of recombination were studied in Refs. 347–349. Elimination of recombination between hydrocarbon ions and electrons by means of imposing an electric field on the gas irradiated by fast electrons results in a lower radiative-chemical hydrogen yield. An apparatus was designed (348) for differentiated investigation of homogeneous and heterogeneous recombination. It permits investigating ion recombination at electrodes in the "pure" form. The composition and energy state of neutrals formed by dissociative recombination of complex ions have not yet been investigated. The experimental technique of pulsed irradiation by fast electrons (350) is of interest for study of recombination in plasma created by ionizing radiation in cold gas at high pressures. With ordinary pulsed gas discharge at pressures somewhat higher than 10 torr the study of elementary reactions is hindered by the difficulty in producing plasma of a prefixed initial concentration that would ensure uniform filling of the cavity. Moreover, a great number of atoms and molecules excited to metastable states is formed in discharge, and this makes difficult the thermalization of electrons. Ionization by a pulsed electron beam eliminated these difficulties. Various applications of beam techniques have been reported recently. These techniques may open up the possibility of studying recombination of molecular ions in prefixed energy states and thus of obtaining more detailed information on the composition and energy states of recombination products. Experiments were carried out (351) using a beam of Cs_2^+ ions. It was passed through the plasma, and the neutrals formed by recombination were recorded at the outlet of the ionized gas region. At an electron temperature of 1380°K the recombination rate constant appeared to be $(2.5 \pm 1.8) \times 10^{-8}$ cm^3 sec^{-1}.

The technique of merging ion and electron beams for measurement of cross-sections and the rate constants for recombination over a range of relative ion and electron energies were described in (352).

Recombination of atomic ions at low densities of charged species occurs at a considerably lower rate compared to recombination of molecular ions, since bimolecular recombination of atomic ions may occur as photorecombination only. The time of electron residence near the ion is considerably shorter than the average time for emission of photons that take up excess energy. As a result of it the photorecombination rate constant is very low (in the order of 10^{-14} cm^3 sec^{-1}).

The most effective recombination of atomic ions in dense low-temperature plasma is that by three-body collisions, when excess energy is taken up by the third body. When the latter is an atom of 10–40 amu or a molecule, the rate constants for three-body recombination will be (353)

$$k \simeq 10^{-31} T_{eV}^{-5/2} \qquad [84]$$

and

$$k \simeq 10^{-30} T_{eV}^{-5/2} \qquad [85]$$

respectively where T_{eV} is the temperature in eV.

When the molecule has a dipole moment, its efficiency as third body is considerably higher. At temperatures of several tenths of eV the theoretical rate constant for electron-ion recombination in a medium of dipole molecules is 10^{-26} cm^6 sec^{-1} (354). When the third body is an electron, the recombination rate constant is (355).

$$k = 10^{-26} T_{eV}^{-9/2} \text{ cm}^6 \text{ sec}^{-1} \qquad [86]$$

If use is made of the Born expression for inelastic transition, the temperature dependence of the rate constant for recombination involving an electron as third particle will be (356)

$$k \sim T^{-11/2} \qquad [87]$$

This dependence is a good approximation to the results of numerical calculations (357) obtained by precise treatment of the problem. The theory implies that the recombination rate constant markedly increases with decreasing temperature. Consequently, it is possible to estimate the pressure range over which two-body recombination of molecular ions will become slower than the three-body one, as increase in the rate constant of the former is considerably less fast.

Let us consider now the recombination of positive and negative ions. It was found (358) that the mechanism of such recombination involves two parallel reactions. One is that of electron transfer from the positive to the negative ion

$$A^+ + B^- \longrightarrow \text{neutrals} \qquad [88]$$

the second represents three body-recombination

$$A^+ + B^- + M \longrightarrow \text{neutrals} \qquad [89]$$

The rate constants for reaction [89] are shown in Table 29 (259). Those for reactions involving He and Ar as inert gases are approximately equal, and

TABLE 29

Rate constants for reactions involving electron transfer from the positive to the negative ion and three-body recombination

System	$k \ (\times 10^7)$, cm^3 sec^{-1}
NO–SF$_6$–He	1.95 ± 0.1
NO–SF$_6$–Ar	2.00 ± 0.1
NO–SF$_6$–Xe	1.5 ± 0.15
C$_6$H$_6$–SF$_6$–He	1.8 ± 0.2
C$_6$H$_6$–SF$_6$–Ar	1.75 ± 0.15
C$_6$H$_6$–SF$_6$–Xe	1.35 ± 0.15
I$_2$–Ar	1.2 ± 0.2
I$_2$–Xe	1.0 ± 0.2

those using Xe are somewhat lower. The latter seems to be accounted for by formation and recombination of NOXe$^+$ and not NO$^+$ ions. It follows from theoretical calculation (360) that the approximate rate constant for [88] is

$$k \simeq 2 \times 10^{-8} T_{\text{eV}}^{-1/2} \text{ cm}^3 \text{ sec}^{-1} \qquad [90]$$

A reaction of the [88] type, namely $N^+ + O^- = N + O$, was studied experimentally by the method of merging beams (361), which permits obtaining the cross-section as a function of the kinetic energies of colliding partners. At kinetic energies of relative motion higher than 0.5 eV the product of the reaction cross-section by the velocity v is 9×10^{-8} cm^3 sec^{-1} and it remains approximately constant.

At energies lower than 0.5 eV the cross-section increase with decreasing energy is considerably more marked, so that at 0.1 eV $\sigma v \simeq 1.4 \times 10^{-7}$ cm^3 sec^{-1}.

The theory of ion-ion recombination by three-body collisions in gas under low pressures has been developed (362–367). Like in other three-body collisions the mechanism considered implies collision of an ion and a neutral in the field of a third body. As a result of this collision the ion gives up to the neutral a portion of energy such that it remains bound. The theoretical research enumerated above yielded results that show fair agreement with each other and with experiment. The rate constants for recombination in air and oxygen are approximated by the expression

$$k \simeq 3 \times 10^{-29} T^{-5/2} \text{ cm}^6 \text{ sec}^{-1} \qquad [91]$$

When the gas density is high, ion recombination occurs as a result of the drift of oppositely charged ions in the Coulomb field. Transition from low to high pressures in air occurs over a range of 1–3 atm. The theory embracing the regions of low, intermediate and high pressures is given in Ref. 363. At the high-pressure limit the effective ion recombination coefficient is given by mobilities K^+ and K^- of positive and negative ions following the Langevin expression (368)

$$\alpha = 4\pi e^2 (K^+ + K^-)$$

The ion-mobility values may be found, for example, in Ref. 6.

X. VIBRATIONAL RELAXATION REACTIONS

Maxwellian distribution over translational and rotational degrees of freedom in molecules is usually attained in times that are low compared to those corresponding to appreciable changes in macroscopic gas parameters, such as density and energy. At temperatures of interest for low-temperature plasma these processes take a time of some ten gas-kinetic collisions. However, tens and hundreds of thousands of collisions are needed for vibrational excitation at temperatures of a thousand or several thousands degrees, for which vibrational relaxation is of practical interest. The particular question of vibrational-translational relaxation for molecular ions was discussed in

Section VI. The kinetic relaxation equation (369) for vibrational excitation and for the back reaction of conversion of vibrational to translational energy is

$$\frac{dE}{dt} = -\frac{|E_e - E|}{\tau} \qquad [92]$$

Here E is the vibrational energy per unit gas volume; $E_e(T)$ is the equilibrium vibrational energy at the same vibrational temperature; τ is the relaxation time. The long relaxation times are due to the long time of interaction compared to the vibrational period (adiabatic collisions). Quantum-mechanical calculation to the adiabatic approximation yields (369) the following temperature dependence of the vibrational-translational relaxation time

$$\left[1 - \exp\left(-\frac{\hbar\omega}{kT} \right) \right] \tau = A \exp(BT^{-1/3}) \qquad [93]$$

Here $\hbar\omega$ is the vibrational quantum energy. The A and B values are usually obtained by plotting the experimental data versus $\tau(T)$. There are also other approximate expressions for the vibrational relaxation times, obtained by classical and quantum-mechanical treatment of the problem (370,371). The most frequently used expression is the Schwartz-Herzfeld expression (370) establishing the relation of the relaxation time to vibrational frequency and to other molecular parameters. In the temperature range of greatest interest this expression coincides, to the accuracy of slowly changing temperature functions, with expression [93]. Experimental data on vibrational relaxation for many pure gases, N_2 (372), O_2 (373,374), NO (375), CO (376), CO_2 (377,378), and their mixtures (379,380) show good agreement with theoretical calculations to the adiabatic approximation. Deviations are observed, when the condition of collision adiabaticity is not fulfilled. The latter takes place even at very low temperatures, for collisions of heavy-atom molecules having low vibrational quanta with light fast species (382,383). For instance, with a mixture of I_2 and He the nonadiabaticity will have an effect even at room temperature (383). For a general case the effectivity of non-adiabatic reactions increases with temperature.

The vibrational relaxation times for mixtures containing polyatomic molecules may be by one to three orders of magnitude lower than those for gases consisting of diatomic molecules. Water molecules are particularly effective in decreasing the relaxation time. This seems to be due to formation of relatively long-lived complexes. Considerably more ready relaxation might probably occur in other cases as well, as mentioned above for ion-molecular reactions.

Experimental determination of vibrational relaxation times usually involves the recording and analysis of the relaxation effect on the hydro-dynamic or optical gas structure in shock waves (18,385).

The experimental dependencies of τ on temperature and pressure for oxygen, nitrogen and carbon monoxide may be given by a general expression (21) with an accuracy to a factor of 2

$$\tau p = 10^{-9} \exp(2.9x^{1/3}) \text{ atm sec} \qquad [94]$$

where $x = D/kT$ and D is the energy of molecular dissociation. The τ values for halogens (21) are given by

$$\tau p = 10^{-9} \exp(1.7x^{1/3}) \text{ atm sec} \qquad [95]$$

approximately to the same accuracy. For instance, at a pressure of 1 atm in O_2, N_2, and CO, the τ values over a temperature range of 2000–5000°K are 10^{-6} to 10^{-4} sec.

The vibrational relaxation of N_2 at 2500°K in various excess gases was investigated (386). The following results were obtained:

$\tau p(N_2-N_2) = 1.9 \times 10^{-4}$ atm sec; $\tau p(N_2-SO_2) = 2.9 \times 10^{-5}$ atm sec;
$\tau p(N_2-H_2) = 1.3 \times 10^{-6}$ atm sec; $\tau p(N_2-Ar) = 4.8 \times 10^{-4}$ atm sec;
$\tau p(N_2-Kr) = 9.4 \times 10^{-4}$ atm sec; $\tau p(N_2-O_2) = 1.2 \times 10^{-5}$ atm sec.

We have discussed the vibrational-translational relaxation of diatomic molecules. Vibrational-vibrational relaxation with transfer of a vibrational quantum from one molecule to another also is of interest for many cases. Its probability is known to be highest, when the vibrational frequencies of colliding molecules are equal, due to resonance. Expression

$$\langle P_{10-01} \rangle = 3.7 \times 10^{-6} T \, \text{sech}^2 \left(\frac{0.174\gamma}{T^{1/2}} \right) \qquad [96]$$

was obtained for the probability of esronance and near-to-resonance transfer of vibrational quanta (387). Here $\langle P_{10-01} \rangle$ is the probability of vibrational quantum transfer in one collision, averaged over the Maxwellian distribution; γ is the difference in vibrational molecular frequencies in cm^{-1}. Expression [96] is valid for molecules with a reduced mass of 20–40 amu, for example, N_2-N_2, CO–NO, CO–N_2, O_2-N_2, N_2–NO.

A specific feature of vibrational relaxation of polyatomic gases and gas mixtures is that such gases display several vibrational frequencies. Every oscillator of a molecule may exchange energy with translational and rotational energy. Moreover, transfer of vibrational quanta from one oscillator to the other may occur by collisions. As a result of fast resonance exchange all groups of oscillators having identical frequencies and initial equilibrium states form equilibrium subsystems with temperatures T_l, $l = 1, 2, 3 \ldots$ (388,389). When the spectrum of vibrational frequencies of a polyatomic molecule ω_1, ω_2 ... has no two adjacent frequencies differing by more than a factor of 2, exchange by vibrational quanta will also be fast, provided the difference in vibrational frequencies does not exceed the collision time reciprocal

$$\Delta\omega \leqslant 5 \times 10^{12} \sqrt{\frac{T}{\mu}} \sec^{-1}$$

It was found (388,389) that the T_l values will be expressed through oscillator frequencies and the temperature of translational rotational motion, the temperature equality for individual oscillator groups setting in simultaneously with complete termination of vibrational relaxation. The expression for relation between T_1, T_l and T (388) is

$$\frac{\omega_l}{T_l} = \frac{\omega_1}{T_1} + \frac{\omega_l - \omega_1}{T} \tag{97}$$

XI. THERMAL DISSOCIATION OF MOLECULES

In accordance with modern concepts, vibrational energy is thought to play the most important part in dissociation. Since its increase upon collisions by one quantum is most probable, dissociation would involve only molecules that were already excited before collision. Consequently, the rate of molecular dissociation depends on the population of upper vibrational levels and, strictly speaking, dissociation and vibrational relaxation cannot be considered as independent.

The limits for describing dissociation of diatomic molecules by means of one parameter, namely the rate constant, either equilibrium or nonequilibrium, were discussed as an example in Section I. The equilibrium dissociation rate constant (390,391) is given by expression [19]. It was found (21) that for elevated temperatures in molecular gases dissociation may be described by a nonequilibrium rate constant determined in the same way as by using [19], but replacing translational temperature T by vibrational T_v. The vibrational temperature for dissociation of O_2, N_2, and CO is given by

$$y = 10 \exp\left(-\frac{x}{1 + y + 2.9x^{1/3}}\right) \tag{98}$$

where $x = D/kT$, $y = T_v/T - 1$. The vibrational temperature is lower than the translational-rotational one, as dissociation represents a sort of drain for highly excited molecules. The mutual effect of vibrational relaxation and oxygen dissociation in a shock wave were considered under different assumptions about the dependencies of dissociation probabilities on the vibrational level number (392). The interesting results obtained throw some light on the relation between the equilibrium and nonequilibrium rate constants. It was found for all plausible dissociation probabilities that k/k^* did not differ essentially from unity at $T < 4000°K$. The mutual effect of vibrational relaxation and dissociation of diatomic molecules at higher than vibrational temperatures was calculated by the Monte-Carlo computer method (393). Models of one-quantum and multiquantum transitions were considered. These yielded close results for O_2 in excess Ar only at temperatures lower than 8×10^3 °K. At 20,000°K and higher, deviation from the results obtained in terms of the Landau-Teller theory (369) became essential.

Detailed investigation of the theoretical and experimental results for reaction

$$O_2 + Ar = O + O + Ar$$

was carried out (394). The theoretical expression for its rate constant is (16,394)

$$k = c'\left[1 - \exp\left(-\frac{\hbar\omega}{kT}\right)\right]\exp\left(-\frac{D}{RT}\right) \qquad [99]$$

where c' is a value that does not depend much on temperature $(c' \sim T^{0+1/6})$ (16). For low temperatures eq. [99] will be reduced to

$$k = c' \exp\left(-\frac{D}{RT}\right) \qquad [100]$$

for high temperatures

$$k = c''T^{-1} \exp\left(-\frac{D}{RT}\right) \qquad [101]$$

The experimental value obtained at high temperatures (5000–18,000°K) (395),

$$k = 2.4(\pm 18\%) \times 10^{18}\, T^{-1} \exp\left(-\frac{D}{RT}\right) \frac{cm^3}{sec\ mole}$$

is in good agreement with the theoretical eq. (101). Correlation of eq. [101] and the experimental dependence yields an expression valid both for low and for high temperatures

$$k = 1.1 \times 10^{15}\left[1 - \exp\left(-\frac{2200}{T}\right)\right] \exp\left(-\frac{D}{RT}\right) \frac{cm_3}{sec\ mole}$$

However, the experimental pre-exponential factor for Br_2 dissociation in argon is $\sim T^{-3/2}$ (396) and for Cl_2 it appears to be $\sim T^{-5/2}$ (397). This discrepancy in temperature dependencies for dissociation of diatomic molecules has yet no explanation.

Detailed analysis of experimental results and their comparison with theoretical data were carried out (398) for the reaction

$$O_2 + O_2 = O + O + O_2$$

The expression

$$k = 1.5 \times 10^{11} \sqrt{T} \left(\frac{D}{RT}\right)^{2.5} \exp\left(-\frac{D}{RT}\right)$$

gives the most accurate description of experimental data for a temperature range of 3000–7000°K.

The results obtained at temperatures of 10^4 °K and higher have shown that the importance of the structures of colliding partners becomes less with increasing temperature (399). For instance, the decrease in the effectivity of O atoms and O_2 molecules with increasing temperatures is such that at 9000–10,000°K it approaches that of argon atoms. The same is observed for hydrogen dissociation: over a temperature range of three to six thousand degrees the rate constant for reaction $H_2 + H \rightarrow 3H$ becomes considerably lower, approaching that for an $H_2 + Ar$ collision. This phenomenon seems to be due to decreasing importance of the attraction forces and of other specific features of the molecular interaction potential for the atom-diatomic molecule complex, as well as to the weaker effect of vibrational quanta exchange on vibrational relaxation and subsequent dissociation. Analysis of experimental data (399) yielded the following recommended rate constants for dissociation at temperatures higher than 10^4 °K:

$$k(O_2 - O) = [1 + 108\theta^{-0.58} \exp(-1.7 \times 10 - 3\theta^{3.3})]k(O_2 - Ar) \quad (\theta > 3)$$

$$k(O_2 - O_2) = [1 + 600\theta^{-2.3} \exp(-4 \times 10 - 9\theta^{9.2})]k(O_2 - Ar) \quad (\theta > 3)$$

$$k(N_2 - N) = [1 + 2200\theta^{-0.9} \exp(-2.85 \times 10 - 7\theta^{6.1})]k(N_2 - Ar) \quad (\theta > 6)$$

$$k(N_2 - N_2) = [1 + 100\theta^{-0.87} \exp(-3.7 \times 10 - 8\theta^{6.5})]k(N_2 - Ar) \quad (\theta > 6)$$

θ is the temperature in characteristic temperature units ($\hbar\omega$).

The thermal dissociation of tri-atomic and polyatomic molecules is known to obey the first and second order kinetic laws at high and low pressures, respectively (400,401). There is an intermediate region betwen these extreme cases, where the reaction order varies from 2 to 1. Use of the transition state method at high pressures, when the intermolecular energy exchange rate is higher than that of intermolecular exchange between vibrational degrees of freedom, yields a satisfactory approximation to the reaction rate constant. The general expression obtained to this approximation (402) is

$$k = g^+ \chi \frac{kT}{2\pi h} \cdot \frac{F_{AB}^+}{F_{AB}} \exp\left(-\frac{D}{kT}\right) \qquad [103]$$

where F_{AB} and F_{AB}^+ are the partition functions for a stable and an activated molecule, respectively; g^+ is the number of independent decay paths: χ is the transmission coefficient. The factor F_{AB}^+ can be considered as known, if the configuration of the activated molecule, or, which is the same as, the critical surface in the phase space intersection of which, shows the completion of the elementary reaction, are known. When the molecule is modelled by a system of harmonic oscillators and the transmission coefficient is close to unity, it follows from eq. [103] that at high temperatures ($kT > \hbar\omega$) the pre-exponential factor will be of the order of vibrational frequency ($10^{14} \sec^{-1}$). The most important evidence of anharmonicity in dissociation is the conversion of certain types of an active molecule vibrations into free rotation. The calculated pre-exponential factor of the rate constant for ethane decomposition to two CH_3 radicals at 600°C is $10^{17} \sec^{-1}$ (403). The pre-exponential factor obtained for a dissociating molecule modelled by a system of s-oscillators and r^+-rotators (398) is

$$A(T) \sim \chi(T) T^{(r^+ + r)/r + 1} \qquad \hbar\omega_i, \hbar\omega_i^+ \gg kT$$

$$A(T) \sim \chi(T) T^{(r - r^+)/r} \qquad \hbar\omega_i, \hbar\omega_i^+ \ll kT$$

r^+ being usually higher than r. Thus, if the transmission coefficient is left aside, A will be characterized by positive and negative temperature dependencies at low and high temperatures, respectively.

A situation when $\chi \ll 1$ is quite possible for nonadiabatic reactions proceeding with change of the electronic state. The temperature dependence $\chi(T)$ will be $\chi(T) \sim T^{-1/2}$, when the relation between terms is due to spin-orbital coupling, and $\chi(T) \sim T^{1/2}$ when it is accounted for by Coriolis forces acting on electrons.

As stated previously, thermal dissociation at low pressures is second order. In this case the pre-exponential factor cannot be calculated in terms of the equilibrium statistical theory. Detailed knowledge of molecular excitation to the dissociation threshold is then necessary. The high-temperature dependence of the pre-exponential factor for strong collision will be (398)

$$A \sim T^{-s - r/2 + 1}$$

and for stepwise excitation of the molecule modelled by harmonic s-oscillators and r-rotators

$$A \sim T^{-s - r/2}$$

The dissociation rate in the region between first and second order reactions is dependent upon competing inter- and intramolecular energy exchange. Thus allowances for kinetics of energy redistribution inside the molecule must be introduced into the dissociation theory. The lifetime distribution function $h\tau$ will be characteristic of such kinetics for active molecules. The information on $h\tau$ is drawn mainly from theoretical investigations of model systems and does not permit unambiguous association of this distribution function with the dynamic characteristics of real molecules (401).

The rate constants for dissociation and recombination of moderately complex molecules in excess inert gas were calculated recently (404) making use of a kinetic equation with transition probabilities and spontaneous decay rates obtained from the statistical theory for reaction rates. The pairs of species investigated are given in Table 30. The rate constants for many reactions of dissociation, recombination, and exchange between neutrals may be found in the handbook (403).

TABLE 30

Species investigated in the dissociation and recombination of moderately complex molecules in the presence of excess inert gas

Dissociation	Recombination	Dissociation	Recombination
$O_3 + Ar$	$O_2 + O$	$NH_3 + Ar$	$NH_2 + H$
$NOCl + Ar$	$NO + Cl$	$(CN)_2 + Ar$	$CN + CN$
$NF_2 + Ar$	$NF + F$	$CF_4 + Ar$	$CF_3 + F$
$NO_2 + Ar$	$NO + O$	$CHF_3 + Ar$	$CF_2 + HF$
$CF_2 + Ar$	$CF + F$	$CH_4 + Ar$	$CH_3 + H$
$H_2O + Ar$	$OH + H$	$N_2O_4 + N_2$	$NO_2 + NO_2$
$SO_2 + Ar$	$SO + O$	$N_2H_4 + Ar$	$NH_2 + NH_2$
$BrCN + Ar$	$CN + Br$	$N_2F_4 + N_2$	$NF_2 + NF_2$
$ClCN + Ar$	$CN + Cl$	$C_2F_4 + Ar$	$CF_2 + CF_2$
$NO_2Cl + Ar$	$NO_2 + Cl$	$C_2H_4 + H_2$	$C_2H_2 + H_2$
$H_2O_2 + N_2$	$OH + OH$		

XII. RECOMBINATION OF NEUTRALS

Recombination of radicals also occurs within two pressure regions where reaction kinetics follow the third and second order laws, as well as within the transition region. Let us consider as an example the recombination of CH_3 (398). Taking

$$CH_3 + CH_3 \underset{k_b}{\overset{k_a}{\rightleftharpoons}} C_2H_6^*$$

$$C_2H_6^* + M \overset{k_c}{=} C_2H_6 + M$$

as the reaction mechanism, and assuming that the concentration of unstable $C_2H_6^*$ molecules is stationary, we obtain for the rate of ethane formation

$$\frac{d(C_2H_6)}{dt} = \frac{k_a k_c (CH_3)^2 (M)}{k_b + k_c(M)}$$

whence the recombination constant k_r will be

$$k_r = \frac{k_a k_c (M)}{k_b + k_c(M)} \qquad [104]$$

It follows from [104] that at high pressures, when $k_c(M) \gg k_b$, k_r becomes

$$k_r^{(2)} = k_a$$

that is, it is actually independent of pressure. In this case the reaction will be second order. However, at low pressures, when $k_c(M) \ll k_b$, we have

$$k_r = \frac{k_a k_c}{k_b} (M)$$

Hence we obtain for the rate constant of third-order reaction

$$k_r^{(3)} = \frac{k_a k_c}{k_b}$$

Different to $k_r^{(2)}$ the constant $k_r^{(3)}$ must depend on the nature of reactant M (through the dependence of k_c on M). As to the temperature dependencies of $k_r^{(2)}$ and $k_r^{(3)}$ the former must be proportional to that of the number of gas-kinetic collisions

$$k_r^{(2)} = A_r^{(2)} \sqrt{T}$$

Then, assuming that the stabilization rate constant for $C_2H_6^*$, k_c is dependent on temperature in accordance with the same law, that is, $k_c = A_c \sqrt{T}$ and that the rate constant for decomposition of $C_2H_6^*$ is $k_b = A_b \exp(-D/RT)$ we get

$$k_r^{(3)} = A_r^{(3)} T \exp\left(\frac{D}{RT}\right)$$

Thus, it will be expected that, different to $k_r^{(2)}$ the rate constant $k_r^{(3)}$ will have a negative temperature coefficient, provided $D > RT$. Analysis of experimental results obtained for methyl radicals (398) shows that all the conclusions are in good agreement with experiment. The recombination rate constants are often calculated from equilibrium ratios from known equilibrium and dissociation rate constants. For example the rate constant for O recombination in excess of the inert gas, argon, was calculated in this way (394). It will be written as

$$k = 4.2 \times 10^{16} \, T^{-1} \, \frac{cm^6}{sec \; mole}$$

for temperatures close to the ambient one, and as

$$k = 2.0 \times 10^{15} T^{-1/2} \, \frac{cm^6}{sec \; mole}$$

for temperatures higher than 3000°K.

Sometimes $A + B$ recombination is possible through formation of a complex with an "inert" component M

$$A + M = AM$$

$$AM + B = AB + M$$

With such a recombination mechanism k must contain an exponential factor $\exp(D'/RT)$, since recombination involves in fact various bound AM pairs with bond energies $D' = 0.5$ to 5 kcal mole^{-1}. The recombination of chlorine atoms in molecular chlorine seems to follow this mechanism (406). Certain recombination rate constants may be found in Refs. 404 and 405.

XIII. EXCHANGE REACTIONS INVOLVING NEUTRALS

Exchange reactions of type

$$A + BC = AB + C$$

represent the most wide and important class of chemical reactions. However, the theory for these reactions is not yet sufficiently developed. The transition state theory (the activated complex theory) (402) seems to be that best developed for reactions of this type. The rate constant expressions for reactions in which A, B, and C are atoms are different for a triangular and a linear complex. The first involves three vibrational and two rotational, and the second two vibrational and three rotational degrees of freedom. The temperature dependence of the rate constant for an exchange reaction (398) is

$$k_{ex} = T^{1/2} \frac{1 - \exp(-\hbar\omega_{AB}/kT)}{\prod_{i=1}^{2} [1 - \exp(-\hbar\omega_i/kT)]} \exp\left(-\frac{E}{RT}\right)$$

$$= \begin{cases} T^{1/2} \exp\left(-\dfrac{E}{RT}\right) & \hbar\omega \gg kT \\[2ex] T^{3/2} \exp\left(-\dfrac{E}{RT}\right) & \hbar\omega \ll kT \end{cases} \qquad [105]$$

for a linear complex, and

$$k_{ex} \sim \frac{1 - \exp(-\hbar\omega_{BC}/kT)}{\prod_{i=1}^{3} [1 - \exp(-\hbar\omega_i^+/kT)]} \exp\left(-\frac{E}{RT}\right)$$

$$= \begin{cases} \exp\left(-\dfrac{E}{RT}\right) & \hbar\omega \gg kT \\[3mm] T \exp\left(-\dfrac{E}{RT}\right) & \hbar\omega \ll kT. \end{cases} \qquad [106]$$

for a triangular complex. The applicability of expressions [105] and [106] at high temperatures may be limited by the request that the overall pre-exponential factor be considerably lower than the number of gas-kinetic collisions. If this request is not fulfilled, the temperature dependence of the pre-exponential factor will be $\sim T^{1/2}$ instead of $\sim T^{3/2}$ and $\sim T$ in eqs. [105] and [106].

Table 31 lists the rate constants for certain simple chemical exchange reactions. Detailed information on rate constants for a wider range of exchange reactions may be found in the handbook (405).

In conclusion let us discuss in brief the experimental techniques for measurement of rate constants of atom and radical reactions. The atoms and radicals may be produced by thermal, photochemical or electrical techniques. Their concentrations are determined in different ways: by the calorimetry technique (419–420); by titration (421); by electron spin resonance (ESR) (422,425); by absorption spectroscopy (415); by mass spectrometry (426–428). The ESR technique is particularly sensitive to the relative content of free radicals and atoms in mixtures. Most extensive information is obtained within one experiment by using the mass spectroscopy.

Mass spectroscopy makes possible both concentration measurements and identification of these species. In prinicple, it may be used for detection of any atoms and radicals. It permits determining the concentration of virtually any molecules of initial, intermediate and end reaction products in the course of the reaction. Unfortunately it is of small value for investigation of slow reactions due to its relatively low sensitivity to the relative content of free radicals in mixtures. This is accounted for by superposition of free-radical mass spectra and of the mass spectra of molecules containing the same radicals in a bound state.

The chemical reactors used for producing reactions of atoms and radicals with molecules may be grouped as follows:

1. Static reactors used for pulse photolysis (429,430), for measurement of rate constants from ignition limits (431,407), for the shock tube technique (432–434) particularly convenient for investigating reactions at very high temperatures.

TABLE 31
Rate constants for some simple exchange reactions

Reaction	Interval, °K	k, cm³ sec⁻¹ mole⁻¹	References
H atom reactions			
$H + O_2 = HO + O$	840–930	$7.8 \times 10^{13} \exp(-15{,}900 \pm 800/RT)$	407
$H + OH = H_2 + O$	300–2000	$10^{12.76 \pm 1.0} \exp(-5800 \pm 1500/RT)$	408
$H + CO_2 = CO + OH$	1200–1350	$3 \times 10^{15} \exp(-33{,}300/RT)$	409
$H + H_2O = H_2 + OH$	300–2000	$10^{14.48 \pm 1.0} \exp(-21{,}100 \pm 1500/RT)$	408
O atom reactions			
$O + NO = O_2 + N$	3000–8000	$3.2 \times 10^9 T \exp(-39{,}100/RT)$	410
$O + H_2 = OH + H$	300–2000	$10^{12.4 \pm 0.7} \exp(-7700 \pm 1000/RT)$	408
$O + H_2O = 2OH$	300–2000	$10^{14.15 \pm 0.8} \exp(-18{,}100 \pm 1000/RT)$	408
$O + OH = O_2 + H$	300–2000	$10^{13.7 \pm 0.3} \exp(-1000 \pm 500/RT)$	408
N atom reactions			
$N + O_2 = NO + O$	several thousands	$13.2 \times 10^9 T \exp(-7074/RT)$	411
$N + NO = N_2 + O$	—	1.6×10^{13}	412
Cl atom reactions			
$Cl + H_2 = HCl + Cl$	298–1000	$9.04 \times 10^{13} \exp(-5500 \pm 200/RT)$	413
$Cl + N_2O = N_2 + ClO$	876–1031	$1.3 \times 10^{14} \exp(-33{,}500/RT)$	414
OH reactions			
$OH + CO = CO_2 + H$	300–2000	$1.5 \times 10^{11} T^{1/2} \exp(-8000/RT)$	415
$OH + OH = H_2O + O$	1750–2750	$3 \times 10^{14} \exp(-2500/RT)$	416
$OH + H_2 = H_2O + H$	300–2000	$10^{13.8 \pm 0.7} \exp(-5900 \pm 1000/RT)$	408
NO reactions			
$NO + NO = N_2 + O_2$	3000–4300	$4.8 \times 10^{23} T^{-5/2} \exp(-85500/RT)$	417
$NO + N_2O = N_2 + NO_2$	924–1028	$2.5 \times 10^{14} \exp(-50{,}000/RT)$	418

2. Flow reactors, the main advantage of which is the possibility of measuring concentrations under stationary conditions and thus of using very sensitive systems for recording of the signals.

There are two kinds of flow reactors: stirred and linear reactors. A stirred reactor usually represents a closed spherical vessel provided with several inlets for admission of the mixture components and with outlets for the uniformly mixed species (435–438). Correct operation of the reactor will be ensured if mixing is completed within a time considerably shorter than that of contact which is taken as equal to the ratio of the reactor volume to the overall rate of the gas withdrawal from the reactor.

With a linear reactor, two or more gases are first mixed in the reactor or premixed before admission into the preheated reactor, flow through a long tube. The concentrations are measured at the end of this tube. The kinetic curves are obtained by measuring the rate constants as a function of the contact time. Corrections must be made for diffusion in the flow and for the velocity distribution. A new diffusion cloud technique has been developed in our laboratory. A schematic view of the reactor is given in Fig. 10 (427,439–

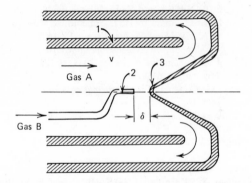

Figure 10   Schematic view of the reactor (441).

441). Molecules are admitted into a linear reactor 1 through a thin capillary 2 adjusted at a certain point of the reactor axis. They are swept away by a fast flow of gas containing atoms and simultaneously diffuse and react with atoms. A sampling cone 3 is located at a certain distance downstream the capillary. The mixture is passed through a small hole in the cone vortex to the mass-spectrometer for analysis. The sampling cone may be placed at various points of the diffusion cloud, which permits measuring the distribution of all reactants in the cloud. For example, the rate constants for reactions

$$H + Cl_2 = HCl + Cl \qquad\qquad [107]$$

$$H + F_2 = HF + F \qquad\qquad [108]$$

were measured by this technique over a temperature range of 294–565°K, and were found to be $k = 6.2 \times 10^{-10} \exp(-1800 \pm 300/RT)$ cm^3 sec^{-1} and $k = 2.0 \times 10^{-10} \exp(-2400 \pm 200/RT)$ cm^3 sec^{-1}, respectively (442). It will be of interest to note that though the heat of reaction [108] is more than twice that of reaction [107] the rate constant of the former is higher due both to lower activation energy and to a higher pre-exponential factor.

The technique of molecular beams developed in recent years (443) is of great interest for investigation of exchange reactions. It permits obtaining information on lifetimes of colliding complexes, on kinetic energies and those of internal excitation of reaction products, on differential cross-section as a function of kinetic energies of the initial species, on the reaction cross-section as a function of the colliding partners orientation. Unfortunately, to date only a small class of reactions occurring, in fact, without an activation energy have been investigated by this technique.

REFERENCES

1. V. N. Kondratiev, E. E. Nikitin, and V. L. Talrose, in *Nizkotemperaturnaya Plasma* [Low-Temperature Plasma], edited by A. E. Scheindlin. Moscow, 1967.
2. L. V. Gurvich and V. A. Kvilidze, *Zh. Fiz. Khim.*, **35**, 1672 (1961).
3. P. Fanchais and N. Manson, in *Nizkotemperaturnaya plasma* [Low-Temperature Plasma], edited by A. E. Scheindlin. Moscow, 1967, p. 122.
4. M. J. Druyvesteyn, *Physica*, **10**, 61(1930).
5. S. Chapman and T. G. Cowling, *The Mathematical Theory of Nonuniform Gases*. Cambridge, 1952, Chap. 18, p. 7.
6. E. W. McDaniel, *Collision Phenomena in Ionized Gases*, New York: Wiley, 1964, Chap. 11.
7. H. N. Allen, *Phys. Rev.*, **52**, 707 (1937).
8. J. A. Smit, *Physica*, **3**, 543 (1936).
9. B. Davydov, *Phys. Z. Sowjetunion*, **8**, 59 (1935).
10. L. G. Christophorou, R. N. Compton, G. S. Hurst, and P. W. Reinhardt, *J. Chem. Phys.*, **43**, 4273 (1965).
11. H. Slumbohm, *Z. Phys.*, **182**, 317 (1965).
12. H. Hessenaner, *Z. Phys.*, **204**, 142 (1967).
13. C. R. Bowman and D. E. Gordon, *J. Chem. Phys.*, **46**, 1878 (1967).
14. A. Kupperman, "Fast Reactions and Primary Processes in Chemical Kinetics." Nobel Symposium 5, p. 131.
15. S. A. Denisik, S. N. Lebedev, Yu. G. Malama, and L. S. Polak, *Khim. Vys. Energ*, **2**, 297 (1968).
16. E. E. Nikitin, *Sovremennye Teorii Termicheskogo Raspada i Isomerisatsii Molekul v Gasovoy Fase*. Moscow: Id-vo Nauka, 1964. (Theory of Thermally Induced Gas-Phase Reactions, Bloomington, Ind.: Indiana University Press, 1966).
17. S. A. Denisik, Yu. G. Malama, L. S. Polak, and R. A. Resvanov, in *Kinetika i Termodinamika Khimicheskikh Reaktsii v Nizkotemperaturonoi Plasme* [Kinetics and Thermodynamics of Chemical Reactions in Low-Temperature Plasma], edited by L. S. Polak. Moscow, 1965, p. 66.

18. E. V. Stupochenko, S. A. Losev, and A. I. Osipov, *Relaksatsionnye Protsessy v Udarnykh Volnakh.* Moscow: Nauka 1965.
19. E. A. Moelwyn-Hughes, *Physical Chemistry.* Oxford: Pergamon Press, 1961.
20. N. S. Snider, *J. Chem. Phys.*, **42**, 548 (1955).
21. N. M. Kuznetsov, *Dokl. Akad. Nauk. SSSR*, **164**, 1097 (1965).
22. N. A. Generalov, B. V. Kuksenko, S. A. Losev, and A. I. Osipov, *Zh. Teor. Eksp. Khim.*, **4**, 311 (1968).
23. A. Temkin, *Phys. Rev. Let.*, **16**, 835 (1966).
24. J. D. Morrison, *J. Appl. Phys.*, **28**, 1409 (1957).
25. J. D. Morrison, *Transfer d'Energie Dans Les Gaz.* New York: Interscience, 1962, p. 397
26. G. M. Wannier, *Phys. Rev.*, **100**, 1180 (1956).
27. C. E. Brion and G. E. Thomas, *V Intern. Conf. Phys. Electron a. Atomic Collisions.* Leningrad: Nauka, 1967, p. 53.
28. J. W. McGowan and E. M. Clarke, *Phys. Rev.*, **167**, 43, (1968).
29. I. A. Beigman and L. A. Vainshtein, *Izv. Akad. Nauk SSSR*, Phys. Series, **27**, 1018 (1963).
30. T. R. Carson, *J. Quant. Spectrosc. Radiat. Transfer*, **6**, 563 (1966).
31. M. Grysinski, *Phys. Rev.*, **138**, 336 (1965).
32. F. E. Stafford, *J. Chem. Phys.*, **45**, 859 (1966).
33. L. Presnyakov, I. Sobelman, and L. Vainstein, *Proc. Phys. Soc.* (L), **89**, 511 (1966).
34. K. Omidvar, *Phys. Rev. Lett.*, **18**, 153 (1967).
35. M. Fabre, *J. Phys. et Radium*, **VIII, X**, 319 (1949).
36. F. Fiquet-Fayard, *J. Chim. Phys.*, **62**, 1065 (1965).
37. B. L. Schram, A. J. H. Berboom, and J. Kistemaker, *Physica*, **32**, 185–197 (1966).
38. Y. Kaneko, and J. Kanomata, *J. Phys. Soc. Japan*, **18**, 1822 (1963).
39. E. Baner and C. D. Barky, *J. Chem. Phys.*, **43**, 2466 (1965).
40. L. J. Kieffer and G. H. Dunn, *Rev. Mod. Phys.*, **38**, 1 (1966).
41. J. Momigny, *Memoires de la Societe Royale des Sciences de Liege.* Cinquieme serie, **XIII**, Fascicule 1. Liege, 1966.
42. G. H. Dunn, *J. Chem. Phys.*, **44**, 2592 (1966).
43. J. Gaulicht, *J. Chem. Phys.*, **43**, 1503 (1965).
44. J. W. McGowan, M. A. Fineman, E. M. Clarke, and H. P. Hanson, *Phys. Rev.*, **167**, 52 (1968).
45. D. P. Stevenson, *J. Chem. Phys.*, **15**, 409 (1947).
46. J. K. Cashion, *J. Chem. Phys.*, **45**, 1663 (1966).
47. C. A. Schaeffer, *J. Chem. Phys.*, **18**, 1501 (1950).
48. A. Cornu and R. Massot, *Compilation of Mass Spectral Data.* London: Heyden, 1966.
49. J. H. Beynon, *Mass Spectrometry and Its Applications to Organic Chemistry.* Amsterdam: Elsevier, 1960.
50. K. Bieman, *Mass Spectrometry. Organic Chemical Applications.* New York: McGraw-Hill, 1962.
51. H. Budzikiewicz, C. Djerassi, and D. H. Williams, *Interpretations of Mass Spectra of Organic Compounds*, San Francisco: Holden-Day, 1964.
52. A. A. Polyakova and R. A. Khmelnitskii, *Vvedenie v Mass-spectrometriyu Organicheskikh Soedinenii*, Moscow-Leningrad: Khimia, 1966.
53. H. M. Rosenstock, M. B. Wallenstein, A. L. Wahrhaftig, and H. Eyring, *Proc. Natl. Acad. Sci., U.S.*, **38**, 667 (1952).
54. H. M. Rosenstock and M. Krauss, *Mass Spectrometry of Organic Ions*, edited by MacLafferty. New York: Academic Press, 1963.

55. G. V. Karachevtsev and V. L. Talrose, *Kinetika i Kataliz*, **8**, 447 (1967).
56. O. Osbergans and Ch. Ottinger, *Phys. Lett.*, **16**, 121 (1965).
57. V. H. Dibeler and H. M. Rosenstock, *J. Chem. Phys.*, **39**, 3106, (1963).
58. S. E. Kuprijanov, *J. Exp. Theor. Phys.* (Russian), **34**, 816 (1964).
59. N. N. Tunitskii, S. E. Kuprijanov, and M. V. Tikhomirov, *Problemy Fisicheskoi Khimii* [Problems in Physical Chemistry], Vol. 1. Moscow, 1958.
60. C. E. Melton, *J. Chem. Phys.*, **37**, 562 (1962).
61. P. Kebarle and E. W. Godbole, *J. Chem. Phys.*, **36**, 302 (1962).
62. J. E. Monahan and H. E. Stanton, *J. Chem. Phys.*, **37**, 2654 (1962).
63. W. A. Chupka and M. Kaminsky, *J. Chem. Phys.*, **35**, 199 (1962).
64. O. Osberghaus and V. R. Taubert, *Z. Phys. Chem.*, **4**, 264 (1955).
65. H. Ehrhardt and O. Osberghaus, *Z. Naturforsch.*, **13a**, No. 1. (1958).
66. G. D. Tantsyrev and V. L. Talrose, *Dokl. Akad. Nauk. SSSR*, **5**, 117, (1957).
67. H. Ehrhardt, F. Linder, and G. Meister, *Z. Naturforsch.*, **B20a**, 48 (1965).
68. M. V. Guriev and S. E. Kuprijanov, *Khim. Vis. Energ.*, **1**, 91 (1967).
69. V. N. Komarov and M. V. Tikhomirov, *Zh. Fiz. Khim.*, **8**, 1951 (1966).
70. M. V. Tikhomirov and V. N. Komarov, *Zh. Fiz. Khim.*, **11**, No. 5 (1967).
71. B. Steiner, C. F. Giese, and M. F. Ingram, *J. Chem. Phys.*, **34**, 189 (1961).
72. L. M. Biberman, Yu. N. Toropkin and K. N. Uljanov, *Zh. Tekh. Fiz.*, **32**, 827 (1962).
73. I. A. Krinberg, *Astronom. Zh.*, **45**, 1061 (1968).
74. D. Rapp and P. Englander-Golden, *J. Chem. Phys.*, **43**, 1464 (1965).
75. R. A. Guljaev, *Astronom. Zh.*, **43**, 948 (1966).
76. I. P. Zapesochnyi and I. S. Aleksakhin, *Zh. Teor. Fiz.*, **55**, 76 (1968).
77. S. I. Pavlov, V. I. Rakhovskii, and G. M. Fedorova, *Zh. Eksp. Teor. Fiz.*, **52**, 21 (1967).
78. K. T. Dolder, M. F. A. Harrison, and P. C. Thonemann, *Proc. Roy. Soc.*, **A264**, 367 (1961).
79. A. M. Emel'yanov, Yu. S. Khodeyev, and L. N. Gorokhov, *V Int. Conf. Phys. Electron a. Atomic Collisions.* Leningrad: Nauka, 1967, p.43.
80. F. A. Barker and J. B. Hasted, *Phil. Trans. Roy. Soc. (L)*, **A261**, 33 (1966).
81. J. Cuthbert, J. Farron, B. S. Prahallada Rao and E. R. Preece, *Proc. Phys. Soc.*, **88**, 91 (1966).
82. N. R. Daly and R. E. Powell, *Proc. Phys. Soc.*, **89**, 281 (1966).
83. P. A. Redhead, *Can. J. Phys.*, **45**, 1791 (1967).
84. K. T. Dolder, M. F. A. Harrison, and P. C. Thonemann, *Proc. Roy. Soc.*, **A274**, 546 (1963).
85. S. E. Kupriyanov and Z. Z. Latypov, *Zh. Eksp. Teor. Fiz.*, **45**, 815 (1963).
86. M. F. A. Harrison, K. T. Dolder, and P. C. Thonemann, *Proc. Phys. Soc.*, **82**, 368 (1963).
87. Z. Z. Latypov, S. E. Kunriyanov, and N. N. Tunitskii, *Zh. Eksp. Teor. Fiz.*, **46**, 833 (1963).
88. W. C. Lineberger, J. W. Hooper, and E. W. McDaniel, *Phys. Rev.*, **141A**, 151 (1966).
89. J. B. Wareing and K. Dolder, *V. Intern. Conf. Phys. Electron a. Atomic Collisions.* Leningrad: Nauka, 1967, p. 43.
90. J. W. Hooper, W. C. Lineberger, and F. M. Bacon, *Phys. Rev.*, **141A**, 165 (1966).
91. E. Hinnov, *J. Opt. Soc. of Am.*, **56**, 1179 (1966).
92. H. J. Kunze, A. H. Gabriel, and H. R. Griem, *V Int. Conf. Phys. Electron a. Atomic Collisions.* Leningrad: Nauka, 1967, p. 362.
93. L. Branscomb, In *Atomic Collision Processes*, edited by McDowell. Amsterdam: North-Holland Publ. Co., 1964.
94. R. S. Berry and C. V. David, *Atomic Collision Processes*, edited by McDowell. Amsterdam: North-Holland Publ. Co., 1964, p. 543.

95. L. M. Branscomb, *Ann. Geoph.*, **20**, 88 (1964).
96. G. Boldt, *Z. Physik.* **154**, 330 (1959).
97. G. E. Norman, *Optika i Spectroskopija*, **17**, 176 (1964).
98. T. F. O'Malley, *Phys. Rev.*, **150**, 14 (1966).
99. V. I. Goldanskii, F. I. Dolidchik, and G. K. Ivanov, *Khim. Vis. Energ.*, **3**, 162 (1969).
100. N. S. Buchelnikova, *Usp. Fiz. Nauk*, **67**, 3 (1958).
101. C. E. Melton, In *Mass-Spectrometry of Organic Ions*, edited by F. W. McLafferty. New York: Academic Press, 1963, p. 163.
102. L. G. Christophorou, and R. N. Compton, *Health Phys.*, **13**, 1277 (1967).
103. L. G. Christophorou and J. A. D. Stockdale, *J. Chem. Phys.*, **48**, 1956 (1968).
104. L. G. Christophorou, R. N. Compton and H. W. Dickson, *J. Chem. Phys.*, **48**, 1949 (1968).
105. G. J. Schulz, *J. Chem. Phys.*, **34**, 1778 (1961).
106. R. N. Compton and L. G. Christophorou, *Phys, Rev.*, **154**, 110 (1967).
107. G. J. Schulz, *J. Chem. Phys.*, **33**, 1661 (1960).
108. G. J. Schulz, *Phys. Rev.*, **128**, 178 (1962).
109. D. Rapp and D. D. Briglia, *J. Chem. Phys.*, **43**, 1480 (1965).
110. D. Rapp, T. E. Shurp, and D. D. Briglia, *Phys. Rev. Lett.*, **14**, 533 (1965).
111. L. G. Christophorou, R. N. Compton, G. S. Hurst, and P. W. Reinhardt, *J. Chem. Phys.*, **43**, 4273 (1965).
112. J. D. Craggs and B. A. Tozer, *Proc. Roy. Soc. (L)*, **A254**, 229 (1960).
113. B. A. Fozer, *Proc. Roy. Soc. (L)*, **A247**, 337 (1958).
114. G. J. Schulz, *Phys. Rev.*, **113**, 816 (1959).
115. G. J. Schulz and R. A. Asundi, *Phys. Rev. Lett.*, **15**, 946 (1965).
116. R. E. Fox, *Phys. Rev.*, **109**, 2008 (1958).
117. M. A. Biondi and R. E. Fox, *Phys. Rev.*, **109**, 2112 (1960).
118. F. K. Tuby, *Phys. Rev.*, **172**, 24 (1968).
119. W. L. Fite, In *Atomic Collision Processes*, edited by McDowell. Amsterdam: North-Holland Publ. Co., 1964, p. 382.
120. G. J. Schulz and D. Spence, *Phys. Rev. Lett.*, **22**, 47 (1969).
121. H. F. Calcote, S. C. Kurzius, and W. J. Miller, *Tenth Symposium on Combustion (International)*, 1965, p. 605.
122. R. N. Compton, L. G. Christophorou, G. S. Hurst, and P. W. Reinhardt, *J. Chem. Phys.*, **45**, 4634 (1966).
123. L. V. Trepha and H. Neuert, *Z. Naturforsch*, **18a**, 1295 (1963).
124. M. I. Chibisov, *Zh. Eksp. Teor. Fiz.*, **49**, 852 (1965).
125. B. M. Smirnov, *Atomnye Stolknoveniya i Elementarnye Protsessy v Plasme*. Moscow-Atomisdat, 1968. p. 233.
126. V. M. Borodin, *V. Intern. Conf. Phys. Electron a. Atomic Collisions*. Leningrad: Nauka, 1967, p. 326.
127. R. Z. Vitlina and A. V. Chaplik, *V. Intern. Conf. Phys. Electron a. Atomic Collisions.* Leningrad: Nauka, 1967, p. 327.
128. R. C. Gunton and T. M. Shaw, *Phys. Rev.*, **140A**, 748 (1965).
129. L. M. Chanin, A. V. Phelps, and M. A. Biondi, *Phys. Rev.*, **128**, 219 (1962).
130. J. L. Pack and A. V. Phelps, *J. Chem. Phys.*, **44**, 1870 (1966).
131. V. B. Brodsky and S. E. Zaychik, *Zh. Tekh. Fiz.*, **36**, 672 (1966).
132. M. A. Biondi, In *Atomic Collision Processes*, edited by McDowell. Amsterdam: North-Holland Publ. Co., 1964, p. 491.
133. A. V. Phelps, *Tenth Symposium on Combustion (International)*, 1965, p. 569.
134. J. B. Hasted, *Physics of Atomic Collisions*. London: Butterworths, 1964.
135. N. S. Buchelnicova, *Pribory i Tekhnika Experimenta*, **6**, 803 (1958).

136. E. Karule and R. K. Peterkop, *Atomnye Stolknovenija*, V. 3. Riga: Linatne, 1965, p. 3.
137. V. I. Ochkur, *Zh. Eskp. Teor. Fiz.*, **45**, 734 (1963).
138. A. V. Elteskii and B. M. Smirnov, *Zh. Tekh. Fiz.*, **38**, 3 (1968).
139. L. A. Vainstein and I. I. Sobelman, *J. Quant. Spectrosc. Radiat. Transfer*, **8**, 1491 (1968).
140. A. V. Phelps, *Phys. Rev.*, **99**, 1307 (1955).
141. R. McFahrland, In *Atomic Collision Processes*, edited by McDowell. Amsterdam: North-Holland Publ. Co., (1964), p. 169.
142. I. P. Zapesochnyi and O. B. Shpenik, *Dokl. Akad. Nauk SSSR*, **150**, 1053 (1965).
143. I. P. Zapesochnyi and O. B. Shpenik, *Zh. Eksp. Teor. Fiz.*, **50**, 890 (1966).
144. I. S. Aleksakhin, I. P. Zapesochnyi, and O. B. Spenik, *V. Intern Conf. Phys. Electron a. Atomic Collisions.* Leningrad: Nauka, 1967, p. 499.
145. D. F. Dance, M. F. A. Harrison, and A. C. H. Smith, *Proc. Roy. Soc.*, **290**, 74 (1966).
146. I. P. Zapesochnyi and L. I. Shimon, *Optika i Spektroskopiya*, **21**, 265 (1966).
147. I. P. Zapesochnyi, *Teplophyzika Visokich Temperatur*, **5**, 7 (1967).
148. V. V. Skubenich and I. P. Zapeschnyi, *V Intern. Conf. Phys. Electron a. Atomic Collisions.* Leningrad: Nauka, 1967, p. 570.
149. G. M. Cunningham and C. C. Lin, *J. Chem. Phys.*, **41**, 3268 (1964).
150. S. E. Kupriyanov, *Optika i Spektroskopiya*, **20**, 163 (1966).
151. G. N. Polyakova, Ya. M. Fogel, and A. V. Zats, *Zh. Eksp. Teor. Fiz.*, **52**, 1495 (1967).
152. A. R. Lee and N. P. Carleton, *Phys. Lett.*, **A27**, 195 (1968).
153. R. C. Elton and W. W. Koppendörfer, *Phys. Rev.*, **160**, 194 (1967).
154. H. R. Griem, *Plasma Spectroscopy.* New York: McGraw-Hill, 1964.
155. M. J. Seaton, In *Atomic and Molecular Processes*, edited by D. R. Bates. New York: Academic Press, 1962.
156. C. W. Allen, *Astrophysical Quantities.* London: The Atholone Press, 2nd ed. 1963.
157. E. Hinnov, *J. Opt. Soc. of Am.*, **56**, 1179 (1966).
158. I. C. Percival, *Nucl. Fusion*, **6** (1966).
159. E. Hinnov, *Phys. Fluids*, **8**, 1541 (1965).
160. E. Hinnov, *Phys. Fluids*, **8**, 118 (1965).
161. E. Hinnov, *Bull. Amer. Phys. Soc.*, **10**, 196 (1965).
162. E. Hinnov, J. G. Hirschberg, F. W. Hofmann and N. Rynn, *Phys. Fluids*, **6**, 1779 (1963).
163. L. C. Johnson, *Bull. Amer. Phys. Soc.*, **9**, 508 (1964).
164. A. B. Bolotin, I. B. Levinson, and L. I. Levin, *Zh. Eksp. Teor. Fiz.*, **50**, 890 (1966).
165. A. B. Bolotin and A. P. Yusuz, *Zh. Eksp. Teor. Fiz.*, **24**, 537 (1953).
166. C. M. Varsavsky, *Astrophys. J. Suppl.*, **6**, 75 (1961).
167. D. R. Bates and A. Damagard, *Phil. Trans. Roy. Soc.* (L), **A242**, 101 (1949).
168. S. E. Frish and Yu. Z. Ionikh, *Optika i spektroskopija*, **25**, 615 (1968).
169. N. Sadeghi and J. C. Pebay-Reyroula, *VIII Intern. Confer. Ion. Phen. in Gas.* Contributed papers. Vienna, 1967, p. 15.
170. G. F. Drukarev and V. I. Ochkur, In *Nizkotemperaturnaya Plasma* [Low-Temperature Plasma] edited by A. E. Sheindlin. Moscow: 1967, p. 47.
171. E. Gerjony and S. Stein, *Phys. Rev.*, **97**, 1671 (1955).
172, A. Dalgarno and R. J. W. Henry, *Proc. Phys. Soc.*, **85**, 679 (1965).
173. M. H. Mentzoni and R. V. Row, *Phys. Rev.*, **130**, 2312 (1963).
174. G. J. Schulz and R. V. Row, *Phys. Rev.*, **112**, 150 (1958).
175. T. R. Carson, *Proc. Phys. Soc.*, **A67**, 909 (1954).
176. G. J. Schulz, *Phys. Rev.*, **135A**, 988 (1964).
177. M. J. W. Boness and G. J. Schulz, *Phys. Rev. Lett.*, **21**, 1031 (1968).

178. J. C. Y. Chen, *J. Chem. Phys.*, **40**, 3513 (1964).
179. J. C. Y. Chen, *Phys. Rev.*, **148**, 66 (1966).
180. A. von Engel, in *Nizkotemperaturnaya Plasma* [Low-Temperature Plasma], edited by A. E. Scheindlin. Moscow: 1967, p. 164.
181. I. R. Hurle, in *Nizkotemperaturnaya Plasma* [Low-Temperature Plasma], edited by A. E. Scheindlin. Moscow: 1967, p. 168.
182. J. R. Cozens, in *Nizkotemperaturnaya Plasma* [Low-Temperature Plasma], edited by A. E. Scheindlin. Moscow: 1967, p. 179.
183. I. R. Hurle, T. M. Sugden, and F. B. Nutt, *Twelfth Symposium (International) on Combustion.* University of Poitiers, France, July 14–20, 1968. Pittsburg: The Combustion Institute, p. 64.
184. L. M. Biberman and A. Kh. Mnatsakyan, *Teplofizika Vysokich Temperatur*, **4**, 491 (1966).
185. R. F. Boikova and V. D. Ob'edkov, *Zh. Eksp. Teor. Fiz.*, **54**, 1439 (1968).
186. J. B. Corrigan, *J. Chem. Phys.*, **43**, 4381 (1965).
187. A. Niehans, *Z. Naturforsch.*, **22a**, 690 (1967).
188. C. E. Melton, *J. Chem. Phys.*, **47**, 1771 (1967).
189. H. Ehrhardt, F. Linder and T. Tekaat, *Z. Naturforsch.*, **22a**, 444 (1967).
190. R. L. Platzman, *J. Chem. Phys.*, **38**, 2775 (1963).
191. B. V. Zyl and G. H. Dunn, *Phys. Rev.*, **153**, 40 (1957).
192. B. V. Zyl and G. H. Dunn, *Phys. Rev.*, **163**, 43 (1967).
193. E. E. Muschlitz, In *Adv. in Chem. Phys.*, Vol. 10, Molecular Beams, edited by J. Ross. New York: Interscience, 1966.
194. D. C. Allison, *Proc. Phys. Soc.*, **89**, 41 (1968).
195. H. S. W. Massey, *Rept. Progr. Phys.*, **12**, 248 (1949).
196. B. M. Smirnov, *Atomnie Stolknovenija i Elementarnie Protsessi v Plasme.* Moscow: Atomisdat, 1968, p. 104
197. E. E. Ferguson, *Phys. Rev.*, **128**, 210 (1962).
198. V. Cermak, *V Intern. Conf. Phys. Electron a. Atomic Collisions.* Leningrad: Nauka, 1967, p. 601.
199. H. P. Broida and J. L. Dunn, *V Intern. Conf. Phys. Electron a. Atomic Collisions.* Leningrad: Nauka, 1967, p. 249.
200. W. W. Robertson, *J. Chem. Phys.*, **44**, 2456 (1966).
201. R. L. Platzman, *J. Phys. Rad.*, **21**, 835, (1960).
202. W. P. Jesse, *J. Chem. Phys.*, **41**, 2060 (1964).
203. V. Cermak and Z. Herman, *Collect. Czech. Chem. Comm.*, **30**, 169 (1965).
204. A. L. Schmeltekopf, E. E. Ferguson, and F. C. Fehsenfeld, *J. Chem. Phys.*, **48**, 2966 (1968).
205. T. Watanabe and K. Katsunra, *J. Chem. Phys.*, **47**, 800 (1967).
206. B. M. Smirnov, *Atomnye Stolknoveniya i Elementarnye Protsessy v Plasme.* Moscow: Atomisdat, 1968, p. 100.
207. S. E. Kupriyanov, *V Intern. Conf. Phys. Electron a. Atomic Collisions.* Leningrad: Nauka, 1967, p. 571.
208. H. Hotop and A. Niehaus, *J. Chem. Phys.*, **47**, 2506 (1967).
209. A. G. Harrison and J. J. Myher, *J. Chem. Phys.*, **46**, 3276 (1967).
210. M. S. B. Munson, J. L. Franklin and, F. H. Field, *J. Chem. Phys.*, **67**, 1542 (1963).
211. R. F. Huffman and D. H. Katayama, *J. Chem. Phys.*, **45**, 138 (1966).
212. V. L. Talrose and E. L. Frankevich, *Zh. Fiz. Khim.*, **34**, 2709 (1960).
213. W. Kaul, V. Lauterbach, and R. Fuchs, *Naturwiss*, **47**, 353 (1960).
214. W. Kaul, *6th Intern. Conf. Ion. Phenom. in Gases.* Paris, 1963, p. 164.

215. P. W. Becker and F. W. Lampe, *J. Chem. Phys.*, **42**, 3857 (1965).
216. J. S. Dahler, J. L. Franklin, M. S. B. Munson, and F. H. Field, *J. Chem. Phys.*, **36**, 3332 (1962).
217. R. A. Young and G. S. John, *J. Chem. Phys.*, **45**, 4156 (1966).
218. T. M. Sugden, *Tenth Symposium (International) on Combustion*. Pittsburgh: The Combustion Institute, 1965, p.539.
219. H. O. Pritchard and A. G. Harrison, *J. Chem. Phys.*, **48**, 2827 (1968).
220. T. M. Sugden, *Tenth Symposium (International) on Combustion*. 1965, p. 539.
221. V. I. Tverdokhlebov and N. N. Chikin, *Dokl. Akad. Nauk SSSR*, **179**, 921 (1968).
222. K. Schofield and T. M. Sugden, *Tenth Symposium (International) on Combustion*. 1965, p. 589.
223. S. A. Losev, V. A. Polyanskii, and G. D. Smekhov, *Khim Vys. Energ.*, **2**, 311 (1968).
224. S. C. Lin and J. D. Teare, *Phys. Fluids*, **6**, 355 (1963).
225. A. J. Kelly, *J. Chem. Phys.*, **45**, 1723 (1966).
226. A. J. Kelly, *J. Chem. Phys.*, **45**, 1733 (1966).
227. I. K. Larin and V. L. Talrose, *Kinetika i Kataliz*, **3**, 305 (1962).
228. Yu. D. Bydin and A. M. Bukhteev, *Dokl. Akad. Nauk SSSR*, **119**, 1131 (1958).
229. Yu. D. Bydin and A. M. Bukhteev, *Zh. Teckh. Fiz.*, **30**, 546 (1960).
230. A. M. Bukhteev and Yu. D. Bydin, *Izv. Akad. Nauk SSSR*, **27**, 1009 (1963).
231. N. G. Utterback, *Phys. Rev.*, **129**, 219 (1963).
232. B. M. Smirnov, *Zh. Eksp. Teor. Fiz.*, **53**, 1400 (1967).
233. H. C. Hayden and N. G. Utterback, *Phys. Rev.*, **A135**, 1575 (1964).
234. J. F. Frichtenight, J. C. Slattery, and D. O. Hausen, *Phys. Rev.*, **163**, 75 (1967).
235. A. M. Bukhteev, Yu. D. Bydin, and V. M. Dukelsii, *Zh. Tekh. Fiz.*, **31**, 638 (1961).
236. P. J. Padley, F. M. Page, and T. M. Sugden, *Trans. Faraday Soc.*, **57**, 1552 (1961).
237. C. Gatz, F. T. Smith, and H. Wise, *J. Chem. Phys.*, **35**, 1500 (1961).
238. V. L. Talrose and A. K. Lyubimova, *Dokl. Akad. Nauk SSSR*, **86**, 909 (1952).
239. V. L. Talrose, Thesis, Inst. Chem Phys, Acad. Sci. USSR, Moscow, 1952.
240. D. P. Stevenson and D. O. Schissler, *J. Chem. Phys.*, **23**, 1353 (1955).
241. F. H. Field, F. W. Lampe, and J. L. Franklin, *J. Amer. Chem. Soc.*, **79**, 2419 (1957).
242. V. L. Talrose and E. L. Frankevich, *Proceedings of the All-Union Conference on Radiation Chemistry*. Acad. Sci. USSR, Moscow, 1958, p.13.
243. D. P. Stevenson, *J. Phys. Chem.*, **61**, 1453 (1957).
244. P. Ausloos and S. G. Lias, in *Action Chimiques et Biologiques de Radiation*, edited by M. Haissinsky. No 11, p. 3. Paris, 1967.
245. V. L. Talrose and G. V. Karachevtsev, *Adv. Mass Spectrom.*, **3**, 211 (1966).
246. "Ion-Molecule Reactions in the Gas Phase," *Adv. in Chem. Series*, No 58. Washington, D.C., 1968.
247. D. P. Stevenson and D. O. Schissler, *J. Chem. Phys.*, **29**, 282 (1958).
248. O. B. Firsov, *Zh. Eksp. Teor. Fiz.*, **42**, 1307 (1962).
249. J. C. Light and J. Lin, *J. Chem. Phys.*, **43**, 3202 (1965).
250. E. E. Nikitin, *Zh. Teor. Eskp. Khim.*, **1**, 428 (1965).
251. F. A. Wolf, *J. Chem. Phys.*, **44**, 1619 (1966).
252. A. Henglein, K. Lacmann, and G. Jacobs, *J. Phys. Chem.*, **69**, 279 (1965).
253. L. Matus, I. Opanszky, D. Hyatt, A. J. Masson, K. Birkinshaw, and M. Henchman, *Disc. Faraday Soc.*, **44**, 146, (1967).
254. G. K. Ivanov and Yu. S. Sayasov, *Zh. Teor. Eksp. Khim.*, **3**, 172, (1967).
255. Z. Herman, J. D. Kerstetter, T. L. Rose, and R. Wolfgang, *J. Chem. Phys.*, **46**, 2845 (1967).
256. T. E. Moran and W. H. Hamill, *J. Chem. Phys.*, **39**, 1413 (1963).

257. V. L. Talrose, M. I. Markin, and I. K. Larin, *Disc. Faraday Soc.*, **33**, 257 (1962).
258. E. E. Fergusson, F.C. Fehsenfeld, P. D. Golden, and A. L. Schmeltekopf, *J. Geophys. Res.*, **70**, 4323 (1965).
259. C. F. Giese, in *Ion-Molecule Reactions in the Gas Phase*. Washington: Am. Chem. Soc., 1966, p. 20.
260. W. A. Chupka and M. E. Russell, *J. Chem. Phys.*, **48**, 1527 (1968).
261. W. A. Chupka, M. E. Russell and, K. Refaev, *J. Chem. Phys.*, **48**, 1518 (1968).
262. T. F. Moran and J. R. Roberts, *J. Chem. Phys.*, **49**, 3411 (1968).
263. D. Rapp and W. E. Francis, *J. Chem. Phys.*, **37**, 263 (1962).
264. D. K. Bohme, J. B. Hasted, and P. P. Ong, *Chem. Phys. Lett.*, **1**, 259 (1967).
265. E. Lindholm, *Z. Naturforsch.*, **9a**, 535 (1954).
266. H. von Koch and E. Lindholm, *Arkiv. Fys.*, **21**, 97 (1962).
267. E. Patterson and E. Lindholm, *Arkiv. Fys.*, **24**, 49 (1963).
268. E. Lindholm, J. Szabo and P. Wilmenius, *Arkiv. Fys.*, **25**, 417 (1963).
269. H. Sjogren and E. Lindholm, *Arkiv. Fys.*, **32**, 275 (1966).
270. E. Lindholm, in *Ion-Molecule Reactions in the Gas Phase*. Washington: Am. Chem. Soc., 1966. p.1.
271. G. Sahlströrm and I. Szabo, *Arkiv. Fys.*, **38**, 145 (1968).
272. G. K. Lavrovskaya, M. I. Markin, and V. L. Talrose, *Kinetika i Kataliz*, **2**, 21 (1961).
273. V. L. Talrose, *Pure Appl. Chem.*, **5**, 455 (1962).
274. E. V. Aparina, M. I. Markin, V. L. Talrose, and G. V. Fridlyanskii, *Khim. Vys. Energ.*, **3**, 291 (1969).
275. M. I. Markin and V. L. Talrose, *Khim. Vys. Energ.*, **3**, 298 (1969).
276. C. F. Giese and W. B. Maier II, *J. Chem. Phys.*, **39**, 197 (1963).
277. W. B. Maier II, *J. Chem. Phys.*, **41**, 2174 (1964).
278. G. V. Karachevtsev, M. I. Markin, and V. L. Talrose, *Izv. Akad. Nauk SSSR*, Chem. series, 1528 (1961).
279. G. V. Karachevtsev, M. I. Markin, and V. L. Talrose, *Kinetika i Kataliz*, **5**, 377 (1964).
280. L. D. Doverspike, R. L. Champion, and T. L. Bailey, *J. Chem. Phys.*, **45**, 4385 (1966).
281. F. C. Fehsenfeld, P. D. Goldan, A. L. Schmeltekopf, and E. E. Ferguson, *Planet. Space Sci.*, **13**, 579 (1965).
282. L. Matus, D. J. Hyatt, and M. J. Henchman, *J. Chem. Phys.*, **46**, 2439 (1967).
283. A. G. Harrison, J. J. Myher, and J. C. J. Thynne, "Ion-Molecule Reactions in the Gas Phase." Amer. Chem. Soc. Washington, 1966, p. 150.
284. V. Lauterback, W. Kaul, and R. Taubert, *Intern. Mass Spectrometry Conference.* Berlin, September 25–29, 1967.
285. M. C. Cress, P. M. Becker, and F. M. Lampe, *J. Chem. Phys.*, **44**, 2212 (1966).
286. R. Taubert, *Z. Naturforsch.*, **19A**, 911 (1964).
287. J. Durup and F. Heitz, *J. Chim. Phys.*, **61**, 470 (1965).
288. V. L. Talrose, *Chemical Effects of Nuclear Transformations*. International Atomic Energy Agency, Vienna, 1961, p. 103.
289. H. E. Stanton and S. Wexler, *J. Chem. Phys.*, **44**, 2959 (1966).
290. M. T. Bowers, D. D. Elleman, and J. L. Beauchamp, *J. Phys. Chem.*, **72**, 3599 (1968).
291. P. Warneck, *J. Chem. Phys.*, **47**, 4279 (1968).
292. V. K. Potapov, *Dokl. Akad. Nauk SSSR*, **183**, 386 (1968).
293. I. Szabo, *Arkiv. Fys.*, **33**, 57 (1967).
294. F. C. Fehsenfeld, A. L. Schmeltekopf, P. Goldan, H. I. Schiff, and E. E. Ferguson, *J. Chem. Phys.*, **44**, 4087 (1966).
295. E. E. Ferguson, F. C. Fehsenfeld, P. D. Goldan, A. L. Schmeltekopf, and H. I. Schiff, *Planet. Space Sci.*, **13**, 823 (1965).

296. G. V. Karachevtsev, *Khim Vys. Energ.* (in press).
297. H. Shin, in *Ion-Molecule Reactions in the Gas Phase*. Am Chem Soc.., Washington, 1966, p. 44.
298. P. Kebarle, R. M. Haynes, and S. Searles, in *Ion-Molecule Reactions in the Gas Phase*. Am. Chem. Soc., Washington, 1966, p. 210.
299. R. E. Harrington, B. S. Rabinovitch, and M. R. Hoare, *J. Chem. Phys.*, **33**, 744 (1960).
300. G. H. Kohlmaier and B. S. Rabinovitch, *J. Chem. Phys.*, **38**, 1692 (1963).
301. B. M. Smirnov, *Zh. Eksp. Teor. Fiz.*, **51**, 1747 (1966).
302. B. M. Smirnov, *Atomnye Stolknoveniya Elementarnye Protsessy v Plasme*. Moscow: Atomisdat, 1968, p. 332.
303. B. H. Mahan, *J. Chem. Phys.*, **43**, 3080 (1965).
304. E. C. Beaty and P. Patterson, *Proceedings of Sixth International Conference Ion. Phen. Gases,* Paris, 1963, **1**, 311, 1964.
305. A. V. Phelps and S. C. Brown, *Phys. Rev.*, **86**, 102 (1952).
306. H. J. Oskam, *Philips Res. Rept.*, **13**, 401 (1958).
307. M. A. Biondi, *Phys. Rev.*, **90**, 730 (1953).
308. J. S. Dalher, J. L. Franklin, M. S. Munson, and F. H. Field, *J. Chem. Phys.*, **36**, 3332 (1962).
309. F. E. Niles and W. W. Robertson, *J. Chem. Phys.*, **40**, 3568 (1964).
310. P. L. Patterson, *J. Chem. Phys.*, **48**, 3625 (1968).
311. T. M. Miller et al., *V Intern. Conf. Phys. Electron a. Atomic Collisions*, Leningrad: Nauka, 1967, p. 251.
312. J. F. Paulson, F. Dale, and R. L. Mosher, *Nature*, **204**, 377 (1964).
313. B. M. Smirnov and O. B. Firsov, *Zh. Eksp. Teor. Fiz.*, **47**, 232 (1964).
314. J. F. Paulson, in *Ion-Molecule Reactions in the Gas Phase*. Am. Chem. Soc., Washington 1966, p. 28.
315. J. G. Dillard and J. L. Franklin, *J. Chem. Phys.*, **48**, 2343 (1968).
316. J. A. D. Stockdale, R. N. Compton, and P. W. Reinhardt, *Phys. Rev. Let.*, **21**, 664 (1968).
317. E. E. Muschlitz, *J. Appl. Phys.*, **28**, 1414 (1957).
318. A. Henglein and G. A. Muccini, *J. Chem. Phys.*, **31**, 1426 (1959).
319. F. C. Fehsenfeld, E. E. Ferguson, and A. L. Schmeltekopf, *J. Chem. Phys.*, **45**, 1844 (1966).
320. D. S. Burch and R. Geballe, *Phys. Rev.*, **106**, 183, 188 (1957).
321. J. L. Moruzzi and A. V. Phelps, *J. Chem. Phys.*, **45**, 4816 (1966).
322. C. E. Melton, in *Mass Spectrometry*, edited by C. A. McDowell. New York: McGraw-Hill 1963, p. 163.
323. D. P. Stevenson, in *Mass Spectrometry*, edited by C. A. McDowell. New York: McGraw-Hill 1963, p. 589.
324. E. J. Robinson and S. Geltman, *Phys. Rev.*, **153**, 4 (1967).
325. B. Steiner, M. L. Seman, and L. M. Branscomb, in *Atomic Collision Processes*, edited by M. R. C. McDowell. Amsterdam: North-Holland Publ. Co., 1964, p. 537.
326. S. Gelman, *Phys. Rev.*, **112**, 176 (1958).
327. J. L. Hall, E. J. Robinson, and L. M. Branscomb, *Phys. Rev. Lett.*, **14**, 1013, (1965).
328. J. L. Hall, *IEEE, J. Quant. Electron,* **2**, 361 (1966).
329. G. C. Tisone and L. M. Branscomb, *Phys. Rev.*, **170**, 169 (1968).
330. B. M. Smirnov and M. I. Chibisov, *Zh. Eksp. Teor. Fiz.*, **49**, 841 (1965).
331. Yu. F. Bydin and V. M. Dukelskii, *Zh. Eksp. Teor. Fiz.*, **31**, 569 (1956).
332. E. A. Mason and J. T. Vanderslice, *J. Chem. Phys.*, **28**, 253 (1958).
333. T. L. Bailey, C. J. May, and E. E. Muschlitz, *J. Chem. Phys.*, **26**, 1446 (1957).

334. H. H. Michels, F. E. Haris, and J. C. Brown, *J. Chem. Phys.*, **48**, 2821 (1968).
335. J. L. Moruzzi, J. W. Ekin Jr., and A V. Phelps, *J. Chem. Phys.*, **48**, 3070 (1968).
336. G. V. Dubrovskii and V. D. Ob'edkov, *Zh. Eksp. Teor. Fiz.*, **2**, 6 (1966).
337. R. A. Young and G. St. John, *Phys. Rev.*, **151**, 25 (1966).
338. C. S. Warke, *Phys. Rev.*, **144**, 120 (1966).
339. M. A. Biondi, T. R. Connor, C. S. Weller, and W. H. Kasher, *Tenth Symposium (International) on Combustion*, 1965, p. 579.
340. C. L. Chen, C. C. Leiby, and L. Goldstein, *Phys. Rev.*, **121**, 1391 (1961).
341. J. N. Fox and R. M. Hobson, *Phys. Rev. Lett.*, **17**, 161 (1966).
342. C. F. Hansen, *Phys. Fluids*, **11**, 904 (1968).
343. R. P. Stein, M. Schiebe, M. W. Syverson, T. M. Shaw, and R. C. Gunton, *Phys. Fluids.*, **7**, 164 (1964).
344. G. R. Court and J. Sayers, *Brit. J. Appl. Phys.*, **15**, 923 (1964).
345. R. King, in *Ionization in High Temperature Gases*, edited by K. E. Schuler. New York: Academic Press, 1963, p. 12.
346. M. H. Mentzoni, *J. Geophys. Res.*, **68**, No. 14 (1963).
347. T. W. Woodward and R. A. Back, *Can. J. Chem.*, **41**, 1463 (1963).
348. I. K. Larin and V. L. Talrose, *Zh. Fiz. Khim.*, **39**, 2071 (1965).
349. V. L. Talrose, in *Action Chimiques et Biologiques des Radiation*, edited by M. Haissinsky. No. 11, p. 87, Paris 1967.
350. V. B. Brodskii and S. E. Zachik, *Nizkotemperaturnaya Plasma* [Low-Temperature Plasma], edited by A. E. Scheindlin, Moscow, 1967.
351. J. M. Hammer and B. B. Aubray, *Phys. Rev.*, **141**, 146 (1966).
352. G. Hagen, *V Intern. Conf. Phys. Electron a. Atomic Collisions*, Leningrad: Nauka, 1967, p. 165.
353. L. P. Pitaevsky, *Zh. Eksp. Teor. Fiz.*, **42**, 1326 (1962).
354. F. I. Dolidchik and Yu. S. Sayasov, *Zh. Eksp. Teor. Fiz.*, **52**, 1593 (1967).
355. A. V. Gurevich and L. P. Pitaevsky, *Zh. Eksp. Teor. Fiz.*, **46**, 1281 (1964).
356. B. M. Smirnov. *Atomnye Stolknoveniya i Elementarnye Protesessy v Plasma*. Moscow: Atomisdat, 1968, p. 312.
357. D. R. Bates, A. E. Kingston, and R. W. P. McWhirter, *Proc. Roy. Soc.*, **A267**, 297 (1962).
358. B. H. Mahan and J. C. Pearson, *J. Chem. Phys.*, **40**, 392 (1964).
359. T. S. Carlton and B. H. Mahan, *J. Chem. Phys.*, **40**, 3683 (1964).
360. D. R. Bates and T. Boyd, *Proc. Phys. Soc.*, **A69**, 910 (1956).
361. W. Aberth, J. R. Peterson, D. C. Lorrents, and C. J. Cook, *Phys. Rev. Lett.*, **20**, 979 (1968).
362. J. J. Thomson, *Phil. Mag.*, **47**, 337 (1924).
363. G. L. Natanson, *Zh. Tekh. Fiz.*, **29**, 1373 (1959).
364. K. A. Brueckner, *J. Chem. Phys.*, **40**, 439 (1964).
365. P. J. Feibelman, *J. Chem. Phys.*, **42**, 2462 (1965).
366. D. R. Bates and R. J. Moffett, *Proc. Roy. Soc.*, **A291**, 1 (1966).
367. B. H. Mahan, *J. Chem. Phys.*, **48**, 2629 (1968).
368. P. Langevin, *Ann. Chim. Phys.*, **28**, 433 (1903).
369. L. D. Landau and E. Teller, *Phys. Z. Sowjetunion*, **10**, 34 (1936).
370. R. N. Schwartz and K. F. Herzfeld, *J. Chem. Phys.*, **22**, 767 (1954).
371. J. G. Parker, *Phys. Fluids*, **2**, 449 (1959).
372. V. H. Blackman, *J. Fluid. Mech.*, **1**, 61 (1956).
373. N. A. Generalov, *Vestnik Mosc. Gosud. Universiteta, Fiz., astron.*, **2**, 51 (1962).
374. M. Camac, *J. Chem. Phys.*, **34**, 448 (1961).

375. W. Roth, *J. Chem. Phys.*, **34**, 999 (1961).
376. D. L. Matthews, *J. Chem. Phys.*, **34**, 639 (1961).
377. N. H. Johannesen. H. K. Zienkiewicz, P. A. Blythe, and J. H. Gerrard, *J. Fluid. Mech.*, **13**, 213 (1962).
378. I. R. Hurle and A. G. Gaydon, *Nature*, **4702**, 184 (1959).
379. R. G. Meyerand and A. F. Haught, *Phys. Rev. Lett.*, **11**, 401 (1963).
380. E. K. Damon and R. G. Tomlinson, *Appl. Opt.*, **2**, 546 (1963).
381. M. N. Safaryan and E. V. Stupochenko, *Priladnaya Matematika i Tekhnicheskaya Fizika*, **1**, 93 (1965).
382. F. D. Schields and K. P. Lur, *J. Chem. Phys.*, **40**, 732 (1964).
383. A. I. Osipov and E. V. Stupochenko, *Uspekhi Fizicheskikh Nauk*, **79**, 81 (1963).
384. J. Lambert, in *Atomic amd Molecular Processes*, edited by D. R. Bates. New York: Academic Press, 1962.
385. N. A. Generalov and S. A. Losev, *J. Quant. Spectrosc. Radiat. Transfer*, **6**, 101 (1966).
386. S. J. Colgan and B. P. Levitt, *Trans. Faraday. Soc.*, **63**, 2898 (1967).
387. D. Rupp, *J. Chem. Phys.*, **43**, 317 (1965).
388. N. M. Kusnetsov, *Dokl. Akad. Nauk SSSR*, **185**, 866 (1969).
389. C. Treanor, J. Rich, and R. Rehm, *J. Chem. Phys.*, **48**, 1798 (1968).
390. O. K. Rice, *J. Chem. Phys.*, **21**, 750 (1953).
391. B. Widom, *J. Chem. Phys.*, **31**, 1027 (1959).
392. C. E. Trenor and P. V. Marrone, *Phys. Fluids*, **6**, 1215 (1963).
393. S. A. Denisik, S. A. Lebedev, Yu. G. Malama, and L. S. Polak, *Khim. Vys. Energ.*, **2**, 304 (1968).
394. V. N. Kondratiev and E. E. Nikitin, *J. Chem. Phys.*, **45**, 1078 (1966).
395. K. L. Wray, *J. Chem. Phys.*, **38**, 1513 (1963).
396. H. B. Palmer and D. F. Hornig, *J. Chem. Phys.*, **26**, 98 (1957).
397. R. W. Diesen and W. J. Felmlee, *J. Chem. Phys.*, **39**, 2115 (1963).
398. V. N. Kondratiev and E. E. Nikitin, *Uspekhi Khimii*, **36**, 2007 (1967).
399. C. A. Losev and O. P. Schatalov, *Khim. Vys. Energ.*, **2**, 377 (1968).
400. V. N. Kondratiev, *Kinetika Khimicheskikh Gasovykh Reaktsii*, Izd. Akad. Nauk SSSR, 1958. (Chemical Kinetics of Gas Reactions). Oxford: Pergamon Press, 1964.
401. D. Bunker, *Theory of Elementary Gas Reaction Rates*. Oxford: Pergamon Press, 1966.
402. S. Glasstone, K. J. Laidler, and H. Eyring, *The Theory of Rate Processes*. New York: McGraw-Hill, 1941.
403. D. W. Setser and B. S. Rabinovitch, *J. Chem. Phys.*, **40**, 2427 (1964).
404. J. Kech and A. Kalelkar, *J. Chem. Phys.*, **49**. 3211 (1968).
405. V. N. Kondratiev, *Konstanty Skorosti Elementarnykh Khimicheskikh Reakstii v Gazovoi Faze, Spravochnik* (in press).
406. E. Hutton, *Nature*, **203**, 835 (1964).
407. V. V. Azatyan, V. V. Voevodskii, and A. B. Nalbandyan, *Kinetika i Kataliz*, **2**, 340 (1961).
408. F. Kaufman and F. P. Del Greco, *Ninth Symposium on Combustion, Discussion on Fundamental Flame Processes*. Maryland, 1962, p. 659.
409. C. P. Fenimore and G. W. Jones, *J. Phys. Chem.*, **62**, 1578 (1958).
410. K. L. Wray and J. D. Teare, *J. Chem. Phys.*, **36**, 2582 (1962).
411. C. B. Kretschmer and H. L. Peterson, *J. Chem. Phys.*, **39**, 1772 (1963).
412. R. E. Duff and N. Davidson, *J. Chem. Phys.*, **31**, 1018 (1959).
413. P. G. Ashmore and J. Chanmugam, *Trans. Faraday Soc.*, **49**, 254 (1953).
414. F. Kaufman, N. J. Gerri, and D. A. Pascal, *J. Chem. Phys.*, **24**, 32 (1956).
415. V. N. Kondratiev, *Spektroskopicheskoe Izuchenie Khimicheskikh Reaktsii*. Moscow: Akad. Nauk SSSR 1944.

416. R. E. Duff, *J. Chem. Phys.*, **28**, 1193 (1958).
417. E. Freedman and J. W. Daiber, *J. Chem. Phys.*, **34**, 1271 (1961).
418. F. Kaufman and J. R. Kelso, *J. Chem. Phys.*, **23**, 602 (1955).
419. E. L. Tollefson and D. J. Le Roy, *J. Chem. Phys.*, **16**, 1057 (1948).
420. W. R. Schulz and D. J. Le Roy, *Can. J. Chem.*, **40**, 2412 (1962).
421. F. Kaufman, *Progr. React. Kinetics*, **1**, 1 (1961).
422. S. Rongelb and M. W. P. Strandberg, *J. Chem. Phys.*, **31**, 1196 (1959).
423. A. A. Westenberg and N. De Haas, *J. Chem. Phys.*, **40**, 3087 (1964).
424. V. N. Panfilov and V. V. Voevodskii, *Kinetika i Kataliz*, **6**, 557 (1965).
425. E. N. Sarkisjan and A. B. Nalbandy, *Dokl. Akad. Nauk SSSR*, **178**, 648 (1968).
426. F. P. Lossing, in *Mass-Spectrometry*, edited by C. A. McDowell. New York: McGraw-Hill, 1963, p. 442.
427. V. L. Talrose, V. P. Strunin, A. F. Dodonov, and G. K. Lavrovskaya, *Adv. Mass. Spectrom.*, **3**, 993 (1964).
428. H. I. Schiff and H. J. Mathias, *Disc. Faraday Soc.*, **37**, 38 (1964).
429. R. G. W. Norrish, G. Porter and, B. A. Thrush, *Proc. Roy. Soc., London*, **A216**, 1651 (1953).
430. G. W. Kistiakowsky, *J. Chem. Phys.*, **35**, 264 (1961).
431. E. Leger, *Can. J. Phys.*, **83**, 74 (1955).
432. J. N. Bradley and G. B. Kistiakowsky, *J. Chem. Phys.*, **35**, 264 (1961).
433. A. P. Modika, *J. Phys. Chem.*, **69**, 2111 (1965).
434. I. R. Hurle, *Rep. Progr. Phys.*, **30**, 149 (1967).
435. G. B. Kistiakowsky and G. G. Volpi, *J. Chem. Phys.*, **27**, 1141 (1957); **28**, 665 (1958).
436. E. L. Wong and A. E. Potter, *J. Chem. Phys.*, **39**, 2211 (1963); **43**, 337 (1965).
437. K. G. Denbigh, *Trans. Faraday Soc.*, **40**, 9 (1944).
438. K. G. Denbigh and F. M. Page, *Disc. Faraday Soc.*, **17**, 145 (1954).
439. A. F. Dodonov, V. P. Strunin, G. K. Lavrovskaya, and V. L. Talrose, *Kinetika i Kataliz*, **7**, 385 (1966).
440. V. P. Strunin, A F. Dodonov, G. K. Lavrovskaya, and V. L. Talrose, *Kinetika i Kataliz*, **7**, 693 (1966).
441. V. L. Talrose, A. F. Dodonov, G. K. Lavrovskaya, and J. Vsesoyusnogo, *Khimicheskogo Obsechestva im. D. I. Mendeleeva*, **11**, 154 (1966).
442. R. G. Albright, A. F. Dodonov, G. K. Lavrovskaya, I. I. Morosov, and V. L. Talrose, *J. Chem. Phys.*, **50**, 3632 (1969).
443. E. E. Greene and J. Ross, *Science*, **159**, 587 (1968).

CHAPTER THIRTEEN

Some Principles of Nonequilibrium
Plasma-Chemical Reaction Kinetics

L. POLAK

I. INTRODUCTION

The study of the time evolution of certain systems is one of the prominent features of modern physics (from both classical and quantum mechanical considerations). The problem of following a change (relaxation, for example) in the state of a system (gas, plasma) has to be considered and solved for any possible initial deviations from equilibrium and must account for the various factors that prevent the system from monotonously approaching the equilibrium state. Various interactions of the system with the external world and those inside the system itself should be included in the consideration. Thus equations describing the system evolution become nonlinear (explicitly or not). This nonlinearity and an explicit dependence of variables upon time are characteristic of the equations describing evolution of systems and make it difficult to solve the equations without the use of electronic digital computers. Moreover some principal problems such as nonreversibility of the systems' behavior and microreversibility, unicursality of time, and so on, should also be solved. All these problems are not yet completely solved and are considered in the elaboration of some new approaches to the study of nonequilibrium systems evolution. These approaches have led also to a change in our comprehension of the nature of equilibrium states and enabled us to understand more profoundly the connection between nonequilibrium and equilibrium states and the importance of fluctuations.

These new trends have expressed themselves in the rapid progress of physical and chemical kinetics* and plasma-chemical kinetics in particular. The subject of plasma chemistry is to study regularities (thermodynamics,

---

*It should be observed that we do not consider nonequilibrium thermodynamics since its characteristic assumption about the linear dependence of fluxes upon gradients is valid only for the Navier-Stokes (hydrodynamic) approach. Hence the nonequilibrium thermodynamics may be applied just for a description of near-equilibrium states. The information accumulated by this method cannot exceed that provided by the first-order calculations of deviations from equilibrium (1). This linear approach cannot be applied for a consideration of chemical reactions since the latter are described by relations far from linear.

kinetics, mechanisms) of chemical reactions under low-temperature plasma conditions. The method of plasma production (arcs, sparks, glow and hf discharges, focused laser radiation, adiabatic compression, etc.) has no importance in a study of the common regularities, though it may certainly influence some of the reactions occurring. In this chapter some kinetic problems of chemical reactions under plasma conditions are discussed.

II. SPECIAL FEATURES OF PLASMA-CHEMICAL REACTIONS AND THEIR KINETICS

Plasma-chemical reactions may be of the nonequilibrium and quasi equilibrium types. Various types of plasma-chemical reactions are enumerated in Table 1.

The kinetics of plasma-chemical reactions as seen from Table 1, can be considered as a particular case of nonequilibrium chemical kinetics.

Plasma-chemical reactions in the gas phase (only these reactions will be discussed further) are characterized by the following:

1. In " hot " gases nonelastic collisions become important as compared to " ordinary " (monoatomic) gases the properties of which are described well by the kinetic theory based upon the consideration of only elastic collisions. The kinetic theory also explains some properties of polyatomic and reacting gases assuming the nonelastic collision frequency to be small; such a treatment fails when the gas temperature is sufficiently increased.

2. The difference between the characteristic times of various physical and chemical processes becomes smaller and it becomes impossible to distinguish between the various processes as it is allowed in the classical chemical kinetics. The values of the characteristic times for various processes occurring at temperatures from 3×10^3 to 1.5×10^4 °K shown in Table 2 confirm the latter statement partly.

3. Chemical kinetics cannot be considered independently of physical kinetics in the region of interest.* In case the reaction rate exceeds the collision frequency for the momentum-transfer collisions, deviations appear from the equilibrium conditions. It can lead to a violation of the equilibrium Maxwell-Boltzmann energy distribution and to a relative decrease of the highly energetic molecules density due to the occurrence of chemical reactions. This highly energetic " tail " of the distribution cannot be maintained at the expense of momentum-transfer collisions since the frequency of such collisions

*Physical kinetic principles have been stated for the first time by L. E. Gurevitch in his classical book *Principles of Physical Kinetics*, Moscow, 1940.

TABLE 1
Types of plasma-chemical reactions

	Processes occurring in the system	Characteristics of the system	Process characteristics
Nonequilibrium	Chemical reactions in nonequilibrium systems[a]	Difference between vibrational and translational temperatures	
		Two subsystems, one being Maxwellian and the other non-Maxwellian	Stationary or relaxing
		Two subsystems with different temperatures	
		Both subsystems are non-Maxwellian	
Quasi-equilibrium	Nonequilibrium in the system due to the occurrence of chemical reactions		Stationary or relaxing

[a] A prominent general feature of nonequilibrium conditions in a gas system or low-temperature plasma is the occurrence of mass, momentum, and energy transfer (or of one of these quantities); this transfer occurs through any small surface element oriented in some way and moving at the speed of the flux (or the mass velocity).

TABLE 2
Characteristic times for various processes at temperatures, 3×10^3–1.5×10^4 °K

(1) Molecular interaction mean time	$\sim 10^{-14}$ sec
(2) Mean time for molecular free path run (of the order of the Maxwellization time)	$\sim 10^{-9}$ sec
(3) Relaxation time for molecular rotation	$\sim 10^{-9}$ sec
(4) Relaxation time for vibrational processes	$\sim 10^{-7}$ sec
(5) Relaxation time for dissociation of oxygen	$\sim 10^{-7}$ sec
(6) Mean time for an effective collision to occur with a barrier energy of $E = 60$ kcal mole^{-1} (~ 2.5 eV)	$\sim 10^{-5}$ sec

is too small. Hence the basic principles of the simple kinetic theory of chemical reactions and of reaction absolute rates theory will be violated. A general solution for the distribution function disturbed by chemical reactions has not yet been found. However, this problem has been studied in some particular cases. The effect of a fast chemical reaction upon the Maxwell-Boltzmann distribution and the effect of the distribution thus produced upon the reaction rate was studied in Ref. (3) using the Monte-Carlo method.

There exist well-known conditions when translational, vibrational, and rotational temperatures are quite different from each other, and/or various components of a system (electrons, ions, and neutral molecules, for instance) have different temperatures, and/or when a system cannot be described at all using the concept of temperature* (nonequilibrium, stationary, and relaxing systems). Strictly speaking, the Arrhenius-type kinetics cannot be used in all these cases and the ordinary expression for the rate of a chemical reaction is quite inapplicable.

4. Multichannel processes should be considered in plasma-chemical kinetics. From the quantum mechanical point of view (we shall consider only two channels for simplicity) it means that in certain energy range two pairs of particles (A_1, B_1) and (A_2, B_2) can exist such that there exist two independent wave functions which satisfy boundary conditions for a given system. As it is known in the case of a one-channel problem the S-matrix contains all the information about interaction properties of the system while in a multi-channel case a similar theorem has not been proved yet(2). Moreover, in order to compose the Hamiltonian using the results of scattering, all the components of the S-matrix should be known for all energies.

5. The barrier-type nature of the reactions (the existence of an energy barrier opposing only the reaction), being peculiar to the Arrhenius classical kinetics, can be completely changed in the case of reactions under plasma conditions. It is necessary to account for possibilities for chemical reactions to occur from different quantum levels of the system and for one of the sub-systems as a whole to have above-barrier energy.†

6. These five special features of plasma-chemical reactions are in reality peculiar to nonequilibrium chemical processes, and chemical reactions under low-temperature plasma conditions are particular cases (but still important) of such processes. In this section some special features of the reactions under plasma conditions will be discussed briefly.

---

*Strictly speaking, the matter is not just that only the temperature concept is inapplicable in the case of a nonequilibrium system. A complete description of a nonequilibrium system becomes impossible if new concepts are not used: first of all level populations (occupation numbers), characteristics of relaxation over various degrees of freedom, distribution function dependence upon time and coordinates.

†A detailed theory of barrier-type phenomena can be found in Ref. 2.

The degree of ionization is known to be the most important characteristic of a plasma under equilibrium conditions; given the temperature and pressure the degree of plasma ionization may be found using the Saha equation that is derived from the mass action law.

Ionization processes (being coupled always to recombination processes) are due to such factors as mutual collisions of heavy particles under high temperatures (energies), their collisions with electrons, photo-ionization, and ion-molecular reactions. A microscopic description of all these processes requires a generalization of the kinetic gas theory for the plasma state. Such a generalization is still under development. In the case of low-temperature plasma containing both neutral and charged particles, there occur long-range collisions, due to electromagnetic interaction between charged particles, in addition to ordinary small-range collisions taking place in gases. Thus very small scattering angles and consequently a great number of interactions resulting in small momentum transfer should be taken into consideration; moreover, interaction of charged particles with external electromagnetic fields should be also accounted for (5–7).

In the case when electron, ion, and molecular gases are not thermally equilibrated, an energy exchange occurs between electrons and neutral particles and between electrons and ions. The latter occurs through Coulomb-type collisions. Both processes may lead either directly or through successive steps of excitation to chemical reactions. The mechanism and probabilities for these reactions are to be studied by plasma-chemical kinetics on the basis of a detailed analysis of all interactions occurring in a system and using the basic principles of nonequilibrium chemical kinetics.*

At present the limited usefulness of Arrhenius kinetics, that is valid just near the equilibrium (for example under small perturbations when a system can be considered yet in quasi-equilibrium), is evident. In other words, this type of kinetics can be used in the case a single value of temperature (being the parameter of the Maxwell-Boltzmann distribution) can be defined for the system.†

---

*Many interesting analogies, worthwhile observing, exist between plasma-chemical kinetics and kinetics of chemical and adsorption processes on the surface of dielectrics and semiconductors.

†In Ref. 8 the temperature as a concept of the kinetic theory is defined from the equation

$$\tfrac{1}{2}m\bar{v}^2 = \tfrac{3}{2}kT \qquad [1]$$

This definition has been discussed in the preface to the Russian edition of the book (8) by Bogolyubov, who observed that gases cannot be considered as a generally valid case for the definition. The most general definition of temperature is made assuming it to be the module of the canonical distribution for equilibrium states and the module of approximately canonical distribution for near-equilibrium states. If a state is far from being statistically in equilibrium the concept of temperature is in general inapplicable (cf. (8), p. 58).

Nonequilibrium distribution of reactants takes place, for instance, when the energy is injected pulsewise into the equilibrium system provided the conditions $\tau_i \ll \tau_{cr}$ is satisfied, where τ_i is the duration of the pulse and τ_{cr} is chemical relaxation time (pulse electrical discharges, shock tubes, flash-photolysis).

In many cases, even when reactions occur under not-too-high energies, the reaction products distribution may prove to be one of nonequilibrium. Some reactions are given here, that result in nonequilibrium distributions of reaction products:

(1) Recombinative excitation

$$A + B + M \longrightarrow AB^* + M$$

$$A + B + M \longrightarrow AB + M^*$$

(2) Dissociative energy transfer

$$AB + M^* \longrightarrow A^* + B + M$$

(3) Exothermic exchange reactions

$$A + BC \longrightarrow AB^* + C$$

$$A + BC \longrightarrow AB + C^*$$

(4) Photodissociation

$$ABC + h\nu \longrightarrow AB^* + C$$

Here the asterisk means excitation into electronic and/or vibrational and/or rotational nonequilibrium states.*

The treatment of kinetic problems that depend more strongly upon the molecular interaction mechanism and molecular quantum level populations† requires far more information about the system of interest.

---

*The excitation of reaction products under molecular beam conditions has been studied in Ref. 10, the reactions of alkali metals with some halogen compounds being used. A kinematical analysis of the angular distribution of the alkali halide molecules produced showed that the greater part of the energy released (equal to the difference between the bond energies of the reactants and products) was contained in the internal excitation of the molecules, and mostly in the vibrational excitation of the newly formed bonds. As the reaction cross-section increases from 10 $Å^2$ to 10^2 $Å^2$ the reaction mechanism becomes a "direct stripping."

†The importance of the effect of vibrational excitation upon the rate of chemical reaction has been confirmed by the results of experiments (11). As the vibrational temperature of N_2 molecules is increased from 1000°K to 6000°K (under $T_{transl} \approx 300°K$) the rate constant for the reaction $O^+ + N_2 \rightarrow N_2^+ + O$ becomes forty times more. (see Fig. 1) The same change in the translational temperature (under $T_{vibr} = const$) would lead in accordance with the Arrhenius equation to a rate constant increase of sixty times. Both effects are quite comparable.

The results of the experiment given in Ref. 12 show that cyclopropane (and carbon dioxide) produced by cyclobutanol photolysis to be vibrationally excited at the ground electronic state. This excitation distribution over vibrational levels is nonequilibrium.

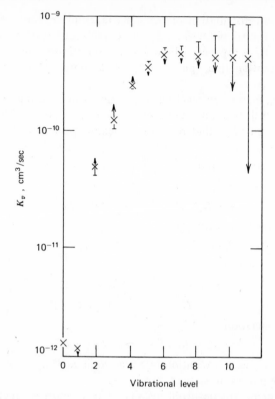

Figure 1 Experimental rate constant dependence on vibrational level number.

Nonequilibrium effects may be observed to appear in a system initially in equilibrium if any processes are occurring at finite rates inside the system. Such processes result inevitably in a violation of the Maxwell distribution. In particular, such a violation may be due to nonelastic collisions resulting in mass exchange and internal energy redistribution of colliding particles. Hence the occurrence of chemical reactions always produces a nonequilibrium in a system.* This nonequilibrium can be neglected (although with a rather vague

---

*Violation of the Maxwell distribution due to chemical reactions has been studied in Ref. 14 using the Enskog-Chapman generalized procedure. As the authors of Ref. 14 have pointed out (Ref. 15), the Enskog-Chapman ordinary procedure is not applicable to the study of finite perturbations of the distribution function. At the same time it is these perturbations that are important for chemical reaction kinetics, since very small ones affect the latter only slightly. Hence calculations made using the Enskog-Chapman ordinary procedure (16–18) are somewhat unconvincing. The Enskog-Chapman generalized procedure developed in Ref. 19 does not appear either to be rigorously founded. (This point requires a special discussion.) However, a conclusion made in Ref. 14 should be mentioned.

degree of accuracy) in the classical Arrhenius kinetics when reaction rates are comparatively small. However, under high temperatures in plasma-chemical processes, radiation chemistry, shock tubes and others, the effects of these reactions have to be accounted for. For instance, thermal dissociation of diatomic molecules is well known not only to violate the Boltzmann distribution but also to decrease the vibrational temperature compared to the translational one. These changes affect both dissociation rate and vibrational relaxation process (13). Nonequilibrium due to a chemical reaction and further occurrence of the reaction under nonequilibrium conditions is the problem for nonequilibrium, generalized, chemical kinetics to be studied. The Arrhenius kinetics appears to be a particularly extreme case of this kinetics and thus will be believed to be rigorously founded, its applicability limits being clearly defined.

Strictly speaking, the solution of this problem must be based upon a consideration of the Pauli equation or the Boltzmann equation (or any equation of the Liouville-type). Using one of these equations and accounting for chemical reactions and relaxation processes of the internal degrees of freedom of reacting molecules,† particular solutions under various conditions can be obtained, including ordinary chemical kinetic equations and expressions for the rate constants for chemical reactions.

Let us define the elementary act of a chemical reaction as a chemical transformation occurring during the time interval less than the collision

---

It is that some calculations made using reaction cross-sections given there show that the distribution function and reaction rate may differ significantly from their equilibrium values. For instance, taking the cross-section in the form

$$\sigma = \begin{cases} 0, & v < v_{cr} \\ 1, & v \geqslant v_{cr} \end{cases}$$

where v_{cr} is the velocity of chemical relaxation, yields $W_{noneq} = 0.17\ W_{eq}$ whereas using the Enskog-Chapman ordinary procedure (18) yields $W_{noneq} = 0.87 W_{eq}$ (W is the rate of reaction).

†From the point of view of interest one of the differences between atoms and molecules is the greater density of the molecules' quantum states due to the existence of rotational and vibrational levels. Moreover, most molecules have far fewer known electronic states than do the corresponding atoms. Almost all molecularly excited states are well above dissociation energy for the ground state and may be of short lifetime due to predissociation or other nonradiative transitions. The number of electronically excited states expected to appear because of chemical processes is determined also by the energies actually reached. For instance, two or three electronically excited states are expected to be important in molecular lasers, so vibrational and rotational sublevels of these states will mainly be important.

mean time. Chemical reaction is a consequence of elementary acts* which yield the following change:

$$\sum_i M_i \rightarrow \sum_j M_j' \qquad [2]$$

where M_i, M_j' are molecules of different kinds; molecules are assumed to be sets of nuclei and electrons having the only value of the minimum potential energy.

The transformation [2] may take place provided a certain configuration in the system under study appears. This configuration is characterized by a special kind of interaction usually represented by either one or another model.†

Three approaches may be suggested to solve the problems under discussion, accounting for the possibility that a set is found of cross-sections σ_i for processes involved; all the information needed about the system can be obtained through a proper averaging.

These three approaches are quantum-mechanical, classical dynamics, and statistical calculations. The former of these is certainly the most rigorous and correct, but it is difficult to carry out because of both the complexity of the many-body system dynamics theory and the rather inadequate knowledge of potential energy surfaces.

A study of classical trajectories on various surfaces of the potential energy allows us to determine the most important features of chemical reaction. Such calculations have been originally carried out in Refs. (20–23). These do not allow us to show the importance of quantum-mechanical effects. Moreover, the probability of transition between the potential energy surfaces amounts to either unity or zero from the classical point of view; this transition takes place under electronically adiabatic reactions. But there exists a large group of reactions which are nonadiabatic and result in electronically excited products (24).

The statistical approach (25–29) provides less information and requires some additional assumptions to be made but still allows quantitative results to be obtained. These results when compared to those of known experiments

---

*Generally accepted in physical chemistry but extremely vague, the term "primary act" is of doubtful use here.

†Trying not to make a rigorous general definition of a model, a formulation that enables us in spite of some deficiency to use the concept of model reasonably can be given. To do this one of the possible definitions of a system has to be given. A system is an arbitrary set of interacting elements. A specific system is given if its (1) elements, (2) structure, (3) possible states, and (4) behavior (the kind of transitions between states) are known. A model is any system similar to another one, taken for an original. A model is assumed to represent the original with respect to some important properties of the latter. Thus modelling implies the existence of a model-creating person and an aim of modelling.

enable us to find the assumption made and to use euristic possibilities of the theory.

Three methods are possible (at least at present) to perform thermal chemical reactions under high temperatures (or energies): heating (with an electric arc, for instance) of "cool" reactants in a mixture prepared beforehand; mixing a "cool" reactant with a heated one (as in a plasma jet, for instance); mixing two heated gases. The second and third methods inevitably include mixing processes. These processes take a finite time during which chemical reactions may occur under nonisotropic and nonisothermic conditions, their rates depending upon time and coordinates.

Equilibrium establishment process in velocity space is known to be significantly different from that in configuration space.

Velocity distribution in any elements of coordinate space approaches monotonically and rather rapidly the Maxwellian local distribution ($\tau \sim 10^{-9}$ sec and is of the order of collision mean time at a pressure of ~ 1 atm). The Maxwellian distribution is never established completely since external forces and the existence of fluxes oppose this process strongly. As for the equilibrium in coordinate space, its establishment occurs not monotonically but requires much more time to be completed (30).

Taking into account chemical reactions, the equilibrium establishment process becomes still more complex because of endothermicity or exothermicity of reactions involved and variations in particle densities (due to association and dissociation) in every element of the space.

Thus, according to experimental data (31) obtained using spectral, probe, and schlieren methods, the time for mixing methane ($T = 300°K$) with argon plasma jet ($T = 3000°K$) amounts to about 3×10^{-5} sec, where as the time of acetylene (from methane formation) under these conditions is approximately 1×10^{-4} sec. Chemical reactions clearly occur partly (and may be mostly) under very complex nonequilibrium conditions.

Hence plasma-chemical kinetics include without exception a study of the mixing of the reacting gases. To study this problem, combined equations of hydrodynamics and chemical kinetics should be solved, using similarity theory methods also (32).

III. FUNDAMENTAL EQUATIONS AND NUMERICAL CALCULATIONS

An equation that should form the basis of nonequilibrium chemical kinetics is difficulty to identify at present.* It may, in general, be the Liouville, Boltzmann, Pauli, or some analogous equation. The Liouville equation has

---

*Chemical kinetic calculations are based, generally speaking, upon the many-particle scattering problem.

the advantage of being the integral of mechanics equations. However, it is difficult to apply because of the irreversibility of systems evolution. Moreover, some practically unsurmountable obstacles arise by its solution.

The application of either the Boltzmann or the Pauli equation make it necessary to use numerical methods and electronic digital computers. This prevents us, of course, from obtaining general regularities. Nevertheless it is for the present the only way to make progress in the solution of nonequilibrium chemical kinetics problems.

Taking into account all the difficulties standing in the way of the experiment and interpretation of its results, the importance of using the mathematical experimentation method (the Monte-Carlo method) and analogous approaches becomes evident.

Naturally, the problem of choosing the basic equation for chemical kinetics still remains. The Boltzmann equation is not likely to be used, although it might seem to be a good selection. Difficulties arising from its solution procedure and excessive computer time stand in the way. Great difficulties also arise because three-body collisions are neglected in the derivation of this equation. The problem of the existence and uniqueness of a solution of this equation is not in general clear.

Now let us consider the Pauli equation. Besides its completely mathematical advantages (from the point of view of the numerical integration procedure), the following important aspects should be mentioned. Strictly speaking, this equation is a balancing one; being correctly composed it is always correct like any balancing equation. It enables us to describe uniformly transitions between levels and also those resulting in chemical transformations. This equation is not only easy to integrate numerically, using computers, but also can conveniently be compared to experimental data.

The Pauli equation is in a sense the result of a direct generalization of chemical-kinetic equations. If transitions between levels are not important it may be reduced to ordinary chemical-kinetics equations. Hence its form and treatment procedure are usual for specialists in classical chemical kinetics.

All this suggests that the Pauli equation should be taken as a principle for chemical kinetics, at least at present. This conclusion cannot be founded rigorously at present but some serious arguments and discussion can be found in Ref. (33) concerning the importance of this equation for the description of irreversible and relaxation processes (apart from chemical kinetics).

Many methods of kinetic problem solution developed in classical chemical kinetics (the quasi-stationary concentration method in particular) will be evidently used in chemical nonequilibrium kinetics. Keep in mind that chemical reaction rates will be discussed classically within certain ranges of temperature (energy), densities of reactants and of reaction products. However, it does not concern those theses of classical kinetics which are based upon equilibrium thermodynamics; these should be reconsidered in chemical nonequilibrium kinetics. In particular such a reconsideration should involve the mass action law, the relation $K = K_{dis}/K_{rec}$. (Here K is the equilibrium constant for a reaction, K_{dis} and K_{rec} are rate constants for dissociation and recombination, respectively).

A. The Pauli Equation

In order to describe completely the time evolution of a multi-channel system, it is necessary to consider excitation and deactivation of all internal degrees of freedom (electronic, vibrational, rotational), the mutual energy exchange between them and the energy transfer from them to the translational degree of freedom (and inversely as well).

An account of transitions between individual quantum levels modifies the classical equation of chemical kinetics and results in the Pauli equation (33).

This equation allows to develop a new method for the investigation of many-particle systems relaxation to the equilibrium state. In the case of a unimolecular reaction occurring in a heat bath of an inert gas the Pauli equation may be written as (31).

$$\frac{dn_i}{dt} = \omega \sum_j P_{ij} n_j(t) - \omega \sum_j P_{ji} n_i(t) - K_i n_i(t) + R_i(t) \qquad [3]$$

where $n_i(t)$ is reacting molecules concentration on the energy level i at the time t; P_{ij} is the probability for a reacting molecule to transit from the state j to the state i due to a collision with inert gas molecule; K_i is the specific rate ("rate constant") for the reaction from the level i; $R_i(t)$ is the rate of excitation of the level i.* When there is no excitation, then $R_i(t) = 0$ and Eq. (3) may be rewritten in a matrix form

$$\frac{dN(t)}{dt} = -JN(t) \qquad [6]$$

where $J = [\omega(I - P) - K]$ is the transport matrix; P is the transition

*Such process can be simply described (neglecting the molecules of the heat bath) with the following scheme:

$$n_j \underset{\omega P_{ji}}{\overset{\omega P_{ij}}{\rightleftarrows}} n_i \overset{K_i}{\longrightarrow} \text{products} \qquad [4]$$
$$\uparrow Rf_i$$

In this case eq. [3] takes the form

$$\frac{dn_i(t)}{dt} = \omega \sum_j P_{ij} n_j(t) - n_i(t)(\omega + K_i) + R(t) f_i \qquad [5]$$

where ω is collision frequency, R is the total rate of excited states production, f_i the probability for the i excited state to be produced.

probability matrix; K is the diagonal matrix for rate constants; N is the vector of concentrations. Thus a problem arises of the eigenvalues for eq. [6] to be found.

Following Ref. 33 we shall point out some special features of eq. [3]:

1. This equation describes the probability density; it is linear and homogeneous.

2. A change in $n_i(t)$ is determined, with balancing between the increase and decrease.

3. The equation may be applied to infinitely great systems provided at least one of the quantum numbers becomes continuous.

4. The time-dependent quantity $n_i(t)$ has the same value both in the left and right parts of the equation; in other words $n_i(t + \Delta t)$ is determined with $n_i(t)$ and does not depend on $n_i(t')$, where $t' < t$ and Δt is much more than a single transition duration; such evolution is called Markovian.

5. Equation [3] describes irreversible motion.

6. The divergence of the transition probability as the system's volume increases to infinity under fixed density conditions is an undesirable feature of eq. [3], but may be overcome by analysing real systems.

Many generalized equations of the Pauli type have been derived during the last few years (34–42). All these equations are given in Ref. 43 and it is shown that they are equivalent though not identical to each other. These generalised equations differ from the Pauli equations (44) in that they involve an explicit integration over a period of time.

These equations have been analyzed in Ref. 45 to find out whether they might be considered Markovian. The Liouville equation

$$i \frac{\partial \rho}{\partial t} = L_\rho(t) \qquad [7]$$

is the original equation. For a classical system $\rho = \rho(q, p, t)$ is the distribution function in the phase space while for a quantum system ρ represents the density matrix composed of the elements ρ_{mn}. In both cases ρ is the N-particle distribution function. Equation [7] is a deterministic equation of motion which describes time-evolution of ρ. The Liouville operator L is quite a dynamic quantity, completely determined by the Hamiltonian of the system under consideration. All the derivations of the generalized principle equation of chemical kinetics are based upon the Liouville operator expansion in perturbed L_1 and unperturbed L_0 terms:

$$L = L_0 + L_1$$

Following Refs. 42 and 45 yields finally

$$\frac{d\rho_{mm}(t)}{dt} = -\int_0^t dt_1 \sum_n K_{mmnn}(t_1)\rho_{nn}(t - t_1) \qquad [8]$$

where ρ_{mm} are diagonal elements of the density matrix ρ;

$$K_{mmnn}(t) = [L_1 \exp(-it(1-D)L) \cdot (1-D)L_1]_{mmnn}$$

D is such an operator, that $(D_\rho)_{mn} = \rho_{mm}\delta_{mn}$. The dynamic quantity K_{mmnn} is the result of the D-operator application to the Liouville operator. Equation [8] has been derived for initial conditions under which the density matrix is diagonal at $t = 0$. This initial condition (usually called "stochastic initial phases assumption") implies no phase correlation at $t = 0$. Under more general initial conditions the kinetic equations for evaluation of the density matrix element or for the density in the phase space (or for its Fourier expansion components) cannot be written in the form of eq. [8]. Thus stochastic ideas are represented in eq. [8] only through the initial condition of stochastic phases at $t = 0$.

The time integration from $t_1 = 0$ to $t_1 = t$ is necessary to find ρ_{mm} at the time t. The value and time evolution of ρ_{mm} at the time t is determined not only with the quantities K_{mmnn} and ρ_{nn} at the time t but also with prehistories of K_{mmnn}, and that must be taken into account explicitly. Thus the future $(t' > t)$ depends not only upon the present $(t' = t)$ but upon the past $(0 \leqslant t' < t)$ as well. It is a system with a memory. The memory is represented through K_{mm} and the density distribution function is assumed to store for the time interval of the order of magnitude of mechanical interaction time t_{int} (of a collision time, for instance). Let us consider the matrix element ρ for a sufficiently long time t that satisfies the inequality $t \gg t_{int}$. Then we have from eq. [8]:

$$\frac{d\rho_{mm}(t)}{dt} \cong -\int_0^\infty \sum_n K_{mmnn}(t_1)\rho_{nn}(t)\,dt_1 \qquad [9]$$

Under some conditions $(t_{int} < t_{rel}$, weak coupling, etc.) the integration of eq. [9] may be carried out for a given physical system (or a model) and yield

$$\frac{d\rho_{mm}}{dt} = -\sum_n K_{mmnn}\rho_{nn}(t) \qquad [10]$$

This is a well-known "master" equation; it does not already contain the prehistories of K and ρ-distribution function, that is, the time evolution of ρ_{nn} at any time $t' > t$ is determined simply with the values of K and ρ at the time t.*

Equation [6] is evidently a system of ordinary differential equations. This system may in general be integrated using one of the known numerical

---

*We shall not dwell upon the point (discussed in Ref. 45) of whether it is correct to consider eqs. [8] and [10] as non-Markovian and Markovian, respectively (in the rigorous mathematical sense). It will be enough to know that these equations describe systems with and without memory, respectively. The authors of Ref. 45 suggested that processes described with eqs. [8] and [10] be named "Paulian" and "non-Paulian," respectively. We shall not use these terms.

methods, initial distribution N_0 being given. The solution of the combined eqs. [6] allows us to distinguish between processes of relaxation and chemical reaction and to evaluate effects produced by their simultaneous presence. Moreover, the evolution of molecules distribution can be found during the processes of relaxation and disintegration.

A general solution of eqs. [6] may also be described analytically with the eigenvectors of the matrix J (46) as

$$N = \sum_{i=0}^{l-1} C_i B^i \exp\left(-\lambda_i t\right) \qquad [11]$$

where C_i is a constant found from initial conditions, and eigenvectors B^i and eigenvalues λ_i satisfy the relation

$$JB^i = \lambda_i B^i \qquad [12]$$

In order to follow the whole process of chemical equilibrium establishment, some additional terms accounting for recombination should be introduced into eq. [6], which becomes nonlinear and thus has to be integrated numerically.

The resulting rate of reaction, that is, the reaction rate experimentally observed is described as

$$\frac{dUN(t)}{dt} = -K_{\exp} UN(t) \qquad [13]$$

where U is matrix-vector of units and $K_{\exp}$ is the reaction rate constant experimentally observed. The rate constant $K_{\exp}$ has been shown in Ref. 46 to be independent of time and the least eigenvalue λ_0 for the transport matrix J after a time τ_{ind}, small compared to the characteristic time of the reaction:

$$JF = K_{\exp} F \qquad [14]*$$

where $F = (N/UN)$ is the vector of the molecules' nonequilibrium distribution over quantum levels at $t > t_{\mathrm{ind}}$. Hence, the solution of eq. [6] may be found considering the problem of the eigenvalues (46). Using eqs. [11] and [12] and the expression for molecule concentration

$$C(t) = UN(t) \qquad [15]$$

yields

$$C(t) = \sum_{j=1}^{l} \sum_{i=0}^{l-1} C_i (B^i)_j \cdot \exp(-\lambda_i t) \qquad [16]$$

*Using eq. [5] under the condition $R(t) = 0$ another matrix expression may be found for $K_{\exp}$ (50):

$$K_{\exp} F = (\omega - W)F \qquad [14a]$$

Let eigenvalues be arranged so that $\lambda_0 \leqslant \lambda_1 \leqslant \ldots \leqslant \lambda_{l-1}$; then from eqs. [15] and [16] the following expression may be derived:

$$K = \lambda_0 - \left\{ \frac{\sum_{j=1}^{l} \sum_{i=1}^{l-1} C_i(B^i)_j(\lambda_0 - \lambda_i) \exp\left(-\lambda_i t\right)}{\sum_{i=0}^{l-1} \sum_{j=1}^{l} C_i(B^i)_j \exp\left(-\lambda_i t\right)} \right\} \tag{17}$$

This expression is written so as to distinguish the least eigenvalue λ_0. For the time greater than the difference between two first eigenvalues

$$K = \lim_{t \to \infty} K(t) = \lambda_0 \tag{18}$$

Thus for relaxation problems described with eq. [6] any theoretical expression for the unimolecular decomposition rate constant should include the least nonzero eigenvalue.

From eqs. [3] and [13] the following expression for $K_{\exp}$ may be obtained (47):

$$K_{\exp} = vKF \tag{19}$$

Thus the resulting rate constant $K_{\exp}$ of a reaction may be found if the distribution F and rate constants for reactions from every level are known. If, on the contrary, a series of $K_{\exp}$ values are known for various distributions F, the problem then is the determination of the K-matrix elements.

Assuming the latter to be the case and the distribution to be in equilibrium, let us see what is necessary to find K. First of all, a certain dependence of K_i on T should be given; for instance $K_i = K_0 \exp(-E_i/kT)$. Then a few values of K have to be known ($m \geqslant ql$, where l is the number of levels for which $K_i > 0$ and q is the number of parameters involved by the arbitrary dependence of K_i on T).

The solution of the inverse problem (which is more important practically) to determine K_i using $K_{\exp}$ data may be carried out by the Helfand-Tsetlin procedure (37), for instance. In case the number of levels considered is not large, the problem may be solved by using a simple iteration procedure (see Ref. 38, for instance, where Tl^+ emission has been studied from two excited electronic levels). Most of such problems are worthwhile considering assuming inert gas heat-bath conditions, the reactants being small additives (so that recombination may be neglected), and conversion degree being small (only initial steps of reactions are considered).

A few attempts have been made on the basis of eq. [3] to develop a general method for the determination of K. Some of these will be discussed here briefly.

The rate factor K has been shown in Ref. 50 to be independent of time for times greater than that of the reaction induction period τ_{ind}. Assuming the mean lifetime of reaction molecules to be defined as

$$\tau = \int_0^\infty \left[\frac{C(t)}{C(0)} \right] dt \qquad [20]$$

where $C(t)$ is reactants concentration, and yield for reactions with $\tau_{ind} \ll \tau$, the value of K may be simply calculated and should be measured experimentally. In case $\tau \sim \tau_{ind}$ (very fast reactions) the value of τ is simpler to calculate than $K(t)$, and just this τ should be measured experimentally.

Neglecting recombination, the Pauli equation may be written as

$$\dot{n}_i = \sum_{j<D} P_{ij} n_j - \omega_i n_i \qquad [21]$$

An analogous equation has been used in Ref. 51 to find the solution of a particular problem, the "nearest neighbor" model being assumed with final states selected to satisfy the condition $i = j + 1$.

The solution has also been obtained in Ref. 52 but the "nearest neighbor" model was not used. However, because of poor convergence it is not applicable to calculations except for those rare cases when the time scale of chemical reactions is determined exactly with that of vibrational relaxation.

If the "nearest neighbor" model is used the transition probability matrix becomes three-diagonal (42–45). Such a probability model has a certain basis in the quantum-mechanical theory of perturbation (57). However, a general rigorous solution for this case has not yet been found. The quantity K may be found if further simplifications are made (58).

The main important result of these studies is perhaps that K is not correctly to be found from the relation $K = \tau^{-1}$ (50). However, this generally accepted assumption has been shown in the same work to be unnecessary.

Numerical methods of eq. [3] using electronic digital computers are discussed thoroughly in Ref. 48; the algorithm and computer programming are also given. Some model and real problems have also been considered there as examples of numerical integration procedure application. Because of the lack of data on cross-sections, transition probabilities, and rate constants for reactions from various quantum states, the main problem is to find all of these quantities using experimental data and eq. [3].

Modern computer techniques enable us to find all or at least most of the quantities needed by using experimental data. It may be done in principle as follows.

Let us see what experimental data are necessary to study a system of Pauli equations and find the lacking values of W_{ij} and K_i. A chemical reaction will be considered as an active component decomposition under inert gas heat-bath conditions.

Taking into account the component nature and the heat-bath temperature, we compose an adequate system of equations. Then we compose the Pauli equations. To solve these equations it is necessary to (1) determine initial conditions (initial populations of all the quantum levels); (2) dispose of the values of allowed transition probabilities between various levels; and (3) dispose of dissociation rate constant values K_{idis} from every level reaction (at the given heat-bath temperature).

Determination of initial conditions depends upon physical processes occurring in the active component before it is placed in the heat bath (for instance, population levels).

The quantities W_{ij} and K_{idis} may be found through theoretical calculations (for example, quantum-mechanical calculations of W_{ij} for vibrational transitions) or from experiments.

The second way will be discussed in some detail. A few versions are possible here depending on the available experimental data:

1. All the population levels are known from experiment all the time. Then all the values of W_{ij} and K_{idis} can be found with a known accuracy using, for instance, the "ravine" method (48).

2. Some population level kinetics is known experimentally. In this case the value of W_{ij} and K_{idis} can be found only partly for those levels.

3. Experimental data include only a total kinetic curve of K_{exp} for the active component decomposition under various heat-bath temperatures. Then the values of W_{ij} and the dependence of K_{idis} on temperature should be somehow given ($K_{idis} = K_{idis}(T_i, \theta)$, where θ are some parameters). It enables us to find the parameters θ for this dependence using the total rate factor K_{exp} observed experimentally. The form of this dependence is determined with the heat-bath temperature and the cross-section dependence upon energy for the dissociation from i level and may be found numerically by the known relation:

$$K_{idis} = \int \sigma(E) E^{1/2} f(E)\, dE$$

As for $\sigma = \sigma(E)$ it can be found (apart from direct experimental procedures using, for instance, molecular beams) by the following procedure:

1. If a theoretically based form of the function $\sigma = \sigma(E, \phi)$ is known, where ϕ are fitting parameters, these ϕ can be fitted using experimentally obtained dependence of σ on E.

2. If intermolecular interaction potential is known, the cross-section dependence on the energy may be found by solving the equation of motion of the system "active component–heat bath" for various initial conditions and further averaging over a multitude of "histories."

3. If the potential is unknown the function $u(r, \theta)$ may be found by solving the reverse problem, provided the cross-section is known from experimental data. Then θ is to be given and dynamic equations are solved to yield σ. The

results obtained are then compared to those available from experiments, and in the case of disagreement the value of θ is corrected to give better agreement. This procedure may be carried out by the "ravine" method.

Thus a combination of computing mathematics and experimental data enable us to find numerical values of W_{ij} and K_{idis}, performing as few as possible difficult, extremely complicated, and sometimes ambiguous experiments.

To study the possibilities of such a treatment, a model problem has been considered in Ref. 59. Three levels have been included, the nature of their excitation being evidently unimportant in this case, since a formal procedure has been used to calculate the value of K_i using experimental data on K_{exp} and expression [12].

Energy levels E_1, E_2, E_3 were assumed to be of 5, 3, and 2 arbitrary units, respectively.* The quantities K_i were believed to be of the Arrhenius type such as

$$K_i = 10 \exp\left(-\frac{E_i}{RT}\right), \qquad i = 1, 2, 3 \tag{22}$$

The values of E_1, E_2, and E_3 were varied rather widely but by preserving the relation $E_1 > E_2 > E_3$. Reacting molecules distribution over the three quantum levels assumed to be Boltzmannian so that eq. [12] could be written as

$$K_{exp} = \frac{10 \exp\left(\dfrac{E_1}{RT}\right)}{\left[1 - \exp\left(-\dfrac{2}{RT}\right) + \exp\left(-\dfrac{3}{RT}\right)\right]}$$

$$+ \frac{10 \exp\left(-\dfrac{E_2}{RT}\right) \exp\left(-\dfrac{2}{RT}\right)}{\left[1 - \exp\left(-\dfrac{2}{RT}\right) + \exp\left(-\dfrac{3}{RT}\right)\right]}$$

$$+ \frac{10 \exp\left(\dfrac{E_3}{RT}\right) \exp\left(-\dfrac{3}{RT}\right)}{\left[1 + \exp\left(-\dfrac{2}{RT}\right) + \exp\left(-\dfrac{3}{RT}\right)\right]} \tag{23}$$

*Arbitrary units were taken because a complete model problem has to be solved.

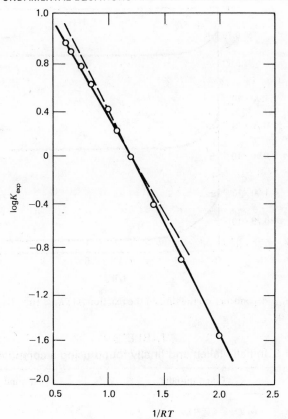

Figure 2   Plot of log K_{exp} as a function of $1/RT$.

The plot of K_{exp} determined with this equation as a function of $1/RT$ is shown in Fig. 2 for $E_1 = 3.5$; $E_2 = 2.5$, and $E_3 = 1.5$ (energy units) M^{-1}. This plot is seen to be practically linear except for small deviations in the high-temperature region. The total value of the activation energy determined by the slope of the plot makes up about 2 (energy units) M^{-1}. An attempt has been made to find parameters E_i included in expression [23] using the ravine method. Eleven points from a plot of the type shown in Fig. 3 have been used. The starting point for the search was that with $E_1 = 5$, $E_2 = 1$, and $E_3 = 2$ (energy units) M^{-1}. The values of E_i initially taken and also found using a computer program are given in Table 3.

An attempt has also been made using the "ravine" method to determine the unknown values of K_i provided the transition probabilities P_{ij} and reactant total concentration and $UN(t)$ are known as functions of time.

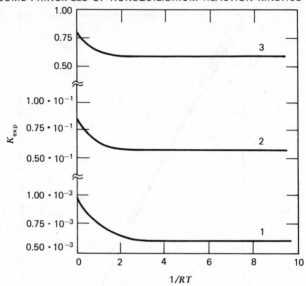

Figure 3 K_{exp} dependence on the time of the reaction: (1) $K_i \approx 10^{-1}\ W_{ij}$; (2) $K_i \approx W_{ij}$; (3) $K_i = 10\ W_{ij}$.

TABLE 3
Values of E_i initially taken and finally found using a computer program

Version	Taken initially			Found		
	E_1	E_2	E_3	E_1	E_2	E_3
1	3.22	2.71	2.30	3.31	2.67	2.28
2	3.50	2.50	1.50	3.50	2.53	1.44
3	3.00	2.00	1.00	2.90	2.05	0.89

In the case of the three levels considered the system of eqs. [2] may be written as

$$\frac{d}{dt}\begin{bmatrix} n_1 \\ n_2 \\ n_3 \end{bmatrix}$$

$$= \begin{bmatrix} -(W_{21} + W_{31}) - K_1 & W_{12} & W_{13} \\ W_{21} & -(W_{32} + W_{12}) - K_2 & W_{23} \\ W_{31} & W_{32} & -(W_{13} + W_{23}) - K_3 \end{bmatrix}$$

$$\times \begin{bmatrix} n_1 \\ n_2 \\ n_3 \end{bmatrix} \qquad [24]$$

Transition probabilities $W_{ij} = \omega P_{ij}$ were taken to be inversely proportional to the differences between energy levels which make up the order of magnitude of the values of K_i.

The system of eqs. [24] was integrated numerically and the reactant total concentration was found for different moments of time:

$$UN(t) = n_1(t) + n_2(t) + n_3(t) \qquad [25]$$

Then, using the ravine method, such values of K_1, K_2, and K_3 were determined that when substituted into eq. [24], eq. [25] was fitted to the best advantage. $K_1 = 0.05$, $K_2 = 0.135$, and $K_3 = 0.368$ (time units)$^{-1}$ were given. The starting values for the search were taken as $K_1 = 0.1$, $K_2 = 0.06$, and $K_3 = 0.25$. The following values were found: $K_1 = 0.047$, $K_2 = 0.064$, and $K_3 = 0.482$. These results show the value of K_1 to be sufficiently correct, K_3 to be somewhat incorrect, and K_2 to be still more incorrect. This disagreement of the K_i values found and given a priori is due to a weak dependence of $UN(t)$ on K_2 and K_3 within the range of K_i variations. In fact, the total reaction rate is determined mainly by the flux from the first level, whereas the fluxes from the second and third levels are 2.5 times as low.

Thus, to find reliable values of K_i using a known dependence [25] such experimental conditions should be selected that the flux from the level of interest is significantly in excess of all the others.

It is interesting to note how the value of K_{exp} is changed during the reaction occurrence. From eq. [13] the following expression may be derived.

$$K_{exp}(t) = \frac{1}{t} \ln \left[\frac{F(0)}{F(t)} \right] \qquad [26]$$

The quantity K_{exp} is determined by the relative values of K_i and W_{ij} so that the less W_{ij} is compared to K_i the more rapidly K_{exp} becomes independent of time. The plot of $K_{exp}(t)$ is shown in Fig. 3 as a function of time (according to eq. [26]).

Kinetics of diatomic molecule dissociation has been studied numerically with electronic digital computer programs using the Pauli equation and the "nearest neighbor" and collision-dominated models (50–51,62).

Table 4 (reported in Ref. 50) shows a maximum value for the rate factor, calculated using the "nearest neighbor" model, differing a few orders of magnitude from the experimental one (except for hydrogen). Taking into account the rotational and electronic degrees of freedom yields an increase in the calculated rate factor. This increase is due partly to the dissociation energy decrease caused by vibrational-rotational transitions occurring in the rotating molecules. The value of the rate factor calculated neglecting the rotation should thus be multiplied by the factor g_{rot} (63). A further increase in the rate factor may be due to higher electronic states, the occurrence of

TABLE 4
Kinetics of the dissociation of diatomic molecules

			Rate factor			
Mole-cule	Tempera-ture, °K	Experi-mental	"Nearest neighbor" model, max value K_{NN}	$K_{NN} \times g_{rot} \times g_e$	Collision-dominated model, max value K_{CD}	$K_{CD} \times g_{rot} \times g_e$
H_2	3000	3×10^{14}	2.2×10^{14}	6.6×10^{14}	1.1×10^{15}	3.3×10^{15}
H_2	4000	3×10^{14}	1.6×10^{14}	4.8×10^{14}	1.3×10^{15}	3.9×10^{15}
O_2	4000	5×10^{14}	1.6×10^{13}	1.4×10^{14}	5×10^{14}	4.5×10^{15}
I_2	300	6×10^{15}	1.3×10^{13}	2×10^{14}	1.4×10^{14}	2.1×10^{15}
I_2	1000	1×10^{15}	4.6×10^{12}	6.9×10^{13}	2.6×10^{14}	3.9×10^{15}
Br_2	1500	1×10^{15}	3.5×10^{12}	6.1×10^{13}	2.8×10^{14}	4.9×10^{15}
Cl_2	2000	7.8×10^{12}	7×10^{12}	1.2×10^{14}	3.7×10^{14}	6.5×10^{15}
Cl_2	3000	3.7×10^{14}	4.5×10^{12}	6.8×10^{13}	4.5×10^{14}	6.8×10^{15}
F_2	2000	1×10^{14}	1×10^{13}	1.5×10^{14}	3.4×10^{14}	5.2×10^{15}

which increases the number of possible routes to dissociation (63). If equilibrium distribution over these states and the ground state is established rapidly, the corresponding increase in the rate factor may be approximately taken into account with the factor g_e (63).

The values of the rate factor multiplied by $(g_e g_{rot})$ are also shown in the same table. The collision-dominated model is seen to yield rate factors greater than those experimentally obtained.

Maximum values of rate factors obtained using the "nearest neighbor" model and multiplied by $(g_e g_{rot})$ are still small (except for hydrogen and fluorine molecules). This suggests that the model of the "nearest neighbor" describes the behavior of diatomic molecules under chemical reaction conditions inadequately. Many quantum transitions appear to be necessary and should be taken into consideration (3).

A theory for chemical reactions occurring in mixtures of reactants with inert gases has been considered in Ref. 60. Although, strictly speaking, chemical reactions in inert gases should be studied under infinite dilution conditions, real pressures of reactants are practically always finite. Therefore, collisions are possible between reacting molecules and inert gas molecules and other molecules of the reactants. A reasonable linear treatment of this problem has been proved to be possible only in case levels with energies lower than a critical energy are maintained in equilibrium.

Let us write once more the equation

$$KF = (\omega - W)F \qquad [14a]$$

where K is the rate factor to be determined, $\mathbf{F}$ is the reactants' distribution vector, ω is the diagonal matrix of collision frequencies, $\mathbf{W} = \mathbf{P}\omega$ is the rate of transitions between all the possible levels due to collisions (the expression [14a] for the "nearest neighbor" model given in Ref. 50). Equation [14a] includes vibrational-vibrational transitions and other bimolecular processes.

In the case of Boltzmann distribution

$$K = \mathbf{U}\mathbf{W}_{21}^{(ur)}\mathbf{F}_1^{(t)} + \mathbf{U}\mathbf{W}_{21}^{(rr)}\mathbf{F}_1^{(t)} \qquad [27]$$

where $\mathbf{U}$ is the unity vector-line (which acts like an operator of summation), $\mathbf{F}_1^{(t)}$ is Boltzmann distribution for bound states; $\omega = \omega^{(ir)} + \omega^{(rr)}$; $\mathbf{W} = \mathbf{W}^{(ir)} + \mathbf{W}^{(rr)}$ where superscripts ir and rr relate to inert gas-reactant and reactant-molecule collisions, respectively.

The second term in eq. [27] is evidently the rate factor for the reaction in pure reactant.

Let us consider the case when the Boltzmann distribution for all the bound states takes no place. The region of applicability of eq. [14a] can be divided into two parts, one of these including low-lying energy levels (where the equilibrium conditions are established with an arbitrary accuracy). The second one (marked further with α) includes higher energy levels but still lower than E_b; the equilibrium distribution here is perturbed strongly with the reaction that occurs. Then the following equation can be derived:

$$K = \mathbf{U}\mathbf{W}_{21}\mathbf{F}_1^{(t)} - \mathbf{U}\mathbf{W}_{2\alpha}(\omega_\alpha - \mathbf{W}_{\alpha\alpha})^{-1}\omega_{2\alpha}\mathbf{F}_\alpha^{(t)} \qquad [28]$$

where the first term is characteristic of the equilibrium value of K (eq. [27]). To derive eq. [28] only the assumption that $K \neq K(t)$ is necessary and the state stability condition is carried out.

If nonequilibrium effects (described with the second term in eq. [28]) are significant, serious difficulties arise in obtaining and interpreting the rate factor using experimental data. For instance, effects of inert gas-reactant and reactant-reactant molecule collisions are impossible to distinguish. Therefore, such parameters of the energy transfer as collision efficiency cannot be found simply even under limited pressure ranges. Moreover, if the main species responsible for the energy transfer is replaced because of certain changes in temperature or concentrations in nonequilibrium region (being still lower than E_b), a corresponding change may be found in the macroscopic rate factor observed.

B. Boltzmann Equations

It has already been shown that any chemical reaction may be considered one of the possible channels of energy exchange between particles undergoing collisions. Being similar to other channels, it has a statistic nature and may be characterized by its differential cross-section. This allows us to describe reaction results using a system of the Boltzmann equation*:

$$\left(\frac{\partial}{\partial t} + V\frac{\partial}{\partial r} + \frac{\bar{x}}{m}\frac{\partial}{\partial v}\right)f = \int |V - \tilde{V}|\,\sigma(f'\tilde{f}' - f\tilde{f})\,d\Omega\,d\tilde{V} \qquad [29]$$

The notations here are generally accepted (see, for instance, Refs. 1 and 65). The function f means the probability density for a given number of particles in a unit volume $(drdv)$ of the phase space. Hence, if this function is known, such characteristics of the system as densities and fluxes may be found.

The use of kinetic equations is one of the possible ways to develop a microscopic theory of chemical reactions. Nevertheless it should be observed that eq. [29] has a number of important drawbacks. It does not describe very fast processes, for instance (66). It is also well known that this equation cannot be derived irreproachably even taking into account only elastic collisions (see, for instance, Ref. 67); an assumption must be made that the cross-section for particle scattering does not depend on external fields. This assumption may prove to be too rough. Moreover, the Boltzmann equation does not take into account three-body collisions. It is at last essentially a classical equation while the objects it describes are in truth quantum-mechanical. Nevertheless the system of equations like

$$\left(\frac{\partial}{\partial t} + V_i\frac{\partial}{\partial r} + \frac{\bar{x}_i}{m_i}\frac{\partial}{\partial v_i}\right)f_i = \sum_{j=1}^{n} K_{ij}^1 f_i' f_j' - K_{ij}^2 f_i f_j)\,d\Omega\,dV_j \qquad [31]$$

has been applied rather successfully to describe gases with chemically reacting molecules (8,68–70). Usually these equations are used to derive generalized hydrodynamic equations, kinetic factors (as in Refs. 69 and 70), and sometimes

---

*The Boltzmann equation has been discussed thoroughly in the literature (see, for example, Ref. 1). Hence, only a few remarks will be made here concerning the nonequilibrium chemical kinetics problem. For the Boltzmann equation derivation, statistical independence of reacting species is to be assumed. Otherwise the reaction rate will not be proportionate to the reactant densities product but will also include a correlation function describing deviations from the statistical independence condition. The necessity of using this function is determined by initial conditions and the ratio of the interaction distance to the mean distance between reactant molecules. In the case of neutral particles and rarefied gases this ratio is small, so that statistical independence assumption may be applied to a macroscopic system. The statistical independence condition may therefore be described as

$$\frac{a}{\lambda} \approx Na^3 \ll 1 \qquad [30]$$

where a is the interaction distance, λ is the mean free path, and N is the total density (64).

equations similar to those of chemical kinetics (71). Equation [31] allows reactions of the type "two into two" to be described:

$$\alpha_1 + \alpha_2 \rightleftharpoons \beta_1 + \beta_2 \qquad [32]$$

Reactions like

$$\alpha_1 + \alpha_2 \rightleftharpoons \beta_1 + \beta_2 + \beta_3 \qquad [33]$$

should be described with an equation containing three-body collisions integral. Such an equation is also known (72–74).

Equations [29] and [31] have already been mentioned to be classical or at least quasiclassical (in the case when quantum differential cross-sections are used). Their quantum versions exist both for monoatomic (75) and polyatomic gases (76). In the latter work the effect of an external field upon particle collisions has been discussed. A method for composing quantum mechanical equations which describe many-body collisions is suggested in Refs. 77 and 78.

Unfortunately, the value of kinetic theory is essentially limited. For a number of reasons great difficulties arise in the solution of eqs. [29] and [31] (apart from more complex equations). The solution is mostly found with the Enskog-Chapman (79,80) or Grad (70,81,82) methods developed to solve eq. [31]. The former method can be applied within a "small vicinity" of the equilibrium distribution (chemical reactions have been shown to violate this distribution strongly); neither of them allows the determination of higher-order approaches due to rapid increase in calculation volume.

Moreover, the Enskog-Chapman procedure does not contain any criterion to determine what deviations from the equilibrium may be allowed.* Hence, the solution of every particular problem needs to be checked up on experimentally, and this is a weak point of the method. Linearization methods have been proved to be inapplicable to a number of cases (see Ref. 83, for example) since the interaction between similar particles is a nonlinear effect.

All these suggest that a digital computer be used as a means of obtaining some particular relations. However, equations of interest are so complex that it is very difficult to make a satisfactory scheme of calculations, so only a few attempts in this direction have been made (84,85), chemical reactions not included. Chemical reactions may be taken into account, of course, but computer time needed will probably turn out to be rather excessive even in the case of the simplest models. The possibility of using numerical methods may be founded upon the theorem proved in Ref. 86 that states eq. [29] to have a single solution within a certain period of time and a sequence of approximations properly arranged to converge evenly to that solution.

---

*In connection with this, an attempt of Alekseeff (87) to apply the Enskog method to the study of far-from-equilibrium systems is very interesting.

However, the Boltzmann equation has not yet been applied to the solution of nonequilibrium chemical kinetics problems. It has been used frequently only to analyze general peculiarities of chemical processes and to find general expressions for the corresponding terms in kinetic equations. Some results of this analysis will be discussed here briefly.

The solution of the Boltzmann equation has been considered in Ref. 16 for homogeneous, bimolecular, gas-phase and isothermic chemical reactions. The equation has been solved first for a system of particles having no internal degrees of freedom using the perturbation theory methods similar to that of Enskog. To find this procedure an assumption has been made that the momentum relaxation time is small compared to that of a chemical reaction. Taking only the zero-order term in the Enskog expansion yields ordinary macroscopic expression for the chemical reaction rate, with the rate factor independent of time and the reactants' chemical nature. An account of higher-order terms results in rate factor depending upon time and the reactants' chemical nature, the mass action law being violated.

Similar results have been obtained for a reacting system of particles having internal degrees of freedom.

Let us discuss briefly some points and mathematical methods developed in Ref. 16. The reaction $A + B \rightleftharpoons C + D$ will be considered. The following equations may be composed:

$$\frac{d(n_A f_A)}{dt} = \sum_M E_{AM} + R_A \tag{34}$$

(and analogously for the rest of the particles). Here

$$E_{AM} \equiv n_A n_M \int \cdots \int \frac{P}{\mu} \sigma_{AM}(P, \Omega)[f_A'(\mathbf{P}_A')f_M'(\mathbf{P}_M') - f_A(\mathbf{P}_A)f_M(\mathbf{P}_M)] \, dP_M \, d\Omega \tag{35}$$

$$R_A \equiv \int \cdots \int \frac{P}{\mu} \sigma_{AB}^*(P\Omega)[n_C n_D f_C(\mathbf{P}_C')f_D(\mathbf{P}_D') - n_A n_B f_A(\mathbf{P}_A)f_B(\mathbf{P}_B)] \, dP_B \, d\Omega \tag{36}$$

E_{AM} is integral of elastic collisions; R_A is the integral of collisions resulting in the chemical reaction; $n_M(t)$ is M-particle density depending on time; $f_M(\mathbf{P}_M, t)$ is one-particle distribution function normalized to unity; $\sigma_{AM}(P, \Omega)$ is differential cross-section for the elastic scattering; $P = |\mathbf{P}_A - \mathbf{P}_M| = |\mathbf{P}_A' - \mathbf{P}_M'|$ is the invariant module of relative momentum; $\sigma_{AB}^*(P, \Omega)$ is the differential cross-section for chemical reaction as a function of $P = |\mathbf{P}_A - \mathbf{P}_B|$ and the solid angle Ω for scattering; μ is the reduced mass of colliding particles.

If internal degrees of freedom must be accounted for, the following equation is valid:

$$\frac{\partial(n_{iA} f_{iA})}{\partial t} = \sum_{j,M} E_{AM}(ij) + \sum_{j,k,l,M} I_{AM}\left(\frac{kl}{ij}\right) + \sum_{j,k,l} R_A\left(\frac{kl}{ij}\right) \qquad [37]$$

where

$$E_{AM}(ij) = n_{iA} n_{jM} \int \cdots \int \frac{P}{\mu} \sigma_{AM}(ij; P, \Omega)[f'_{iA} f'_{jM} - f_{iA} f_{jM}] \, d\mathbf{P}_M \, d\Omega \qquad [38]$$

$$I_{AM}\left(\frac{kl}{ij}\right) \equiv \int \cdots \int \frac{P}{\mu} \sigma_{AM}\left(\frac{kl}{ij}; P, \Omega\right)$$

$$\times [n_{kA} n_{lM} f'_{kA} f'_{lM} - n_{AM} n_{jM} f_{iA} f_{jM}] \, d\mathbf{P}_M \, d\Omega \qquad [39]$$

$$R_A\left(\frac{kl}{ij}\right) \equiv \int \cdots \int \frac{P}{\mu} \sigma^*\left(\frac{kl}{ij}; P\Omega\right)[n_{kC} n_{lD} f'_{kl} f'_{lD} - n_{iA} n_{jB} f_{iA} f_{jB}] \, d\mathbf{P}_B \, d\Omega$$

$$[40]$$

In these expressions $E_{AM}(ij)$ is the integral of elastic collisions between A molecule in a quantum state i and M molecule in a quantum state j, $I_{AM}(kl/ij)$ is the integral of inelastic collisions between A and M molecules resulting in internal transitions; $R_A(kl/ij)$ is the integral of inelastic collisions resulting in chemical reactions such as

$$A(i) + B(j) \; \xrightleftharpoons{} \; C(k) + D(l) \qquad [41]$$

If we make some assumptions these equations may be tranformed and integrated. The results obtained are in general not progressive and this work (16) should be considered preparative for much more interesting work (88). Chemical reactions have been pointed out above to perturb distributions over both internal and translational degrees of freedom (cf. for example (89–98)). In the work (88) the development of just this physically reasonable point has been made. The reaction $A + B \rightleftharpoons C + D$ has been considered (or its specific version $A + M \rightleftharpoons B + M$ under a great excess of the inert gas M).

The equation for A-reactant is

$$-\frac{dn_A}{dt} = K_{f,t} n_A n_B - K_{r,t} n_C n_D \qquad [42]$$

where $K_{f,t}$ and $K_{r,t}$ are rate factors obtained by an averaging of the corresponding cross-sections over the nonequilibrium distribution. In general, $K_{f,t}$ and $K_{r,t}$ depend on reacting mixture composition and only under chemical equilibrium conditions does the ratio of these factors amount to the equilibrium constant K. The rate factors corresponding to the equilibrium distribution are $K_{f,t}^{(o)}$ and $K_{r,t}^{(o)}$ so that $K = \dfrac{K_{f,t}^{(o)}}{K_{r,t}^{(o)}}$. In ordinary kinetic expression

$$-\frac{dn_A}{dt} = K_f n_A n_B - K_r n_C n_D \qquad [43]$$

where K_f and K_r do not depend evidently upon the composition and time and $K = K_f K_r$.

Rice (99,100) observed in the case of dissociation and recombination reactions that

$$K_{f,t} > K_f \quad \text{and} \quad K_{r,t} > K_r \qquad [44]$$

For the reaction under consideration eq. [43] may be derived from eq. [42] and the quantities $K_{f,t}$ and $K_{r,t}$ reduce to K_f and K_r, respectively, provided (1) one reactant is present in great excess and (2) the reaction rate is sufficiently small that perturbations produced by the reaction are negligible for the distribution over internal degrees of freedom.

To calculate rate factors the values of cross-sections for chemical reactions and for inelastic collisions between reactants and reaction products are necessary.

Let us consider a homogeneous isothermic mixture of ideal gases acted upon by external forces. Every reactant and product of A, B, C, and D may be present in internal quantum states. Time-evolution of such a system is described by eq. [37]. Assuming the distribution over the translational degree of freedom to be Maxwellian and integrating over $\mathbf{P}_A$ yields:

$$\frac{dn_{iA}}{dt} = \sum_{j,k,l,M}^{V} \left[K_{AM}\left(\frac{kl}{ij}\right) n_{kA} n_{lM} - K_{AM}\left(\frac{ij}{kl}\right) n_{iA} n_{jM} \right]$$

$$+ \sum_{j,k,l} \left[K_r\left(\frac{kl}{ij}\right) n_{kC} n_{lD} - K_f\left(\frac{ij}{kl}\right) n_{iA} n_{jB} \right] \qquad [45]$$

where

$$K_{AM}\left(\frac{ij}{kl}\right) = \iiint \frac{P_{AM}}{\mu_{AM}} \sigma_{AM}\left(\frac{ij}{kl}; P_{AM}, \Omega\right) f_A^{(o)} f_M^{(o)} \, d\Omega \, d\mathbf{P}_A \, d\mathbf{P}_M \qquad [46]$$

$$K_r\left(\frac{kl}{ij}\right) = \iiint \frac{P_{CD}}{\mu_{CD}} \sigma_{CD}^*\left(\frac{kl}{ij}; P_{CD}, \Omega\right) f_C^{(o)} f_D^{(o)} \, d\Omega \, d\mathbf{P}_C \, d\mathbf{P}_D \qquad [47]$$

$$K_f\left(\frac{ij}{kl}\right) = \iiint \frac{P_{AB}}{\mu_{AB}} \sigma_{AB}^*\left(\frac{ij}{kl}; P_{AB}, \Omega\right) f_A^{(o)} f_B^{(o)} \, d\Omega \, d\mathbf{P}_A \, d\mathbf{P}_B \qquad [48]$$

Let us introduce $X_{iM} = n_{iM}/n_M$ which after some time depends on time inexplicitly (through n_A, n_B, n_C, and n_D).

Making summation over A in eq. [45] yields eq. [42] in which

$$K_{f,t} = \sum_{i,j,k,l} X_{iA} X_{jB} X_f\left(\frac{ij}{kl}\right)$$

$$K_{r,t} = \sum_{i,j,k,l} X_{kC} X_{lD} X_r\left(\frac{kl}{ij}\right)$$

$$[49]$$

These factors depend on time inexplicitly (through concentrations).
When the ordinary eq. [43] of chemical kinetics is valid these factors reduce
to K_f and K_r. There are three cases when this takes place.

1. For the reaction $A + B \rightleftharpoons C + D$ provided one of the reactants is
present in great excess;

2. For the reaction $A + B \rightleftharpoons C + D$ occurring so slowly that the distribution is perturbed negligibly over the internal degrees of freedom of A, B, C,
and D molecules.

3. For the reaction $A + M \rightleftharpoons B + M$ occurring under a great excess of
inert gas molecules M.

In general, an experimental measurement of $K_{f,t}$ and $K_{r,t}$ is rather difficult.
It requires the cross-sections for chemical reactions to be measured together
with nonequilibrium distributions over internal states during the reaction
occurrence. There is a certain progress in the measurements of these quantities,
but at present reasonably accurate measurements of the theoretical rate
factors may be performed only for systems where these factors are reduced to
$K_{f,t}^{(o)}$ and $K_{r,t}^{(o)}$.

The calculations of other rate factors requires cross-sections, both for
chemical reactions and inelastic collisions, to be known. These cross-sections
may principally be obtained from either very accurate experimental scattering
measurements or theoretical calculations of scattering. If the values of cross-
sections are known they may be used to determine nonequilibrium internal
distribution. Then the quantities $K_{f,t}$ and $K_{r,t}$ may be found using a proper
averaging procedure. To calculate $K_{f,t}^{(o)}$ and $K_{r,t}^{(o)}$ it is sufficient to know the
values of cross-sections and the equilibrium internal distribution.

Thus, even phenomenological rate factors depend on inelastic cross-sections.
Hence, temperature variations of these factors are determined not by chemical
reaction cross-sections only. This point is very important in the dissociation
and recombination theory of diatomic molecules where rate constants had to
be considered as dependent upon inelastic cross-sections to explain their
abnormal temperature dependence.

C. The Schrödinger Equation and Quantum Mechanical Probability for the Reaction

Quatum-mechanical calculations are evidently the most accurate at present.
However, great difficulties arise in the performing of these calculations even if
electronic digital computers are used, since the potential energy surfaces have
to be known. Such information is poor, especially concerning rather complex
systems, and also is difficult to obtain.

Let us consider a numerical method developed in Ref. (106) as an example of
a quantum-mechanical treatment. An exchange reaction of the type $BC + A \rightarrow$

$\rightarrow B + CA$ occurring at temperature T was considered. The reaction was the result of colinear collisions, the molecule BC being initially either in the ground or in the first vibrational state. A sufficiently general method for numerical integration of the nonstationary Schrödinger equation allows the use of triatomic potential surfaces. To find an averaged quantum-mechanical probability for the above exchange reaction was the purpose of the calculations making use of triatomic functions of interatomic distances.

The quantum-mechanical probability $K(i, P_A)$ for the exchange reaction depends on relative momentum P_A of A and BC particles and in what vibrational state i the BC molecule is present.

An experimental study of a gas-phase reaction results in the reaction probability being averaged over the totality of relative momenta and other impact characteristics. Hence, a numerical procedure is developed in Ref. (106) to determine directly the quantity $K(i, P_A)$ averaged overall momenta,

$$\langle K(i) \rangle = \int F(P_A) K(i, P_A) \, dP_A \qquad [50]$$

where $F(P_A)$ is the ratio of the number of collisions occurring per second with the relative momentum P_A to the total number of collisions.

The form of the $F(P_A)$ function was selected using the results of the work (107) and may be described as

$$F(P_A) \, dP_A = \begin{cases} \dfrac{(\mu_A kT)^{-2}}{2} |P|^3 \exp\left[-\dfrac{P_A^2}{(2\mu_A kT)}\right] dP_A; & P_A \leqslant 0 \\ 0; & P_A > 0 \end{cases} \qquad [51]$$

The averaged reaction probability $\langle K \rangle$ is then

$$\langle K \rangle = \frac{\sum_i \langle K(i) \rangle \exp\left[-\dfrac{E_{iv}}{kT}\right]}{\sum_i \exp\left[-\dfrac{E_{iv}}{kT}\right]} \qquad [52]$$

where E_{iv} is the vibrational energy of the molecule in the i-vibrational state.

Let us write the Schrödinger equation for a colinear triatomic system in coordinate system relative to the center of mass with its origin placed at the C atom:

$$i\hbar \frac{\partial \psi}{\partial t} = -\frac{\hbar^2}{2}\left\{\frac{1}{m_1} + \frac{1}{m_2}\frac{\partial^2}{\partial r_1^2} + \left(\frac{1}{m_2} + \frac{1}{m_3}\right)\frac{\partial}{\partial r^2} - \frac{2}{m_2}\frac{\partial^2}{\partial r \, \partial r_2}\right\}\psi + V(r_1, r_2)\psi \qquad [53]$$

where m_1, m_2, and m_3 are masses of B, C, and A atoms, respectively; r_1 is the distance between B and C atoms in the BC molecule, r_2 is the distance between the incident A atom and C atom; $V(r_1, r_2)$ is the potential energy for the three atoms' interaction which is calculated by quantum-mechanical methods (107,108). Isopotential curves for this energy are shown in Fig. 4. A

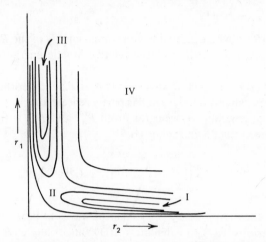

Figure 4 The potential energy surface as a function of interatomic distances for a tri-atomic system; r_1 is the distance between C atom (of the BC molecules) and the incident A atom.

point in the region I corresponds to a configuration in which r_1 is about the intermolecular equilibrium distance, and r_2 is so great that there is practically no interaction between BC and A.

The point O in the configuration space where the energy of interaction between BC and A is practically zero, and potential energy of the BC molecule is minimum, is taken for zero-potential-energy configuration. The points in the region IV of the configuration space correspond to the three separated atoms and are not considered because the total energy of the $(BC + A)$ system is significantly less than the BC molecular dissociation energy.

The packet of waves representing the colliding system's initial state with the averaged relative momentum $P_A^{(0)}$ (of the A atom and the BC molecule center of mass) and with the BC molecule present in i-vibrational state may be described as

$$\psi(r_1, r_2 ; 0) = \psi_{ir}(r_1) \cdot \psi_{tr}(R_A ; P_A^{(0)}) \qquad [54]$$

where $R_A = r_2 + (m_1/m_1 + m_2)r_1$ is the distance between A and BC center of mass, and

$$\psi_{tr}(R_A ; P_A^{(0)}) = (2\pi\delta^2)^{-1/4} \exp\left\{ -\frac{(R_A - P_A^{(0)})^2}{4\delta^2} + iP_A^{(0)} \frac{R_A}{h} \right\} \qquad [55]$$

In the region I the system energy is calculated using the expression

$$\iint_{\text{region I}} \psi^*(r_1, r_2, 0) H \psi(r, r_2, 0)\, dr_1\, dr_2 \qquad [56]$$

is $E_{iv} + (1/2\mu_A)P_A^{(0)2}$ where E_{iv} is the vibrational energy of the BC molecule in the i state; $(1/2\mu_A)P_A^{(0)2}$ is the average relative kinetic energy of BC and A before the collision.

Moving further, the packet of waves [54] approaches the corner of region II, partly passes through its boundary and is partly reflected back. The probability for the exchange reaction to occur (at given $P_A^{(0)}$ and E_{iv}) is the probability that the reacting system is in region III,

$$K(E_{iv}, P_A^{(0)}) = \iint_{\text{region III}} |\psi(r_1, r_2, t_f)|^2\, dr_1\, dr_2 \qquad [57]$$

where t_f is the time required by the packet of waves to pass into region III.

There are various ways to calculate $\langle K(i) \rangle$ but in any case the following physical assumptions are necessary concerning the packet of waves and the reacting system:

1. The initial packet of waves $\psi(r_1, r_2, 0)$ is placed in region I and may be expressed as the product of two probability functions.

$$\psi(r_1, r_2, 0) = \psi_0(r_1)\psi(R_A) \qquad [58]$$

where $\psi(R_A)$ is composed of numerous negative components of the relative momentum and $\psi(r_1)$ relates only to the vibrational state of BC. In this case

$$|\psi(r_1, r_2, 0)|^2 \longrightarrow 0 \quad \text{when} \quad R_A \longrightarrow 0 \quad \text{or} \quad R_A \longrightarrow \infty$$

2. After a sufficiently great time t_f the packet of waves is composed of two parts, one moving on to region III and the other backward to region I. Moreover, at the time t_f the centers of both packets are far from the corner of region II so that in this region $|\psi(r_1, r_2, t_f)|^2 \sim 0$

3. Stationary solutions of the Schrödinger equation [53] exist in the form

$$\psi^{(E)}(r_1, r_2) \exp\left(-\frac{iEt}{\hbar}\right)$$

where $i = \sqrt{-1}$ and E is the total energy. The solutions of the type $\psi^{(E)}(r_1, r_2)$, which are considered in the case of the exchange reaction, may be described asymptotically in regions I and III, respectively, as:

region I

$$\psi_{iA}^{(E)}(r_1, r_2) \sim \psi_{iA}(r_1) \exp\left(-\frac{iP_A R_A}{\hbar}\right) + \sum B_{iA,i'_A}^{P_A;P'_A} \psi_{iA}(r_1) \exp\left(\frac{iP_A R_A}{\hbar}\right)$$

[59]

and

region III

$$\psi_{iB}^{(E)}(r_1 r_2) \sim \sum K_{iA;iB}^{P_A;P_B} \psi_{iB}(r_2) \exp\left(\frac{iP_B R_B}{\hbar}\right)$$

[60]

The quantities iA, P_A, and R_A relate to a vibrational state of the BC molecule, A momentum being relative to the mass center of BC and A momentums corresponding coordinate, respectively; the quantities $i'A$, P'_A describe the reflected state of the $(BC + A)$ system in which no reaction occurs, this energy state still being equal to E; the quantities iB, P_B, R_B relate to a vibrational state of the CA molecule, B momentum being relative to the mass center of CA and B momentums corresponding coordinate, respectively.

The values of passed and reflected amplitudes $K_{iA,iB}^{P_A;P_B}$ and $K_{iA,i'_A}^{P_A;P'_A}$ deposed on the interaction potential $V(r_1, r_2)$ and masses m_1, m_2, m_3.

Reducing the expressions obtained yields a relation for the probability amplitude $\psi(R_A)$ which is sufficiently convenient to be numerically treated using electronic computers.

The details of calculations and expressions used may be found in Ref. (106).

Thus a detailed knowledge of the potential energy surface is necessary for quantum-mechanical calculations to be carried out. The same must be known in the reaction absolute rates theory that includes the calculation of the potential energy surfaces for a reacting system and relates real rates of reactions to these potential surfaces. These points have been studied by Eyring and his associates (9) assuming the equilibrium to occur between reactants and activated complexes that exist within the vicinity of the " saddlewise " point on the potential energy surface. Such equilibrium assumption cannot be rigorously founded and to obtain more accurate data on interaction of reacting particles their motion equations have to be solved, the potential energy surfaces accounting for coupling of particles.

Great difficulties arise (especially for polyatomic molecules) from actually rigorous quantum-mechanical calculations in which reflection and passing of the wave packets are considered in the fields of much more complex form than those shown in Fig. 4.

It is also difficult to judge which way is simpler—to determine the values of cross-sections or to find the potential energy surfaces in complex cases. However, some progress in the solution of these difficult problems has been made during the last few years because of the rapid development of computation mathematics and electronic digital computer technique.

D. The S-matrix

A rule must be found in quantum-mechanics that would make it possible to compare the initial and final states of a system characterized by a set of quantum numbers describing both the motion and the structure of the particles involved.

Let a wave function $\psi_n(x)$ describe a state of the system where n is the notation for a set of quantum numbers which define this state, and x is a set of variables. The Schrödinger equation for this function is

$$i \frac{\partial \psi}{\partial t} = \hat{H}\psi \qquad [61]$$

If Δt is a certain period of time, then

$$\psi(t + \Delta t) = \psi(t) - i \int_t^{t + \Delta t} \hat{H}\psi(t)\, dt \qquad [62]$$

and an operator may be introduced as

$$\hat{u}(t + \Delta t, t) = 1 - i \hat{H} \Delta t \qquad [63]$$

which transforms the function ψ at the moment t into that at $(t + \Delta t)$. The integral operator $\hat{u}(t, t_0)$ transforms then $\psi(t_0)$ into $\psi(t)$ where $(t - t_0)$ is a finite termination. It is not diffcult to show that

$$i \frac{\partial \hat{u}}{\partial t} = \hat{H}\hat{u} \qquad [64]$$

Now the reaction of the type "two into two" will be considered: $A + B \rightarrow C + D$.

Equation [61] has a solution ψ that becomes $\psi_i(x)$ as $t \rightarrow -\infty$, the function $\psi_i(x)$ describing two noninteracting particles A and B. As $t \rightarrow +\infty$ the function ψ describes two noninteracting particles C and D. Since in any experiment the states of noninteracting particles are observed before and after the collision, that is, at $t \rightarrow -\infty$ and $t \rightarrow +\infty$, respectively, an operator should be found which transforms $\psi(-\infty)$ into $\psi(+\infty)$ so that

$$\lim \hat{u}(t, t_0) = \hat{S}, \qquad t_0 \rightarrow -\infty, \qquad t \rightarrow +\infty \qquad [65]$$

$$\psi_f(+\infty) = \hat{S}\psi_i(-\infty)$$

The operator $\hat{S}$ is usually called S-matrix. Let us show the squares of the S-matrix elements to determine the probability of the transition from the initial to final state (the probability for the dynamic variables to be of certain values at the final state provided they were given at the initial state).

Let us expand $\psi_i(-\infty)$ and $\psi_f(+\infty)$ in eigenfunctions of an operator $\hat{Q}$ which describes a dynamic variable

$$\hat{Q}\psi_q = qW_q, \qquad [66]$$

where q are eigenvalues of $\hat{Q}$,

$$\psi_i(-\infty) = \sum_q C_q^i \psi_q$$
$$\psi_f(+\infty) = \sum_q C_q^f \psi_q \qquad [67]$$

Substituting these expansions into eq. [66] yields

$$C_q^f = \sum_q S_{q'q} C_q^i \qquad [68]$$

At the initial moment let $q = q_0$ so that $C_q^i = \delta_{qq_0}$ where δ_{qq_0} is the Kronecker symbol. Then

$$C_{q'}^f = S_{q'q_0} \qquad [69]$$

Since $|C_{q'}^f|^2$ is the probability for the variable q' to be at the state f the quantity $|S_{q'q_0}|^2$ determines the probability of the transition from the state q_0 into the state q'.

As the function ψ is orthogonally normalized and the S-matrix is unitary the diagonal elements of the latter must satisfy the following equation:

$$\sum_j |S_{ij}|^2 = 1 \qquad [70]$$

which means that the sum of all the transition probabilities is equal to unity.

Making use of the S-matrix properties a relativistically invariant expression may be found for the cross-section (Möller formula). A general quantum-mechanical expression for the cross-section presented in Ref. 57 may be reduced in the quasiclassical case to a simple formula

$$\sigma = \pi\lambda^2(2l' + 1) \qquad [71]$$

where λ is the De Broglie wavelength and l' is the orbital momentum of particles which may take part in the reaction. The square of the matrix element of the S-matrix for the corresponding reaction is assumed here to be equal to unity as well. From the theory of the S-matrix a few general conclusions may be drawn concerning the cross-sections for the elastic and nonelastic processes.

1. The partial cross-section of any nonelastic process cannot be in excess of $\pi\lambda^2(2l' + 1)$.

2. All the nonelastic processes are always accompanied by simultaneous elastic scattering processes.

3.   The scattering process may be described with a set of real parameters (phases). If the characteristic distance of interaction is about the wavelength of particles involved, the cross-section may be determined to a high accuracy with a small number of phases.

The S-matrix is used widely in nuclear reaction studies.*

E. The Green Function

The Green quantum-mechanical function has been applied to the study of chemical kinetics in Refs. 103 and 104 in accordance with the Kadanoff and Baym approach (102). This approach is based upon the principle that properties of like particle systems may be conveniently described using Heisenberg operators of formation $\psi^+(r, t)$ and destruction $\psi(r, t)$. The former operator modifies the system state by adding one particle to this state at a space-time point (r, t), while the latter removes one particle from the same point. All the macroscopic operators may be expressed through the product of ψ and ψ^+ operators.

Green's one-particle function may be defined as follows:

$$G(\mathbf{r}, t, \mathbf{r}_1 t_1) = \frac{1}{i} \langle T(\psi(\mathbf{r}, t)\psi^+(\mathbf{r}, t)) \rangle \qquad [72]$$

where T is an operator which acts upon the operators' products and arranges them so that operators relating to an earlier moment of time are placed to the right of operators relating to a later moment of time. The Green one-particle function describes the propagation of a perturbation under which one particle is added to or removed from a many-particle equilibrium system. The authors of Ref. 104 use the results of the work (105) which show experimental data to be in disagreement with a calculated time of relaxation τ for a fast chemical reaction of the type $A + B \rightleftharpoons C$. Near the equilibrium,

$$\tau = \frac{1}{K_{12}} (n_A + n_B) \qquad [73]$$

where n_A and n_B are equilibrium densities of the reactants A and B, respectively. The authors of Ref. 104 suggested that this disagreement is due to the fact that the linearized kinetic equation describing the relaxation time is actually

*A profound analogy apparently exists between nonequilibrium chemical kinetics (being yet under development) and some approaches of nuclear reaction kinematics. An account of the latter was made in Ref. 101. This analogy will be observed to become still more profound and important when the necessity of explaining experimental results requires us to develop relativistic nonequilibrium chemical kinetics. Such a situation is surely not so far off, but this interesting point is beyond the scope of the present survey.

insufficient since it involves only Markov terms. Using the Hamiltonian for this reaction and calculating the Green function with methods developed by the authors of Ref. 102 a kinetic equation may be composed which involves both Markov and non-Markov terms:

$$\frac{\partial n_A}{\partial t} = [K_{12} n_A n_B - K_{21} n_C] - K_{12} n_A n_B (n_A + n_B)\alpha_1$$

$$+ K_{21} n_C (n_A + n_B)\alpha_1 + K_{12}(n_A n_B - K_{21} n_C)\alpha_2 \quad [74]$$

Here the square parentheses contain ordinary Markov terms and the others are correction (non-Markov) terms. The terms containing certain integral expressions α_1 and α_2 account for non-Markov chemical reactions. Calculations that have resulted in this equation are rather cumbersome and will not be discussed here. The authors of Ref. 102 have evaluated numerically the ratio

$$\frac{K_{12} n_A n_B (n_A + n_B)\alpha_1}{K_{12} n_A n_B} = (n_A + n_B)\alpha_1 \quad [75]$$

which is seen to be dependent on both the concentrations and α_1. In particular case ($U_0 = 10^2$, $T = 10^2$, and the constant Γ contained in the expression for the Bright-Wigner cross-section is equal to zero) the results of corresponding calculations are given in Table 5.

TABLE 5
Calculated correction (non-Markov) terms

K_{12}	Concentrations, mole cm^{-3}	$\dfrac{\text{Correction term}}{\text{main term}}$, %
10^{12}	10^{-3}	0.01
10^{12}	10^{-1}	1.0
10^{13}	10^{-3}	0.1
10^{13}	10^{-1}	10.0

The correction term is seen from the table to be significant in the case of comparatively fast reactions and small concentrations, so that the time may become a nonlinear variable for the reaction. All these calculations are valid near the equilibrium. Let us now see how the correction term changes with temperature. The expression for α_1 is as follows:

$$\alpha_1 \sim \exp\left(\frac{U_0}{kT}\right) I(\overline{U}, T) \quad [76]$$

where

$$I(\overline{U}, \dot{T}) = \int_0^\infty E^{1/2} \frac{[(E - U_0)/K)^2 - \Gamma^2]}{[K^{3/2}(E - U_0)/K)^2 + \Gamma^2]} \exp\left(-\frac{E}{kT}\right) dE \quad [76a]$$

The latter integral I has been shown to rise with temperature. Therefore, α_1 is increased with temperature as well. However, in general the behavior of α_1 is not quite clear because of the complexity of the expression [76a].

F. The Hamilton Equation with Pseudo-stochastic Initial Conditions

The modern computing techniques allow us to carry out numerical integration of rather complicated differential equation systems. Therefore, the problem of the study of collisions can be solved for as many particles and collisions that the results obtained (both under classical and quantum-mechanical treatment) may be representative of a gas with a great number of particles. From such a solution a great deal of information can naturally be obtained concerning the dynamics of collisions. It is also possible to combine this solution with results obtained by using some statistical approaches.

This combined method seems to be very fruitful, especially in the case when a combination of dynamic and Monte Carlo methods is used. It implies in truth a direct solution of the Liouville equation with a corresponding selection of pseudo-stochastic initial conditions.

Wall, Hiller and Mazur (21), using the classical approach, have solved the problem of the frontal collision of H_2 molecule with H atom by considering a general case of noncolinear collisions. Initial pseudo-stochastic conditions have been used to account for the fact that at the initial state the molecule may have different values of translational, rotational, and vibrational energies.

The space disposition of atoms considered was arbitrary. The potential energy of the system was represented as a function of the three distances r_{12}, r_{13}, and r_{23} of the London-Polanyi-Eyring type. As the system was characterized with nine coordinates and nine momenta the Hamilton 18 equations had to be integrated. However, the number of these equations was reduced from 18 to 12 using the integral of the center-of-mass motion. To do this new coordinates were introduced: Cartesian coordinates of the first and the second atoms relative to the third one and initial coordinates of the third atom. Six initial components of the momenta of the first and the second atom and three components of the whole system form the new momenta system. By this tangent transformation of variables the Hamilton equation is preserved (109,110). The new Hamiltonian lacks three coordinates of the third atom. Moreover, the three components of the system momentum correspond to the integrals of the third atom coordinates and are therefore constants.

These are conveniently taken as equal to zero, which implies the center of mass of the system to be at rest.

The Hamiltonian of the system is

$$H = T(P_1 \dots P_6) + V(q_1 \dots q_6) \qquad [77]$$

and the equation of motion

$$\frac{\partial H}{\partial P_i} = \dot{q}_i \qquad \frac{\partial H}{\partial q_i} = -\dot{P}_i \qquad [78]$$

If $|q_i|_{t=0}$ and $|P_i|_{t=0}$ are given an integration of the Hamilton equations will result in the values of q and p for any $t > 0$. Such a solution has been carried out numerically using the Runge-Kutta-procedure.*

The number of the equations may be diminished still more by making use of the fact that H and M must be constant (where M is momentum's momentum). However, it proves better to preserve the 12 equations and use corresponding relations for H and M to check up on the results of calculations. Deviations from these relations show the errors of calculations and the necessity of correcting the numerical integration procedure. Solutions of the motion equation for 700 collisions showed most collisions to be " sliding " ones resulting in energy transfer but with no particle transfer (an exchange reaction has been considered). Only six of these 700 collisions result in the exchange reaction, the initial molecule having zero rotational energy in four of these six cases and having small rotational energy in the other two cases. The reaction probability is maximum when the potential energy of the tri-atomic system is minimum. The latter occurs provided the system is colinear. Thus the effect of rotation on the reaction probability is determined using the fact that a molecule having a significant potential energy cannot possibly form a colinear configuration on collisions with atoms.

The effect of vibrational energy on the chemical reaction should be observed. An increase in the vibrational energy does not lead to the increase in the reaction probability. However, in five of the above six cases the reaction is accompanied by a decrease in the vibrational energy. This suggests that the molecule having initially small rotational and some vibrational energies is transformed into a molecule with smaller vibrational energy but with higher rotational energy. It is the most general conclusion drawn from these calculations.

*The potential energy of the diatomic molecule is approached with the Morse function under the following conditions: the energy of dissociation $D = 108.5$ kcal mole^{-1}, the equilibrium internuclear distance $r_o = 0.74$Å, the frequency of harmonic vibration $v_o = 1.379 \times 10^{14}$ sec^{-1}. The time interval corresponding to one step of the numerical integration procedure is taken as 2.01×10^{-16} sec; it was small as compared to the period of H_2 inherent vibration and suitable for the Runge-Kutta-Gill method to be applied (111).

The dynamic method has been applied, for example, to compute equilibrium and thermodynamic properties of liquids and liquid argon in particular (112, 113). In both works equations of motion have been solved for 864 particles using the Lennard-Jones potential curve. The results of these calculations proved to be in a reasonable agreement with experimental data available and showed that the argon equilibrium state may be described with a binary potential.

G. The Hamilton-Jacobi Equation and Its Analytical Solution for the Exchange Reaction

Any mechanical motion (including collisions resulting in mass rearrangements, that is, chemical reactions) may be considered as progressive development of the contact transformation (109,110). The generating function S of this transformation must satisfy the Hamilton-Jacobi partial differential equation which may be solved completely provided the S function can possibly be presented in the form

$$S = S_1(q_1) + S_2(q_2) + \ldots + S_n(q_n) \tag{79}$$

In such a case the S function is usually called separable. If the solution [79] exists the momentum

$$P_k = \frac{\partial S}{\partial q_k} = \frac{\partial S_k(q_k)}{\partial q_k} \tag{80}$$

becomes dependent only upon q_k. After the separation

$$P_k = f_k(q_k, \alpha_1 \ldots \alpha_{n-1}, E) \tag{81}$$

where $\alpha_1 \ldots \alpha_{n-1}$ are arbitrary constants appearing as a result of the separation of variables; E is the system's total energy.

As a result, the solution for S_k may be obtained through quadratives as

$$S_k = \int f_k(q_k, \alpha_1 \ldots \alpha_{n-1}, E)\, dq_k + C_k \tag{82}$$

Thus the correct selection of variables completely determines the procedure of the Hamilton-Jacobi equation solution for any problem considered. The separation procedure, being impossible to carry out in a given coordinate system, may be successfully performed using a corresponding canonical transformation of coordinates resulting in $P_k = P_k(q_k)$.

The authors of Refs. 117–119 used the Hamilton-Jacobi equation to study a bimolecular reaction of the type $AB + C \rightarrow A + BC$.

In these works the problem of the dynamic description of the systems motion along the potential energy surface was considered for the above reactions in the cases of linear (117) and planar (119) collisions. A coordinate system was introduced (called by Markus the "natural collision coordinates") which allowed the transition from reacting particles system before collisions to that of reaction products after collisions to be smooth.

Let us consider the potential energy path that is at the "valley" corresponding to the configuration of the initial reactants. This path is finished at the reaction product "valley" and passes through a "hill" placed between the two valleys. We shall call such a curve the "reaction path" in the coordinate space. It is a curved path in the interaction region and a straight path in the regions of separated reactants and reaction products. A motion normal to this path is vibrational. Let us mark the reaction path curve with C; let the distance from a point in the space to the nearest point on this curve be X and the path length along the curve C from the beginning to the latter point be S. The kinetic energy may be described then as

$$T = \left(\frac{P_X^2}{2\mu}\right) + P_s^2[2\mu(1 + kX)^2] \qquad [83]$$

where K is the curvature of the curve C at the point (X, S) and μ is the reduced mass of the representing point.

The potential energy is

$$V = V_1(S) + V_2(X, S) \qquad [84]$$

$$V_2(0, S) = 0 \qquad [85]$$

where $V_1(S)$ is the potential energy along the curve C and $V_2(X, S)$ is defined pith both eqs. [84] and [85]. If the curve C is the reaction path then $C_2(X, S)$ is the vibrational potential energy of the Morse type which depends on X and may slightly depend on S.

The Hamilton-Jacobi equation may be written using [84] and [85] as

$$\left(\frac{1}{2\mu(1 + kX)^2}\right)\left[\left(\frac{\partial W}{\partial S}\right)^2 + 2\mu V_1(S)\right] + \frac{1}{2\mu}\left(\frac{\partial W}{\partial X}\right)^2 + U_2(X, S) = \alpha_1 \quad [86]$$

where

$$U_2(X, S) = [1 - (1 + kX)^{-2}]V_1(S) + V_2(X, S); \qquad [87]$$

α_1 is the total energy, $W(X, S, \alpha)$ is a Hamiltonian characteristic function. The latter is the generating function for the canonical transformation

$$P_i = \frac{\partial W}{\partial q_i} \qquad Q_i = \frac{\partial W}{\partial \alpha_i} \qquad [88]$$

where P_i, q_i are initial (before collisions) momenta (P_X, P_S) and coordinates (X, S), respectively. The motion constants are new momenta and Q_i are new coordinates. For some potential surfaces $U_2(X, S)$ depends slightly upon S and to a first approximation

$$W \cong W_1(S, \alpha) + W_2(X, \alpha) \qquad [89]$$

From eq. [87] it may be found then as follows:

$$(2\mu)^{-1}\left(\frac{\partial W_1}{\partial S}\right)^2 + V_1(S) = \left[-(2\mu)^{-1}\left(\frac{\partial W_2}{\partial X}\right)^2 + \alpha_1 - U_2(X, S)\right][(1 + kX)^2] \qquad [90]$$

The left part of this equation does not depend on X. If the right part were not dependent on S both the parts would be equal to the constant quantity α_2. However, the right part, and thus α_2, depend slightly upon S allowing an adiabatic approximation to be used as

$$(2\mu)^{-1}\left(\frac{dW_1}{dS}\right)^2 + V_1(S) = \alpha_2(S) \qquad [91]$$

$$(2\mu)^{-1}\left(\frac{dW_2}{dX}\right) + U_2(X, S) + \left[\frac{\alpha_2}{(1 + kX)^2}\right] = \alpha_1 \qquad [92]$$

Since $P_s = dW_1/ds$ the quantity α_2 is a slowly varying energy for the angular motion which is described with the curve C.

Let us introduce a function $U_3(X, S)$ to represent the effective potential energy of the vibrational motion as

$$U_3(X, S) = U_2(X, S) + \left[\frac{\alpha_2}{(1 + kX)^2}\right] \qquad [93]$$

This function is minimum at $X = X_0$. Therefore

$$\frac{\partial V_2(X_0, S)}{\partial X_0} = (\alpha_2 - V_1)\frac{2k}{(1 + kX_0)^3} \qquad [94]$$

The curve $X = X_0(S)$ is the reaction coordinate. If the curve C is the reaction path, then functions $V_1(S)$ and $V_2(X, S)$ may be expressed simply. Let us take the curve C so that $X_0(S) = 0$. Then C becomes the reaction coordinate and according to eq. [94]

$$\frac{\partial V_2(X_0, S)}{\partial X_0} = (\alpha_2 - V_1)2k \qquad [95]$$

Equation [90] may be written as

$$\left[(2\mu)^{-1}\left(\frac{\partial W_2}{\partial X}\right)^2 + U_3(X,S) - U_3(X_0,S)\right]$$

$$+ V_1(S) + V_2(X_0,S) + \left\{\frac{P_S^2}{2\mu(1+kX)^2}\right\} = \alpha_1 \quad [96]$$

The term in the square brackets is the local vibrational energy at the point S. The sum of the next two terms is the potential energy corresponding to the point S at the reaction coordinate because $V_1(S)$ is the potential energy along the reaction path C and $V_2(X_0, S)$ is an additional energy needed to pass from the curve C to the reaction coordinate at the same value of S. The last term is the kinetic energy for the motion along the curve of the reaction coordinate. The sum of all these terms is the total energy α_1.

To approach the vibrational motion adiabatically, let us use "angle-action" coordinates. Then the action is $I = \text{const} = I_0$ during the motion (I_0 is the initial meaning of U), and the local vibrational energy is

$$E(I_0 S) = (2\mu)^{-1}\left(\frac{dW_2}{dX}\right)^2 + U_3(X,S) - U_3(X_0,S) \quad [97]$$

and

$$\alpha_2 = \alpha_1 - E(I_0, S) + [1 - (1 + kX_0)^{-2}](\alpha_2 - V_1) \quad [98]$$

Equations [94] and [98] may solved to yield $\alpha_2(S)$ and $X_0(S)$; after that a solution of eq. [91] may be found because

$$P_S = \frac{dW_1}{dS} = \mu\dot{S}(1 + kX_0)^2$$

at the curve C,

$$\int_{S_0}^{S} \mu^{1/2}(1 + kX_0)^2 \frac{dS}{[2(\alpha_2 - V_1)]^{1/2}} = t - t_0 \quad [99]$$

where S_0 is the value of S at $t = t_0$ and hence does not depend upon where the beginning of S is taken.

Taking the curve C so that it represents the reaction coordinate yields $X_0 = 0$ and

$$\alpha_2 = \alpha_1 - E(I_0, S) \quad [100]$$

$$\mu^{1/2}\int_{S_0}^{S}\frac{dS}{[2(\alpha_2 - V_1)]^{1/2}} = t - t_0$$

In the case of a harmonic oscillator

$$E(I_0, S) = I_0 \frac{\omega_2}{2\pi} \tag{101}$$

where

$$\mu\omega_2^2 = \left(\frac{\partial^2 V_2}{\partial X_0^2}\right) + [\sigma(\alpha_2 - V_1)k^2(1 + kX_0)^4]$$

and if C is the reaction path then

$$\frac{\partial^2 V(X_0 S)}{\partial X_0^2} = \mu\omega^2$$

Accounting for nonadiabaticity the change in the vibrational energy due to the transition to the region of separated products (where C is linear) is as follows:

$$E_{\text{vibr}} = \frac{(\omega_\infty - \omega_0)I_0}{2\pi} + \left(\frac{I_0\mu\omega_\infty}{\omega_0 \pi}\right)^{1/2} \int_{-\infty}^{+\infty} \cos(\omega_0 \tau' + \delta)G(\tau')d\tau'$$

$$+ \frac{\mu}{2}\frac{\omega_\infty}{\omega_0}\left|\int_{-\infty}^{+\infty} \exp(i\omega_0 \tau')G(\tau')\,d\tau'\right|^2 \tag{102}$$

Coming back to the initial "valley" and surmounting no potential barrier opposing the reaction yields an increase in the vibrational energy as

$$E_{\text{vibr}} = \left(\frac{I_0\mu\omega_0}{\pi}\right)^{1/2} \int_{-\infty}^{+\infty} \cos(\omega_0 \tau' + \delta)G(\tau')\,d\tau'$$

$$+ \frac{\mu}{2}\left|\int_{-\infty}^{+\infty} \exp(i\omega_0 \tau')G(\tau')\,d\tau'\right|^2 \tag{103}$$

where ω_∞, ω_0 are the values of ω at $t = \infty$ and $t = 0$, respectively; δ is a constant;

$$G \equiv \omega_0^2 X_0\left(\frac{\omega_2}{\omega_0}\right)^{1/2} + X\frac{d^2}{d\tau^2}\left(\frac{\omega_2}{\omega_0}\right)^{1/2}$$

the second term in this expression being usually negligibly small.

Thus the problem has been solved as a whole, in principle, and the solutions of particular problems may be found as well provided concrete potential energy surfaces are given.

In more complicated cases new mathematical difficulties may arise. The method by itself, however, has one significant advantage. Being successfully and consistently applied it yields all the information about what is generally accepted to be called "primary act" for a chemical reaction. Therefore the results of its application may be compared to those of known statistical methods.

Since Hamilton-Jacobi and Schrödinger equations are profoundly coupled from the logical point of view quantum mechanical effects may also be taken into consideration (110).

H. Summary

Thus a set of methods (far from being exhaustive) is at our service to solve kinetic problems. These methods enable us to get information about macroscopic quantities dependent on time and parameters of systems, and also about the characteristics of primary acts for the interaction of molecules both with each other and with environments. A combined application of these methods allows us in principle to find desirable relations between the microscopic and macroscopic characteristics of kinetics and give a complete (but not exceedingly detailed) description of a chemical reaction occurrence. At present both quantum-mechanical and classical methods are under development; some ways have been outlined of combining computational and experimental methods to use the most information that the latter yield; various analytical and numerical methods have been suggested to solve kinetic problems.

Nevertheless, a detailed calculation of the kinetics of nonequilibrium chemical reactions is not yet feasible due to the lack of data needed on transition probabilities for various levels, energy-dependent cross-sections for various processes, potential energy surface characteristics, and correct interaction potential functions.

Also, few data are available on the evolution of distribution functions, relaxation curves, and times under chemical reaction conditions.

Quantum-mechanical calculations of molecule structures are still far from being useful for consideration of kinetic problems and for detailed analysis of collisions resulting from chemical reactions.

Methods for the treatment of ordinary kinetic experimental data are not quite clear from the point of view of nonequilibrium chemical kinetics; it is not clear what changes should be made in the ordinary course of the chemical experiment.

IV. THE MONTE-CARLO METHOD IN PHYSICAL AND CHEMICAL KINETICS

The Monte-Carlo method (MCM) is well known to consist of a statistical modelling of a random quantity in order to find parameters of this quantity's distribution. Problems of physical and chemical kinetics may be considered as those of time evolution of certain quantities' distributions which describe the state and behavior of ensembles composed in general of molecules (atoms, radicals, etc.), ions, electrons, and so on.

Since the MCM may be applied to the solution of any problems which allow a statistical description it is possible to use it to study, first of all, relaxation processes and, more generally, any transitions of molecular systems from their initial states to final (equilibrium) states. The MCM does not permit us to deal with gas-kinetic equations but permits us to perform something of the kind of mathematical "experiment" which models simultaneous occurrence of relaxation and chemical reaction considered as atoms rearrangement due to collisions.

The essence of the MCM consists of an inversion of an ordinary procedure when an integral equation (or sometimes a differential equation) is composed and solved using various methods (numerical ones as well) for a certain stochastic process. Instead, it was suggested first in Ref. 114 that to solve this equation the stochastic process of interest might be modelled and statistical calculations of the probability used to solve approximately analytical problems.

Such a procedure has been successfully used to solve problems of neutron penetration through matter and has become widely used in studies of such processes as equilibrium distribution establishment, rotational and vibrational relaxation, dissociation, and ionization. The most important advantage of the MCM over analytical and other numerical methods is the possibility of composing models which allow us to overcome great difficulties arising under the analytical solution procedure of a number of problems.

When a problem is to be solved using the MCM, the system under study is divided into the "medium" of "field particles" and the ensemble of "trying particles." The state of the medium is described with such parameters as density and temperature. The only interaction accounted for is that between "trying" and "field" particles. Since the number of particles is usually very great in systems under study, and modern computer storage is rather confined, periodical boundary condition (PBC) procedure has been suggested. According to this procedure, the space is divided into a number of elementary cells, every one of them containing the same number of particles (~ 100) and the relative positions of particles inside the cells assumed to be the same .The PBC procedure has not yet been strictly established, although the results obtained show its application to be possible. Using the PBC procedure clearly leads to the loss of the opportunity of considering the space correlations of the particles. However, it is more interesting to determine "kinetic" features than space characteristics of the problem. The MCM has been applied to solutions of similar problems in a number of works and an account of them is given in Ref. 4.

There is another scheme of MCM application which does not require PBC to be used, but may be applied only to problems with isotropic velocity distributions (so that only the velocity module is important). According to this scheme, the space of the velocity module is divided into a number of "stripes." Then the problem is reduced to that of finding a solution of a system of balance equations describing every population level. Such a model (it resembles, evidently, the many-group theory for neutron transfer) has a number of advantages. First, the computer time is significantly reduced; the imitation of a collision now takes an order less time in the case of 200 levels due to the simplification of calculations. Calculations made using this procedure (henceforth to be called velocity discrete space procedure) have shown that the results obtained are only slightly sensitive to the number of levels included and allow us to save a great amount of computer time.

The problem of Maxwellization of a mixture of two gases with different initial temperatures has been considered using the velocity discrete space (VDS) procedure.

The mixture consisted of methane and argon molecules at temperatures $3 \times 10^2 \, ^\circ K$ and $1 \times 10^4 \, ^\circ K$, respectively.

The system was assumed to be homogeneous and molecules were approached with solid noninteracting balls. Methane and argon molecule densities were taken as equal to each other and amounted to $5 \times 10^{17} \, cm^{-3}$. The total number of particles was 4×10^4; that led to a statistical error not more than 1 %. The most important results of the calculations are as follows:

Two steps are observed in the Maxwellization of the system. During the initial "nonadiabatic" step the process of energy transfer from "hot" molecules to "cold" ones is considerably faster than that of Maxwellization inside every individual gas. This step lasts for a time up to $t = 3\tau_c$, where τ_c is a mean time between collisions under equilibrium conditions. During the second "nearly adiabatic" step a dynamic equilibrium occurs between the rates of these processes.

The system reached the total equilibrium at the moment $t = 12\tau_c$.

Up to the time $t < 3.5\tau_c$ the concept of temperature has no sense either for the whole system or for its individual components, since molecular velocity distributions differ greatly from a Maxwellian distribution. The highly energetic "tail" of the cold gas molecules' velocity distribution, which appears at the initial moment of time, must have a strong effect upon the kinetics of other processes including, for instance, chemical reactions.

This effect has been studied by the example of thermal decompositions of methane and $SiCl_4$ molecules in mixtures with argon (see Fig. 5). To

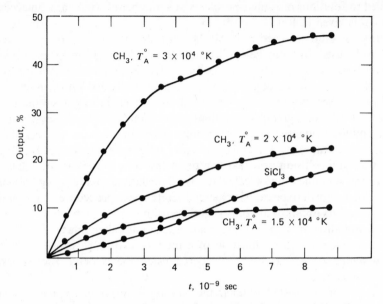

Figure 5 CH_3 and $SiCl_3$ formation rates as functions of time.

simplify the calculations the following assumptions were made: (1) Molecules are solid balls. (2) Reactions occur according to the scheme

$$CH_4 \rightarrow CH_3 + H \qquad [104]$$

$$SiCl_4 \rightarrow SiCl_3 + Cl \qquad [105]$$

(3) Reaction cross-sections are zero at $E_k < E_a$ and constant at $E_k \geqslant E_a$, where E_k is the kinetic energy of molecules and E_a is the activation energy for the reactions [104] and [105]. (4) The lifetime of the molecules with $E_k \geqslant E_a$ does not depend on E_k and may be described as

$$\rho(t) = \tau^{-1} \exp\left(-\frac{t}{\tau}\right) \qquad [106]$$

where τ is the mean lifetime.

Initial temperatures of CH_4 and $SiCl_4$ molecules were taken as $3 \times 10^2 \, ^\circ K$ while argon's initial temperature was varied from 1.5×10^4 to $3 \times 10^4 \, ^\circ K$. Initial densities of argon and reactants were $5 \times 10^{17} \, cm^{-3}$. Recombination was not accounted for. The values of the activation energy for the decomposition of CH_4 and $SiCl_4$ were taken as 91 and 89 kcal/mole, respectively.

All the calculations were carried out assuming the velocity space to be continuous. The system was composed of 108 particles; the accuracy of the results obtained was about $\pm 2\%$. The kinetics of CH_4 decomposition has appeared to differ significantly from that of $SiCl_4$. Thus the rate of CH_3 radical formation is especially high during the initial moments of time ($t < 3 \times 10^{-9}$ sec) and then decreases sharply. It may be due to the appearance of the highly energetic "tail" of methane molecule distribution. In other words, the "nonadiabatic" process of the energy transfer from argon atoms to methane molecules significantly affects the rate of the second-order reaction [104].

The fall of the radicals' formation rate after $t = 3 \times 10^{-9}$ sec may be explained by the fact that under adiabatic Maxwellization the decrease in density of hot methane molecule due to the chemical reaction, cannot be made up by the methane molecules activation due to their collisions with argon atoms.

The decomposition of $SiCl_4$ molecules occurs as follows: Although at initial moments of time the highly energetic "tail" of the velocity distribution of $SiCl_4$ molecules does appear, the rate of $SiCl_3$ radical formation remains practically the same. This may be explained as follows. Since the lifetime of $SiCl_4$ molecules in activated states (2×10^{-9} sec) is more than the collision mean time, the rates of both activation and deactivation of $SiCl_4$ molecules significantly exceeds the rate of decomposition of these molecules. This implies that the rate of $SiCl_3$ radical formation can be determined with the stationary population of the velocity range corresponding to $E_k \geqslant E_a$ but not with the rate of highly energetic $SiCl_4$ molecule formation. Hence, the rate of $SiCl_3$ formation must not depend on the nature of the Maxwellization process since during both stages of Maxwellization the highly energetic "tail" of the distribution function is changed only slightly. At initial moments of time the rate of CH_3 radical formation greatly exceeds that of $SiCl_3$ radicals in spite of $(E_a)_{CH_4} > (E_a)_{SiCl_4}$. Thus, a strong nonequilibrium of distribution functions at initial moments of time significantly affects molecule decompositions provided these reactions are of the second order. The initial nonequilibrium will be very important until (E_a/kT) is not too great. Therefore, this effect is to take place under comparatively low temperatures for the reactions with small activation energies.

From the results of calculations performed a conclusion may be drawn that for the reactions of the second order radical yield at initial moments of time will be more in the case of a two-component mixture with different temperatures of components than in the case of the initially equilibrium system with both components having equal temperatures.

Equilibrium distribution perturbations due to chemical reactions and reverse effects of the distribution produced upon reaction rates are very interesting points.* These may be studied also with the MCM method.

In Ref. 3 molecular velocity distribution has been studied under the occurrence of the reaction $CH_4 \rightarrow CH_3 + H$ in an inert gas environment.

This reaction cross-section was assumed to be zero at $E_k < D$ and constant at $E_k \geqslant D$, where D is dissociation energy. The lifetime was determined with the relation [106] at $E_k \geqslant D$. Chemical reaction was believed to have occurred if the lifetime obtained using eq. [106] proved to be less than the free-path time of molecules. In opposite cases an elastic collision was mathematically "drawn" of molecules with inert gas atoms. The value of D was taken as 86.4 kcal mole^{-1} and the inert gas density as 10^{10} cm^{-3}.

Calculations were carried out for $T = (5, 7.5, 10, 125, 150) \times 10^3$ °K, where T is the inert gas temperature. Under each of these temperatures the mean lifetime of molecules with the energies $E_k \geqslant D$ was varied and this resulted in a change of the reaction order. The number of molecules was 5×10^4 so that the statistical error did not exceed $\sim 1\%$. The results of these calculations describe both the kinetics of the systems transition from the initial state to the equilibrium state and the equilibrium state itself.

The results obtained show the highly energetic tail of the distribution ($E_k \geqslant D$) to be absent† practically under $\tau = 2 \times 10^{-14}$ sec (see Fig. 6). This is because under $\tau \ll \tau_c$ the chemical reaction rate greatly exceeds that of the molecule activation by their collisions with the inert gas atoms.

Under $\tau \gg \tau_c$ the equilibrium distributions differ from the initial ones only slightly. The decrease of molecules with energies as $E_k \geqslant D$ is made up practically in no time with the molecules' collisional activation.

*It was pointed out in Ref. 13 that "noticeable perturbations of the Maxwell distribution and as a result a finite change in the reaction rate may be observed only for chemical reactions with the values of cross-sections for the primary acts of the order of unity. This fact may be reasonably explained. The point is that processes of two types are occurring under chemical reaction conditions. The chemical reaction results in the decrease of molecule density having translational energy of the order of the activation energy. This decrease is compensated due to elastic molecular collisions which have cross-sections of the order of the gas kinetic cross-sections, so that these collisions are very effective. Thus a chemical reaction may perturb finitely the distribution in the high-energy region only if the cross-section for the primary act of the reaction is of the order of the gas kinetic cross-section in the same region."

†The problem concerning a chemical reaction effect on the distribution has not yet been solved in general. Many attempts have been made to solve a more simple problem: to find the effect of small perturbations on the reaction rate. An account of such works has been made in Ref. 53 and 115. It was shown that the reaction rates under perturbed distribution conditions differ from those under equilibrium. However, these differences are small ($\sim 10\%$ under $(E_a/kT) \geqslant 5 - 10$). Thus the equilibrium approach may be applied. Nevertheless, it should be observed that great deviations from equilibrium values of corresponding quantities are not possible to obtain until an ordinary perturbation theory is used.

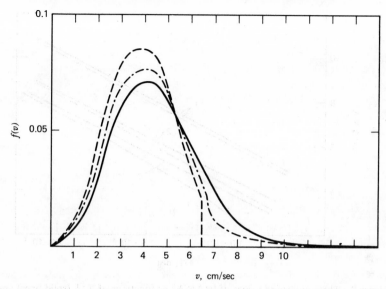

Figure 6 The equilibrium velocity distribution perturbation produced with a fast chemical reaction.

The calculation results show also the pre-exponential factors in the well-known Arrhenius equation describing the reaction rate to be dependent upon temperature. This effect may be explained with the argument that the distribution function is decreased in the region $\langle\!\langle E_k \rangle\!\rangle < E_k < D$ (where $\langle\!\langle E_k \rangle\!\rangle$ is the mean kinetic energy of molecules under equilibrium) as compared to the equilibrium distribution function (see for details Ref. 3).

Under experimental data treatment the value of the heat bath temperature is usually substituted in the Arrhenius equation. The plots of the quantity $\ln(\Delta N/N)$ as a function of T^{-1} for some three values of the lifetime τ for molecules with $E_k \geqslant D$ are shown in Fig. 7. The rate constants in all these cases are seen to be described by the Arrhenius equation.

Since the molecular distributions differ greatly from Maxwellian ones the concept of the temperature has no sense for the system as a whole. Nevertheless, let us take $T^* = \frac{2}{3}\bar{E}/R$ (where $\bar{E}$ is the mean kinetic energy of molecules under the equilibrium conditions). The temperature dependence of the rate constant is seen from Fig. 7 to be described with the Arrhenius equation under $\tau = 5 \times 10^{-9}$ sec and 5×10^{-10} sec while under $\tau = 2 \times 10^{-14}$ sec are not described like this. It is due to the reaction rate in the first two cases being determined mainly with the stationary velocity distribution of molecules while in the third case the reaction rate is determined with the frequency of the molecule collisions with the heat bath atoms resulting in the molecule activation.

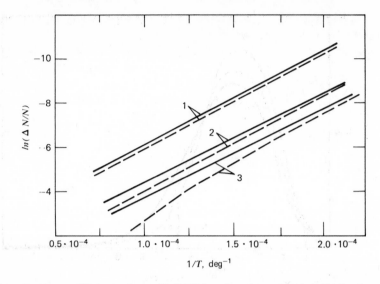

Figure 7   The equilibrium values of $\ln(\Delta N/N)$ as functions of T^{-1} (solid lines) and of $(T^*)^{-1}$ (dotted lines): (1) $\tau = 5 \times 10^{-9}$ sec; (2) $\tau = 5 \times 10^{-10}$ sec; (3) $\tau = 2 \times 10^{-14}$ sec. $T^* = 2\bar{E}/3R$, where E is the molecular mean kinetic energy at the equilibrium state.

This frequency is determined mainly by the highly energetic tail of the heat-bath atoms distribution (which according to the model considered is assumed to be Maxwellian).

In nonisothermic cases only the quantity T^* can be substituted for temperature into the Arrhenius equation. Therefore, the rates of the second-order reactions of thermal decomposition ($\tau \ll t_{chem}$) cannot be described with an Arrhenius expression. In this case the deviations from the Maxwell distribution are the most significant.

It is clear from the above account that the MCM may be successfully applied to study vibrational relaxation of molecules by taking into consideration their dissociation. This problem has been discussed thoroughly in Ref. 3. Some results obtained will be considered here briefly.

In a rough outline the calculation procedure was similar to that discussed previously. The calculations show the Boltzmann distribution at the first moments of time provided there are no many-quantum transitions. Further, the process of dissociation decreases the upper-level populations. If many-quantum transitions are to be accounted for, the common vibrational temperature cannot be defined even when dissociation may be neglected due to a stronger dependence of transition probabilities upon the vibrational energy than in the case of the harmonic oscillator model.

All the results discussed show convincingly that the Monte-Carlo method must become one of the main ways to study properties of molecular systems and evolution of distributions in various problems of physical and chemical kinetics.

V. THE RATE FACTOR FOR NONEQUILIBRIUM CHEMICAL REACTIONS

The basic equation of classical chemical kinetics is known to be written as

$$\frac{dn_i}{dt} = \sum_{j=1}^{n} K_{ij} n_i n_j \qquad [107]$$

where K_{ij} is the rate constant for a chemical reaction and n_i, n_j are concentrations of the i and j species, respectively. The terms describing binary processes, omitted here for simplicity, may be derived from some general principles (postulates) of statistical theory. In particular, postulates of collisions, statistical independence and some others have to be used (116). In the case of classical kinetics the equilibrium (or quasi-equilibrium) postulate should be added.

Equation [107] may be derived naturally from the Boltzmann kinetic equation. As a result it becomes more general and may be used to describe both physical kinetic phenomena (quantum population levels, ionization) and chemical kinetic phenomena.

Let us write the Boltzmann equation as*

$$\frac{df_i}{dt} = \sum_{j,k,l} I_{ij}^{kl} \qquad [108]$$

where f_i is particle velocity distribution function and I_{ij} are integrals of binary collisions (both elastic and nonelastic). Subscripts i, j are notations for both the kinds of particles and their states. The spreading of collision integrals over many-multiple cases will not change, when applied, the meaning of the lower transformations. Let us write collision integrals according to Refs. 69 and 120 in the form

$$I_{ij}^{kl} = \iint_{4\pi} \iiint_{-\infty}^{+\infty} (f_k f_l - f_i f_j) \dot{V}_{ij} \sigma_{ij}^{kl} \, d\Omega \, dp_j \qquad [109]$$

where

$$V_{ij} \equiv \left| \frac{1}{m_i} p_i - \frac{1}{m_j} p_j \right|$$

*The absence of the flux term does not restrict further discussions.

and f functions are normalized to densities $n(t)$. Substituting $f_i \equiv n_i F_i$, where

$$\iiint_{-\infty}^{+\infty} F_i \, dp_i = 1$$

and making integration of the eq. [108] over momenta p_i yields the equation system

$$\frac{dn_i}{dt} = \sum_{ikl} (W_{kl}^{ij} n_k n_l - W_{ij}^{kl} n_i n_j) \qquad [110]$$

where

$$W_{ij}^{kl} = \iint_{-4\pi} \iiint_{-\infty}^{+\infty} \iiint_{-\infty}^{+\infty} V_{ij} \sigma_{ij}^{kl} F_i F_j \, d\Omega \, dp_i \, dp_j \qquad [111]$$

and σ_{ij}^{kl} is the differential cross-section for the collision of i and j particles (these collisions result in appearance of k and l particles);

$$d\Omega \equiv \sin \theta \, d\theta \, d\phi$$

where θ and ϕ are the angles of scattering;

$$dp_i \equiv dp_{i1} \, dp_{i2} \, dp_{i3}; \qquad dp_j \equiv dp_{j1} \, dp_{j2} \, dp_{j3}$$

Equations like these are discussed thoroughly in Refs. 7, 34–36, and 47.

Thus the quantities W_{ij}^{kl} are transition probabilities averaged over the particle energy distribution and may be considered as rate factors K_c for chemical reactions.*

In general, the rate factor for a chemical reaction K_c depends upon cross-sections of corresponding processes, momentum distributions of reactant and product particles and quantum-level populations of molecular internal

---

*Theoretical rate factor (rate constant) for a chemical reaction is a function of the type

$$K_c \sim K_c(U, f) \sim K_\sigma(\sigma, f) \qquad [112]$$

where U is the potential function for the molecular interaction. The nature of K_c is rather like that of transfer coefficients, so many results may be obtained analogously. It should be observed that generally speaking

$$f = f(\mathbf{r}, \mathbf{v}, E_{in}, t)$$

where E_{in} is molecular quantum level energies (vibrational energies) and K_c may prove to be not only a time-dependent but also a density-dependent function. A special study is necessary to find how far the analogy between K_c and transfer coefficients may be spread (see, for instance, Ref. 121).

degrees of freedom (122). In classical (Arrhenius) kinetics, translational momentum distributions of particles are believed to be Maxwellian, internal degrees of freedom are not taken into account, and molecular interactions are assumed to be those of solid balls. Under these assumptions it may be simply derived that

$$K \sim \exp\left(-\frac{E_a}{kT}\right) \qquad [113]$$

where E_a is the activation energy, and T is the temperature (the concept of temperature may be used because of the equilibrium conditions).

Possible changes in the form and magnitude of K_c due to the rejection of "solid balls" model and/or Maxwellian (equilibrium) distribution of particle velocities have been discussed in the literature (8,113). In particular, the applicability of eq. [113] under either $E_a \lesssim kT^*$ conditions (which may take place at high temperatures, for example) or when the Maxwellian distribution does not take place is considered in Refs. 115 and 64, respectively. The results obtained allow neither quantitative evaluation nor development of a method for such an evaluation of changes in K due to nonequilibrium distributions and different models of molecular interaction.

In chemical kinetics K is not calculated but is found from experimental data as K_{exp}.† Expression [112] shows K_c to be a certain combination of the reaction cross-section $\sigma(E)$, being energy-dependent, and the particle distribution function $f(\mathbf{r}, \mathbf{v}, E_{in}, t)$. However, the determination of K_c based upon equations of the type of eq. [112] is difficult not only because of the computing procedure but also because of the absence of sufficiently accurate values of $\sigma(E)$. Assuming $\sigma(E)$ and f to be known, a method of calculating K_c may be suggested that appears to be suitable for any forms of cross-sections and distributions. Since K_c depends on both $\sigma(E)$ and $f(\mathbf{r}, \mathbf{v}, E_{in}, t)$ it is necessary to find out the effect of the latter on the size of region of the K_c applicability.

Using some models (64) or more general statistical laws (16,34,124) different (but close by meaning) equations for K_c may be derived.

Let us consider an irreversible gas-phase reaction

$$A(i) + B(j) \rightarrow C(k) + D(l) \qquad [114]$$

---

*Here and further on k is the Boltzmann constant.

†The concept of K_{exp} is valid only for the equilibrium or near it; just in these cases K_{exp} is actually a constant which is time- and reactant-densities-independent and depends only upon the temperature. This follows from the Arrhenius procedure of K_{exp} determination by experimental data.

A careful derivation of K_{exp} for a nonequilibrium chemical reaction (where there are no possibilities to obtain the Arrhenius plot) will be carried out further to show K_{exp} to be a function of the reactant's initial densities and time.

where i, j, k, l are characteristics of the particle quantum states. Relating the rate of reaction [114] to the number of collisions between particles $A(i)$ and $B(j)$ yields the expression for the reaction rate factor as

$$K_c \equiv \sum_{ijlm} X_{A(i)} X_{B(j)} \iiint_{-\infty}^{+\infty} \iiint_{-\infty}^{+\infty} V_{AB}\,\sigma(ml/ij;\,V_{AB})F_{A(i)}\,F_{B(j)}(V_B)\,dV_A\,dV_B \qquad [115]$$

where $X_{A(i)}$ and $X_{B(j)}$ are relative densities of particles in quantum states i and j, respectively; $\sigma(ml/ij;\,V_{AB})$ are total cross-sections for the corresponding scattering processes (dependent on quantum numbers and velocities of relative motion) considered in the coordinate system of the colliding particle's center of mass; $F_{A(i)}$ and $F_{B(j)}$ are distribution functions (normalized to unity) of A and B particles in i and j quantum states, respectively; V_{AB} is the relative velocity module of A and B particles.

The rate factor for the reaction to occur from an ith level may be expressed as follows:

$$K_i = \int_{V_A} \int_{V_B} \sigma(ij;\,V_{AB})\,|\overline{V}_{AB}| \cdot F_{A(i)}(V_{A(i)}) \cdot F_{B(j)}(V_{B(j)})\,d\overline{V}_{A(i)}\,dV_{B(j)} \qquad [115a]$$

In case only one of the reactants has internal degrees of freedom

$$K_c = \sum_i X_{A(i)} \int_{V_A} \int_{V_B} \sigma(i;\,V_{AB})F_{A(i)}(V_{A(i)})F_{V_B}(V_B)\,d\overline{V}_{A(i)}\,d\overline{V}_B \qquad [115b]$$

or, in brief,

$$K_c = \sum_i X_i K_i = \sum_i \tilde{K}_i$$

where $\tilde{K}_i$ is the contribution of an ith level into the brutto rate factor, supposing the distribution over vibrational levels X_i to be given. (Here we suppose molecules to have only vibrational levels. However, the completely correct consideration requires rotational levels to be included.)

From the physical point of view an essential difference between K_i and K_c should be emphasized. K_i is the fundamental quantity and describes any given molecule through the cross-section $\sigma(\varepsilon)$. Strictly speaking, K_i depends upon the molecular interaction potential defined under given quantum states and distribution function $F_i(\varepsilon, t)$. K_i is the only rate factor for the elementary act of the chemical reaction. The rate factor K, measured in a chemical experiment and defined by eq. [115], is always a complex parameter depending on σ and F and also upon level populations, and may coincide with K_i only in very rare particular cases. Such cases may occur most probably under low-temperature conditions and for slow reactions (preferably thermoneutral). In a general case, K depends upon level populations, for example, upon concentrations of molecules in given quantum states. These concentrations are varied widely. Evidently K will change with temperature (even under Maxwell-Boltzmann distribution conditions) because of changes in various K_i contributions into K. Thus a reconstruction of K with the help of K_i gives not an Arrhenius-type but a more complex dependence of K on temperature. Under low-temperature conditions the rate factor is determined with the reactions occurring from lowest level, and the dependence $K = K(1/T_{tr})$ coincides asymptotically with that for the first vibrational level. Under high temperatures the rate factor is changed, and the activation energies too being correspondingly changed. Therefore, the dependence of log $K \sim 1/T_{tr}$ will not be linear but curved. Thus an Arrhenius-type treatment of experimental data is physically wrong especially in cases such as highly exothermic reactions, chain-branching through excited molecules, and so on, even if translational and vibrational temperatures are equal. Also wrong are the conclusions drawn concerning reaction mechanism changes based upon the bending of the Arrhenius plot. In all these (and many other) cases the Arrhenius type kinetics and its methods of treatment and interpretation of experimental data prevent the correct understanding of the nature of chemical reactions.

Thus we have shown the plot of the brutto rate factor $K_c = \sum_i X_i K_i$ of a chemical reaction, as a function of temperature, will not be a straight line in the Arrhenius coordinates even if all K_i are described with the Arrhenius-type equation and there exists in the system the Maxwell-Boltzmann distribution.

From eq. [115] it follows that (1) K_c may be determined for any given cross-sections and distributions and is not related to the concept of temperature which cannot be defined simply for nonequilibrium systems. (2) K_c also depends inexplicitly on time for nonequilibrium processes since $F_{A(i)}$ and $F_{B(j)}$ are time-dependent. The value of K_c may be determined from eq. [115] using the Monte-Carlo procedure (125) for any given σ and f.

From K_c calculations for different non-Maxwellian distributions, making use of the solid ball model, the limits of classical chemical kinetics application may be found. In particular, these calculations will allow us to determine possibilities for the Arrhenius rate constant K_{exp} to be used to interpret the data of chemical kinetic experiments.*

A resulting close approximation of experimental data with the Arrhenius plot in (log K_{exp}, $1/T$) coordinates is not a proof that the solid balls model* is

*Only the solid balls model is considered for the following reasons:
1. This model is used in equilibrium chemical kinetics and allows a sufficiently great number of problems to be solved with reasonable accuracy.
2. The question is to be answered: how is K_c changed due to the substitution of the equilibrium distribution postulated in the Arrhenius kinetics with various nonequilibrium distributions (preserving the solid balls model implies the consideration of a nonequilibrium produced with chemical reactions).
3. Other more real models cannot be considered for the lack of cross-section data for various processes.

correct or that the Maxwell distribution occurs under the conditions of the experiment. If chemical kinetic experimental data cannot be approximated with a single Arrhenius plot, then usually either a few plots with different slopes are used or the experimental data are considered to be insufficiently correct. It would certainly be more reasonable to compare K_{exp} with K_c for different possible distribution functions and only after that to interpret the values of K_{exp}. Such treatment is usually difficult to use because of great difficulties in K_c calculations. Nevertheless, the value $E_a \approx E_b{}^*$ must be determined from experimental data no matter what form the distribution function takes.

Currently it is possible to carry out this calculation provided eq. [113] may be applied. Therefore, it is important to investigate within what limits and with what accuracy such a procedure of experimental data treatment may be applied in the case of non-Maxwellian distribution.

Let us take the total cross-section σ_{AB} dependence upon the energy E_{AB} of the relative motion of colliding particles in the form which is used usually in classical chemical kinetics (as in the case of the solid balls model)

$$\sigma_{AB} = \begin{cases} 0, & E_{AB} < E_n \\ 1, & E_{AB} \geq E_n \end{cases} \qquad [116]$$

where E_b is the energy barrier opposing the reaction of the type [114]†.

In Ref. 126 the following cases have been studied taking a system composed of (1) two subsystems with like temperatures (stationary Maxwellian distribution) (Fig. 8a); (2) two Maxwellian subsystems with different mean energies (Fig. 8b); (3) two subsystems, one Maxwellian and the other different from Maxwellian in the low-energy region (Fig. 8c); (4) a Maxwellian subsystem and a subsystem different from Maxwellian in the high-energy region (Fig. 8d); (5) A Maxwellian subsystem and a system with the energy distribution in the form of the δ-function (Fig. 8e); (6) two systems with δ-function-like energy distributions (Fig. 8f).

These nonequilibrium systems are comparatively simple and frequent to be dealt with. An application of the procedure under consideration to other distributions and cross-sections appears to be simple.

---

*Here E_a is activation energy and E_b is the energy barrier opposing the reaction (a minimum energy above which the reaction proceeds from a given quantum state).

†The cross-section in the form of [116] is certainly approximate. According to quantum mechanics there is always quantum-mechanical tunneling through the energy barrier and reflection from the barrier of a particle, the energy of which is above the height of the barrier. In other words the cross-section σ_{AB} can be equal to neither zero nor unity except for some exotic deliberately constructed potentials. The cross-section in the form of [116] is essentially classical in approximation and is not valid if the barrier is narrow or the mass of the species crossing it is small (so it cannot be applied to the consideration of electron-atomic and electron-ionic collisions).

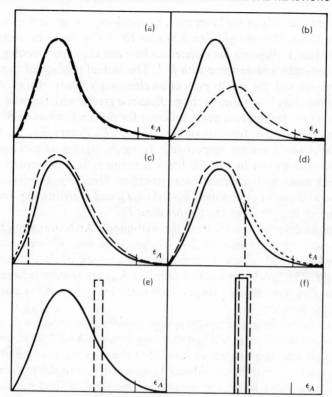

Figure 8 The distribution functions under study of the components A and B of the gaseous system. ϕ_A is the Maxwell function with $\bar{E}_A > 0.15\, E_b$ (solid line) and ϕ_B is shown by the broken line: (a) $\phi_A = \phi_B$; (b) ϕ_B is the Maxwell function with different values of $\bar{E}_B$; (c) ϕ_B is the Maxwell function being "cut off" under low energies; (d) ϕ_B is the Maxwell function being "cut off" under high energies; (e) ϕ_B is the monoenergetic distribution; (f) ϕ_A and ϕ_B are similar monoenergetic distributions.

It is worthwhile observing that conditions like (2) may take place, for instance, under glow discharges or VHF (very high frequency) discharges (where the electron temperature is significantly higher than that of heavy particles); conditions like (5) may occur when a gas jet is injected into a volume filled with an equilibrium gas; and conditions like (6) are possible under reactions proceeding in monoenergetic beams, etc.

The plots of log K_c as functions of $\beta = E_b/kT$ are shown in Fig. 9a for five cases including (1) $T_A = T_B$, (2) $T_B = 1.5T_A$, (3) $T_A = 10T_B$, (4) $T_B = 30T_A$, (5) A particles are characterized by the temperature T_A, B particles have Maxwellian distribution "cutoff" at $E_B = E_b$.

Since kT_A is taken to be constant the dependence of log K_c on β may differ from straight line only in the latter case. Interestingly enough it does not take place here (126). The straight line 5 is seen from Fig. 9a to be everywhere lower than that 1 although the differences between the corresponding values of log K_c are small and decrease with β^{-1}. The mutual position of these plots is in agreement with the results even of an elementary kinetic theory. A comparison of the plots 1–4 of Fig. 9a shows K_c to rise greatly with the ratio T_B/T_A, the character of this increase being different for different values of β.

The plot of log K_c as function of the ratio $\bar{E}_A/\bar{E}_B$ (where $\bar{E}_A$, $\bar{E}_B$ are the energies of A and B species, respectively, being averaged over corresponding distributions) is shown in Fig. 9b for a reacting system composed of two Maxwellian gases with different mean energies. Since $\bar{E}_A$ was taken to be constant and $\bar{E}_B = kT_B$ the ratio $(\bar{E}_A/\bar{E}_B) : 1/T_B$ and therefore the Arrhenius plot shown in Fig. 9b is for the temperature T_B.

These plots differ noticeably from the well-known Arrhenius straight lines. They may be approximated by 3–4 straight lines with different slopes in particular for $\beta = 50$, which is somewhat characteristic of classical chemical experiments. The breaks on the like plots for K_{exp} are usually believed to be due to reaction mechanism changes. However, this conclusion is clearly not the only one possible.

A practically important case is the system including electrons, singly charged ions and neutral molecules (atoms) that may occur in VHF, glow, and other discharges. Under low degrees of ionization the ions are not important, so chemical reactions may be considered to proceed due to electron-molecule collisions only. In such two-component systems electrons and neutral molecules may have Maxwellian distributions, their temperatures being greatly different (usually $T_e \sim 2$–5 eV and $T_M \sim 0.03$–0.05 eV where T_e and T_M are the electron and molecular temperatures, respectively). In this case the expression for K_c may be reduced to that for a one-component system, introducing some "effective" temperature which may be defined as

$$T_{eff} = \frac{m_e T_M + m_M T_e}{m_e + m_M} \qquad [117]$$

where m_e, T_e and m_M, T_M are masses and temperatures of electrons and neutral particles, respectively. For the system under consideration $T_{eff} \approx T_e$ due to that $m_e/m \approx 5 \times 10^{-4}$.

The dependence of K_c^{ion} on heavy particle temperature proved to be slight as it has been expected. For instance, taking $\bar{E}_e = 3$ eV and assuming neutral particle velocity distribution to be Maxwellian yields the results given in Table 6 for cases when electrons have either Maxwellian or Druvesteyen distributions.

The dependence of K_c^{ion} on E_e under the condition $(E_b/kT) = 50$ may be illustrated with the data given in Table 7.

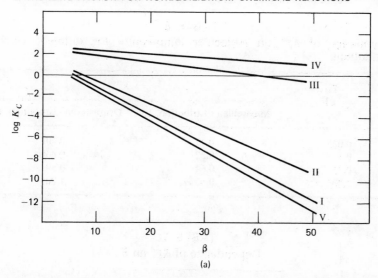

(a)

Figure 9(a)   The quantity $\log K_c$ as a function of β; ϕ_A (solid line) is the Maxwell function with $E_A = 0.15 \, E_b$. Curves: (I) $\phi_A = \phi_B$; (II) ϕ_B is the Maxwell function with $\bar{E}_B = 1.5 \, \bar{E}_A$; (III) ϕ_B is the Maxwell function with $\bar{E}_B = 10 \, \bar{E}_A$; (IV) ϕ_B is the Maxwell function with $\bar{E}_B = 30 \, \bar{E}_A$; (V) ϕ_B is the Maxwell function being cut off at the energy $\bar{E}_B = \bar{E}_b$; $\bar{E}_B = \bar{E}_A$.

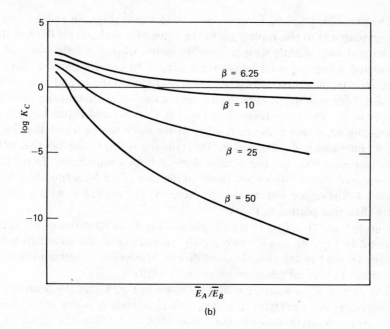

(b)

Figure 9(b)   The quantity $\log K_c$ as a function of $(\bar{E}_A/\bar{E}_B)$.

TABLE 6

Dependence of K_c^{ion} on molecular temperature for different electron distributions

T_M, eV	K_c^{ion}	
	Maxwellian distribution, 10^{-4}	Druvesteyen distribution, 10^{-6}
0.025	0.17	0.40
0.5	0.52	0.66
0.75	0.64	0.89
1.00	0.93	1.20

TABLE 7
Dependence of K_c^{ion} on E_e

E_e/E_b	10	30	50
$\log K_c^{ion}$	3.81	2.56	1.11

The plot of $\log K_c$ as a function of E_b is shown in Figs. 8b and 8c. Log K_c is seen (curve I) to rise rapidly up to the value of $\gamma = (\bar{E}_B/E_b) = 0.5$ and then is changed only slightly with γ. In other words when $\gamma > 1$ the value of K_c calculated using the solid balls model cannot be considered as a quantity characteristic of relative rates of chemical reactions. If the second reactant has the distribution in the form of the δ-function the log K_c-dependence upon γ is similar to the above one (curve 2 in Fig. 10). Curves I and II (see Fig. 10) are interesting since they cross each other in the same region where the rate of log K_c increases and γ diminishes. This crossing is due to the fact that in the two-temperature system the distributions of both components always have low-energy " wings " which are absent in the case of the δ-function-like distribution. In the region where $\gamma > 1$ the factor K_c plotted in Fig. 8e is 2–3 times more than that plotted in Fig. 8b.

Curves I and II in Fig. 11 are the plots of log K_c as functions of γ that correspond to Figs. 8c and 8f, respectively. In both cases the solid ball model cannot be used in the consideration of non-Maxwellian systems to describe the rates of chemical reactions using the quantity K_c.

The plot of K_c as a function of γ is shown in Fig. 12 for the distributions shown in Fig. 8d. The factor K_c is seen to increase linearly with γ up to $\gamma \approx 0.75$ and approach asymptotically the value of $K_c = 1$. Thus the factor K_c is practically insensitive to the form of B-particle distribution at $\gamma \approx 1$ and is not

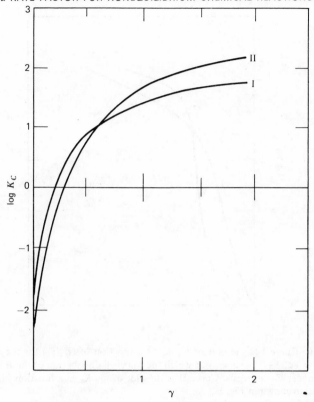

Figure 10 The quantity $\log K_c$ as a function of γ. Curves: (I) corresponds to the distribution shown in Fig. 8b; (II) corresponds to the distribution shown in Fig. 8e.

characteristic of the chemical reaction due evidently to the extreme simplification of the model used.

All these results show the Arrhenius procedure of describing chemical reactions may lead even in the most simple cases to significant errors both in the rate factor K_c and in the understanding of the chemical reaction mechanism. Thus three problems arise: (1) The factor K_c is to be found for various more real models of molecular structure and interaction using equilibrium and nonequilibrium distributions of the energy and level populations. (2) A procedure is to be developed to distinguish between nonequilibrium and Arrhenius reactions under chemical kinetics experiments. (3) A means is to be found to determine $E_b \approx E_a$ and reaction rate factors as functions of energies and level populations. The discussion of problems (1) and (2) is beyond the scope of the present survey. As for problem (3) some remarks may be made here which may be useful under the treatment of nonequilibrium kinetic experimental data. If both subsystems of a nonequilibrium system are Maxwellian, $\bar{E}_A$ and

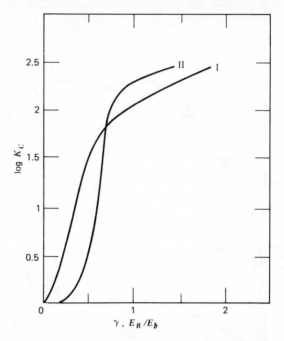

Figure 11   Curve I is the plot of $\log K_c$ as a function of (E_B/E_b) for the distribution shown in Fig. 8c; E_B is the energy at which the Maxwell distribution of the B molecules is "cut off" under low energies. Curve II is the plot of $\log K_c$ as a function of $(\bar{E}_B/E_b)$ for the distribution shown in Fig. 8f.

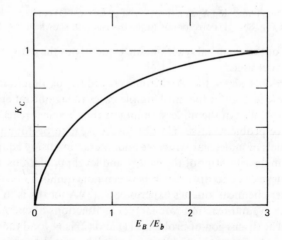

Figure 12   The quantity K_c as a function of $(\bar{E}_B/E_b)$ for the distribution shown in Fig. 8d; $\bar{E}_B$ is the energy at which the Maxwell distribution of B molecules is "cut off" under high energies.

$\bar{E}_B$ are known and K_{exp} is determined for a few values of the ratio $\alpha = \bar{E}_A/\bar{E}_B$. The plot of K_{exp} as a function of α should be compared to the plots shown in Fig. 9b (here $\beta = E_B/E_A$ is a parameter for the curves shown). The value of E_B may be determined then by the coincidence of the experimental and one of the calculated plots. It is interesting to compare the value of E_b to the value of E_a obtained from the Arrhenius plot.

Quite an analogous procedure is known to be used in geophysics in the consideration of the inverse problem of the potential. Digital electronic computers may be successfully used in such a treatment of experimental data.

VI. THEORIES FOR DISSOCIATION, RECOMBINATION, AND REACTIONS OCCURRING UNDER PULSE ELECTROMAGNETIC FIELD CONDITIONS

Since there is no general theory for plasma-chemical reaction kinetics yet (as a part of nonequilibrium chemical kinetics) the study of simple and frequently met reactions (somewhat model reactions) is important.

Such a study may reasonably combine the dynamic approach and statistical physics methods. A number of problems have been considered and for some of them, reasonable and sometimes fruitful calculation procedures have been suggested (127–129).

Here only those reactions will be discussed that are important in the study of stationary, pulse, and decaying plasmas. These reactions have been investigated frequently from various points of view and include dissociation and recombination reactions in stationary and decaying plasmas and ionization reaction in pulse electrical (or VHF) discharges. The importance of the two former reactions does not need to be proved. The only approaches to their description that will be discussed are approaches which seem to contain basic features and which may prove to be useful from the point of view of the general theory of nonequilibrium chemical kinetics.

Chemical reactions in a pulse discharge are a particular but still important case for the theory, partly because the pulse characteristics allow us to describe the reactions more completely and closely. A reaction of ionization occurring in a pulse VHF discharge will be considered as an example of such reactions.*

A. Dissociation Reactions

Diatomic molecule decomposition under low-temperature conditions may occur through thermal dissociation and due to electron impact.

*The kinetics of ionic reactions may be described using one of the possible kinds of eq. [3]. A detailed account of these kinetic reactions may be found, for instance, in Refs. 130 and 131.

Thermal dissociation is the transition of molecules from discrete vibrational states into the continuum (132). A calculation of K_d should be based on the solution of the system of eq. [3] describing transitions both from discrete state into continuum and between discrete states themselves.

The basic assumption of the ordinary (low-temperature) theory for thermal dissociation, that is the equality T_t and T_v $(\tau_d \gg \tau_v)$* during the whole process of the vibrational relaxation, is well known to be invalid under high-temperature conditions (here and henceforth K_d is the rate constant for dissociation, T_t is translational temperature, T_v is vibrational temperature, τ_d is the characteristic time for the dissociation, and τ_v is the characteristic time for vibrational relaxation). This important point may be illustrated with the experimental results obtained in Ref. 133 and given here in Table 8.

TABLE 8
Dissociation delay time Δt in an $O_2 +$ Ar mixture

$T_t, °K$	$\Delta t / \tau_v$	T_v / T_t at the moment Δt of time
5500	2.4	0.93
8000	1.1	0.71
11000	0.55	0.48
14000	0.45	0.41
18000	0.40	0.37

Vibrational and translational temperatures are seen from Table 8 to be unequal in oxygen beginning from 8000°K.

Thus vibrational relaxation and thermal dissociation should be considered simultaneously; both the processes affect each other greatly (135,136).

Two aspects may be observed in the theory of dissociation. Rice (137) assumed that the transition of the molecule from the bound vibrational states into two free atoms occurs only from upper vibrational states. This assumption implies that the molecule must rise over vibrational states from lower levels to upper ones by means of one-quantum transitions and be near the dissociation limit (within the interval $\sim kT$) to dissociate after the nearest collision.

Careri (138–141) assumed that the dissociation may occur by means of a direct transition from lower vibrational levels due to the occurrence of some strong collisions.

*Rotational relaxation is not considered here because usually $\tau_r \ll \tau_v$. This relation, however, appears to be not always valid. Thus, as it has been shown in Ref. 134 the number of collisions needed for the rotational equilibrium to be established increase with the temperature, that is, results are quite opposite from those obtained for the vibrational relaxation.

A simultaneous consideration of vibrational relaxation and dissociation has been carried out in Ref. 142. Translational temperature appeared to be changed monotonously behind the shock-wave front in oxygen while T_v passed through a maximum; nevertheless, in nitrogen T_v was changed monotonously. This work is important because it is a principal approach describing simultaneous occurrence of vibrational relaxation and thermal dissociation. The results of the calculations have to be considered rather questionable; however, since dissociation was assumed not to disturb the Boltzmann distribution of molecules over vibrational levels, which is undoubtedly wrong.

This assumption was omitted in Ref. 13 where a consistent analysis of the problem was carried out for the system of "cut off" harmonic oscillators. This analysis showed the rate of dissociation to be determined mainly with vibrational (but not translational) and has not yet been completed up to the moment of dissociation. Dissociation significantly affects the rate of vibrational relaxation. In the opinion of the author of Ref. 13 one can still speak about an "establishment of some quasi-stationary conditions under which vibrational energy is determined with the rate of dissociation at the same moment of time." However, the same author asserts further that "quasi-stationary distribution establishment precedes dissociation and is experimentally observed as time-delay of dissociation" (13). These two assertions are contradictory (143).

Calculations of cross-sections for vibrational excitation are based as a rule on some model potentials. However, the vibrational excitation cross-section has been shown in Refs. 144–147, by considering vibrational energy transfer in the system (He + H_2) to be very sensitive to the form of the potential curve used. Molecular potentials are usually formed using additive interatomic potentials taken in pairs (the latter are approximated with exponential functions, their parameters being fitted to that of the Lennard-Jones potential). Such approximation does not result in the matrix elements or transition probabilities which are usually obtained using the rigorous potentials. A transition probability has been generally accepted to be determined mainly with colinear frontal collisions.*

This point proved to be unconfirmed with the calculation results using the rigorous potentials; the transition probability appeared to be determined mainly with collisions occurring at an angle of $40°$. Disregarding of small

*From the collision theory point of view collisions resulting in dissociation are non-adiabatic, that is, these are highly effective strong collisions, the relative kinetic energy of colliding particles being of the order of a few electron-volts. A collision may be imagined to occur as follows. After a fast rapproachement of colliding particles and mutual penetration of their electronic covers, a strong repulsion occurs due to a very rapid increase in the repulsion potential under small distances between colliding particles (in other words, collisions are nonadiabatic, according to Ehrenfest).

differences between matrix diagonal elements of the interaction potential results in great errors in the transition probability values. Thus the consideration of molecules as harmonic oscillators and the linearization of the interaction potential are inadmissible. The anharmonicity of molecules is shown in Ref. 147 to yield values of transition probabilities $10-10^3$ times less than the true ones.

Thus the problem of the model potential selection and application to precise calculations must be specially studied and established, since even for a simple system such as He + H_2 the utilization of a model potential results in great errors.

Observed dissociation rate depends upon level populations and probabilities for dissociation occurring from separate vibrational levels. Under plasma-chemical temperatures ($\sim 10^4$ °K) the time of vibrational relaxation is about that of thermal dissociation. Hence, vibrational nonequilibrium and differences between dissociation probabilities from different excited levels largely determine the total rate of molecule dissociation. An attempt has been made in Ref. 148 to calculate the dissociation rate assuming dissociation to occur mainly from a high vibrational level. The effect of vibrational excitation on dissociation has been discussed earlier in Refs. 142 and 149 using the Landau-Teller model.* An adverse effect of dissociation upon vibrational relaxation has been accounted for in Refs. 73 and 150. These vibration-dissociation models contain two important assumptions: (1) Vibrational relaxation resulting in a Boltzmann distribution over vibrational levels is assumed to occur through a number of Boltzmann distributions.† (2) Dissociation probabilities from any vibrational level are the same under collisions with sufficient energy.

---

*Landau and Teller (151) assumed the interaction potential in the form $A \exp(-r/s)$ where "r" is the intermolecular distance and s is the effective distance, for the intermolecular forces to act. Using the Ehrenfest principle the authors of Ref. 151 concluded that only repulsion forces which act at small distances have to be accounted for. They found the quantity τ (or $P_{1,0}$) to depend upon the temperature as

$$\tau \sim T^{-1/2} \exp(T^{-1/3}) \qquad [118]$$

†This is far from being always valid. Thus, in Ref. 152 the relaxation of harmonic oscillator's nonequilibrium vibrational distribution was considered. Using the transition probabilities calculated for such oscillators, the relaxation to the final equilibrium distribution of the Boltzmann initial distribution and of the distribution in the form of the δ-function were studied. The transition to the final distribution with the temperature T_k appeared to occur through a series of intermediate Boltzmann distributions with the temperatures $T = T(t)$ and $T_o \geqslant T(t) \geqslant T_k$ provided the initial distribution was Boltzmannian with a certain initial temperature T_o. The initial δ-function-like distribution appeared to relax to the final distribution, passing through a series of nonequilibrium distributions. The mean energy relaxation depends only on its initial value and does not depend on the form of the initial distribution; the time of its relaxation is $(K_{1,0} \theta)^{-1}$, where $K_{1,0}$ is the probability for the transition between the ground and first excited levels and $\theta = h\nu/KT_v$. It should be observed

In Ref. 71 assumption (1) has been retained, but instead of assumption (2) different dissociation probabilities have been taken from different vibrational levels.

The equation for the vibrational relaxation accounting for dissociation and recombination may be written as

$$\frac{\partial \varepsilon}{\partial t} = \frac{\varepsilon(T_t) - \varepsilon}{\tau_k} - \frac{[\bar{E}(T_t, T_v) - \varepsilon]}{[n_M]}\left(\frac{d[n_M]}{dt}\right)_f + \frac{[\bar{E}(T_t, T_t) - \varepsilon]}{[n_M]}\left(\frac{d[n_M]}{dt}\right)_r$$

[119]

where n_M is the dissociating molecule's density;

$$\left(\frac{d[n_M]}{dt}\right)_f, \qquad \left(\frac{d[n_M]}{dt}\right)_r$$

are rates of dissociation and recombination, respectively;

$$\bar{E}(T_t, T_v), \qquad \bar{E}(T_t, T_t)$$

are the mean energy transferred from the vibrational degree of freedom into dissociation and the mean energy transferred to the vibrational degree of freedom from recombination, respectively; T_t and T_v are translational and vibrational temperatures, respectively (the latter corresponds to the Boltzmann distribution of the vibrational energy ε).

The effect of vibrational relaxation upon dissociation may be expressed through the ratio $\alpha = K_d/K_{dl}$ where K_{dl} is the rate constant for dissociation under vibrational equilibrium and $T_t = $ const; since $T_v < T_t$ the quantity α is always less than unity. There are some reasons to consider dissociation probability to be higher from upper vibrational levels (theoretical evidence for this may be found in Refs. 75–77 and experimental evidence in Ref. 133). In Ref. 142 the probability exponential distribution has been used as a possible approach:

$$F_j = \exp\left[-\frac{D - E_j}{KU}\right]$$

[120]

where D is the energy of dissociation, E_j is the energy of j vibrational level, U is the fitting parameter. The rate of dissociation of molecules behind the shock wave was calculated using the above model. Numerical solutions were found for $(O_2 + Ar)$ mixtures. The time of dissociation delay calculated for

---

that in the work under discussion an exponential form was assumed for the transition probability dependence upon the vibrational quantum number, unlike the Landau-Teller approach, where this dependence was assumed to be linear. The proceeding relaxations proved to be determined mainly by the form of this dependence.

$U = \infty$ was much less than that experimentally observed. Making use of an extrapolated value of τ_k from Ref. 156 and of $U = D/3k$ yields the time delay and rate constants for dissociation, which are in a good agreement with experimental values of Ref. 133. Assuming $U = D/6k$ and using τ_k two times less yields nearly the same results. Vibrational nonequilibrium results in a temperature dependence of the pre-exponential factor of the rate constant for dissociation. In case $U = \infty$ and $U = D/6k$ this dependence is as T^{-1} and T^{-3}, respectively, in the temperature range 4000–8000°K. Unfortunately, the introduction of physically vague U parameters is undoubtedly a disadvantage of this interesting work.

A general case has been considered in Ref. 157, with no quantitative results being obtained. Harmonic oscillators were considered having initially the Boltzmann distribution under the heat-bath conditions. Such conditions may take place in shock-tube experiments.*

In a series of works surveyed in Ref. 160 both dynamic and statistical methods have been used to analyze shock-tube experimental data on vibrational excitation and dissociation of diatomic molecules. Hamilton equations have been solved with classical mechanics methods under various initial states of colliding particles, and then the kinetic problem was considered. The solution of the dynamic part of the problem was represented by a set of distribution functions, $f(E'_v, E_v, E_n)$, where E'_v, E_v are energies of initial and excited vibrational states. As a result, probabilities P_{ij} for dissociation from i levels were calculated.

The quantities P_{ij} proved to be independent of temperature and increased with level quantum number at temperatures $3000 \leqslant T \leqslant 20,000°K$ and $j > 20$; the probability for many-quantum transitions to occur is high within this temperature region.

These results differ greatly from those of the Landau-Teller theory. As to dissociation, its probability from high vibrational levels may exceed that for the transition to the next level.

A natural desire to avoid strictly limiting assumptions of the theory of absolute rates of reactions has led to the development of some alternative approaches. These are theories which consider chemical reaction rates in terms of nonequilibrium statistical mechanics (161–164). In these works (and

---

*Refs. 158 and 159 will not be discussed. In the former the effect of vibrational relaxation upon dissociation has been considered neglecting recombination and using diffusion theory with $(\tau_v/\tau_d) > 1$ and $t > \tau_v$, with some physically unfounded assumptions being made (as the authors themselves observed). In the latter work a procedure of calculation has been suggested (to the same approximations) which has been founded on quantum-mechanical theory of dissociation; some results on dissociation kinetics have been obtained for $t > \tau_v$.

especially in Ref. 164) the rate constant for a chemical reaction was assumed to be the same both under near- and far-from-equilibrium conditions.

Montroll and Shuler (53), making use of the stochastic processes theory, considered dissociation as a stochastic roam over vibrational levels between reflecting and absorbing barriers. The recombination of the dissociated components was not accounted for (the corresponding equation did not contain the second order terms) and in the beginning the temperature of reacting molecules is less than that of the heat-bath environment. Reacting molecules were assumed to be excited with collisions and passed from one level to another (step by step) until they reached the $(N + 1)$ level; then they disappeared irreversibly from the reacting system. According to the stochastic processes theory, this process may be considered a stochastic roam between a reflecting barrier at $m = 0$ and an absorbing barrier at $m = (N + 1)$. The problem is to determine an average time τ of the "first appearance," that is, an average time necessary for the roaming particle (an excited molecule) to reach the absorbing barrier for the first time.* Finally, every molecule dissociated and left the heat bath. Montroll and Shuler used the Landau-Teller collisional transition probabilities calculated for the "cut-off" harmonic oscillator accounting for only one-quantum transitions selection rules. The initial distribution was not Boltzmannian, all the molecules, existing in the ground states. The value of τ found corresponded to the rate of dissociation as 10^{11} cm^3 mole^{-1} sec^{-1} while the experimental value amounted to 10^{16} cm^3 mole^{-1} sec^{-1}. Such a high rate of dissociation experimentally observed cannot be explained from a theoretical point of view unless many-quantum transitions are assumed not to occur (Ref. 3, Chapter 3).

The results of the calculations showed the rate of the chemical reaction under $(E_a/kT) = 5$ to differ by $\sim 20\%$ from that calculated using the equilibrium theory; under $(E_a/kT) = 10$ this difference is negligibly small; in the case of $(E_a/kT) = <5$ (being interesting from the plasma-chemical reaction kinetics point of view) the theory does not allow us to draw certain conclusions. The authors of Refs. 17 and 166 obtained some analogous results.

The effect of internal degrees of freedom perturbations produced with chemical reaction occurrence upon the reaction rate has been studied in Refs. 166 and 167. The effect of nonequilibrium vibrational distribution upon the chemical reaction rate has been found negligible up to $E_b > 10kT$ assuming harmonic oscillator model, one-quantum transitions, and the Maxwell velocity distribution. This criterion should be observed to be about the same

---

*Such an approach has been used earlier by Kramers (165), who considered chemical reaction as the diffusion through the potential barrier of a particle in Brownian motion. In Ref. 53 a quantum-mechanical version of Kramer's model has been suggested.

as in the case of Maxwell velocity distribution perturbations. However a connection between these cannot be pointed out since deviations from Boltzmann and Maxwell distributions differ completely from the physical point of view.

Dependence of dissociation rate on pressure is determined also with deviations from equilibrium populations of vibrational levels.

The thermal dissociation is known to be the first- and the second-order reaction under high and low pressures, respectively (168,169). A transitional region occurs between these extreme cases within which the reaction order is changed from the second to the first. The dependence of dissociation rate factors upon the pressure is due to deviations from equilibrium distributions over the internal degrees of freedom of reacting molecules. Under high pressures, when the rate of intermolecular energy exchange is more than that of the molecule's degrees of freedom inside, the equilibrium distribution perturbations are small. Under low pressures, however, any perturbations of the Boltzmann distribution greatly affects the dissociation rate.* That is why the method of the transitional state is not applicable in this case (170) to calculate K_d.

The change of a reaction rate with pressure has been predicted by Lindeman (171), who considered the simultaneous occurrence of the chemical reaction perturbing the distribution and the deactivation of excited molecules according to the scheme

$$B + B \underset{K_{deact}}{\overset{K_{act}}{\rightleftharpoons}} B^* + B \qquad [121]$$

$$B^* \xrightarrow{K_c} products$$

The rate constant K_i for the monomolecular reaction (being dependent on the pressure) is usually found according to Rice, Ramsperger, and Kassel through the averaging of the quantity $[\omega K_i/(\omega + K_i)]$ over the equilibrium distribution (here ω is the effective collision frequency, K_i is the rate constant for the molecule's dissociation from i excited state (172)). The mechanism of strong collisions and a stochastic character of dissociation are believed to be valid here; dissociation thus occurs with a probability $K_i \Delta t$, where Δt is a small interval of time (172). According to Kassel's theory K_i is assumed to be

---

*Great nonequilibrium effects may occur at low pressures under the following physical conditions [47]: 1. There are many molecules on internal levels with energies more than E_b; this takes place under high T and small ratios of E_b/kT. 2. The probability is great for the deactivation of levels with energies higher than E_b to the levels with energies lower than E_b, but still near E_b. 3. The probability is great for the molecules to be kept excited on levels lower than E_b but still near E_b.

dependent on E_i; the form of this dependence has to be found using statistical physics methods (173).

Slater (172) suggested a more detailed model of intermolecular interaction causing dissociation. He assumed that (1) only the vibrational motion is important to determine K_i, (2) this vibrational motion is harmonic, (3) the reaction occurs under sufficiently great (and discoverable) value of the reaction coordinate. The second assumption has been shown later (174,175) to be extremely simplified. An analysis of this problem has been carried out in Ref. 176 using numerical procedures to integrate the motion equations; the small-perturbation method cannot be applied to molecules approaching the dissociation (the anharmonicity rises). An accounting for the anharmonicity proved to be extremely necessary.

The details of the molecular model also affect the deviations from the Maxwell velocity distribution and the Boltzmann distribution produced with chemical reactions.

Only in the case of simplest and most unreal models the effect of chemical reactions upon the Maxwell distribution is small and does not depend practically on the assumptions of models. This is the case, for instance, for the following models:

$$
\begin{cases}
\sigma^* = 0 & E < E_B \\[2mm]
\dfrac{\sigma^*}{\sigma} = 1 & E > E_b \\[2mm]
\dfrac{\sigma^*}{\sigma} = 1 - \exp\left(-\dfrac{E}{2E_b}\right)
\end{cases}
$$

$$
\begin{cases}
\sigma^* = 0 & E < E_b \\[2mm]
\sigma^* = 1 - \exp\left(\dfrac{E_b}{E}\right) & E > E_b
\end{cases}
$$

where E is the initial relative kinetic energy and E_b is the energy barrier opposing the reaction. The results of calculations carried out in Refs. 17 and 18 are mainly in good agreement with each other; thus, the distribution perturbation is negligibly small until $E_b \geqslant 10\,kT$. However, these calculations have been shown by Takayanagi (177) to be doubtful because the expansion of the Boltzmann equation's solution for chemical reaction in Sonin polynomials is divergent. This point needs to be further studied.

The ratio of the reactants' masses was shown in Ref. 177 to be important for a nonequilibrium production; momentum distribution proved to be significantly perturbed in the case of a light molecule taking part in the reaction that may greatly affect the reaction rate.

Although the solid ball model proves to be reasonable for the consideration of a rather great number of chemical reactions, it is extremely simplified from the point of view of elastic collisions theory. As a matter of fact, the differential cross-section for the elastic scattering in the case of more real interaction models is increased rapidly for small scattering angles and small relative energies, while in the case of the solid ball model this cross-section does not depend on the angle and energy. Collisions at small angles may be very important for the establishment of the Maxwell distribution.

As a conclusion, some useful references are given here on vibrational relaxation (188) and dissociation (132) times.

B. Recombination Reactions

The recombination of two atoms (or radicals) to form a molecule results in a rather greater energy release.* This energy must be removed from a vibrationally excited molecule just formed, since otherwise the molecule will dissociate again. This excess of vibrational energy contained in the highly excited molecule M^{**} may be removed due to its collision with a third particle M' that results in M^{**} deactivating into an upper stable vibrational state M^* and in a translational energy increase in M' (the collision of the second kind). Thus the recombination reaction may be described as

$$R + R \rightleftharpoons M^{**}$$

$$M^{**} + M' \rightleftharpoons M^* + M$$

[122]

or alternatively as

$$R + M' \rightleftharpoons M'R^{**}$$

$$M'R^{**} + M' \rightleftharpoons M'R^* + M'$$

[123]

$$M'R^* + R \rightarrow M^* + M'$$

The expression for the recombination rate factor K_r may be obtained using any of these mechanisms.

Numerous experimental studies of recombination show the quantity K_r to be slowly decreasing with temperature under equilibrium conditions (in the

*Recombination reactions are especially important in the studies of decaying plasmas and quenching processes (forced lowering of the system's temperature at the rate of $dT/dt = f(t, \mathbf{r})$). The energy removal from the system increases the probability for recombination to occur under collisions (recombination is assumed here to include any reactions of the types $e + M^+ \rightarrow M$, $R + R' \rightarrow RR'$ where R, R' are atoms, radicals and so on, and M molecules).

case of recombination under triple collisions*). Hence, the K_r temperature dependence may be described with a "negative activation energy." Since the triple collision probability is small the activation energy should be small too; if the activation energy were large the recombination would be impossible. In the equilibrium theories for recombination a transitional binary complex is assumed to occur, the lifetime of which is decreasing with temperature, causing the activation energy to be negative.

The theory of absolute rates of chemical reactions allows the value of K_r to be predicted, which may be in agreement with its value experimentally observed within a rather narrow temperature range but does not give any account of the K_r temperature dependence. This theory does not describe in reality the recombination under nonequilibrium conditions.

A far more interesting and general approach was developed as early as 1939 by Wigner (178–180). The three recombining atoms were considered in these works as being components of a canonical ensemble. A volume of the phase space containing these three particles may be divided into two regions. In the first region of recombination, two atoms are recombining in the presence of the third one, and all three atoms exist independently within the second "free" region. The problem is as follows: At the initial moment of time the three atoms are present in the free region and the probability must be found for the particles to be in the recombination region after a certain period of time. Since the trajectories of the three particles are a line in the phase space, the rate of the reaction may be interpreted as the number of trajectories which proceed from the free region to that of recombination. The rate of the reaction may be defined mathematically using the density of the points in the phase space and the corresponding velocity component of the representing point, i.e., instantaneous values of atoms' coordinates and momentum in terms of the Hamilton mechanics.

A certain arbitrariness should be observed taking place in the definition of the size of the recombination region. This is due to a possibility that the three particles are just near each other but still not recombined. As it has been suggested in Ref. 93, to reject this arbitrariness, the recombination region should be defined so that the reaction rate constant is minimum within this region and under the third particle removal from the newly formed molecule the latter passes into the actual region of recombination. This problem has been solved in Ref. 181 where the effects of the rotational barrier and the van der Waals attraction forces between the third particle M' and every recombining particle R during the recombination were accounted for. Sufficiently

---

*The three-body recombination takes place in the case of atoms and diatomic molecules. In the case of more complex polyatomic fragments binary recombination is possible; the energy thus released is distributed over the numerous bonds of the colliding particles.

arbitrary model interaction potentials were taken in this work although the result of calculations is rather sensitive to their forms. Nevertheless, the results obtained in Ref. 181 are the upper limits for experimental values, the agreement between them becoming worse with temperature due to insufficient account for those recombination acts which are followed by immediate dissociation. The rate increases with temperature. On the whole, the theory developed in Ref. 181 is a great success; a further development may imply the correction of the interaction potential to be made so that it would allow the phase space regions to be more correctly defined.

Another interesting approach to the problem of recombination has been developed in Ref. 25. The main assumption was that electronic transitions do not occur during recombination in molecules, so that the interaction potential for the system may be simply defined. As distinguished from the calculations of vibrational excitation made in Ref. 182, collisions were considered on the basis of classical mechanics. That was possible because the De Broglie wavelength of interacting atoms is small compared to the size of the interaction region of these atoms, and moreover, the energy transferred under the recombination is great compared to the energy gaps between the levels of the newly formed molecule.

The theories for the recombination rate developed in Refs. 25 and 178–180 are really equilibrium ones; that is, the rate of reaction may be found by the rate of dissociation using the equilibrium constant. It has been shown in Refs. 183 and 184 that $(K_d)_{ne} < (K_d)_e$ (where subscripts "ne" and "e" mean nonequilibrium and equilibrium, respectively) while nonequilibrium conditions do not affect K_r because the rate of recombination is determined by the time two free colliding atoms take to transit into one of the possible bound states (this transition occurs in one step). Thus the rate of recombination does not depend on the vibrational level population. If this is the case, the classical relation $K = K_d/K_r$ is not valid under nonequilibrium conditions and cannot be used to determine K_d and K_r.

Dissociation and recombination may be considered as the representing points of motion in the phase space. The regions of the phase space where recombination may occur are evidently limited by the laws of conservation of total momentum, angular momentum, and energy. The rate of recombination may be expressed as the product of the probability for recombination and collision frequency of dynamic systems satisfying the laws of conservation. The former factor is a function of three-body interaction potential and of trajectories in which the three particles are moving along; presently it is not possible to find it in the case of three particles with about equal masses. The latter factor may be calculated using the kinetic theory methods.

Keck (25) has suggested that the probability for recombination be calculated statistically. Then reasonable values of the rate factor for recombination may be found. The experimental quantity K_r, however, diminishes with temperature more rapidly than expected according to this theory. It implies that the statistical evolution analysis of the complex formed under collision is insufficient and that the detailed mechanism for three-body collision is certainly important. Thus the analysis made in Ref. 25 has to be corrected to account for the interaction dynamics.*

In Ref. 185 classical dynamics methods have been applied to study the recombination reaction

$$I + I + Ar \longrightarrow I_2 + Ar$$

We take interest not in the results of this work but in some important features of the dynamic approach used. The problem has been considered in the case of a central potential field $V(r)$ using polar coordinates.

The time to pass any path is easily determined under dynamic calculations using the concept of the sight distance. To determine the lifetime of the complex formed under collision the integration is carried out along the trajectory from some r_{max} where the collision begins. The value of r_{max} may be simply determined since the quantity dr/dt is minimum under some values of the sight distance and the distance between particles. The reaction rate constant is determined through the integration of an expression containing the product of collision frequency by the complex's lifetime over all the sight distance and over all the values of the initial kinetic energy (the interaction potential has to be cut off at very great and very small distances between particles).

The results of shock tubes, flash photolysis, and plasma-chemical experiments suggest that nonequilibrium dissociation-recombination theory must necessarily be developed. Thus, nonequilibrium atomic recombination theory, for instance, predicts K_r to be independent of temperature. At the same time experimental data available show K_r to be decreased as T^{-1} at low temperatures and apparently as T^{-2} at high temperatures. Simple nonequilibrium theories account explicitly for the reaction and vibrational relaxation rates and result in the correct dependence of $K_r \sim T^{-1}$ at low temperatures (186,187).

---

*Calculations based upon mechanics yield results, however, in good agreement with those of statistical calculations and suggest that other conclusions may be made, at least in a particular case. Thus the calculated rate constant for the reaction

$$I + I \; \rightleftharpoons \; I_2^*(^1\Sigma)$$

$$I_2^* + M \longrightarrow I_2 + M$$

is in good agreement with the rate constant statistically found (25). These calculated results allow the following conclusions to be made: (1) The system characteristics are determined by collisions having the largest possible angular momentum. (2) Atom collisions are not necessarily adiabatic. (3) The detailed mechanism of collisions under recombination is not important, at least in the case of heavy particles, as it has been suggested in Ref. 25.

This problem has been considered in Ref. 55 using the Pauli equation. The equilibrium conditions will be discussed first, atoms and molecules being placed in an inert gas heat bath (inert gas molecules are marked with M). The rate of the reaction may be described macroscopically as

$$\frac{d[A_2]}{dt} = K_r[M][A]^2 - K_d[M][A_2] \tag{124}$$

This macroscopic description requires naturally vibrational (and rotational) transitions in the excited molecules to be accounted for as

$$\frac{[dA_{i2}]}{dt} = K_{ri}[M][A]^2 - K_{di}[M][A_{i2}]$$
$$+ [M]\sum_{i \neq n} K_{ni}[A_{n2}] - [M]\sum_{j \neq n} K_{ji}[A_{i2}] \tag{125}$$

Let us take

$$\frac{d[A_2]}{dt} = \sum_{i=0}^{N} \frac{d[A_{i2}]}{dt} \tag{126}$$

where N is the number of the energy levels. Using eq. [125] the following expression may be found:

$$\frac{d[A_2]}{dt} = [M][A]^2 \sum_{i=0}^{N} K_{ri} - [M]\sum_{i=0}^{N} K_{di}[A_{i2}] \tag{127}$$

If the distributions are in equilibrium inside the internal degrees of freedom of the diatomic molecule, then

$$[A_{i2}] = \frac{\exp\left(-\dfrac{E_i}{kT}\right)[A_2]}{\displaystyle\sum_{n=0}^{N} \exp\left(-E_n/kT\right)} \equiv \gamma_i[A_2] \tag{128}$$

As a result eq. [127] becomes

$$V_0 \equiv \frac{d[A_2]}{dt} = [M][A]^2 \sum_{i=0}^{N} K_{ri} - [M][A_2]\sum_{i=0}^{N} K_{di}\gamma_i \tag{129}$$

Comparing eqs. [124] and [129] yields

$$K_r = \sum_{i=0}^{N} K_{ri}$$

$$K_d = \sum_{i=0}^{N} K_{di\gamma i} \tag{130}$$

Under $d(A_2)/dt \neq 0$ the assumption about the equilibrium distributions over internal degrees of freedom is not valid because of perturbations produced by chemical reactions; nonequilibrium distributions produced affect the rate of the chemical reaction.

The derivation of the kinetic equation in the case of nonequilibrium recombination-dissociation theory is carried out like that in the case of the equilibrium theory; the distribution function over internal degrees of freedom is necessarily included in the consideration.

Not dwelling upon the derivation of this equation, we shall only point out that the method used is similar to that of Enskog. Finally, the equation for nonequilibrium recombination-dissociation kinetics of diatomic molecules may be described (instead of eq. [129]) as:

$$\frac{d[A_2]}{dt} = V_0 - [M][A_2]V_0 \sum_{i=0}^{N} K_{di} \gamma_i f_i$$

$$= V_0 \left(1 - [M][A_2] \sum_{i=0}^{N} K_{di} \gamma_i f_i \right) = V_0[1 - I(T)] \qquad [131]$$

where f_i is the distribution function. Thus chemical and vibrational relaxations are connected through the function $I(T)$ which is the first term of the nonequilibrium process rate expansion as

$$V = V_0[1 - I(T) + I^2(T) - I^3(T) + \cdots + (-1)^n I^n(T)] = \varphi(T)V_0 \quad [132]$$

The macroscopic equation in the nonequilibrium case is like eq. [124] except that

$$K_r = \varphi(T) \sum_{i=0}^{N} K_{ri} \qquad K_d = \varphi(T) \sum_{i=0}^{N} \gamma_i K_{di} \qquad [133]$$

The problem is considered using the perturbation theory procedure near the equilibrium so that when the reaction rate approaches that for vibrational relaxation, higher-order terms may have to be accounted for.

In the case of the "nearest neighbor" model (one-quantum transitions) the function $\varphi(T)$ is

$$\varphi(T) = \left\{ 1 + \gamma_N K_{dN} \left[\sum_{i=0}^{N} \frac{(\sum_n^i \gamma_n)^2 (i-1)}{K_{i-1,i} \gamma_i} \right] \right\}^{-1} \qquad [134]$$

Calculations show K_r to decrease with temperature as T^{-2} at sufficiently high temperatures. Although this conclusion has been drawn for a particular case, the main equations above are sufficiently general and may be used to study more real models.

C. Reactions Under Electromagnetic Pulse Conditions

Processes initiated by electron impact and also reactions of ions, excited particles and so on, are known to be important for the kinetics of chemical reactions occurring under electric discharge conditions at pressures ~ 0.1 atm and lower due to the fact that the electron mean energy may exceed, by orders of magnitude, the translational mean energy of the heavy particles under these conditions. Moreover, field intensities in pulse discharges are usually very high, which results in a nonequilibrium distribution of electron energy (while translational energy distribution for heavy particles may be in equilibrium). Thus data are needed on concentrations and energy distribution functions of charged particles to study chemical reactions under the given conditions.

The density and energy of charged particles (electrons mainly) also determine the electrodynamic characteristics of the pulse discharge plasma which affect the field intensities inside the latter. Therefore, to study chemical processes under these conditions simultaneous equations are necessarily considered in chemical kinetics, energy, and electrodynamics.*

An approximate phenomenological procedure will be considered here for nonequilibrium chemical reaction kinetics calculations using electronic digital computer programs. The reactions are assumed to occur under electromagnetic hf and VHF pulse conditions. In particular, ionization kinetics of N_2 under VHF pulse conditions has been studied in such a way that allows us to find space-time density distributions of electrons, ions, and N atoms. The results of the calculations are compared to those of an experiment.

In studies of electromagnetic wave interaction with plasmas simultaneous equations of chemical kinetics and electrodynamics must also be solved. (These have been carried out in Refs. 189–199 and surveyed briefly in Ref. 200.) Due to that, the authors of these works took interest mainly in wave propagation processes in plasmas and physical-chemical process kinetics has been significantly simplified.

The mathematical model for the process under study consists of two parts: (1) equations of homogeneous chemical reactions kinetics†

$$\frac{\partial N_i}{\partial t} = \sum_j d_{ij} N_j + \sum_j \sum_k \beta_{ijk} N_j N_k \qquad [135]$$

---

*Hydrodynamic processes are not considered, although these may be important in general in the case of moving plasmas.

†Generally, diffusion processes must be accounted for in these equations. In the present case the diffusion terms may be shown to be small (200).

where N_j is the density of any possible reactant (electrons, positive and negative ions, excited and neutral particles); α_{ij} and β_{ijk} are rate factors for various possible processes* (ionization, recombination, dissociation), which may not be of the Arrhenius type and may depend on the electric field intensity (200); (2) Maxwell's equation†

$$\text{rot } \mathbf{H} = \frac{1}{c}\frac{\partial \mathbf{D}}{\partial t} + \frac{4\pi}{c}\mathbf{J}_{\text{ext}} \qquad [136a]$$

$$\text{div } \mathbf{D} = 4\pi\rho_{\text{ext}} \qquad [136b]$$

$$\text{rot } \mathbf{E} = -\frac{1}{c}\frac{\partial \mathbf{H}}{\partial t} \qquad [136c]$$

$$\text{div } \mathbf{H} = 0 \qquad [136d]$$

$$\mathbf{D} = \varepsilon'\mathbf{E} \qquad [136e]$$

where $\mathbf{E}$ and $\mathbf{D}$ are the intensity and induction of the electric field; $\mathbf{H}$ is the intensity of magnetic field; $\mathbf{J}_{\text{ext}}$ and ρ_{ext} are the current and charge densities, respectively, of external sources; c is the light velocity; ε' is the complex dielectric constant which is characteristic of the plasma. For the isotropic plasma

$$\varepsilon' = \varepsilon - i\,\frac{4\pi}{\omega}\,\sigma \qquad [137]$$

where ε is the dielectric permeability, σ is the plasma conductivity, ω is the electromagnetic field frequency. The values of ε and σ are determined mainly by the electron density (199)

$$\varepsilon = 1 - \frac{4\pi e^2 N_e}{m(\omega^2 + v_{\text{eff}}^2)} \qquad [138]$$

$$\sigma = \frac{e^2 N_e v_{\text{eff}}}{m(\omega^2 + v_{\text{eff}}^2)}$$

where e, m are the charge and mass of the electron, N_e is the electron density, v_{eff} is the effective collision frequency (for electron-heavy particle collisions resulting in the momentum transfer) which depends on the electron energy and particle densities.

---

*Zero- and third-order reactions are not considered since they occur rarely and may if necessary be included.

†It is assumed here that the magnetic permeability is unity for a plasma (199).

Using eqs. [136a–136e] and assuming (200),

$$\left| \frac{\partial \varepsilon}{\partial t} \frac{\partial \mathbf{E}}{\partial t} \right| \ll \left| \varepsilon' \frac{\partial^2 \mathbf{E}}{\partial t^2} \right|$$

[139]

$$\left| \frac{\partial^2 \varepsilon'}{\partial t^2} \mathbf{E} \right| \ll \left| \varepsilon' \frac{\partial^2 \mathbf{E}}{\partial t^2} \right|$$

yields a well-known stationary wave equation:

$$\Delta \mathbf{E(r)} - \text{grad div } \mathbf{E(r)} + \frac{\omega^2}{c^2} \varepsilon' \mathbf{E(r)} = 0 \qquad [140]$$

where ε' depends upon time and coordinates.

Simultaneous partial differential equations [135] and [140] are essentially nonlinear. This nonlinearity is due to the fact that the rate factors α_{ij} and β_{ijk} may depend on the electric field intensity which is the solution of the wave eq. [140]. At the same time the quantity ε' in eq. [140] depends in turn upon both time-dependent electron density, found as a result of the solution of eq. [135], and the electric field intensity itself (through ν_{eff}).

Thus, the mathematical model of the process under consideration consists of simultaneous nonstationary chemical kinetic (SNCK) eqs. [135] and stationary wave (SW) equations [140] with corresponding initial and boundary conditions.

To solve this system of equations the SNCK eq. [135] are to be numerically integrated first, resulting in all the particle densities at every moment of time and the complex dielectric permeability ε'. Then the SW equation [140] is solved with boundary conditions being found under the solution procedure using integration procedure (200).

Let us apply the integration procedure just described to the study of N_2 ionization kinetics under VHF plasmotron conditions (Fig. 13). A quasi-monochromatic wave H_{10} is excited during VHF pulses of τ duration in a rectangular wave guide ($a = 7.2$ cm and $b = 3.4$ cm are shown in Fig. 13), possibly with some repetition rate. For this wave the electric field may be described as

$$E_r = E_0 \sin \frac{\pi x}{a} e^{-ik'y} e^{-i\omega t}$$

[141]

$$K = \sqrt{\frac{\omega^2}{c^2} - \frac{\pi^2}{a^2}}$$

where x and y are the coordinates; t is the time; ω is the wave frequency; $i = \sqrt{-1}$, and E_0 is the amplitude of the electric field intensity.

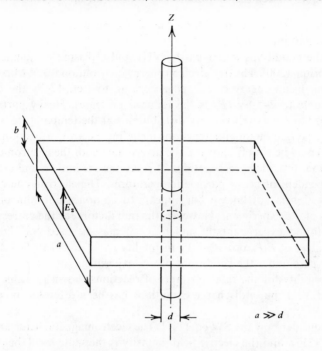

Figure 13   The model for the VHF plasmotron.

Let us compose the chemical kinetic equations for the processes occurring in nitrogen under the action of VHF electromagnetic fields.

Possible reactions are shown in Table 9; the corresponding rate constants are available from the literature references shown in this table.

TABLE 9
Reactions possible in N_2 subjected to VHF electromagnetic fields

No.	Reaction	References
1.	$e + N_2 \rightarrow N_2^+ + 2e$	202,203
2.	$N_2^+ + N_2 \rightarrow N_3^+ + N$	204
3.	$N_2^+ + N_2 + M \rightleftharpoons N_4^+ + M$	206,207
4.	$N_2^+ + N \rightarrow N_2 + N^+$	208
5.	$N^+ + N_2 + N_2 \rightleftharpoons N_3^+ + N_2$	206
6.	$N_2^+ + e \rightarrow 2N$	209,210
7.	$N_3^+ + e \rightarrow 3N$	211,212
8.	$N_4^+ + e \rightarrow 2N + N_2$	211,212
9.	$N^+ + e \rightarrow N^* + h\nu$	208
10.	$N + N + M \rightarrow N_2 + M$	205,213

In this table M is a third body, N^* is the excited nitrogen atom, and hv is the radiation quantum.

Under the conditions discussed the VHF pulse plasma is significantly in nonequilibrium (200). The free electron energy distribution is not Maxwellian; the electron mean energy calculated according to Ref. 17 by the quantity E/P_0 amounts to 2–5 eV (P_0 is the reduced pressure). Heavy particles are assumed to have Maxwell velocity distributions at the temperature $\sim 300°K$. Therefore, the rate factors for reactions including electrons (reactions [1,6–9] in Table 9) may be simply shown to be determined with the electron distribution function, provided cross-sections of reactions are known and are practically independent of heavy particle temperatures. The electron energy distribution function is not known but appears to be nonequilibrium under the conditions of the experiment. However, the rate factors for the corresponding reactions found experimentally under $\omega = 0$ may be used for the corresponding values of E/P_0 provided the inequality $v_{eff}^2 \ll \omega^2$ is satisfied (214,215) as was the case under the conditions of our experiment.

The possibility for the rate constants of reactions shown in Table 9 to be used under VHF pulse discharge conditions has been discussed in detail in Ref. 216.

Let us consider now the SW eq. [140]. The electromagnetic fields are quasi-stationary (217), and the electric field intensity is the same in all the points of the surface (201) since the wavelength in the waveguide is great compared to the plasmotron tube radius. According to the symmetry condition the quantities E and ε' depend only on the distance r from the tube axis. The SW eq. [140] in cylindrical coordinates may be described as

$$\frac{d^2E(r)}{dr^2} + \frac{1}{r}\frac{dE(r)}{dr} + \frac{\omega^2}{c^2}\varepsilon'(r)E(r) = 0 \qquad [142]$$

The boundary condition in this case is

$$\tilde{E}(t) = E_0(t) - \tilde{E}_{refl}(t) \qquad [143]$$

To solve the SW equation the plasma has to be divided into small regions with particle densities being the same within each of these (200). In the present consideration the cylindrical plasma slab is divided naturally into l homogeneous cylindrical layers. Within each of these the solution of eq. [142] may be described (200,217) as

$$E_j(r) = C_j J_0(K_j r) \qquad [144]$$

where C_j is a constant being determined from the condition [143] for j layer; J_0 is the Bessel function of zero order; K_j is the complex wave number for j layer described as

$$K_j = \frac{\omega}{C}\sqrt{\varepsilon_j'} \qquad [145]$$

where E_j is the complex dielectric permeability for j layer.

Using the values of E_j ($j = 1, 2, \ldots, L$) found, the quantity E_{refl} on the cylinder's surface (201,212) may be found as

$$\bar{E}_{\text{refl}} = 0.4 \cdot 10^{-2}\pi \sum_{m=1}^{\infty} \frac{i\omega}{ac\Gamma_m} I \sin\frac{m\pi}{r} \sin\frac{m\pi(a/2) + R}{a} \qquad [146]$$

where

$$\Gamma_m = \sqrt{\frac{m^2\pi^2}{a^2} - \frac{\omega^2}{c^2}}$$

The total current within the plasma is

$$I = \int_0^R \tilde{\sigma}E2\pi rdr = 2\pi \sum_{j=1}^{N} \int_{r_j}^{r_{j+1}} \tilde{\sigma}_j E_j rdr \qquad [147]$$

where $\tilde{\sigma}_j = \sigma_j + i(\omega/4\pi)\varepsilon_i$ is the complex electrical conductivity of the plasma j layer; σ_j and E_j are the conductivity and dielectric permeability, respectively, of the plasma j layer.

Thus the electron density and electrical field space distributions are necessarily given initially to solve the simultaneous eqs. [141] and [142] using the procedure suggested in Ref. 200.

The initial density of electrons was taken as 10^2–10^4 cm^{-3}. The conductivity of the medium inside tube is negligibly small and its electrodynamic properties are practically those inside the waveguide medium under such electron concentrations. The electric field thus is not absorbed by the gas inside the tube at the initial moment, so $E(r) = E_0$ (218).

The results of the experimental study of nitrogen ionization under pulse VHF discharge conditions include time-space distributions of the electric field, reflection index "r" for the plasma slab and the energy E_p absorbed with the plasma (the experimental arrangement is described in Ref. 219).

So that a comparison is possible of the calculation results obtained for a single pulse with those of the experiment (where a series of pulses was used), the experimental conditions have to be analyzed thoroughly. Such an analysis has been carried out in Ref. 219 and showed: (1) The initial electron density increase up to values of about 10^8 cm^{-3} do not affect the calculation results. (2) Relatively small ($\sim 20\%$) changes in the gas temperature (and thus in the value of the reduced pressure) significantly affect time-space distributions of the plasma characteristics.

The plots of N_e, E and the electron mean energy as functions of time are shown in Fig. 14 for the axis (marked with O) and the boundary (marked with R) at a pressure of 30 torr. Experimental and calculated values are seen to be in good agreement. The experimental and calculated values of Γ and E_p are in

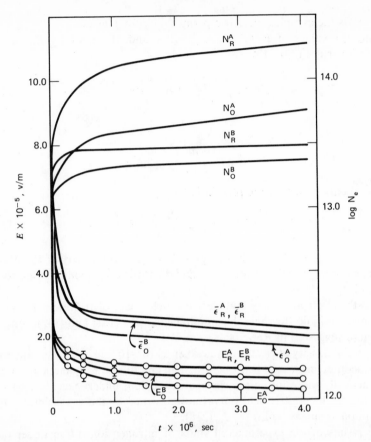

Figure 14 The electron density N_e, electric field intensity E, and the electron mean energy ε as functions of time for the plasma axis (O) and boundary (R); $P = 30$ torr; the incident wave electric field is $E_i = 9.6 \times 10^5$ v m^{-1} (A) and $E_i = 6 \times 10^5$ v m^{-1} (B); experimental points are marked with I.

good agreement too (differences between these do not exceed ~ 5 and 10%, respectively).

The plots of N_e, N_2^+, N_3^+, N_4^+, and N densities as functions of time are shown in Fig. 15.

At the beginning of the pulse up to the time of $10^{-7} - 10^{-8}$ sec the only positive ion N_2^+ occurs to provide the plasma quasineutrality; then only N_4^+ ions are important. This agrees with experimental data reported in Refs. 208, 212, and 220 which show the main important ions in the nitrogen plasma to be N_4^+ and N_3^+ under pressures 0.1–7.0 torr and values of the ratio E/P_0 up to 60 cm^{-1} torr^{-1}.

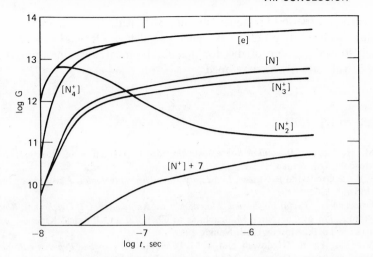

Figure 15   The electron N_e, atoms N, and ions N_2^+, N_3^+, N_4^+, N^+ densities as functions of time at the plasma slab boundary under VHF pulse discharge conditions; pulse power is 0.5 Mw; pulse duration is 4×10^{-6} sec; the pressure is 30 torr.

The N^+ ion density is 8–11 orders of magnitude less than other nitrogen ion densities.

Nitrogen atom density at the end of the VHF pulse amounts to 10^{-2}– 10^{13} cm^{-3} (under different intensities of the electric field and pressure of 30 torr). This value is at least 1–2 orders of magnitude less than that experimentally observed (221).

Thus the ionic mechanism for nitrogen atom formation does not provide for the atoms' density under the VHF pulse conditions. The energy removal by the formation of all the above particles (N, N^+, N_2^+, N_3^+, N_4^+) from N_2 molecules is observed to be significantly less than that supplied into the plasma under the experimental conditions (which were measured accurately).

Both the disagreements enable us to assume that the above mechanism of atomic nitrogen formation under the VHF pulse conditions is not complete and that it does not account for a possible way of N-atom formation through vibrationally and electronically excited nitrogen molecules and ions.

VII. CONCLUSION

In this account the incompleteness and fragmentary nature are due to the condition of the study of the problems considered. Many of these problems are only to be principally set, their consistent and rigorous solutions being still far away.

A reasonable period for nonequilibrium chemical kinetics to be developed for plasma chemical processes is difficult to define. Optimal ways are also difficult to evaluate and predict for this development. Just one thing is now clear: it will certainly be developed.

REFERENCES

1. M. N. Kogan, *Dinamika Razrezhennykh Gazova* [Dynamics of Rarefied Gases]. Moscow: Izd. Nauka, 1967.
2. S. R. de Groot and P. Mazur, *Non-Equilibrium Thermodynamics*. Amsterdam: North-Holland, 1962.
3. *Primeneneiye Vychilistelshchnoi Matematiki v. Khimicheskoi i Fizicheskoi Kinetike* [Application of Computor Mathematics to Chemical and Physical Kinetics], edited by L. S. Polak. Moscow: Izd. Nauka, 1969.
4. A. I. Baz, Ya. B. Zelydovich, and A. M. Perelomov, *Rasseyanie Reaktsii i Raspady v Nerelyativistskoi Kvantovoi Mekhanik* [Non-Relativistic Quantum Mechanics of Dispersion, Reaction and Dissociation]. Moscow: Izd. Nauka, 1966.
5. A. von Engel, *Ionized Gases*. Oxford: Clarendon Press, 1955.
6. L. Spitzer, *Physics of Fully Ionized Gases*. New York: Interscience, 1962.
7. Shih-J-Pai, *Magneto Gas Dynamics and Plasma Dynamics*. Vienna: Springer, 1962.
8. S. Chapman and T. G. Cowling, *The Mathematical Theory of Non-Uniform Gases*. Cambridge: University Press, 1952.
9. S. Glasstone, K. J. Laidler, and H. Eyring, *The Theory of Rate Processes*. New York: Academic Press, 1941.
10. D. R. Herschbach, "Chemical Lasers." *Appl. Optics, Suppl.*, **2**, pp. 128–144 (1965).
11. A. L. Schmeltekopf, E. E. Ferguson, and F. C. Fehsenfeld, *J. Chem. Phys.*, **48**, 2966 (1968).
12. K. J. Campbell and E. W. Schlag, *J. Chem. Soc.*, **89**, 20 5103 (1967).
13. A. I. Osirov, *Teor. Eksp. Khim.*, **2**, 649 (1966).
14. E. V. Stupochenko and A. I. Osirov, *Teor. Eksp. Khim.*, **3**, 76 (1967).
15. E. V. Stupochenko, Dissertation, Moscow, 1951.
16. J. Ross and P. Mazur, *J. Chem. Phys.*, **35**, 19 (1961).
17. R. D. Present, *J. Chem. Phys.*, **31**, 747 (1959).
18. I. Prigogine and E. Xhrouet, *Physica*, **15**, 913 (1949).
19. E. V. Stupochenko, *Doklady Akad. Nauk SSSR*, **67**, 447, 635 (1949).
20. F. T. Wall, L. A. Hiller, and J. Mazur, *J. Chem. Phys.*, **29**, 255 (1958).
21. F. T. Wall, L. A. Hiller, and J. Mazur, *J. Chem. Phys.*, **35**, 1284 (1961).
22. N. C. Blais and D. L. Bunker, *J. Chem. Phys.*, **37**, 2713 (1962).
23. N. C. Blais and D. L. Bunker, *J. Chem. Phys.*, **39**, 315 (1963).
24. K. S. Shuler, T. Carrington, and J. C. Light, *Appl. Optics, Suppl.*, **2**, 81 (1965).
25. J. C. Keck, *J. Chem. Phys.*, **29**, 410 (1958).
26. O. B. Firsov, *Zh. Eksp. Teor. Fiz.*, **42**, 1307 (1962).
27. J. C. Light, *J. Chem. Phys.*, **40**, 3221 (1964).
28. E. E. Nikitin, *Zh. Teor. Eksp. Khim.*, **1**, 428 (1965).
29. J. C. Light, *Discussions Faraday Soc.*, **44**, 13 (1967).
30. G. E. Uhlenbeck and G. W. Ford, *Lectures in Statistical Mechanics*, Am. Math. Soc., 1963.

31. A. A. Ovsyannicov, L. S. Polak, M. V. Safonova, and M. S. Fedorova, *Teplophyzika Visokich Temperatur*, **7** (1969).

32. *Kinetika i Termodinamika Khimicheskikh Reaktsii v Nizkotemperaturnoi Plazme* [Kinetics and Thermodynamics of Chemical Reactions in Low Temperature Plasma], edited by L. S. Polak. Moscow: Nauka, 1965.

33. S. Fujita, *Introduction to Non-Equilibrium Quantum Statistical Mechanics*. Philadelphia, Pa.: Saunders, 1966.

34. I. Prigogine, *Non-Equilibrium Statistical Mechanics*. New York: Interscience, 1962.

35. R. V. Serauskas and E. W. Schlag, *J. Chem. Phys.*, **42**, 3009 (1965).

36. G. Chester, *Rep. Progr. Phys.*, **26**, 411 (1963).

37. L. van Hove, *Physica*, **23**, 441 (1954).

38. S. Nakayama, *Progr. Theoret. Phys.* (Kyoto), **20**, 948 (1958).

39. R. Zwanzig, *J. Chem. Phys.*, **33**, 1338 (1960).

40. I. Prigogine and P. Resibois, *Physica*, **27**, 629 (1961).

41. P. Resibois, *Physica*, **29**, 721 (1963).

42. E. W. Montroll, in *Fundamental Problems in Statistical Mechanics*. Amsterdam: North-Holland, 1962.

43. R. Zwanzig, *Physica*, **30**, 1109 (1964).

44. W. Pauli, *Probleme der Modernen Physik*. Leipzig: Hirzel, 1928.

45. J. Oppenheim and K. E. Shuler, *Phys. Rev.*, **138**, B1011 (1965).

46. W. G. Valance and E. W. Schlag, *J. Chem. Phys.*, **45**, 216 (1966).

47. W. G. Valance and E. W. Schlag, *J. Chem. Phys.*, **45**, 4280 (1966).

48. I. M. Gelefand and M. L. Tsetlin, *Doklady Akad. Nauk SSSR*, **137**, 2 (1961).

49. P. D. Thomson and F. E. Williams, *J. Chem. Phys.*, **20**, 124 (1952).

50. W. G. Valance, E. W. Schlag, and J. P. Elwood, *J. Chem. Phys.*, **47**, 3284 (1967).

51. S. K. Kim, *J. Chem. Phys.*, **28**, 1057 (1958).

52. B. Widom, *Advan. Chem. Phys.*, **5**, 353 (1961).

53. E. W. Montroll and K. E. Shuler, *Advan. Chem. Phys.*, **1**, 361 (1958).

54. M. Hoare, *J. Chem. Phys.*, **41**, 2356 (1964).

55. H. J. Kolker, *J. Chem. Phys.*, **44**, 582 (1966).

56. J. Keck and G. Carrier, *J. Chem. Phys.*, **43**, 2284 (1965).

57. L. D. Landau and E. M. Lifshitz, *Teoreticheskaye Fizika, t.z, Kvantovaye Mekhanika, Nerelyetivistskaye Teorii* [Theoretical Physics, Quantum Mechanics, Non-relativistic Theory]. Moscow: Fizmatgiz, 1963.

58. E. E. Nikitin, *Sovremennye Teorii Termicheskogo Raspada i Izomerizatsii Molekul v Gazovoi Phaze* [Modern Theory of Thermal Dissociation and Isomerization of Gas Phase Molecules]. Moscow: Izd. Nauka, 1964.

59. S. G. Gagarin and L. S. Polak, *Kinetika i Kataliz*, **6** (1969).

60. E. W. Schlag and W. G. Valance, *J. Chem. Phys.*, **49**, 605 (1968).

61. W. G. Valance and E. W. Schlag, *J. Chem. Phys.*, **47**, 3292 (1967).

62. W. G. Valance and E. W. Schlag, *J. Chem. Phys.*, **47**, 3277 (1967).

63. E. E. Nikitin, *J. Chem. Phys.*, **41**, 90 (1964).

64. K. E. Shuler, *Chemische Elementarprocese*. Heidelberg: Springer, 1968, pp. 1–22.

65. V. P. Shidlovskii, *Vvedenie v Dinamiku Razrezhennogo Gaza* [Introduction to Rarefied Gas Dynamics]. Moscow: Nauka, 1965.

66. K. Huang, *Statistical Mechanics*, New York: Wiley, 1963.

67. M. Kac, *Probability and Related Topics in Physical Sciences*. New York: Interscience, 1958.

68. J. O. Hirschfelder, C. F. Curtis, and R. B. Bird, *Molecular Theory of Gases and Liquids*. New York: Wiley, 1954.

69. J. Bond, K. Watson, and J. Welch, *Atomic Theory of Gas Dynamics*. Reading, Mass.: Addison-Wesley, 1965.
70. A. Ivanovskii, A. Repnev, and E. Shvidkovskii, *Kineticheskaya Teoriya Verkhnei Atmosferi, Gidrometeorologiya* [Kinetic Theory of the Upper Atmosphere, Hydrometeorology]. Izd-VO, 1967.
71. N. S. Snider and J. Ross, *J. Chem. Phys.*, **44**, 1087 (1966).
72. F. C. Andrews, *J. Chem. Phys.*, **35**, 922 (1961).
73. E. G. Cohen, *Physica*, **28**, 1025 (1962).
74. M. S. Green, *Phys. Rev.*, **136**, 905 (1964).
75. E. Uehling and G. Uhlenbeck, *Phys. Rev.*, **43**, 522 (1933).
76. S. Hess, *Z. Naturforsch.*, **22a**, 1871 (1967).
77. A. M. Kogan, *Doklady Akad. Nauk SSSR*, **175**, 785 (1967).
78. N. R. Sibgatulin, *Doklady Akad. Nauk SSSR*, **180**, 48 (1968).
79. J. T. O'Toole and J. Dahler, *J. Chem. Phys.*, **39**, 3214 (1963).
80. S. V. Vallander, I. A. Egorova, and M. A. Rydalpvskaya, *Vestnik Leningradskogo Universiteta*, **7**, 155 (1964).
81. H. Grad, *Phys. Fluids*, **6**, 147 (1963).
82. H. Grad, *Rarefied Gas Dynamics*, Vol. 1. New York: Academic Press, 1963.
83. R. F. Snider, *J. Chem. Phys.*, **41**, 591 (1964).
84 V. A. Rykov and T. I. Chukanova, in *All-Union Conference on Theoretical and Applied Mechanics*. Moscow, 1968, p. 202.
85. M. Wachman and B. B. Hamel, *Rarefied Gas Dynamics*, **1**, 675 (1967).
86. A. N. Temchni, *Inzh-Fizich. Zh.*, **16**, 5 (1969).
87. B. V. Alekseev, *Dokl. Akad. Nauk SSSR*, **182**, 2, 288 (1968).
88. N. S. Snider, *J. Chem. Phys.*, **44**, 1087 (1966).
89. J. Ross, *Advan. Chem. Phys.*, **10** (1966).
90. P. Hammering, J. D. Teare, and B. Kivel, *Phys. Fluids*, **2**, 422 (1959).
91. H. O. Pritchard, *J. Phys. Chem.*, **66**, 2111 (1962).
92. K. E. Shuler and G. H. Weiss, *J. Chem. Phys.*, **38**, 505 (1963).
93. C. W. Pyun and J. Ross, *J. Chem. Phys.*, **40**, 2572 (1964).
94. J. T. O'Toole and J. S. Dahler, *J. Chem. Phys.*, **39**, 3214 (1963).
95. S. H. Bauer, *Science*, **141**, 867 (1963).
96. O. K. Rice, *J. Chem. Phys.*, **9**, 258 (1941).
97. A. G. Gaydon and I. R. Hurle, *The Shock Tube in High Temperature Chemical Physics*. New York: Reinhold, 1963.
98. "The Study of Fast Reactions." *Discussions Faraday Soc.*, **17** (1954).
99. O. K. Rice, *J. Phys. Chem.*, **65**, 1972 (1961).
100. O. K. Rice, *J. Phys. Chem.*, **67**, 1733 (1963).
101. A. M. Baldin, V. I. Golidanskii, V. M. Maksimenko, and I. L. Rozental, *Kinematika Yadernikh Reakstsii* [Kinetics of Nuclear Reactions]. Moscow: Atomizdat, 1968.
102. L. Kadanoff and G. Baym, *Quantun Statistical Mechanics. Green's Function Methods in Equilibrium and Non-equilibrium Problems*. New York: Benjamin, 1962.
103. R. Paul and C. N. Fowler, *J. Chem. Phys.*, **48**, 56 (1968).
104. R. Paul, C. N. Fowler, and W. G. Laidlaw, *J. Chem. Phys.*, **48**, 63 (1968).
105. M. Fleischman, J. N. Hiddleston, A. Bewick, and W. F. K. Wynne-Jones, *Discussions Faraday Soc.*, **39**, 149 (1965).
106 J. Mazur and R. J. Rubin, *J. Chem. Phys.*, **31**, 1395 (1959).
107. H. Eyring, J. Walter, and G. E. Kimball, *Quantum Chemistry*. New York: Wiley, 1948.
108. H. M. Hulburt and J. Hirschfelder, *J. Chem. Phys.*, **11**, 276 (1943).

109. E. T. Whittaker, *Analytical Dynamics*. New York: Dover, 1959.
110. L. S. Polak, *Variatsionnye Printsipy Mekhaniski, ikh Razvitie i Primeneniya v Fizike* [Variational Principles of Mechanics, Their Development and Application to Physics]. Moscow: Fizmatgiz, 1960.
111. S. Gill, *Proc. Phil. Soc.*, **47**, 96 (1951).
112. A. Rahman, *Phys. Rev.*, **136**, A405 (1964).
113. L. Verlot, *Phys. Rev.*, **159**, 98 (1967).
114. N. Metropolis and S. Vlam, *J. Amer. Stat. Assoc.*, **44**, N247, 335 (1949).
115. K. Shuler, *Fifth Symposium (International) on Combustion*. New York: Reinhold, 1955.
116. Yu. A. Kolbanovskii and L. S. Polak, *Kinetika i Kataliz*, **10** (1969).
117. R. A. Markus, *J. Chem. Phys.*, **45**, 4500 (1966).
118. R. A. Markus, *J. Chem. Phys.*, **49**, 2610 (1968).
119. R. A. Markus, *J. Chem. Phys.*, **49**, 2617 (1968).
120. L. D. Landau and E. M. Lifshitz, *Teoreticheskaya Fizika*, tom **5**, Statisticheskaya Fizika [Theoretical Physics, Vol. 5, Statistical Physics]. Moscow: Nauka, 1964.
121. C. S. Wang-Chang and G. E. Uhlenbeck, *Transport Phenomena in Polyatomic Molecules*. Ann Arbor: University of Michigan, 1951.
122. R. H. Fowler and E. A. Guggenheim, *Statistical Thermodynamics*. Cambridge: University Press, 1939.
123. L. S. Polak, Vvedenie k Knige, *Primenenie Vychislitelinoi Matematiki v Khimicheskoi i Fizicheskoi Kinetike* [Introduction to the book, Application of Computer Mathematics to Chemical and Physical Kinetics]. Moscow: Izd. Nauka, 1969.
124. M. Eliason and J. Hirschfelder, *J. Chem. Phys.*, **30**, 1426 (1959).
125. N. P. Buslenko, D. I. Golenko, I. M. Soboli, B. G. Sragovich, and Yu. A. Shneider, *Metod Statisticheskikh Ispytanii, Metod Monte-Karlo* [Method of Statistical Analysis, Monte-Carlo Method]. Moscow: Izd.-FM, 1963.
126. L. S. Polak, A. N. Temchin, and A. V. Khochoyan, *Kinetika i Kataliz*, **6** (1969).
127. D. L. Bunker, *Theory of Elementary Gas Reaction Rates*. New York: Pergamon Press, 1966.
128. K. J. Laidler and J. C. Polanyi, *Progr. Reaction Kinetics*, **3**, 1 (1965).
129. V. N. Kondratiev, E. E. Nikitin, and V. L. Tal'rose, in *Nizkotemperaturnai Plazma* [Low-Temperature Plasma]. Moscow: Mir, 1967.
130. R. C. Whitten and I. G. Poppof, *Physics of the Lower Ionosphere*. Englewood Cliffs, N. J.: Prentice-Hall, 1965.
131. H. S. W. Massey and E. N. Burhop, *Electronic and Ionic Impact Phenomena*. Oxford: Clarendon Press, 1952.
132. E. V. Stupochenko, S. A. Losev, and A. I. Osipov, *Relaksatsionnye Protseccy v Udarniykh Volnakh* [Relaxation Processes in Shock Waves]. Moscow: Izd. Nauka, 1965.
133. K. L. Wray, *J. Chem. Phys.*, **37**, 1254 (1962).
134. J. G. Parker, *Phys. Fluids*, **2**, 449 (1959).
135. Ya. B. Zeldovich and Yu. P. Raizer, *Fizika Udarniyk Voln i Vysokotemperaturnykh Gidrodinamicheskikh Yavlenii* [Physics of Shock Waves and High Temperature Hydrodynamic Phenomena]. Moscow: Fizmatgiz, 1963.
136. O. A. Malkin, *Kinetika Relaksatsionnik Protsessov v Gaze* [Kinetics of Relaxation Processes in Gases]. Moscow: Izd. Mifi, 1968.
137. O. K. Rice, *J. Chem. Phys.*, **21**, 750 (1953).
138. G. Careri, *J. Chem. Phys.*, **21**, 749 (1953).
139. G. Careri, *Nuovo Cimento*, **6**, 94 (1949).

140. G. Careri, *Nuovo Cimento*, 7, 155 (1950).
141. G. Careri, *Advan. Chem. Phys.*, 1, 119 (1958).
142. Ch. E. Treanor and F. V. Marrone, *Phys. Fluids*, 5, 1022 (1962).
143. N. M. Kuznetsov, *Dokl. Akad. Nauk SSSR*, 164, 1097 (1965).
144. M. Krauss and F. H. Mies, *J. Chem. Phys.*, 42, 2703 (1965).
145. F. H. Mies, *J. Chem. Phys.*, 42, 2709 (1965).
146. F. H. Mies, *J. Chem. Phys.*, 40, 523 (1964).
147. F. H. Mies, *J. Chem. Phys.*, 41, 913 (1964).
148. P. V. Marrone and Ch. E. Treanor, *Phys. Fluids*, 6, 1215 (1963).
149. P. Hammerling, J. D. Teare, and B. Kivel, *Phys. Fluids*, 2, 422 (1959).
150. S. P. Heims, *J. Chem. Phys.*, 38, 603 (1963).
151. L. Landau and E. Teller, *Phys. Z. Sowjet.*, 10, 34 (1936).
152. R. J. Rubin and K. E. Shuler, *J. Chem. Phys.*, 25, 59 (1956).
153. S. W. Benson, *Ninth Symposium (International) on Combustion*. Ithaca, N.Y.: Cornell University Press, 1963.
154. J. Keck, *Discussions Faraday Soc.*, 33, 173 (1962).
155. O. K. Rice, *J. Chem. Phys.*, 9, 258 (1941).
156. M. Camac, *J. Chem. Phys.*, 34, 448 (1961).
157. S. K. Kim, *J. Chem. Phys.*, 28, 1057 (1958).
158. C. A. Brau, J. C. Keck, and G. F. Carrier, *Phys. Fluids*, 9, 1885 (1966).
159. C. A. Brau, *J. Chem. Phys.*, 47, 1153 (1967).
160. S. A. Losev, Dissertation, Moscow, 1968.
161. C. F. Curtiss, Report CM-476. University of Wisconsin, 1948.
162. I. Prigogine and M. Mahieu, *Physica*, 16, 51 (1950).
163. B. H. Mahan, *J. Chem. Phys.*, 32, 362 (1960).
164. T. Yamamoto, *J. Chem. Phys.*, 33, 281 (1960).
165. H. A. Kramers, *Physica*, 7, 284 (1940).
166. B. J. Zwolinski and H. Eyring, *J. Amer. Chem. Soc.*, 69, 2702 (1947).
167. E. W. Montroll and K. E. Shuler, *Advan. Chem. Phys.*, 1, 361 (1958).
168. V. N. Kondratiev, *Kinetika Khimicheskikh Gazovykh Reaktsii* [Chemical Kinetics of Gas Phase Reactions]. Moscow: Izd. Akad. Nauk SSSR, 1958.
169. S. W. Benson, *The Foundations of Chemical Kinetics*. New York: McGraw-Hill, 1960.
170. V. N. Kondratiev and E. E. Nikitin, *Uspekhi Khim.*, 36, 2007 (1967).
171. F. A. Lindeman, *Trans. Faraday Soc.*, 17, 598 (1922).
172. N. B. Slater, *Theory of Unimolecular Reactions*. Ithaca, N.Y.: Cornell University Press, 1959.
173. L. S. Kassel, *Kinetics of Homogeneous Gas Reactions*, ACS Monograph No. 57. New York: Am. Chem. Soc., 1932.
174. E. Thiele and D. J. Wilson, *Canadian J. Chem.*, 37, 1035 (1959).
175. E. Thiele and D. J. Wilson, *J. Phys. Chem.*, 64, 473 (1960).
176. E. Thiele and D. J. Wilson, *J. Chem. Phys.*, 35, 1256 (1961).
177. K. Takayanagi, *Progr. Theor. Phys.* (Kyoto), 6, 486 (1951).
178. J. Wigner, *J. Chem. Phys.*, 5, 720 (1937).
179. J. Wigner, *J. Chem. Phys.*, 6, 29 (1938).
180. J. Wigner, *J. Chem. Phys.*, 7, 646 (1939).
181. J. C. Keck, *J. Chem. Phys.*, 32, 1035 (1960).
182. M. Salkoff and E. Bauer, *J. Chem. Phys.*, 29, 26 (1958); 30, 1614 (1959).
183. B. Widom, *J. Chem. Phys.*, 34, 2050 (1961).
184. E. Nikitin and N. Sokolov, *J. Chem. Phys.*, 31, 1371 (1959).

185. D. L. Bunker, *J. Chem. Phys.*, **32**, 1001 (1960).

186. S. W. Benson and T. Fueno, *J. Chem. Phys.*, **36**, 1597 (1962).

187. E. V. Stupochenko and A. I. Osipov, *Zh. Fiz. Khim.*, **33**, 36 (1959).

188. A. M. Read, *Progr. Reaction Kinetics*, **3**, 203 (1965).

189. V. L. Ginzburg and A. V. Gurevich, *Usp. Fiz. Nauk*, **70**, 201 (1960).

190. A. V. Gurevich, *Zh. Eksp. Teor. Fiz.*, **35**, 271 (1959).

191. M. Epstein, *Phys. Fluids*, **3**, 1016 (1960).

192. M. S. Sodha, *Appl. Sci.*, Sect. **B8**, 208 (1960).

193. K. T. Yen, *Phys. Fluids*, **7**, 1612 (1964).

194. K. T. Yen, *A.I.A.A.J.*, **2**, 71 (1964).

195. M. Epstein, *Phys. Fluids*, **7**, 121 (1964).

196. R. J. Papa and G. T. Case, *Canadian J. Phys.*, **43**, 2021 (1965).

197. R. J. Papa and G. T. Case, *Canadian J. Phys.*, **43**, 38 (1965).

198. R. J. Papa, *Canadian J. Phys.*, **46**, 889 (1968).

199. J. T. Mayhan and R. V. de Vore, *J. Appl. Phys.*, **39**, 5746 (1968).

200. F. B. Vurzel, G. V. Lysov, L. S. Polak, Yu. L. Khait, and E. N. Chervochkin, *Khim. Vysokikh Energii*, **3**, (1969).

201. L. Levin, *Sovremennaya Teoriya Volnovodov* [Modern Wave Theory]. Moscow: Izd. Il., 1954.

202. A. G. Engelhardt, A. V. Phelps, and C. G. Risk, *Phys. Rev.*, **135**, A1566 (1964).

203. S. Brown, *Elementarnye Protsessy v Plazme Gazovogo Razpyada* [Elementary Processes in Gas Discharge Plasmas]. Moscow: Gosatomizdat, 1961.

204. I. Leventhal and L. Friedman, *J. Chem. Phys.*, **46**, 997 (1967).

205. J. Heicklen, *A.I.A.A.J.*, **5**, 4 (1967).

206. P. Warneck, *J. Chem. Phys.*, **46**, 502 (1967).

207. L. A. McKnight, K. B. McAfee, and D. P. Sipler, *Phys. Rev.*, **164**, 62 (1967).

208. E. W. McDaniel, *Protsessy Stolknovenii v Ionizovannykh Gazek* [Collision Processes in Ionized Gases]. Moscow: Izd. Mir., 1967.

209. L. Frommohold and M. A. Biondi, *Bull. Amer. Phys. Soc.*, **12**, 217 (1967).

210. P. Hackam, *Planet. Space Sci.*, **13**, 667 (1965).

211. J. B. Hasted, *Fizika Atomnykh Stolknovenii* [Physics of Atomic Collisions]. Moscow: Izd. Mir., 1965.

212. W. H. Kasner, W. A. Rogers, and M. A. Biondi, *Phys. Rev. Lett.*, **7**, 321 (1961).

213. K. Evenson and D. Burch, *J. Chem. Phys.*, **45**, 2450 (1966).

214. V. E. Golant, *Usp. Fiz. Nauk*, **65**, 39 (1958).

215. V. L. Granovskii, *Elektricheskii Tok v Gaze* [Flow of Electricity in Gases], Vol. **1**. Moscow-Leningrad: Gittl, 1952.

216. F. B. Vurzel, L. S. Polak, Yu. L. Khait, and E. N. Chervochkin, *Khim. Vysokikh Energii*, **3** (1969).

217. L. D. Landau and E. M. Lifshitz, *Elektrodinamika Sploshnykh Sred* [Electrodynamics of Continuous Fluids]. Moscow: Gittl, 1957.

218. L. A. Vainshtein, *Elektromagnitnye Volny* [Electromagnetic Waves]. Moscow: Izd. Sov. Radio, 1957.

219. F. B. Vurzel, G. V. Lysov, L. S. Polak, and E. N. Chervochkin, *Khim. Vysokikh Energii*, **3** (1969).

220. M. Saporoschenko, *Phys. Rev.*, **111**, 1550 (1958).

221. R. A. Young, R. L. Sharpless, and R. Stringham, *J. Chem. Phys.*, **40**, 117 (1964).

CHAPTER FOURTEEN

Chemical Reactions in Electrical Discharges

M. M. SHAHIN

I. PRODUCTION AND REACTIONS OF ATOMIC SPECIES

One of the major uses of electrical discharges in the laboratory is in the production of atomic species. The techniques used are varied depending on the instrumentation available and the specific requirements of the experiments. However, all the systems which were described in the chapter on Electrical Discharge Plasmas (Vol. I, Chapter 5), namely, coronas, glows, and arcs, could be utilized to produce the desired atomic species. In recent years, several reviews (1–5) have appeared in the literature describing the details of some of these techniques for use in the laboratory. This growing interest indicates the widespread application of discharges in many areas of chemistry.

A. General Mechanisms

In electrical discharges, the major source of energy for the dissociation of molecules is derived from inelastic collisions with energetic electrons. Although molecules can store energy in many forms, only simple vibrational and electronic excitations will, in general, contribute to molecular dissociation. This is because rotational and translational energies are rapidly exchanged with other molecules by collisions and therefore are unlikely to substantially depart from kinetic temperature equilibrium. Vibrational-translation interchange, however, is very inefficient especially for strongly bound homonuclear diatomic molecules. Electron impact excitation of vibrational energy is a highly specific process with cross-sections varying by two orders of magnitude from one molecule to another. Certain molecules like N_2, CO and CO_2 have large cross-sections (6–9) of the order of $1-5 \times 10^{-16}$ cm^2, while others such as H_2 and O_2 have cross-sections which are smaller by a factor of 10–50. The vibrationally excited molecules are further excited by electron impact to dissociative states. However, because of their internal energy, low energy electrons can also participate in this process.

Electron impact excitation of molecules to higher electronic states also occurs with reasonable cross-sections. When excitation occurs to a radiatively allowed state, the cross-section rises to a broad maximum and then slowly decreases. For radiatively forbidden states, however, the cross-section is sharply peaked at the corresponding energy and decreases rapidly at higher energies. The peak cross-sections are of the order of $10^{-17}-10^{-16}$ cm^2 for transitions requiring 5 to 10 eV. All transitions will take place within the limitations set by the Frank-Condon principle.

The dissociation of molecule into neutral fragments occurs by one of three principle routes, following electron impact excitation to an electronic state which contains an energy greater than D, the dissociation energy. These are:

(a) excitation to a repulsive state which allows the molecule to dissociate upon its first pseudo-vibration, that is, in about 10^{-13} sec; (b) excitation to a bound state, with the molecule being formed at a point above the dissociative energy of that state. This will again lead to dissociation within one vibration in about 10^{-13} sec; (c) excitation to a bound state, with energy less than the dissociation energy of that state, but there is another state of lower dissociation energy with which the first state may interact. Near the crossing point of the two potential energy curves, the states are mixed and there is a finite probability of crossing and subsequent dissociation. Because the degree of mixing may vary, the dissociation step is slower than the first two cases. In all three cases, however, the probability for dissociation is about unity because collisional or radiative lifetimes of the excited states is not shorter than 10^{-7}–10^{-8} sec.

Electron-ion recombination at the wall or in the gas phase should also be mentioned as possible mechanisms for the formation of atomic species within the discharge, for example $e + H_2^+ \rightarrow 2H$. It is clear, however, that the upper limit to this process is determined by the total rate of ionization, but nevertheless may be important in some special cases.

A general observation should be made on the number of dissociation events in the discharge as compared with those of ionizations for which a rough experimental measure is usually available through current measurements. The energy of the electrons within the discharge can generally be approximated by a Maxwellian distribution. It is, therefore, easy to conceive that a far greater number of electrons will have the energy required for excitation than for ionization; the latter usually requiring several electron-volt higher energies. Since the cross-sections for the two processes are usually similar, it would be expected that excitation and subsequent dissociation events surpass the number of ionization acts by about two orders of magnitude within the discharge.

B. Hydrogen Atoms

The production of hydrogen atoms in glow discharges at pressures of 0.2–1.0 torr pressure has been known for some time (10–12). One of the earlier investigators in this area was Wood (10) who used a low-frequency electrode discharge in hydrogen at 0.2–1.0 torr pressure and obtained more than 50% dissociation of the gas into atoms. Systematic studies of the effects of pressure, power, and the yield of atoms both for low-frequency and microwave discharges have been carried out by various investigators (1). Using microwave discharge at 3000 MC/S, Shaw (1,12) reports some 90% dissociation of hydrogen at 0.5 torr and 100 watts power. Small amounts (0.1–0.3%) of added gases such as H_2O or O_2 have been found to increase the yield of hydrogen atom substantially. This is thought to be due to the effects of these gases on the surface of the tube in reducing the probability of surface recombination (13). Below 0.1 torr, the effect of these impurities is less pronounced.

Using phosphoric acid or Drifilm (a mixture of methyltrichlorosilane and dimethyldichlorosilane), it has been possible to coat the walls of the vessel and pump the hydrogen atoms for considerable distances from the discharge region. Details of the various apparatus which can be used for the production of hydrogen atoms have been described in Chapter 5, Vol. I of Reactions Under Plasma Conditions.

Hydrogen atoms are extremely labile and can act as strong reducing agents, initiate polymerization, and react with various elements including carbon to form various hydrides. Various reactions of hydrogen atoms produced by electrical discharges have recently been reviewed by McTaggert (4).

Several techniques have been used to quantitatively estimate the concentration of atomic species in the gas stream. The physical methods include Wrede (14,15) pressure gauge and calorimetry (16) while chemical methods involve reactions with metal mirrors (17) or color solids (17) such as MoO_3.

C. Oxygen Atoms

The use of discharge tubes with internal electrodes is generally undesirable for the production of oxygen atoms, since the severe oxidation of the metal could release impurities into the gas stream. The presence of the metal in the discharge tube also leads to surface catalyzed recombination of the atomic species which will reduce the overall yield. Thus, generally either ozonizers or other electrodeless (RF or microwave) systems have been used for this purpose. Kaufman (18,19) used a microwave discharge (3000 MC/S) in dry oxygen at pressures of 0.2–1.6 torr, with up to 800 watts of power to produce 12–20 % oxygen atoms. Large catalytic effects by N_2, NO, H_2, or water vapor have also been reported in these investigations. While very pure oxygen, for example, gave only 0.6 % atoms, the addition of small quantities (0.01–0.05 %) of N_2, N_2O, or NO produced oxygen atoms at the rate of 40–45 per added N and similar additions of H_2 produced 160–200 oxygen atoms per added H_2. This catalytic effect can be understood for H_2 in terms of the formation of water and its coverage on the surface of the tube. However, such an explanation cannot be used for the action of nitrogen compounds since they are not strongly absorbed on the surface. Conceivably, NO^+ or NO_2^+, strong Lewis acids, may be involved in poisoning the surface and thus reducing the efficiency of the main loss process which occurs through atom recombinations. The addition of Ar, He, or CO_2 had no effect in these experiments.

Dissociated oxygen, unlike the hydrogen system, contains considerable concentration of excited metastable molecules as well as small traces of ozone. Using a mass spectrometer for detection, Herron and Schiff (20) measured some 8 % atomic oxygen as well as 10–20 % of excited molecules in a micro-wave discharge of oxygen at 1 torr. The presence of these excited molecules has been demonstrated physically by Elias et al. (21) through their thermal effect after the removal of oxygen atoms from the system. These excited molecules were probably in the $^1\Delta_g$ state.

Oxygen atoms are strong oxidizing agents and react with a variety of elements and molecules. A brief summary of these reactions has recently been compiled by McTaggart (4). Among these reactions, the production of ozone has probably been of the greatest historical importance since electrical discharges have long been used in ozonizers for this purpose. Reactions with oxides of nitrogen and specifically NO_2 have also been of special importance since the latter is routinely used for the titration of oxygen atoms (22). The procedure for this titration is to add NO_2 to the gas stream. The fast reaction

$$O + NO_2 \longrightarrow O_2 + NO \qquad [1]$$

provides a source of NO molecules which can act as an indicator in the titration by the following slow reactions

$$O + NO \longrightarrow NO_2^* \qquad [2]$$

$$NO_2^* \longrightarrow NO_2 + hv \qquad [3]$$

The disappearance of a yellow-green glow due to eq. [3] indicates the end of titration.

D. Nitrogen Atoms

Production of "active nitrogen" by electrical discharges has been investi-gated by many workers over the last fifty years. A review by Mannella (23) and a recent book by Wright and Winkler (23) summarize the physical and some of the chemical aspects of these investigations. Winkler and co-workers (24, 25) have shown that the most efficient technique for the production of atomic nitrogen is the use of Woods type (electroded) tube with a pulsed condensed discharge of 30–60 pulses per second. The atom yield from this system approaches almost 100 %. Fontana (26) has shown that a microwave discharge is apparently less efficient for the production of nitrogen atoms than a pulsed discharge apparatus. The presence of small quantities of water vapor, SF_6, NO, or O_2, however, is known to increase the atom yield considerably (27).

Active nitrogen has been shown (28,29) to contain a variety of species which include excited atoms, molecules, as well as ground state ^4S atoms. Kaufman and Kelso (30) have presented strong evidence for the presence of vibrationally excited N_2 molecules with lifetime of some 50 milliseconds at 1 torr pressure in the products of a microwave discharge. It is generally agreed that although all discharges through nitrogen produce predominantly ^{4}S atomic species, there are interesting differences in the proportion of these to excited molecules between various types of discharges. The microwave systems appear to produce large concentrations of vibrationally excited ground state molecules (30,31) while the condensed and radio-frequency discharges produce them to a much lesser extent (32). However, the condensed discharge does seem to produce large amounts of electronically excited molecules (33). The chemical reactivity of active nitrogen is mainly due to the ground state and excited atoms. Vibrationally excited molecules have, however, been shown by Winkler and co-workers (34) to participate in reactions with hydrocarbons.

The great complexity of " active nitrogen " is probably due to the large cross-sections for vibrational excitations of nitrogen molecules and also due to the existence of metastable electronically excited states below the dissociation limit of ground state N_2. As a result, extensive vibrational excitation persists for times much longer than those spent in the discharge zone. This leads to chemi-ionization in regions such as the " pink glow " well downstream of the discharge. The absence of the lowest triplet state, A, $^3\sum_u^+$, in active nitrogen (35) containing N atoms is probably indicative of the efficient quenching of these states by nitrogen atoms and thus, vibrationally highly excited ground-state molecules are the principle carriers of excitation energy to downstream regions.

Nitrogen atoms react with a variety of compounds giving rise to various nitrogenated species. A summary of the more important reactions of " active nitrogen " have recently been reviewed by McTaggart (4).

Quantitative estimation (36) of nitrogen atoms in a gas stream could be made similar to that of oxygen through its reaction with NO according to the fast reaction

$$N + NO \longrightarrow N_2 + O \tag{4}$$

As NO is added, the afterglow of the discharge is weakened because N atoms are removed. Some of the oxygen atoms produced through the above reaction would subsequently react with NO by the slow reaction $N + O + M \rightarrow NO^* + M$ and the emission from the excited NO^* may give rise to a pinkish-blue coloration. At the end point, this color as well as the afterglow of the discharge will disappear and any excess NO produces the yellow-green color due to $O + NO \rightarrow NO_2 + hv$.

E. Halogens, Other Atoms

The use of electrical discharges for the production of halogen atoms has been known for many years. Earlier investigators (37), however, were unable to produce halogen atoms in reasonable concentrations owing to the rapid recombination reaction on the metal electrodes or on the wall of the discharge tube. Schwab (37), for example, discovered that almost every collision of Br atoms with the wall resulted in recombination irrespective of various surfaces that he used. Systematic work of Ogryslo (38), however, showed that although many surfaces such as bare pyrex, quartz tubes, or when coated with polyethylene, teflon, sodium chloride, sodium hydroxide, had no effect in preventing surface recombination of Cl or Br atoms, high yields of dissociated atoms could be obtained when the discharge tube was coated with such compounds as phosphoric acid, sulphuric acid, hypochloric acid, or boric acid. These oxyacids are well known as poisoning agents for surfaces. High concentrations of Cl and Br atoms have thus been obtained at discharge pressures of 0.3–4.0 torr. Even with such coatings, iodine atoms could not be produced in reasonable yields and fluorine atoms were difficult to handle. Using a microwave discharge, Vanderkool and MacKenzie (39) have reported complete dissociation of Cl_2 and Br_2 but only partial dissociation of F_2 in a discharge tube which was coated with sulphuric or phosphoric acid. RF discharge has also been successfully used (40) to generate fluorine atoms in a fast flowing system.

Chlorine and bromine atom concentrations can best be determined (38) by titration with NOCl or the corresponding bromine analogue through the fast reaction

$$Cl + NOCl \longrightarrow NO + Cl_2 \qquad [5]$$

which is followed by the side reaction as $Cl + NO + M \to NOCl + M$ or $Cl_2 + 2NO \to 2NOCl$. These side reactions are relatively slow and will not appreciably affect the end point. The end point of the titration is determined by the use of an isothermal calorimetric device 2 cm downstream from the point of entry of the NOCl. The rate of introduction of NOCl is initially adjusted in excess of the equivalent amount of halogen atom and is later reduced until the atoms just reach the calorimeter and are detected.

Production of phosphorus atoms was achieved by Zabolotny and Gesser (41) who passed a stream of argon gas through a bulb containing phosphorus at 25–100°C and introduced the mixture into a microwave discharge at a pressure of about 1 torr. The production of atoms was inferred through its reactions with hydrocarbons to form PH_3 among other products. Production of excited atomic species of sulphur has been reported by Vastola and Stacy (5) through dissociation of hydrogen sulphide in a plasma jet. These authors have studied the reactions of these species with methane and neopentane.

F. Free Radicals

The mechanism of the production of free-radicals from polyatomic molecules in electrical discharges is, in general, very complicated since electron impact excitation of these molecules gives rise to fragmentation in many modes, generating a number of reactive species as well as molecular by-products. Consequently, many other reactions most of which are much slower than the electron impact processes and may require long residence time in the discharge tube to reach a steady state, will have to be considered.

As an example of this complexity, it may be noted that although spectroscopic evidence for the presence of hydroxyl radicals in the discharge through water vapor has been commonly known, this scheme has failed as a source of OH radicals. Space-resolved spectroscopy (42) in fast flow systems has shown that negligible amounts of OH radicals were present a few milliseconds downstream of the discharge. A small number of these radicals are, however, formed further downstream by slow reactions such as $H + O_2 + M \rightarrow HO_2 + M$ and $H + HO_2 \rightarrow 2OH$, indicating that this discharge is a good source of H atoms. Apparently, continued excitation and dissociation of OH radicals within the discharge is so common that oxygen atoms are also formed and the very fast reaction $O + OH \rightarrow O_2 + H$ accounts for the major discharge products which are hydrogen atoms and molecular oxygen. When the dissociation of OH does not occur extensively in the discharge, then the fast reactions $2OH \rightarrow H_2O + O$ and $OH + O \rightarrow O_2 + H$ will effectively produce the same result.

Thus, even in the case of moderately complex molecules, the prediction of the output of the discharge requires detailed information on many complicated events which not only require the knowledge of electron impact ionization and dissociation rates as well as surface recombination rates, but also neutral-neutral reaction rates and their temperature dependence in and out of the discharge.

In general, the action of the discharge on polyatomic molecules could be regarded as breakdown into fragments and regrouping into new molecular species. Thus, Coats (43) found that when n-hexane was passed through a microwave discharge at 1 torr pressure, some 25 different hydrocarbon compounds were formed. Streitweiser and Ward (44) diluted toluene with helium before passing it through a microwave discharge and again found numerous compounds among which some tarry substances as well as benzene, ethylbenzene, styrene, and phenylacetylene were isolated. Mild discharges such as coronas or low-power RF could, however, be profitably employed to bring about minimum of molecular energization and breakdown. For example, Bindley et al. (45) have used RF power with external electrodes at 6 Mc sec^{-1} in o-, m-, and p-fluorotoluenes to produce the corresponding $FC_6H_4CH_2$ radicals which combined to form dimers. Jen et al. (46) found that a mild discharge of CH_4 was a convenient source of CH_3 radicals. Pulsed discharge is also suitable to produce limited fragmentation of the molecule if the discharge period and its repetition rate is properly chosen.

Recent reviews on the many complexities of the breakdown and regrouping of organic molecules which have been subjected to electrical discharges have appeared in the literature (4,5).

II. SYNTHESIS OF NOVEL CHEMICALS

One of the more common usages of electrical discharges in the laboratory is in the synthesis of novel compounds for which often no other straightforward reaction routes could be found. In general, the synthesis of compounds which are thermodynamically unstable with respect to the starting materials, for example, NO from N_2 and O_2, or O_3 from O_2, are most conveniently carried out in electrical discharges. In spite of the generally low yields which are derived from the present discharge equipment, the simplicity of their operation and their unique capability have remained of great value to the chemist.

A. Synthesis of Inorganic Hydrides

Hydrogen atoms produced in electrical discharges could be reacted with various metals and nonmetals in an elementary form to produce volatile hydrides. Thus, various hydrides of phosphorus, sulphur, arsenic and antimony were synthesized by Bonhoeffer (47). Others (48) have synthesized volatile hydrides of germanium, tin, arsenic, antimony and tellurium.

When simple volatile hydrides are passed through ozonizer type discharge (corona) near atmospheric pressure or through a glow discharge at low pressure, fairly good yields of higher homologs of the hydrides are obtained. Kotlensky and Shaeffer (49), for example, used a mixture of B_2H_6 with helium in an ozonizer to produce B_4H_{10} (40% yield), B_5H_9 (20%), B_5H_{11} (30%), and small amounts of B_6H_{10}, $B_{10}H_{15}$, and B_9H_{15}. Decaborane-16 ($B_{10}H_{16}$) was produced by Grimes et al. (50) from a mixture of B_5H_9 and hydrogen. The unusual compound $B_{20}H_{16}$ in which there are fewer hydrogen atoms than B atoms was prepared from a mixture $B_{10}H_{14}$ and hydrogen in an electrical discharge (51).

Formation of various hydrides of germanium (germanes) up to Ge_9 have been reported by Drake and Jolly (52) who passed GeH_4 at a pressure of 300 torr through an ozonizer which was kept at $-78°C$. Using fractional distillation followed by various analytical techniques, they concluded that a large number of isomers analogous to those found in the paraffin series were present.

Spanier and MacDiarmid (53) who used similar techniques to those described for germanes but at lower pressure, found that silanes could also be converted to a mixture of higher homologs. The products contained some 66% SiH_6, 23% Si_3H_8, and 11% of higher silanes such as Si_4H_{10}. Gokdale and Jolly (54) prepared two isomers of Si_4H_{10} from SiH_4 in a similar apparatus. Jolly's later work shows preparation of Si_8H_{18} from silane and conversion of arsine to diarsine.

When mixtures of relatively simple hydrides are passed through electric discharges (such as, ozonizers) higher molecular weight ternary hydrides are formed. Thus, by using equimolar mixtures of GeH_4 and PH_3, Drake and Jolly (55) prepared GeH_3PH_2, Ge_2PH_7, Ge_3PH_9 and many other higher mixed homologs. In a mixture of GeH_4–AsH_3, the only mixed hydride found was GeH_3–AsH_2. This compound was separated from the germanes by fractional distillation. Mixtures of GeH_4 and SiH_4 in an ozonizer type discharge produced a new compound H_2GeSiH_3 in reasonably good yields.

Using the ozonizer type discharge, Gokdale and Jolly (56) prepared two isomers of Si_2PH_7, namely disilanyl phosphine $(Si_2H_5PH_2)$ and disilylphosphine $[(SiH_3)_2PH]$, and identified them by nuclear magnetic spectroscopy. Mixed hydrides of silicon and arsenic were also synthesized by Jolly and co-workers (55) using a mixture of SiH_4 and AsH_3.

B. Synthesis of Halides

When volatile halides are passed through glow discharges at low pressures, small yields of the higher homologs are obtained if provisions are made to separate the products from the by-product chlorine through fractional condensation, in order to avoid reverse reaction to reform the starting materials. The yields can, however, be considerably improved if a reducing agent which can react with chlorine is included in the discharge zone or immediately after the discharge zone. Mercury and copper wool have been found to be very effective reducing agents for this purpose. As an example, P_2Cl_4 can be obtained (57) from a discharge in a mixture of $H_2 + PCl_3$ or from a PCl_3 discharge followed by copper wool, whereas no P_2Cl_4 has been produced in the absence of reducing agents.

B_2Cl_4 has been synthesized by Wartik et al. (58) by circulating BCl_3 at a pressure of 1–2 torr through a glow discharge mercury electrode. The volatile product was trapped at $-78°C$. Here again, mercury acts to remove the chlorine from the scene of reaction. More recently, other techniques (59) including microwave discharge have been used for the preparation of B_2Cl_4. Holliday and Massey (60) have recently reviewed both the properties of boron halides as well as the details of the discharge techniques used for their preparation.

Ge_2Cl_6 has been produced in reasonable yields by Jolly (57) and co-workers from $GeCl_4$ at low pressures by placing bronze wool downstream from the discharge zone or by operating a series of 60 cycle AC discharges between bronze wool plugs.

C. Synthesis of Fluorinated Compounds

Using a high voltage (2900–5000 V) discharge between mercury electrodes Frazer (61) has produced tetrafluorohydrazine and difluorodiazine (N_2F_2) from NF_3 at a pressure of 1–4 torr in very high yields: N_2F_4, 50–60%; N_2F_2, 12–14%. The entire discharge tube was heated to a suitable temperature for this reaction. The presence of mercury also gave rise to nitrogen and mercury fluorides which formed a coating on the walls of the reactor and prevented the corrosion of the pyrex glass apparatus.

A number of the compounds of oxygen fluorides (O_2F_2, O_3F_2, O_4F_2, O_5F_2 and O_6F_2) have been prepared (62,63) by subjecting mixtures of oxygen and fluorine to electric discharge at very low temperatures and at pressures of 5–15 torr. All these compounds are very unstable and on warming, they decompose to oxygen and fluorine.

XeF_4 was produced by Kirstenbaum et al. (64) by passing a mixture of one volume xenon to two volumes fluorine into a glow discharge tube kept at $-78°C$ at pressures ranging between 2 and 15 torr. The gases were quantitatively converted to XeF_4. When the composition of the input gas was changed to one volume Xe and 3 volumes F_2, xenon hexafluoride was reported to be formed (65). Hoppe et al. (66) and Milligan and Sears (67) have prepared XeF_2 in a discharge when mixtures of Xe and F_2 or xenon and either CF_4 or SiF_4 vapor were used in a refrigerated flow apparatus.

III. ION-MOLECULE REACTIONS IN ELECTRIC DISCHARGES

Studies of ion-molecule reactions which occur within electrical discharges have received considerable attention in recent years and a number of reviews on this subject have appeared (3,68,69). The impetus for this work has come not only from the development of new and improved vacuum instrumentation and mass spectrometers which are particularly suited for such work, but also because of the frequent use of these systems by the chemists in the laboratory and the realization that electrical discharges are extremely convenient sources of both ionic as well as atomic species. This interest has generated a great deal of activity in this area with the hope that it would lead to a better understanding of the chemical processes which occur within these systems. In general, the knowledge of the nature of charge carriers would considerably help in understanding many other properties of the discharge. Such properties as ion-mobility, ion-electrode interactions, emission of radiation, and to some extent, the production of neutral by-products in the discharge are all influenced by the exact nature of the ionic species. Studies of these systems are, however, often complicated by the fact that primary ionic species which are generally formed by direct electron bombardment on neutral gas molecules may undergo processes in which their identity is lost before they are sampled and detected by a mass spectrometer. It is, therefore, of great interest to learn not only the identity of the final charge carriers in these systems but also to trace their possible precursors in order to understand both the properties of the discharge at various locations of the tube as well as to unravel the mechanisms of the chemical reactions in which ionic species participate.

Two main processes, namely, simple charge exchange and ion-molecule reactions will change the nature of the primary ionic species within the discharge. The simple charge exchange occurs between the ionic species and either the parent neutral molecule (resonance) or with other neutral molecular species for which the reaction is exothermic. In the latter case, the identity of the ion is completely changed while the former will strongly influence the mobility of the ion and its energy distribution within the discharge and can produce highly energetic neutral species as side-products. These energetic species may then dissociate and contribute to free-radical reactions within the discharge. The processes designated as ion-molecule reactions will completely change the nature of charge carriers. These latter reactions are particularly interesting since they are some of the fastest known and provide the opportunity to study the influence of direct coulombic forces on chemical reactions. The specific characteristics of electric discharges, however, often complicate determination of meaningful cross-sections for various ion-molecule reactions which occur within these systems. This is due mainly to the complex dependence of the cross-section on ionic velocities and the variation of the latter, not only in the presence of electric fields which are generally variable within the discharge and from discharge to discharge, but also the drastic modification of ion velocities by both resonance charge exchange processes and elastic collisions which arise from the relatively high pressures used in these systems.

Attempts to explain the variation of reaction cross-section with ionic energy have been made by a number of investigators. Giomousis and Stevenson (70) have derived a precise expression for the collision cross-section based on Langevin's (71) treatment for polarizable systems. Their expression shows the collision cross-section σ to be:

$$\sigma = \frac{2e\pi}{v_i} \left(\frac{\alpha}{\mu}\right)^{1/2} \qquad [6]$$

where α is the polarizability of the neutral species, v_i is the velocity of the ion, μ is the reduced mass and e the charge on the electron. If the ion has a mass m_i and an energy E, then

$$v_i = \left(\frac{2E}{m_i}\right)^{1/2} \qquad [7]$$

and therefore σ will vary as $E^{1/2}$. Further, since $k = \sigma v$, then

$$k = 2e\pi\left(\frac{\alpha}{\mu}\right)^{1/2}$$ [8]

and thus the rate constant k is independent of ionic velocity or energy. This equation, however, does not agree with the great body of information which is now available on ion-molecule reactions, although it appears to hold for some. Hammil and his co-workers (72,73), on the other hand, have modified the assumptions involving point particles and have considered the neutral species to exhibit a hard core to high energy collisions while being deformable in low energy collisions. These workers subsequently showed that for small ion energies σ obeys the Giomousis and Stevenson relationship, but for large energies $\sigma \alpha E^{-1}$ which agrees with a greater body of the experiments. Hamil et al. (74,75) have also extended their treatment to ion-molecule reactions involving neutral species which have permanent dipoles to obtain a better agreement with experimental results.

A further complication in studying the ionic species of electric discharges arises in the process of transferring the ions from the discharge into a mass analyzer. While there is little difficulty when the pressure is below 10 microns, the interaction of sampling probe with the discharge becomes increasingly more complex as the pressure increases. This is attributed to the fact that ions and electrons diffuse to the wall at different rates, thereby establishing an electric field which promotes the process of ambipolar diffusion. The presence of this electric field changes the energy distribution of various charged species. Under most conditions, an ion sheath is formed on any surface including that of a sampling probe within the discharge. Ions and electrons must have or be given sufficient energy to pass through this sheath in order to be sampled. Ionic collisions within the sheath could therefore bring about reactions which are not representative of the main discharge and would alter the nature of the species to be analyzed. This is probably the major source of uncertainty in these measurements. Under certain circumstances (76,77) (for example, low charge density) these difficulties may, however, be avoided. Other complications involved in the sampling process as well as various equipment used for these studies have been reviewed in detail by Knewstubb (3) and others (78) recently.

A. Studies in Glow Discharges

As has been discussed before (79), glow discharges have several distinctive regions. Thus, the electrical characteristics of such regions as the cathode dark-space, the negative glow or the positive column are quite different. It would, therefore, be expected that the different electron and ion energy distributions which control the properties of these regions would also strongly influence the type of ion-molecule reactions which occur within these regions.

1. **Cathode Region.** Studies of ionic species which arrive at the cathode of various glow discharges have been made by Shahin (69) using a quadrupole mass spectrometer which sampled the ions through a small port in the cathode. The specific properties of the cathode (80) region require that the majority of these ions originate in the negative glow where the electric field is almost zero, and the ions have thermal energies. As they move through the cathode dark space in an intense electric field, they pick up considerable amounts of energy and later move beam-like the length of the distance to the cathode. The ion-energy distribution as measured (81) at the cathode is relatively wide and is primarily determined by the resonance charge-exchange cross-section for the particular gas and the cathode fall potential. Because the average ionic energy could be many electron volts, exothermic as well as endothermic ion-molecule reactions which are governed by their threshold energies could take place within this region. Mass-spectral data of the relative abundances of the various ions at the cathode and their variation with discharge conditions reflect the effect of these ion-molecule reactions occurring within the cathode dark-space.

In pure nitrogen as well as a mixture of argon and nitrogen, Shahin (69) studied several processes of dissociative ionization, for example,

$$N_2^+ + N_2 \longrightarrow N^+ + N + N_2 \qquad [9]$$

$$Ar^+ + N_2 \longrightarrow N^+ + N + Ar \qquad [10]$$

Careful analysis of the data based on the conditions within the discharge showed, as expected, that the cross sections for both these reactions varied with ion energy, being negligible close to the threshold and rising to a maximum of 0.5×10^{-16} cm^2 for reaction [9] and 2×10^{-16} cm^2 for reaction [10]. These values are in reasonably good agreement with measurements made for these reactions in a more conventional apparatus (82). Similar decomposition of the molecular ions was also observed in pure oxygen as well as mixtures of nitrogen and oxygen. In the latter case, using very small concentrations of oxygen, the dissociative ionization of oxygen by collisions with nitrogen ions,

$$N_2^+ + O_2 \longrightarrow O^+ + O + N_2 \qquad [11]$$

was studied.

2. **Negative Glow and Positive Column.** As mentioned earlier, although the edge of the negative glow close to the cathode dark space has a reasonably high electric field, by far in the major part of the negative glow the electric field is close to zero. The electric field in the positive column is also very small

and is no more than a few volts per cm. These considerations have been previously discussed in detail in Chapter 5, Vol. I. Another major difference is the number density of the ions within the negative glow which is some one to two orders of magnitude greater than the positive column through which the ions drift with relatively small energies. Apart from the extraneous effects within the ion sheath around the sampling port, it is therefore expected that only exothermic ion-molecule reactions occur within these regions of the discharge.

Mass-spectrometric studies of discharges in rare gases have been carried out by several workers (83,84) showing the presence of atomic as well as molecular ions of these gases in both the negative glow and positive column. Knewstubb has shown that there is considerable variation in their relative concentration between these two regions (85). Two processes have been proposed for the formation of the molecular species. These are the three-body mechanisms

$$X^+ + 2X \longrightarrow X_2^+ + X \qquad [12]$$

where X represents any rare gas atom, and the Hornbeck-Molnar process involving a highly excited state of the atom (86)

$$X^* + X \longrightarrow X_2^+ + e \qquad [13]$$

Because of the squared dependence of reaction [12] on pressure, it is likely that the three-body process be of importance only in high pressures, for example, above a few torr. On the other hand, reaction [13] predominates at pressures below 0.1 torr while in the pressure range of 0.1–1 torr, the relative importance of the two reactions depends on which one of the X^+ or X^* species is preferentially produced. Knewstubb (85) concludes that in the negative glow, ionization is enhanced relative to high electronic excitation and therefore, reaction [12] is more favored in this region. The positive column he argues favors reaction [13]. Franklin et al. (68), studying microwave discharges which only exhibit positive columns, also conclude that the formation of He_2^+ in their experiments within the same pressure region, must arise from reaction [13], if the rate constant for reaction [12] would be no higher than 10^{-30} cm^6 molecule^{-2} sec^{-1}.

Glow discharges in hydrogen have been studied by a number of investigators (87,88). In these systems, the formation of H_3^+ was first reported by Braesfield (87). He observed the increasing importance of H_3^+ ions as the discharge pressure was increased. Luhr (88), using a mixture of H_2 and D_2 showed the formation H_3^+ and D_3^+ in the positive column of the discharge. As expected, the presence of triatomic ions has also been observed in microwave discharges (89). These studies have thus firmly confirmed the occurrence of the ion-molecule reaction

$$H_2^+ + H_2 \longrightarrow H_3^+ + H \qquad [14]$$

in hydrogen discharges.

In glow discharges in nitrogen, any of the four ionic species, namely N^+, N_2^+, N_3^+, and N_4^+ can be observed under the suitable discharge conditions. Thus, Knewstubb (85) found that N_3^+ and N_4^+ do not appear in significant amounts in the ions drawn from a positive column. The N_4^+ ion appears in the region of the discharge where the lowest field is expected and N_3^+ ion is found in the negative glow where high-energy electrons from the cathode region arrive in considerable number. The purity of the gas and the system is critical for the observation of these ions since reaction with hydrogenous molecules produces N_2H^+, or with traces of oxygen, O_2^+ and NO^+ is observed (85,90). The formation of N_4^+ below 1 torr is now believed (91,92) to involve three-body reactions

$$N_2^+ + 2N_2 \longrightarrow N_4^+ + N_2 \qquad [15]$$

while at higher pressures it behaves as a bimolecular reaction (90,92). Formation of N_3^+ ion is most probably due to the presence of excited nitrogen molecules (93). In agreement with the results of Knewstubb, the lack of N_4^+ ions has also been reported by Franklin et al. (68) when sampling from a microwave discharge which is simply a positive column discharge (79). These authors observe only N^+, N_2, and N_3^+ with varying intensities within 0.01–0.3 torr pressure.

Studies of the positive ions from oxygen discharges have been reported by several workers (85,94–96). These workers have also observed the presence of all four ions, namely O^+, O_2^+, O_3^+, and O_4^+ under specific discharge conditions. It is firmly believed (95), however, that the fast charge exchange reaction

$$O^+ + O_2 \longrightarrow O_2^+ + O \qquad [16]$$

plays an important role in these discharges. Using microwave discharge, Franklin et al. (68) only observe O^+ and O_2^+. This is again expected from the higher field which is present in the positive column of the discharge as compared to the Faraday dark-space and the negative glow.

Knewstubb and Tickner (97) have studied the ionic species of the glow discharge in water vapor at 0.4 torr and have reported the presence of H_3O^+ as the major ionic species which forms clusters with other water molecules. The general formula of these clusters is $H^+(H_2O)_n$ which may be referred to as solvated protons. In these studies, values of n between 1 and 5 have been observed. These authors observed only traces of H_2O^+ which apparently reacted with water molecules according to:

$$H_2O^+ + H_2O \longrightarrow H_3O^+ + OH \qquad [17]$$

to yield H_3O^+ ion. A similar tendency has been noticed for NH_4^+ ion which appears in glow discharges of ammonia and gives rise to clusters of the general formula $H^+(NH_3)_n$.

B. Studies in Corona Discharges

Mass-spectrometric studies of corona discharges have recently been pioneered in the author's laboratory (90,98–100), because of their widespread use as electrostatic charge generators as well as their general application as ozonizer type discharges for the controlled synthesis of many novel inorganic compounds. These discharges are very mild and run at much lower currents than those for glows and can be operated at pressures from a few torr to atmospheric, both in the positive and negative modes for many applications. Generally, the most stable form of corona discharges is established between two concentric electrodes. The electrodes could be covered with a thin layer of dielectric (for example, glass) as in ozonizers or the central electrode could be a thin, nonreactive (for example, platinum) bare wire, placed at high potential with respect to a coaxial cylindrical cathode. A high-voltage power supply together with a limiting resistor usually ensures a stable corona for most gases. On the application of the high voltage to the central wire and the occurrence of breakdown, a glow appears around the wire. Because of the rectangular hyperbolic field distribution between the two electrodes, electrons can gain sufficient energy for ionization only at small distances from the wire and thus the gas molecules are ionized primarily near the wire. At low currents where the effect of space charge is minimized, the system with positive potential resembles a line source for generating positive ions which then move through the gas in an almost constant field and perpendicular to the axis, undergoing various interactions with the gas molecules before reaching the cathode. The system with negative wire potential may generate, through various attachment processes, negative ions which will behave in a similar fashion. The pressure reduced electric field E/P for the most part of the ion path is very small and of the order 10–20 volt cm^{-1} torr. This characteristic low E/P and the high frequency of charge transfer and elastic collisions maintain the ion energy close to thermal energies. Thus, ion-molecule reactions which occur in these systems are all generally exothermic and are reflected in the mass spectral data which is obtained when the ionic species are sampled through a port at the cathode. (90)

1. *Positive Coronas*. The results of the discharge experiments carried out at atmospheric pressure in nitrogen, oxygen and air show (98) the importance of trace quantities of impurities such as water vapor in these systems. In all gases described previously unless extreme precautions were taken, the major ionic species observed appear to be hydrated protons; all of the general formula $(H_2O)_nH^+$ where $n = 1, 2, 3, \ldots$. The highest number observed for n was 8, obtained with some 20% relative humidity in air. As the concentration of water vapor was reduced in air, the distribution of ions moved to a

lower value of n. At water concentrations below 300 ppm in air, other ionic species such as $NO^+(H_2)O_n$ and $NO_2^+(H_2O)_n$ with $n = 0, 1$, and 2 were observed. In nitrogen at low water concentrations, mixed clusters of the general formula $(NH_3)_n(H_2O)_m H^+$ as well as N_4^+ ion was observed. Ammonia was apparently the neutral by-product of the discharge in nitrogen and water vapor and was formed in trace quantities. In oxygen at low water concentrations $O_2^+(H_2O)_n$ where $n = 1$, or 2, as well as O_4^+ were observed.

To study the processes which are responsible for the conversion of the primary ions to hydrated protons in all these discharges, low-pressure discharges were investigated in order to limit the number of collisions that the primary ions would undergo with the background gas molecules before reaching the cathode. In experiments with nitrogen (90) containing 130 ppm of water vapor, it was observed that while at 5 torr, the principle ions were N_2^+, N_2H^+, and to a smaller extent N_4^+, their intensities were diminished as the pressure was increased and those of H_2O^+, H_3O^+, and $H_5O_2^+$ were increased. These results are consistent with the following reactions:

$$N_2^+ + N_2 \longrightarrow N_4^+ \qquad [18]$$

$$N_2^+ + H_2O \longrightarrow N_2H^+ + OH \qquad [19]$$

$$N_2^+ + H_2O \longrightarrow H_2O^+ + N_2 \qquad [20]$$

$$N_4^+ + H_2O \longrightarrow H_2O^+ + 2N_2 \qquad [21]$$

$$N_2H^+ + H_2O \longrightarrow H_3O^+ + N_2 \qquad [22]$$

$$H_2O^+ + H_2O \longrightarrow H_3O^+ + OH \qquad [23]$$

which apparently bring about the complete conversion of the ionic species in nitrogen to those of hydrated protons. Quantitative analysis of the behavior of the ions in this system allows determination of the cross-section of most of the above reactions (90).

Studies in low pressure discharges of oxygen containing some 200 ppm of water vapor similarly show (100) that the initial appearance of O_2^+ is decreased at pressures above 10 torr, while species such as $O_2^+(H_2O)$, $O_2^+(H_2O)_2$, O_4^+, and $(H_2O)_2^+$ or $(H_3O^+ \cdot OH)$ ions appear. At higher pressures, these latter ions are also reduced in intensity while $H_5O_2^+$ and $H_7O_3^+$ become dominant. There is thus clear indication that mono and dihydrates of O_2^+ ion as well as $(H_2O)_2^+$ ion somehow participate as intermediates in this sequence of reactions. A possible reaction sequence may involve the following:

$$O_2^+(H_2O)_2 \rightleftharpoons (H_2O)_2^+ + O_2 \qquad [24]$$

$$(H_2O)_2^+ + M \longrightarrow H_3O^+ + OH + M \qquad [25]$$

Experiments in corona discharges of a mixture of nitrogen and some 4.4

pp 10^3 of oxygen have demonstrated (90) that reaction [18] as well as the charge-exchange reactions,

$$N_2^+ + O_2 \longrightarrow O_2^+ + N_2 \qquad [26]$$

$$N_4^+ + O_2 \longrightarrow O_2^+ + 2N_2 \qquad [27]$$

occur between discharge pressures of 5–20 torr. Again, the analysis of the data allowed calculation of the thermal cross-sections for these reactions as well as demonstrating that reaction [18] is bimolecular above 5 torr pressure used in these experiments.

Experiments in air at low pressures and very low water concentrations have shown (100) that although initially O_2^+ is the major ion, arising mainly from reaction [26], its intensity is reduced above 10 torr and that of O_4^+ rises to become a major species. A small amount of NO^+ is also observed.

2. **Negative Coronas.** Using a negative corona in which a high negative potential is applied to the central wire electrode, experiments (99) have been carried out on the nature of the ionic species which are present in discharges of air and oxygen at pressures ranging from a few torr to atmospheric. The major ionic species in air at 25 torr has been found to be O^-, O_3^-, CO_3^-, and small traces of $O_3^-(H_2O)$, and $CO_3^-(H_2O)$. The origin of CO_3^- was traced in these experiments to the small quantity of CO_2 (~ 300 ppm) which is present in air. After removing this gas through an absorption column, no trace of the ion could be found at this pressure, but instead the contributions of O^- and O_3^- were found to increase. The presence of these ions could be explained through the following known reactions:

$$e + O_2 \longrightarrow O^- + O \qquad [28]$$

$$O^- + O_2 + M \longrightarrow O_3^- + M \qquad [29]$$

$$O^- + CO_2 + M \longrightarrow CO_3^- + M \qquad [30]$$

$$O_3^- + CO_2 \longrightarrow CO_3^- + O_2 \qquad [31]$$

At higher air pressures in the discharge, the contribution of both of O^- and O_3^- were found to diminish while that of CO_3^- increased sharply reaching almost 100% at atmospheric pressure. Efforts to remove the trace CO_2 through absorption had no effect on the appearance of CO_3^- at atmospheric pressure, indicating that there were sufficient collisions with the remaining CO_2 molecules in the system to convert all the ionic species to CO_3^-. Calculations based on known rate constants for reactions [28–31] show that only 40 ppm of CO_2 is necessary for such a behavior.

The results of the experiments carried out in pure oxygen (99) showed a remarkable similarity to that of air. At discharge pressures of 60 torr the major ionic species was O_3^-, with O^- and O_3^- (H_2O) being present in small quantities. As the pressure of oxygen was increased, however, initially a trace amount of CO_3^- was observed, but with increasing pressure the contribution of this ion increased until at atmospheric pressure more than 90% ionic yield was due to CO_3^-. Efforts to remove the trace CO_2 from the gas stream through either absorption columns or cold traps were unsuccessful, indicating that the source of carbon dioxide might possibly be due to the reaction of the oxidative atmosphere of the discharge with the carbonaceous material from the wall of the discharge tube. This effect has also been regarded as the major source carbon-dioxide impurity by other workers (101).

REFERENCES

1. A. M. Bass and H. P. Broida, eds., *Formation and Trapping of Free Radicals*. New York: Academic Press, 1960.
2. K. R. Jennings, *Quarterly Reviews*, **15**, 237 (1961).
3. P. P. Knewstubb, "Mass Spectrometry of Ions from Electrical Discharges, Flames and Other Sources." In *Mass Spectrometry of Organic Ions*, edited by F. W. McLafferty. New York: Academic Press, 1963.
4. F. K. McTaggart, *Plasma Chemistry in Electrical Discharges*. New York: Elsevier Publishing Co., 1967. See also M. Venugopalan and R. A. Jones, *Chemistry of Dissociated Water Vapor and Related Systems*. New York: Interscience, 1968.
5. *Chemical Reactions in Electrical Discharges*. Advances in Chemistry Series No. 80. American Chemical Society, Washington, D.C., 1969.
6. A. G. Engelhardt and A. V. Phelps, *Phys. Rev.*, **131**, 2115 (1963).
7. J. B. Corrigan, *J. Chem. Phys.*, **43**, 4381 (1966).
8. R. D. Hake, Jr. and A. V. Phelps, Westinghouse Research Laboratories Paper 66-IE2-Gases-P1, October 1966.
9. A. G. Engelhardt, A. V. Phelps, and C. G. Risk, *Phys. Rev.*, **135**, A1566, (1966).
10. R. W. Wood, *Proc. Roy. Soc.*, **A102**, 1, (1922).
11. H. G. Poole, *Proc. Roy. Soc.*, **A163**, 415, 424 (1937).
12. T. M. Shaw, Gen. Elec. Microwave Lab. Rep. No. TISR-58ELM115 (1958).
13. C. C. Goodyear and A. von Engel, *Proc. Phys. Soc.*, **79**, 732 (1962).
14. H. Blades and C. A. Winkler, *Can. J. Chem.*, **29**, 1022 (1951).
15. J. C. Greaves and J. W. Linnett, *Trans. Farad. Soc.*, **55**, 1338 (1959).
16. H. G. Poole, *Proc. Roy. Soc.*, **A163**, 404 (1937).
17. E. W. R. Steacie, *Atomic and Free Radical Reactions*. 2nd Edition, Chapter 2. New York: Reinhold, 1954.
18. F. Kaufman, *J. Chem. Phys.*, **28**, 352 (1958).
19. F. Kaufman and J. R. Kelso, *J. Chem. Phys.*, **32**, 301 (1960).
20. J. T. Herron and H. I. Schiff, *Can. J. Chem.*, **36**, 1159 (1958).
21. L. Elias, E. A. Ogryzlo, and H. I. Schiff, *Can. J. Chem.*, **37**, 1680 (1959).
22. G. B. Kistiakowski and P. H. Kydd, *J. Amer. Chem. Soc.*, **79**, 4825 (1957).
23. G. G. Mannella, *Chem. Rev.*, **63**, 1 (1963); A. N. Wright and C. A. Winkler, *Active Nitrogen*. New York: Academic Press, 1968.
24. D. A. Armstrong and C. A. Winkler, *J. Phys. Chem.*, **60**, 1100 (1956).
25. R. Kelly and C. A. Winkler, *Can. J. Chem.*, **37**, 62 (1959).

26. B. J. Fontana, *J. Appl. Phys.*, **29**, 1668 (1958).
27. R. A. Young, R. L. Sharpless, and R. L. Stringham, *J. Chem. Phys.*, **40**, 111 (1964).
28. Y. Tanaka, A. Jursa, and F. LeBlanc, *The Threshold of Space*. London: Pergamon, 1957, p. 89.
29. D. S. Jackson and H. I. Schiff, *J. Chem. Phys.*, **23**, 2333 (1955).
30. F. Kaufman and J. R. Kelso, *J. Chem. Phys.*, **28**, 510 (1958).
31. K. Dressler, *J. Chem. Phys.*, **30**, 1621 (1959).
32. A. N. Wright, R. L. Nelson, and C. A. Winkler, *Can. J. Chem.*, **40**, 1082 (1962).
33. A. Fontyn and D. E. Rosner, *Can. J. Chem.*, **42**, 2440 (1964).
34. W. E. Jones and C. A. Winkler, *Can. J. Chem.*, **34**, 1217 (1956).
35. R. A. Young, *Can. J. Chem.*, **44**, 1171 (1966).
36. P. Harteck, R. R. Reeves, and G. G. Mannella, *J. Chem. Phys.*, **29**, 608 (1958).
37. G. M. Schwab, *Z. Physik Chem.*, **B27**, 452 (1935).
38. E. A. Ogryslo, *Can J. Chem.*, **39**, 2556 (1961).
39. N. Vanderkool and MacKenzie, "Free Radicals in Organic Chemistry," Chapter 9, *Advances in Chem. Series*, No. 36 (1962).
40. H. E. Radford, V. W. Hughes, and V. Beltran-Lopez, *Phys. Rev.*, **123**, 153 (1961).
41. E. R. Zabolotny and H. Gesser, *J. Amer. Chem. Soc.*, **81**, 6091 (1959).
42. F. P. DelGreco and F. Kaufman, *Disc. Farad. Soc.*, **33**, 128 (1962); M. Venugopalan and R. A. Jones, *Chemistry of Dissociated Water Vapor and Related Systems*. New York: Interscience, 1968.
43. A. D. Coates, U.S. Dept. Comm. Office Tech. Serv. A.D. 419–618 (1962).
44. A. Streitwieser and H. R. Ward, *J. Amer. Chem. Soc.*, **85**, 539 (1962).
45. T. F. Bindley, A. T. Watts, and S. Walker, *Trans. Farad. Soc.*, **60**, 1 (1964).
46. C. K. Jen, S. N. Foner, E. L. Cochran, and V. A. Bowers, *Phys. Rev.*, **112**, 1169 (1958).
47. K. F. Bonhoeffer, *Z. Phys. Chem.*, **113**, 199 (1924).
48. T. G. Pearson, P. L. Robinson, and E. M. Stoddart, *Proc. Roy. Soc.*, **A142**, 275 (1933).
49. W. V. Kotlensky and R. Schaeffer, *J. Amer. Chem. Soc.*, **80**, 4517 (1958).
50. R. Grimes, F. E. Wang, R. Lewin, and W. N. Lipscomb, *Proc. Natl. Acad. Sci. U.S.*, **47**, 996 (1961).
51. L. B. Friedman, R. D. Dobrott, and W. N. Lipscomb, *J. Amer. Chem. Soc.*, **85**, 3505 (1963).
52. J. E. Drake and W. L. Jolly, *J. Chem. Soc.*, 2807 (1962).
53. E. J. Spanier and A. G. MacDiarmid, *Inorg. Chem.*, **1**, 432 (1962).
54. S. D. Gokdale and W. L. Jolly, *Inorg. Chem.*, **3**, 946 (1964).
55. J. E. Drake and W. L. Jolly, *Chem. Ind.*, 1470 (1962).
56. S. D. Gokdale and W. L. Jolly, *Inorg. Chem.*, **3**, 1141 (1964); **4**, 596 (1965).
57. W. L. Jolly, C. B. Lindahl and R. W. Kopp, *Inorg. Chem.*, **1**, 958 (1962).
58. T. Wartik, R. Moore, and H. I. Schlesinger, *J. Amer. Chem. Soc.*, **71**, 3265 (1949).
59. A. G. Massey, 20th Intern. Congr. IUPAC, Moscow, July 1965.
60. A. K. Holliday and A. G. Massey, *Chem. Rev.*, **62**, 303 (1962).
61. J. W. Frazer, *J. Inorg. Nucl. Chem.*, **11**, 166 (1959).
62. A. V. Grosse and A. D. Kirstenbaum, *J. Amer. Chem. Soc.*, **81**, 1277 (1959).
63. A. V. Grosse, A. D. Kirstenbaum, and A. G. Streng, *J. Amer. Chem. Soc.*, **83**, 1004 (1961).
64. A. D. Kirstenbaum, L. V. String, A. V. String, and A. V. Gross, *J. Amer. Chem. Soc.*, **85**, 360 (1963).
65. A. D. Kirstenbaum, L. V. String, A. V. String, and A. V. Gross, *Noble Gas Compounds*. Chicago: University of Chicago Press, 1963, p. 73.

66. R. Hoppe, W. Dahne, H. Mallanch, and K. M. Rodder, *Z. Anorg. Allg. Chem.*, **324**, 214 (1963).

67. A. D. Milligan and D. Sears, *J. Amer. Chem. Soc.*, **85**, 823 (1963).

68. J. L. Franklin, P. K. Gosh, and S. Studniary, "Chemical Reactions in Electrical Discharges." *Advances in Chemistry Series*, No. 80, p. 59. Washington, D.C.: American Chemical Soc., 1969.

69. M. M. Shahin, "Ion-Molecule Reactions in the Gas Phase." *Advances in Chemistry Series*, No. 58, p. 315. Washington, D.C.: American Chemical Soc., 1966.

70. G. Gioumousis and D. P. Stevenson, *J. Chem. Phys.*, **29**, 294 (1958).

71. P. Langevin, *Ann. Chim. Phys.*, **5**, 245 (1905).

72. N. Boelrijk and W. H. Hamill, *J. Amer. Chem. Soc.*, **84**, 730 (1962).

73. D. A. Kubose and W. A. Hamill, *J. Amer. Chem. Soc.*, **85**, 125 (1963).

74. L. P. Theard and W. H. Hamill, *J. Amer. Chem. Soc.*, **84**, 1135 (1962).

75. T. F. Moran and W. H. Hamill, *J. Chem. Phys.*, **39**, 1413 (1963).

76. See Debye Sheath, "Electrical Discharge Plasmas," this book, Vol. I, Chapter 5.

77. J. D. Cobine, *Gaseous Conductors*. Dover Publications, 1958.

78. F. T. Green and T. A. Miln, *J. Chem. Phys.*, **39**, 3150 (1963); R. E. Lechenby, E. J. Robins, and P. A. Trevalion, *Proc. Roy. Soc.*, **A280**, 409 (1964).

79. See "Electrical Discharge Plasmas," this book, Vol. I, Chapter 5.

80. A. vonEngel, *Ionized Gases*. London: Oxford University Press, 1965.

81. W. D. Davis and T. A. Vanderslice, *Phys. Rev.*, **131**, 219 (1963).

82. C. F. Giese and W. B. Maier, *J. Chem. Phys.*, **39**, 197 (1963); W. B. Maier, *J. Chem. Phys.*, **47**, 859 (1967).

83. D. Morris, *Proc. Phys. Soc.*, **A68**, 11 (1955).

84. M. Pahl and U. Weiner, *Z. Naturforsch*, **13a**, 753 (1958).

85. P. F. Knewstubb and A. W. Tickner, *J. Chem. Phys.*, **36**, 674, 684 (1962); *J. Chem. Phys.*, **37**, 2941 (1962); *J. Chem. Phys.*, **38**, 464 (1963).

86. J. A. Hornbeck and J. P. Molnar, *Phys., Rev.*, **84**, 621 (1951).

87. C. J. Braesfield, *Phys. Rev.*, **31**, 52 (1928).

88. O. Luhr, *J. Chem. Phys.*, **3**, 146 (1935).

89. L. B. Ortenburger, M. Hertzburg, and R. A. Ogg, *J. Chem. Phys.*, **33**, 579 (1960).

90. M. M. Shahin, *J. Chem. Phys.*, **47**, 4392 (1967).

91. G. Junk and H. J. Svec, *J. Amer. Chem. Soc.*, **80**, 2908 (1958).

92. D. K. Bohme, D. B. Dunkin, F. C. Fehsenfeld, and E. E. Ferguson, *J. Chem. Phys.*, **51**, 863 (1969).

93. R. K. Asundi, G. J. Schulz, and P. J. Chantry, *J. Chem. Phys.*, **47**, 1584 (1967).

94. O. Luhr, *Phys. Rev.*, **44**, 459 (1933).

95. P. H. G. Dickinson and J. Sayers, *Proc. Phys. Soc.*, **A76**, 137 (1960).

96. G. Brederlow, *Ann. Physik* [8], **5**, 414 (1960).

97. P. F. Knewstubb and A. W. Tickner, *J. Chem. Phys.*, **38**, 464 (1963).

98. M. M. Shahin, *J. Chem. Phys.*, **45**, 2600 (1966).

99. M. M. Shahin, *Appl. Optics*, Supplement on Electrophotography, p. 106 (1969).

100. M. M. Shahin, "Chemical Reactions in Electrical Discharges." *Advances in Chemistry Series*, No. 80. Washington, D.C.: American Chemical Soc., 1969, p. 48.

101. W. L. Fite and J. A. Rutherford, *Disc. Farad. Soc.*, **37**, 192 (1964).

CHAPTER FIFTEEN

Chemical Reactions in Plasma Jets

CHARLES S. STOKES

I. INTRODUCTION

The plasma jet is a relatively new device for the production of high temperatures beyond the range of chemical-combustion flames or the ordinary electric arc. Its range may be defined as about $5000°K$–$50,000°K$.

The production of compounds with the plasma jet depends on the temperature achieved and the quenching velocity of the compounds formed at these temperatures. The process of the formation of compounds by using a plasma jet as the high-temperature source may be considered as occurring in two principal steps; primarily, the decomposition of the molecules, either of the reactive plasma gas or of the molecules fed into the plasma "flame," into atoms or activated atoms; and secondarily, the freezing out of the chemical equilibrium attained at these high plasma temperatures by using fast quenching methods.

According to the two steps described above, two essentially different types of chemical reactions might be carried out successfully by the use of the plasma jet temperatures:

First, the decomposition of compounds into their elements or less energetic compounds, for example,

$$2\,NH_3 \longrightarrow N_2 + 3H_2$$

$$CH_4 \longrightarrow C + 2\,H_2 \quad \text{or} \quad Al_2O_3 \longrightarrow 2Al + \tfrac{3}{2}O_2$$

Second, the formation of endothermic compounds by freezing the chemical equilibria obtained at high temperatures by the use of fast quenching methods. The formation of exothermic compounds, such as ammonia from nitrogen with hydrogen, is not probable, since the chemical equilibrium at high temperatures is less favorable for ammonia than for nitrogen and hydrogen.

The reactions investigated so far show that by the use of the high plasma jet temperatures with appropriate quenching, gaseous endothermic compounds, such as NO, C_2H_2, HCN, and $(CN)_2$ are obtained in as good or better yields than by some available industrial processes.

II. TYPES OF CHEMICAL-PLASMA JETS AND RELATED EQUIPMENT

Plasma arc devices have been found suitable for a variety of uses. The electric arc, which is constricted into a smaller circular cross-section than would ordinarily exist in an open arc-type device, generates a very high temperature. This superheated-plasma working fluid can be channeled through an orifice and used as a reactive medium for chemical synthesis.

Plasma generators are classified as the nontransferred arc and the transferred arc. The difference between the two is related to the position of the electrodes with respect to each other and to the arc plume. A nontransferred arc consists usually of a cathode and an anode with an orifice or channel so that when the arc is struck, the arc plume emerges through this opening. The transferred-arc cathode is spaced some distance away from the anode and the arc is constricted between both electrodes. Both systems have been used in chemical synthesis studies.

Although many types of plasma jets have been perfected for various purposes, the most-used type for chemical studies is a direct-current gas stabilized plasma arc of the general type shown in Fig. 1.

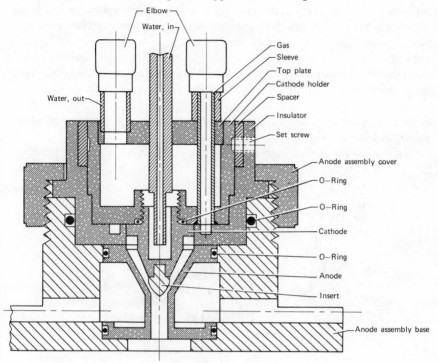

Figure 1   Typical plasma jet.

Gage's constricted-arc (see General References—Staff Feature), gas-fed torch, developed by the Linde Company, was the first commercial plasma jet. In studying the arc properties of rare gases, Gage had observed the flames produced when the arcs struck a water-cooled copper anode. By drilling a hole in the anode, he made the "flame" pass through it, and gas flow under pressure produced a crude plasma jet. Finally, the hole was reduced in size to form a nozzle which constricted the arc and the plasma. The plasma equipment commercially available consists of torches and accessories for their control. However, complete plasma systems for chemical synthesis are not available commercially. The nature and complexity of the laboratory equipment necessary to carry out plasma reactions are dictated by the chemical process under investigation.

A plasma jet for chemical purposes can be varied in its design to meet the requirements of the process, such as the introduction of a reactant at a certain point along the flame path.

Consumable cathodes have been used in experiments in which carbon was one of the reactants. Many experiments used carbon vaporized from a graphite cathode in the chemical studies. The introduction of powder carried in a gas stream or as a constituent of a gas either admixed or premixed has also been used to enter reactant into the plasma stream.

Tungsten or 2%-thoriated tungsten electrodes are the most frequently used water-cooled nonconsumable cathodes. Water-cooled copper anodes have been widely used in many arc generators designed for chemical synthesis.

The reactor chamber may be of any configuration desired to accommodate different feeding and quenching devices. A schematic of a plasma reactor is shown in Fig. 2.

Gases or powders have been injected into the plasma from a ring attached

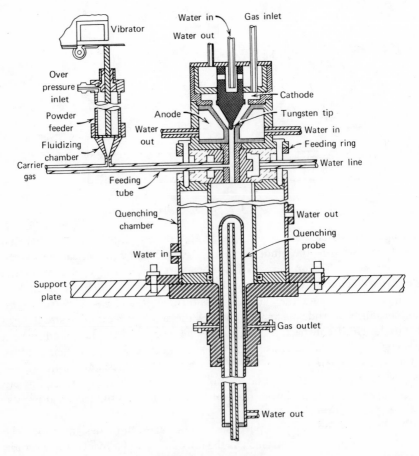

Figure 2 Plasma reactor.

to the bottom of the plasma generator. The chamber can be fitted with variously shaped quench tubes to cool the products.

In general, methods for feeding and quenching reactions, collection of samples, and other processes must be studied for each particular reaction.

III. PLASMA JET REACTIONS

A. Decomposition Reactions

1. *Iron Ore Reduction.* Recently Gillis and Clump (1) have studied the reduction of iron ore with hydrogen in a DC plasma jet. The apparatus consisted of a plasma jet equipped with a special anode for injecting ore coupled to a reactor approximately 5 inches in diameter × 2 ft long. This reactor was equipped with a quench plate approximately 5 inches in diameter which could be placed at several distances from the plasma jet anode. Typical operating conditions of several production runs are given in Table 1.

TABLE 1
Iron ore reduction

Ore mesh size	Plasma gas		Ore conveying		Distance from anode to quench plate, in.	Plasma power		
	Mole %, H_2	Flow, SCFH	Gas, SCFH	Rate, g min^{-1}		Gross, Kw	Watts per SCFH, plasma gas	Ore reduction, %
−270, +325	100	143	8.4	0.83	5.75	14.4	41.7	33.7
−270, +325	100	141	5.4	0.92	5.75	21.8	62.0	53.5
−270, +325	100	118	9.5	0.85	5.75	30.4	86.0	69.2
−200, +230	100	144	6.6	1.04	5.75	15.0	43.0	21.8
−200, +230	100	122	9.5	1.04	5.75	31.6	89.3	64.0
−270, +325	25	83	9.5	0.91	7.75	17.0	61.5	27.5
−270, +325	25	82	9.5	0.96	7.75	22.7	84.4	42.1
−200, +230	25	83	9.5	1.01	7.75	16.5	59.4	15.7

The plasma jet used a mixture of hydrogen and argon; Carol Lake concentrate (which was approximately 67% iron) was used as a feed material. The results of these studies show that iron ore can be reduced very rapidly and efficiently using a plasma jet apparatus.

2. Metal Oxides Reduction

a. TUNGSTEN TRIOXIDE REDUCTION. The reduction of tungsten trioxide has been successfully carried out in the plasma jet (2, 3) according to the reaction:

$$WO_3 + 3H_2 \longrightarrow W + 3H_2O$$

Tungsten trioxide powder was carried in a hydrogen stream into the "flame" of a helium plasma jet. The copper cold finger was placed about 5 inches below the feeding ring.

The conditions and results of some of the runs are given in Table 2.

TABLE 2
Tungsten trioxide reduction

Helium flow, liters min^{-1}	H$_2$ Flow, liters min^{-1}	WO$_3$ Input, g min^{-1}	Operating power, Kw	W Formation %	g min^{-1}
34	13.6	4.36	14.8	80	2.77
34	13.6	2.11	11.4	90	1.51
34	13.6	2.60	15.2	95	1.96

The product formation is based on the W input as WO$_3$. The highest yield obtained was 95%. The calculated residence time of the particles in the flame was 0.26 milliseconds. The product obtained in this reaction was highly pyrophoric in nature. The average particle size of the product was from 0.5 to 1 micron.

From Table 2 it can be shown that for a certain power input to the jet, the yield of W increases with a decrease in WO$_3$ powder flow. Also, at a certain WO$_3$ powder flow rate, the yield of W increases with an increase in power.

b. FERRIC OXIDE REDUCTION. Ferric oxide reduction has been successfully carried out using the plasma jet (2, 3). Ferric oxide powder has been injected into a helium plasma through a feeding ring. Hydrogen was used as the carrier gas and the copper cold finger was used at a distance of 5 inches from the feeding ring. Typical plasma conditions were He flow, 34 liters min^{-1} at a power of 15.5 Kw; hydrogen flow, 13.6 liters min^{-1} and the powder flow rate 0.3 g min^{-1}. The product obtained consisted of a submicron, black and highly pyrophoric iron powder (yield 100%).

c. TITANIUM DIOXIDE REDUCTION. Several attempts have been made to reduce TiO$_2$ in the plasma jet, all with unsuccessful results (2, 3). No reduction has been obtained by any of the methods studied. An outline of the different procedures used in carrying out the reactions is presented in Table 3. All runs were made with TiO$_2$ powder (325 mesh size).

TABLE 3
Titanium dioxide reduction

Powder flow, g min^{-1}	Power input, Kw	Plasma		Carrier and overpressure gas, liters min^{-1}		Quenching method
		Gas, liters min^{-1}				
0.5	12	N$_2$	5.2	N$_2$	3.4	None
0.37	14.4	N$_2$	5.9	N$_2$	2.4	Copper cold finger (6 in. below feeding ring)
0.6	12	N$_2$	5.2	N$_2$	3.4	Quenching probe
0.4	10.5	He	34	H$_2$	13.7	Quenching probe
0.4	15.5	He	34	H$_2$	13.7	Cold finger (6 in. below feeding ring)

d. ZIRCONIUM OXIDE REDUCTION. ZrO$_2$ reduction has been attempted in the plasma jet (2, 4). ZrO$_2$ powder was injected into the flame of a helium plasma; hydrogen gas was used as the carrier and overpressure for the powder. The helium flow was 34 liters min^{-1} at a power of 15 Kw. They hydrogen flow was 13.6 liters min^{-1} and the powder flow rate was 0.8 g min^{-1}. No reduction was obtained, as shown by the X-ray diffraction analysis of the product.

e. REDUCTION OF TANTALUM PENTOXIDE WITH H$_2$. The reduction of tantalum pentoxide (Ta$_2$O$_5$) was successfully carried out in the helium plasma (2, 4) according to the equation:

$$Ta_2O_5 + 5H_2 \longrightarrow 2Ta + 5H_2O$$

Commercial grade tantalum pentoxide powder was carried in a hydrogen stream into the flame of a helium plasma jet. A copper cold finger was used either at 0.5 inch or 5 inches below the feeding ring; therefore, two different residence times in the flame were studied. With the cold finger at a 0.5 inch distance, the residence time of the particles in the flame was 0.10 milliseconds and with the cold finger at a 5 inch distance, the calculated residence time was 0.18 milliseconds. A much faster quenching of the products was produced with the cold finger at 0.5 inch below the feeding ring. The helium flow rate was 34 liters min^{-1} and the hydrogen flow rate was 6.5 liters min^{-1}.

Figure 3 and Table 4 show the results of these experiments. Note the higher conversion of Ta$_2$O$_5$ to Ta at the higher quenching rate. Also note the difference in slope of the two lines, showing the importance of the position of the quench probe. Figure 3 shows that the higher the Kwhr g^{-1} input the greater the conversion in either case.

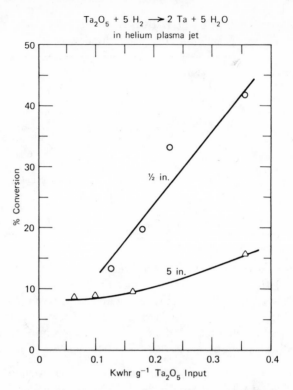

$$Ta_2O_5 + 5 H_2 \longrightarrow 2 Ta + 5 H_2O$$
in helium plasma jet

Figure 3   Reduction of Ta_2O_5 with hydrogen. (2)

TABLE 4
Ta_2O_5 Reduction with H_2

Powder flow, g min^{-1}	Kwhr g^{-1}, Input	Operating power, Kw	Cold finger quench, inches	Ta Formation %	g min^{-1}
0.77	0.350	16.20	0.5	42.8	0.27
1.25	0.216	16.20	0.5	33.3	0.34
0.88	0.178	9.36	0.5	20.0	0.14
1.40	0.114	9.60	0.5	13.1	0.15
0.78	0.350	16.56	5	15.8	0.10
3.17	0.085	16.20	5	9.3	0.24
0.34	0.047	9.60	5	9.3	0.03
1.04	0.154	9.60	5	9.3	0.08

f. THE REDUCTION OF ALUMINUM OXIDE.   The use of the high temperature of the plasma jet to carry out the reduction of aluminum oxide is an attractive possibility (3,5). Several were made both with an argon plasma jet and a helium plasma jet. Into the flame of the jet powdered Al_2O_3, 200 mesh or 325 mesh, was fed as a suspension in either hydrogen, methane, or argon by a powder-feeding apparatus. The residence time of the particles in the plasma flame was calculated to range between 5 and 20 milliseconds. The solid products formed, after fast quenching with either a water-cooled funnel located 1.5 inches below the anode end or a cold finger placed at several different distances from the anode, were collected in the copper collector attached to the reaction chamber.

The results obtained are listed in Table 5. The reduction to aluminum metal was very poor in all of the reactions, although aluminum metal was definitely formed.

TABLE 5
Reduction of aluminum oxide

Powder		Power input Kw	Plasma		Carrier and overpressure		Quenching method	% Al
Type	g min⁻¹		Gas	liters min⁻¹	Gas	liters min⁻¹		
Al_2O_3 (325 mesh)	0.8	13.6	He	34	H_2	8.6	Quenching probe	
Al_2O_3 (325 mesh)	0.5	11.6	He	34	H_2	13.7	Graphite tube between feeding ring and probe[a]	
Al_2O_3 (325 mesh)	0.7	11.4	He H_2	31 2.8	H_2	13.7	Quenching probe	
Al_2O_3 (325 mesh)	2.5	13	He	34	H_2	13.7	Cold finger 6 inches below ring	
Al_2O_3 (325 mesh)	2	13.3	He	34	H_2	9.7	Cold finger ½ inch below ring	
Al_2O_3 (325 mesh) and C powder (1 mole Al_2O_3 to 7 moles C)	0.48	14.9	He	34	Ar	3.8	Cold finger 6 inches below ring	
Al_2O_3 (particle size reduced in plasma jet)	0.33	15.5	He	34	H_2	8.9	Cold finger 6 inches below ring	
Al_2O_3 (200 mesh)	6	8.55	Ar	15.5	H_2	12.0⎫	Water-cooled funnel at 1.5 inches below anode	1.25
Al_2O_3 (200 mesh)	1.5	8.9	Ar	11.9	CH_4	8.5⎬		0.20
Al_2O_3 (200 mesh)	3	9.6	Ar	11.9	CH_4	8.7⎭		0.20

[a] The graphite tube used had $\frac{7}{16}$ inch inside diameter and $\frac{1}{8}$ inch wall thickness.

Since the particle size of the collected reaction product, which consisted essentially of aluminum oxide, was the same as the size of the starting material, it is assumed that either the residence time in the plasma flame was too short or the products were not added into a hot enough part of the flame, thereby limiting the decomposition of the alumina.

g. URANIUM DIOXIDE REDUCTION. Gibson and Weidman (6) have reduced uranium dioxide with carbon producing uranium carbide using a high-intensity arc apparatus with consumable homogeneous electrodes. Although not a pure plasma jet, such a system would lend itself to a plasma jet process.

B. Gas Decomposition Reactions

1. *Production of Acetylene.* For many years there has been a strong interest in the production of acetylene from methane via a plasma jet. Anderson and Case (7) investigated the production of acetylene using a hydrogen plasma jet and admixing methane. A complete analysis of the reaction was undertaken and yields as high as 80% were obtained based on the methane input. The authors predicted and obtained the optimum cracking conditions for methane which would be the formation of acetylene in a yield of 80% at an input requirement of 340,000 BTU lb^{-1} mole acetylene. The optimum calculated values were obtained at a hydrogen-in-methane flow rate ratio of 0.497. The experimental results were in excellent agreement with the technical analysis.

Leutner and Stokes (8) produced acetylene by admixing methane to an argon plasma jet. Using a consumable carbon cathode an 80% yield was obtained under the following operating conditions:

Argon arc	6.84 Kw
Argon flow	8.9 liters min^{-1}
Total methane input	1.65 liters min^{-1}
Total carbon input	0.9 g min^{-1}

Chemical Week (9) presented the production of acetylene by a pseudo plasma jet or long arc developed by duPont and commercially produced acetylene from methane. With a graphite electrode, the methane is fed directly into the arc around the graphite cathode. The arc is then rotated by magnetic coil and a quench hydrocarbon, usually propane, is fed below the magnetic coil into the arc stream. Below the quench hydrocarbon inlet is a quench water spray which further cools the reactant mixture. For each 100 lbs of acetylene produced, about 120 lbs of methane and 40 lbs of propane are required.

Chemical Week reported that the methane fed to propane quench weight ratio was 12:3 and the burner consumed 6 Kwhr lb^{-1} of acetylene produced at yields of 78%. This process looks particularly economical where low electric costs can be obtained.

Gulyaev et al. (10) of the Soviet Union have shown that the acetylene yield from an argon stabilized arc admixing methane depends on the methane flow rate, the arc power consumption and the nozzle design; 80% conversions were reported.

Stokes and Smith (2, 11) on the production of acetylene from methane using an argon jet showed that using a ratio of argon to methane of 0.3 the minimum (60 Kwhr) power is required to produce 100 ft³ of acetylene. Figure 4

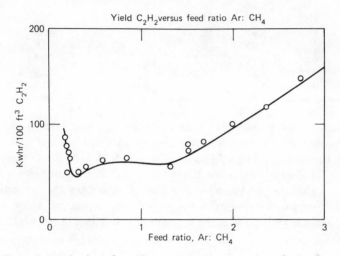

Figure 4 Production of acetylene versus argon to methane feed ratio. (2)

shows the dependence of the feed ratio of argon to methane on the Kwhr/100 ft³ of yield. Typical running conditions are given in Table 6.

Recent developments by Westinghouse scientists Maniero et al. (12) and Hirayama and Maniero (13) utilizing an AC arc in the multimegawatt range, magnetically rotated using a pure methane flow, have produced acetylene at 2.7 Kwhr lb⁻¹ (19.6 Kwhr/100 ft³). This energy input is only slightly in excess of the required amount of the heat of reaction and leaves little heat available for the formation of other products.

2. Cracking Rate Studies

a. DECOMPOSITION OF CARBON DIOXIDE. The production of oxygen from the reduction of carbon dioxide has been investigated by Blanchet and Lavallee (14). Using an argon plasma jet operating at 3 and 6 Kw, 1 and 3% yields of oxygen were obtained by passing carbon dioxide into the exit plume of the jet. Flow rates of argon ranged from 3 to 30 liters min⁻¹.

TABLE 6
Production of acetylene from methane using an argon plasma jet

Total flow, liters min^{-1} Ar + CH$_4$	Ar–CH$_4$ Ratio	Power, Kw	Product analysis, %			Conversion CH$_4$ to C$_2$H$_2$, %	Kwhr 100 ft^3 C$_2$H$_2$
			C$_2$H$_2$	C$_2$H$_4$	C$_2$H$_6$		
20.2	3.05	5.66	3.1	—	—	29.2	366.0
21.4	2.45	6.05	10.1	1.5	—	73.4	125.0
22.8	2.00	6.05	11.5	1.6	—	70.5	107.0
25.2	1.52	6.05	12.3	0.8	—	64.0	89.0
30.4	1.00	5.90	10.2	1.8	—	46.0	79.5
45.2	0.51	5.90	8.6	1.5	1.5	26.0	69.0
48.0	0.26	5.38	5.3	1.4	1.8	22.4	59.0
52.0	0.24	5.31	6.0	1.5	2.2	15.9	75.0
56.4	0.21	5.55	6.4	1.6	2.5	13.8	81.5

b. DECOMPOSITION OF AMMONIA AND METHANE. Kinetic rate studies of the decomposition of ammonia and methane in an argon plasma jet has been shown to be rate limited by a diffusion process (15). A good fit of experimental data to a proposed model for the process has been shown with several quantities calculatable, among them time distribution of decomposition products spent on the reactor, time-temperature profile of argon effluing from jet, and the temperatures the reactant contacts as it diffuses into the hot zone.

C. Gas Reactions

1. The Preparation of Hydrogen Cyanide

a. FROM METHANE AND NITROGEN. By feeding methane into a nitrogen plasma, the decomposition into carbon and hydrogen would yield the carbon supply and at the same time provide the hydrogen necessary for HCN formation.

Table 7 gives the experimental data and the results obtained by Leutner (16) in these experiments. All of these reactions were carried out without a quenching device.

As it is shown in Table 7, higher HCN yields are obtained by using a large excess of nitrogen. With a pyrolytic graphite cathode and nitrogen in the C : N proportion of 1 : 717, a conversion into HCN and C$_2$H$_2$ of 91.3% of the total carbon input was achieved although the amount of products formed is relatively low compared with 1.9 g min^{-1} of HCN and 1.5 g min^{-1}

TABLE 7
Production of hydrogen cyanide

Methane input, liters min⁻¹	Starting ratio C : N	Starting ratio C : H	Power input, Kw	HCN Formation[a] %	HCN Formation[a] g min⁻¹	C_2H_2 Formation[a] %	C_2H_2 Formation[a] g min⁻¹
(a) Using graphite cathodes							
2.0	1 : 4	1 : 2.5	12.7	31.5	1.5	40.3	0.9
4.0	1 : 3.1	1 : 2.9	12.2	21.1	1.4	39.4	1.3
2.0	1 : 7.7	1 : 3.6	12.5	45.7	1.2	45.6	0.6
(b) Using 2% thoriated tungsten cathodes							
3.25	1 : 1.5	1 : 3.17	11.5	23.2	1.0	62.3	1.4
8.0	1 : 1	1 : 4	12.5	19.5	1.9	31.75	1.5

[a]Product formation is based on the total (cathode plus methane) carbon input.

of C_2H_2, using a stoichiometric C : N ratio, high gas flows and a 2% thoriated tungsten cathode. Other hydrocarbons besides C_2H_2 were not present; cyanogen was found in not quantitatively detectable amounts.

Freeman (17) investigated the production of hydrogen cyanide in a nitrogen plasma jet using methane as the carbon-hydrogen source. In this work the reactor configuration was varied in order to investigate the production rate of hydrogen cyanide versus the input rate of methane. The reactor consisted of a plasma jet with intermediate nozzle section, which is shown in Fig. 5. The data show that the formation of hydrogen cyanide by admixing methane

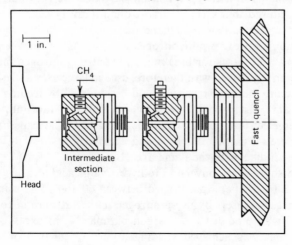

Figure 5 Plasma reactor of Freeman (17).

into a nitrogen plasma is a true "titration" and is governed by the heat flow at the mixing point; the titration curve is shown in Fig. 6. As shown in the figure, the observed curve first shows an initial rise. then an equivalent point, and last a plateau region, which rises slowly. The production of hydrogen cyanide was independent of the length of the reactor. When argon was substituted for nitrogen in the plasma jet, the absolute production rate of hydrogen cyanide appears to be a constant.

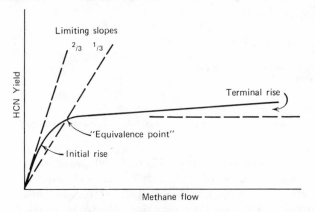

Figure 6 Titration curve. (17)

b. FROM AMMONIA AND METHANE. In the following experiments, stoichiometric mixtures of ammonia and methane were fed into the "flame" of either an argon plasma jet or a nitrogen plasma jet. Since the previously described experiments showed that CH_4 is almost quantitatively decomposed into its elements in the plasma flame, methane was chosen as carbon and hydrogen source. Ammonia instead of pure nitrogen was used as the nitrogen source, in order to avoid heat losses for breaking up the strong nitrogen molecule into atomic nitrogen; hydrogen was, therefore, used in large excess (from NH_3 and CH_4). Essentially the same results should be obtained by feeding a nitrogen-methane mixture instead of an ammonia-methane mixture into the plasma flame; higher electrical power would be necessary. The experiments listed in Table 8 were all carried out by using a circular gas-feeding device with gas input perpendicular to the flame axis (16).

As Table 8 shows, the conversion to hydrocyanic acid and acetylene based on the carbon (methane) input ranged between 60 and 75%, using argon or nitrogen as plasma gases. By using nitrogen, either as pure nitrogen plasma or added in small amounts to an argon plasma (N_2 in excess), preferably HCN formation was achieved yielding up to 50% based on the carbon (methane) input. With argon as plasma gas, C_2H_2 formation has the prefer-

TABLE 8
Conversion to hydrocyanic acid and acetylene

Plasma gas flow, liters min^{-1}	Starting ratio C : N	C : H	Power input, Kw	Stoich. CH$_4$ + NH$_3$ input, liters min^{-1}	HCN Formation^a, % g min^{-1}	C$_2$H$_2$ Formation^a, % g min^{-1}	Quenching device
(a) Argon as plasma gas							
14.35	1 : 1	1 : 7.25	8.8	4.0	32.2	42.9	yes
					0.78	0.45	
15.75	1 : 1	1 : 6.7	8.6	6.0	31.9	30.0	no
					1.15	0.52	
11.9	1 : 1	1 : 7.0	9.9	10.0	30.8	39.75	no
					1.86	1.18	
11.9	1 : 0.97	1 : 6.8	9.2	10.0	28.55	44.1	yes
					1.74	1.3	
11.9	1 : 0.97	1 : 6.8	15.6	10.0	25.0	48.7	no
					1.67	1.6	
11.9^b	1 : 1.56	1 : 6.7	11.2	10.0^c	36.0	25.7	no
					2.2	0.7	
(b) Nitrogen as plasma gas							
7.0	1 : 8	1 : 7.1	15.5	4.0	47.2	21.6	yes
					1.13	0.25	
5.0	1 : 4.3	1 : 4.7	14.8	6.0	51.7	20.7	no
					1.88	0.38	
4.15	1 : 2.6	1 : 6.8	14.0	10.0	40.0	32.9	no
					2.4	1.0	

^{a}For each run the first value is % formation and the second value is g min^{-1} formed.
^{b}1.7 liters min^{-1} nitrogen was added to the plasma gas.
^{c}The gas mixture was fed through the circular gas feeding ring with a 30° angle versus the plasma flame.

ence, the respective yields being reversed. The preference of HCN respective to C$_2$H$_2$ formation is dependent on the quenching rate. Since acetylene is a more endothermic compound than hydrocyanic acid (-54.3 Kcal/mole for C$_2$H$_2$ compared to -30.1 Kcal/mole for HCN), the faster the quenching the higher the C$_2$H$_2$ formation.

The quenching rate obviously varied with the electrical power input, the plasma gas flow used, the feeding rate of the reactive gases, and the quenching effect of the cooling devices.

With the reaction conditions and the apparatus described, fast quenching with a cooling funnel introduced 1½ inches underneath the anode favored the C$_2$H$_2$ formation using argon as plasma gas. When using the same quenching devices, higher power input through the argon plasma jet also favored the formation of acetylene (because of the rising temperature) in accordance with the theory. Highest HCN conversions were obtained in a nitrogen plasma jet with gas flows between 5 and 7 liters per minute. Lowering the gas flow rates, causing higher plasma jet temperatures, again favored the acetylene formation. The residence time of the particles in the plasma was calculated to range between 1 and 20 milliseconds depending on the gas flow rates.

Besides HCN and C_2H_2, small quantities of cyanogen, $(CN)_2$, were formed; the maximum amount of $(CN)_2$ found was 0.8%, based on the carbon input.

c. FROM AMMONIA AND CARBON MONOXIDE.   An additional possibility for the production of HCN in a plasma jet seems to be the reaction of water gas $(C + H_2O \rightarrow CO + H_2)$ with generator gas $(C + Air \rightarrow CO + N_2)$ according to

$$N_2 + 3H_2 + 2CO \longrightarrow 2HCN + 2H_2O$$

Stoichiometric mixtures of carbon monoxide and ammonia were fed into an argon plasma jet and into a nitrogen plasma jet. Only the ammonia decomposed into its elements and no HCN was formed. The carbon monoxide was not decomposed under the conditions of the investigation (4).

2. *Water-Gas Reaction.*   The production of reducer gas has been proposed by Damon and White (18) according to the equation

$$CH_4 \text{ (or other hydrocarbons)} + H_2O \longrightarrow CO + 3H_2$$

The source material would be natural gas or propane and the steam-methane refining process would operate at temperatures between 3000 and 6000°F.

3. *Flourocarbon Reactions.*   The production of tetrafluoroethylene by the reaction of carbon with carbon tetrafluoride in an electric arc has been achieved by Baddour and Bronfin (19) using an arc reactor with a consumable graphite anode and a hollow graphite cathode. Operating in the range of 7.5 to 25 Kw and feeding carbon tetrafluoride through a center bore in the anode at rates in the range of 0.4 to 50 cc sec^{-1}, up to 69 mole% tetrafluoroethylene was produced. The effect of the variation of quench probe location was studied and it was shown that the further the sampling probe was withdrawn from the hot zone, the lower was the yield of tetrafluoroethylene. Also, perfluoropropane was formed in small quantities (about 3%). Typical run conditions are given in Table 9.

As can be seen from the table, the yield of C_2F_4 increases with decreasing pressure, which is probably due to the enhancement of the process of mixing the reactant material with the carbon plasma.

TABLE 9
Reaction of CF_4 in consumable electrode arc

Power Kw	CF_4 Feed rate, cc sec^{-1}	Mole % C_2F_4, product	Pressure, atm
12	50	7.5	1
12	25	14	1
25	50	34	1
21	25	31	1
11	0.4	20	0.5
9	10	15	0.5
10	25	25	0.5
23	10	51	0.5
16	25	57	0.5
7.5	10	11	0.1
9	25	30	0.1
17	10	60	0.1
17	25	69	0.1

In another study by Bronfin and Hazlett (20), nitrogen plasma was reacted with carbon tetrafluoride and sulphur hexafluoride. Using a 20 Kw nitrogen plasma jet with the nitrogen feed at 75 SCFH and a 15 SCFH feed of carbon tetrafluoride, the following compounds were formed: NF_3, C_2F_6, N_2F_4, CF_3NF_2.

The concentrations of these materials varied with the location of the probe intake position. The nitrogen plasma jet was coupled to a water-cooled reactor with a volume of about 0.1 ft^3. The gas sampling probe was water-cooled and was placed at a distance up to 2 inches from the plasma jet exit. The total yield of fixed nitrogen products was about 1 % of the input nitrogen for typical conditions. Using sulfur hexafluoride as a fluorine carrier, only NF_3 was detected in the product stream with the total yield of nitrogen products being about 1 %. For both reactants the yield increases with increasing power input and with increasing F/N ratio in the plasma, and the results of the experiments suggest the formation of FCN as the primary reaction path for the CF_4 gas.

4. Nitrogen Fixation Studies.

a. NITROGEN-HYDROGEN REACTION. Gaseous endothermic compounds are easily obtained at the temperatures of the plasma jet. By feeding hydrogen into the "flame" of a nitrogen plasma, it is possible to cause the formation of ammonia or hydrazine.

$$N_2 + 3H_2 \longrightarrow 2NH_3 + 11 \text{ Kcal}$$
$$N_2 + 2H_2 \longrightarrow N_2H_4$$

The plasma jet apparatus used a 2% thoriated tungsten rod as cathode. With gas flows of 5.1 liters min^{-1} of nitrogen and 8.8 liters min^{-1} of hydrogen and a power input of 13.2 Kw, no ammonia could be detected. Probably small amounts of hydrazine, N_2H_4, (heat of formation: -1.7 Kcal/mole) were formed instead of the ammonia (21).

Harnisch et al. (22) investigated the preparation of hydrazine via a plasma jet using an arc fluid of either ammonia, nitrogen, or argon and admixing cold anhydrous ammonia to the flame, quenching it immediately. Trace amounts of hydrazine were formed with the maximum conversion of 0.05% or 0.2 grams of hydrazine per Kwhr. Although the yield was quite small, more efficient and rapid methods of quenching may aid in the production of hydrazine in this manner.

b. PREPARATION OF OXIDES OF NITROGEN. The formation of nitric oxide in a DC plasma jet has been carried out (23) by using a 13 Kw nitrogen plasma with N_2 flow of 9.5 liters min^{-1} and injecting oxygen at a rate of 8.25 liters min^{-1}. The average conversion based on the oxygen was 2%.

In the later work of Stokes et al (21) liquid air at various oxygen-to-nitrogen ratios was fed perpendicularly to the axis of a helium plasma. The product was collected in a dewar flask at the bottom of the reaction chamber, together with the unreacted liquid.

Table 10 gives the data on the conditions and results of some of these experiments.

TABLE 10
Nitrogen fixation studies

Liquid air rate, lb min^{-1}	Liquid air composition, % N_2 by weight	Power, Kw	NO Formation, ppm	NO$_2$ Formation, ppm
2.69	41.5	8.48	279	517
1.04	55.0	9.28	457	332
0.75	35.0	11.20	844	472
0.75	70.0	10.70	589	357

The helium flow was maintained at 34 liters min^{-1} and the average run time was 30 seconds. Ozone was formed also as was evidenced by the strong ozone odor. No differentiation was made in the quantitative analysis between ozone and nitric oxide.

By increasing the flow rate of liquid air, NO formation was decreased. It is evident from the data that increasing the power increases the formation of NO$_2$; also, the NO formation increased.

C. THE REACTION OF LIQUID NITROGEN WITH LIQUID OXYGEN IN A HELIUM PLASMA JET. Experiments have been reported (21) using separate streams of liquid N_2 and O_2. Either liquid oxygen or nitrogen was fed close to the "flame" of the jet, and liquid nitrogen or oxygen was fed below the former. The helium flow was maintained constant at 34 liters min^{-1} and the average run time was 1 minute. The total flow composition was maintained at essentially the composition of air.

Table 11 gives the data on the conditions and results of some of the experiments with the liquid nitrogen fed close to the flame.

TABLE 11

Nitrogen fixation studies using liquid N_2 and liquid O_2 (liquid N_2 fed close to plasma exit)

Liquid N_2 rate, lb min^{-1}	Liquid O_2 rate, lb min^{-1}	Total flow composition, % N_2 by weight	Power, Kw	NO Formation,[a] ppm
3.65	1.88	66	10.5	433.5
4.90	2.60	65	10.5	386.6
5.50	3.24	63	10.5	286.7

[a]Includes O_3 formed; calculated as NO.

NO_2 was not found in the product. It is evident from Table 11 that the NO formation decreases as the liquid flow increases.

Table 12 gives the data on the conditions and results of some of the experiments with the liquid oxygen fed close to the flame. NO_2 was not found in the product. At this time no differentiation was made in the quantitative analysis between ozone and nitric oxide. But the amount of ozone present in the

TABLE 12

Nitrogen fixation studies using liquid N_2 and liquid O_2 (liquid O_2 fed close to plasma exit)

Liquid N_2 rate, lb min^{-1}	Liquid O_2 rate, lb min^{-1}	Total flow composition, % N_2 by weight	Power, Kw	NO Formation,[a] ppm
3.65	1.88	66	10.2	1067
4.90	2.60	65	10.2	915
5.50	3.24	63	9.8	665

[a]Includes O_3 formed; calculated as NO.

product was greater in the last set of experiments, evidenced by the strong ozone odor and dark blue color of the liquid product.

As is shown in Fig. 7, the NO formation was much larger with the second set-up. This set-up consisted of feeding the oxygen close to the flame.

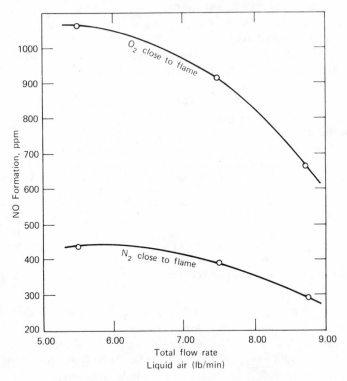

Figure 7   Formation of NO from liquid air.

5. *Reduction of Silicon Tetrachloride.* The reduction of silicon tetra-chloride has been studied by Harnisch, Meymer, and Schallus (22) using a DC plasma torch utilizing hydrogen as the plasma fluid coupled to a reactor which contained a copper cooling drum surrounded by a water-cooled jacket. The gaseous silicon tetrachloride was introduced into the flame of the plasma arc at the rate of 6–7 kg hr^{-1}. Up to 70% was converted to trichlorosilane (SiHCl$_3$) in a single pass which corresponds to 4 Kwhr per kg produced.

Plasma arc conditions were:

Current amp	100–250
Arc voltage V	100–200
Power Kw	15–30
Hydrogen flow rate, M^3 hr^{-1}	3–5

6. **Reduction of Titanium Tetrachloride.** The reduction of titanium tetrachloride was carried out by Harnisch et al. (22) by feeding a 6 : 1 mole ratio of hydrogen to titanium tetrachloride into a plasma jet. Titanium trichloride was obtained with conversion up to 60% per pass. The energy consumption was about 5Kwhr per kg. Also, when the rate was increased further, small amounts of titanium dichloride were produced, up to about 10%.

7. **Reduction of Nickel Carbonyl.** Selover (24) produced nickel fume by the decomposition of volatile nickel carbonyl when fed into an argon plasma jet of 9.9 Kw with 1.03 SCFM argon flow rate and feeding nickel carbonyl at the rate of 4.25×10^{-3} SCFM. Product analysis showed 70% nickel oxide and 30% free nickel at a production rate of 2.75×10^{-4} lb min^{-1}. The nickel fume produced was more resistant to sintering at higher temperatures in an oxygen atmosphere than in hydrogen. This study included the influence of the argon gas rate on the surface area of the reaction product produced, a quench chamber temperature profile, and an analysis of the impurities in the arc stream.

D. Solid Reactions

1. Solid Carbon Reactions Including Coal Yielding Acetylene

a. PREPARATION OF ACETYLENE USING CARBON. Leutner and Stokes (8) produced acetylene in yields up to 34% using a consumable graphite anode. Typical conditions for the experiment were: gas flow 4.5 liters min^{-1}, H_2–Ar ratio 1 : 3.5, carbon input rate 67 mg min^{-1}, power 9 Kw. Some methane was also formed.

Experiments with an argon plasma jet, a consumable graphite electrode as carbon source, and hydrogen fed into the plasma flame gave higher yields and 10 times higher C_2H_2 formation rates per time as shown in Table 13 (5). Baddour and Iwasyk (25) designed and fabricated a high-intensity arc reactor (pseudo plasma jet) to carry out the reaction of carbon vapor and hydrogen. The reaction products were quenched with a water-cooled probe. The probe was placed at different distances from the arc and several power inputs were used; with the anode as the carbon source, hydrogen was fed around the anode

TABLE 13

Acetylene production using an argon plasma jet feeding hydrogen and carbon (5)

Argon flow, liters min^{-1}	Hydrogen flow, liters min^{-1}	Carbon input, g min^{-1}	Power input, Kw	% C_2H_2 Conversion
23.2	6.5	1.05	8.8	42.2
16.1	6.85	0.86	9.0	39.2

and thence carried down a hollow cathode pipe where the sample probe was placed. Arc running conditions were as follows:

Anode vaporization rate	$0-9.2$ g min^{-1} carbon
Power, Kw	$2.5-14$
Hydrogen feed rate, liters min^{-1}	$0-5.5$

The best results of these studies showed a yield of 18.6 vol % acetylene operating at 7.5 Kw, hydrogen flow at 2.75 liters min^{-1}, and the probe 1.5 inches from arc. Approximately 0.6 vol % ethylene was also produced, together with trace amounts of diacetylene (0.4%), vinyl acetylene (0.04%) and benzene (trace). By using a helium diluent, 63.6% of hydrogen flow, a 23.8% yield of acetylene was obtained. Using a similar reactor, Baddour and Blanchet (26) increased the yield of acetylene to 26% using a carbon anode reacted with hydrogen by operating at higher power. With methane instead of hydrogen, a yield of 52% acetylene was obtained under the following conditions: power 26 Kw, methane flow 1.5 liters min^{-1}, probe distance 0.5 inch (0.135 inch diameter).

b. REACTION OF COAL IN A PLASMA JET. Graves, Kawa, and Kiteshue (27) have studied the reactions of coal in a plasma jet. Coal input ratio ranged from 0.74 to 3.14 lb hr^{-1} carried in 0.26 SCFM of argon. An argon plasma jet was used in the studies operating at 1.17 SCFM of argon with total power input in the range of 3.8 to 12.6 Kw—jet efficiency was about 50%. Typical yields and residue composition are given in Table 14.

TABLE 14

Typical yields and residue compositions of argon plasma jet reactions of high-volatile a. bituminous coal

Coal size	70 × 100 mesh		−325 mesh	
Coal rate, lb hr^{-1}	3.06	1.11	1.03	0.74
Total power Kw^a	7.3	12.6	4.8	10.2
Net power, Kw	3.2	4.7	2.4	4.9
Products				
Solids	89.2	78.3	73.6	45.3
H$_2$	0.8	1.7	2.4	3.9
CH$_4$	0.2	0.2	2.7	0.6
C$_2$H$_2$	3.5	6.0	9.5	15.4
C$_4$H$_2$	0.3	0.6	Trace	Trace
CO	5.3	11.0	18.1	24.3
CO$_2$	—	—	1.4	0.0

^{a}Argon flow 1.17 SCFM working gas and 0.26 SCFM coal carrier gas.

Bond et al. (28) passed high-volatile coal of 72 mesh size at rates up to 1 g min^{-1} carried in argon into a 9 Kw argon-10% hydrogen plasma jet, total gas flow about 10 liters min^{-1}. Analysis of the products showed methane, ethane, ethylene, propane, and acetylene to be present. Conversions to acetylene of 25% with a pure argon plasma jet and 45% with the argon-hydrogen mixture based on the carbon input were obtained. Similar experiments have been reported by Kawana et al. (29).

2. *The Preparation of Cyanogen.* The preparation of cyanogen according to the endothermic reaction:

$$2C + N_2 \longrightarrow (CN)_2, \ -71 \text{ Kcal}$$

was carried out by Stokes and Knipe (23), Leutner (30), and Grosse et al. (5). The reaction was investigated by reacting the carbon vaporized from an ordinary graphite cathode with a nitrogen jet—or an argon jet with nitrogen fed into the flame of the jet. Both methods gave the same results—conversions up to 15%, based on the carbon input, even when the electrical characteristics and the carbon-nitrogen ratios were quite different. The unconverted carbon (80%) was collected as very fine soot. No paracyanogen was present in the soot.

Surprisingly, fast quenching had a negative effect on the yields not yet explained, reducing them to one-half of the yields obtained without cooling. The reduction might be due to a too short reaction time or to a catalytic decomposition of cyanogen by the copper of the cooling funnel. The reaction time in the plasma flame was calculated to be in the range of 5 to 50 milliseconds, depending on the gas flow rate. The reaction temperature was not measured, but was certainly substantially higher than 4000°C, since all the carbon was definitely vaporized. Besides cyanogen and soot, only paracyanogen could be observed qualitatively, especially when relatively large quantities of carbon were consumed. Table 15 gives the typical data on the conditions and results of some of the investigations.

3. *The Preparation of Hydrogen Cyanide.*

a. FROM THE ELEMENTS.   The formation of hydrogen cyanide in a plasma jet is likely since the heat of formation from the elements of gaseous hydrocyanic acid is -30.1 Kcal mole^{-1}, similar to the heat of formation of acetylene (-54.3 Kcal mole^{-1}), and since any cyanogen formed should react at the high temperatures of the plasma jet with hydrogen to form HCN. The preparation of hydrogen cyanide from the elements (4,5,16) according to the reaction:

$$2C + H_2 + N_2 \longrightarrow 2HCN, \quad -60.2 \text{ Kcal}$$

Solid carbon in a hydrogen-gas suspension may be fed into the flame of a nitrogen plasma to give, after fast quenching, HCN. In order to avoid energy

TABLE 15
Production of cyanogen

Gas flows, liters min^{-1}	Electrical characteristics			Nitrogen-carbon ratios	Carbon consumed, mg min^{-1}	Cyanogen obtained, mg min^{-1}	% Conversion based on carbon input
	V	amp	Kw				
Nitrogen as plasma gas without quench							
7.0	44.0	270	11.9	17.0 : 1	440	130.0	13.55
7.0	41.0	300	12.3	13.7 : 1	492	147.6	13.9
Nitrogen as plasma gas with quench							
7.0	42.5	235	10.0	15.8 : 1	474	74.5	7.3
7.0	43.0	280	12.0	12.8 : 1	542	92.7	7.1
Argon as plasma gas without quench. Nitrogen feed rate 2.0 liters min^{-1}							
11.9	23.5	410	9.6	3.8 : 1	566	177.0	14.45
17.9	24.0	400	9.6	2.1 : 1	1045	342.0	14.95
Argon as plasma gas with quench. Nitrogen feed rate 2.0 liters min^{-1}							
17.9	22.8	405	9.25	2.12 : 1	1007	168.0	7.7
17.9	24.0	400	9.6	1.40 : 1	1509	215.0	6.7

and time consumption for heating up the carbon particles, experiments were carried out using a consumable graphite cathode as the carbon source, nitrogen as plasma gas, and hydrogen fed through a gas-feeding ring into the flame of the plasma gas. In order to maintain unchanging electrical characteristics, the cathode was pushed continuously towards the anode to compensate for the vaporization of the graphite cathode. Table 16 shows the experimental data and the results obtained in these experiments.

Over 50% conversion into HCN, based on the carbon input, was obtained. The only significant by-product of the reaction was acetylene. Other hydrocarbons were formed but in yields of less than 2%, based on the carbon input

TABLE 16
Production of hydrogen cyanide from the elements

Starting ratio		Power input, Kw	HCN Formation[a]		C_2H_2 Formation[a]	
C : N	C : H		%	g min^{-1}	%	g min^{-1}
1 : 9.6	1 : 7.8	13.3	43.3	1.0	13.9	0.18
1 : 9.2	1 : 4.6	12.8	51.1	1.0	12.9	0.12[b]

[a]Product formation is based on the carbon input.
[b]Without fast quenching of the products formed.

as the gas analysis of the collected gases showed. The remaining carbon input was collected as finely divided soot in the cooling chamber. A limiting factor of the method described is the relatively small vaporization rate of the graphite cathode (approximately 1 g min^{-1}). When quenching was not so pronounced (by omitting the water-cooled quenching device), higher HCN yields were observed.

b. FROM CARBON AND AMMONIA. A method for the preparation of hydrogen cyanide by feeding ammonia into the "flame" of a nitrogen plasma jet which has a vaporizing graphite cathode has been described by Leutner (16). The results were similar to those obtained by using hydrogen. Ammonia was decomposed quantitatively into nitrogen and hydrogen while passing through the plasma "flame." Table 17 shows the data.

TABLE 17

Production of hydrogen cyanide from carbon and ammonia

Starting ratio		Power input, Kw	HCN Formation[a]		C$_2$H$_2$ Formation[a]	
C : N	C : H		%	g min^{-1}	%	g min^{-1}
1 : 7.8	1 : 2.8	13.3	33.8	1.0	No values	
1 : 10	1 : 6	13.6	37.3	1.0	6.9	0.1
1 : 9	1 : 6.7	12.9	39.0	1.0	17.8	0.2[b]

[a]Product formation is based on the carbon input.
[b]Without using a cooling funnel for fast quenching of the products formed.

4. Refractory Metal Nitride Formation.

a. TITANIUM NITRIDE FORMATION. Titanium nitride production has been successfully accomplished using the plasma jet (3,23), Two hundred mesh titanium powder was fed into a nitrogen plasma using a feeding ring below the plasma generator. Nitrogen gas was used as carrier for the powder. The nitrogen flow was about 5 liters min^{-1} and the carrier flow about 1 liter min^{-1}. The average power was 12 Kw and the powder flow was about 0.5 g min^{-1}. The reaction product was a finely divided black powder. This product was analyzed by means of X-ray diffraction and proved to be 100% titanium nitride. The titanium nitride particles were measured under the microscope and were found to range from 0.75 to 7.5 microns. Large particles were easily broken down into smaller particles.

Titanium nitride was found occasionally in the form of large compact crystals that were golden-yellow and shiny. The black color is attributed to the finely divided state of the product.

b. TUNGSTEN NITRIDE FORMATION. Tungsten powder (200 mesh size) was fed into a nitrogen jet by means of a feeding ring below the plasma generator. Nitrogen flow was 5 liters min^{-1} at a power of 6 Kw. A cold quenching tube $\frac{1}{4}$ inch below the feeding ring served to cool the product. The X-ray diffraction analysis showed 25% conversion to WN (3).

c. THE PREPARATION OF BORON NITRIDE. Basch and deVynck (31) have synthesized boron nitride using a nitrogen or ammonia plasma jet. Using a 1.5 m^3 hr^{-1} flow of ammonia and operating the jet at 135 volts and 110 amps, fine boron powder was added to the jet. Boron nitride in the form of a fine crystalline powder was formed.

d. MAGNESIUM NITRIDE FORMATION. Using a nitrogen plasma operating at 12 to 15 Kw with nitrogen flow at 2.5 liters min^{-1} and injecting magnesium at about 2 g min^{-1}, a 40% conversion to Mg$_3$N$_2$ was obtained by Stokes and Knipe (23).

5. *Reaction of Methane with Metals.*

a. PREPARATION OF TUNGSTEN CARBIDE.

(1) *From Micron-Size Powdered Tungsten.* Micron-size powdered tungsten obtained via tungsten trioxide reduction with hydrogen (see Section III, A-2), was fed into a helium plasma jet. The powder was carried in a methane stream. Methane was chosen as the carbon source because of the ease in feeding. A water-cooled quench tube was placed 5 inches below the jet exit.

Table 18 shows the experimental conditions and results (4). Carbon was

TABLE 18

Tungsten carbides from micron-size tungsten

Powder Input g min^{-1}	Operating power, Kw	Kwhr g^{-1}	W$_2$C Formation		WC Formation		% Total conversion
			%	g min^{-1}	%	g min^{-1}	
1.25	14.8	0.978	27.0	0.35	5.5	0.07	32.5
1.10	9.8	0.148	32.2	0.37	3.3	0.04	35.5
0.54	15.8	0.487	39.5	0.22	7.9	0.05	47.4
0.37	10.3	0.465	40.4	0.15	5.7	0.02	46.1
0.36	16.3	0.755	38.5	0.14	10.9	0.04	49.4
0.33	14.4	0.746	39.5	0.13	7.9	0.03	47.4

always used in excess, the methane flow being kept constant at 6.5 liters min^{-1} in all experiments. The plasma gas flow rate was 34 liters min^{-1}. Calculated residence time of particles in the flame was 0.31 milliseconds.

(2) *From Tungsten Metal Powder and Methane.* Stokes et al. (4) reported the preparation of tungsten carbide by using commercial-grade tungsten

metal powder (325 mesh size) carried in the methane gas stream into the flame of a helium plasma jet. The methane flow rate was kept constant at 6.5 liters min^{-1} and the helium flow at 34 liters min^{-1} in all experiments. A copper water-cooled quench tube was used at about 5 inches below the feeding ring. Calculated residence time of particles in the jet flame was 0.31 milliseconds.

Table 19 gives the experimental data and the results obtained in these experiments.

TABLE 19
Tungsten carbides from tungsten metal powder and methane

Tungsten flow, g min^{-1}	Operating power, Kw	Kwhr g^{-1}	W$_2$C Formation %	g min^{-1}	WC Formation %	g min^{-1}	% Total conversion
9.80	14.43	0.0246	22.5	2.28	2.3	0.24	24.8
7.92	10.53	0.0221	23.0	1.88	—	—	23.0
5.28	14.80	0.0467	22.5	1.23	2.3	0.13	24.8
4.95	12.95	0.0436	23.0	1.18	—	—	23.0
4.21	14.44	0.0573	36.2	1.57	3.6	0.16	39.8
3.88	15.84	0.0678	36.5	1.46	2.8	0.12	39.3
2.86	14.06	0.0817	42.5	1.26	4.3	0.13	46.8
2.35	14.80	0.105	27.6	0.67	3.4	0.09	31.0
1.12	15.75	0.234	33.6	0.39	10.5	0.13	44.1

Figure 8 shows a plot of the results. As can be seen, the WC conversion is directly proportional to the power output level (Kwhr g^{-1} W). The plot for the production of W$_2$C shows a maximum at approximately 0.5 Kwhr g^{-1} W. Several points in the range 0.05 to 0.1K whr g^{-1} W do not follow the curve and no plausible explanation can be given for this at

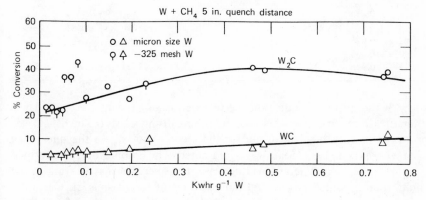

Figure 8 Preparation of tungsten carbide from tungsten and methane. (2) (5 in. quench distance; O, △ micron size W; ♀ ⚣ 325 mesh W.)

this writing. Conversions to W_2C ranged from 22.5 to 42.5% and those of WC from 2.3 to 10.9%. Higher conversions to W_2C may be due to the large excess of carbon present in the reaction zone.

b. PREPARATION OF TANTALUM CARBIDE FROM THE REACTION OF TANTALUM METAL AND METHANE.   Tantalum carbides were also produced by the reaction of tantalum metal with methane in a helium plasma jet (2, 4).

Commercial grade tantalum metal powder (325 mesh size) was used in these experiments. The metal powder was carried in a methane stream into the flame of a helium plasma jet. Helium flow rate was kept constant at 34 liters min^{-1} and the methane flow at 6.5 liters min^{-1} in all experiments.

The results of these runs are shown in Table 20 and Fig. 9. Here again the

TABLE 20
Production of tantalum carbides from tantalum powder and methane

Ta Flow g min^{-1}	Ta Kwhr g^{-1}	Oper- ating power, Kw	Cold finger quench, inches	TaC Formation		Ta_2C Formation		% Total con- version
				%	g min^{-1}	%	g min^{-1}	
2.68	0.104	16.65	0.5	71.6	2.04	15.3	0.42	86.9
3.22	0.086	16.65	0.5	40.9	1.40	11.3	0.38	52.2
3.30	0.084	16.65	0.5	44.0	1.55	—	—	—
1.90	0.082	9.36	0.5	—	—	10.6	0.21	—
4.06	0.070	17.02	0.5	37.5	1.62	—	—	—
3.25	0.048	9.36	0.5	12.7	0.53	6.2	0.25	18.9
8.70	0.018	9.36	0.5	8.2	0.91	1.5	0.17	9.7
2.15	0.130	16.65	5	21.8	0.50	15.3	0.34	37.1
1.54	0.102	9.36	5	—	—	8.0	0.13	—
2.84	0.098	16.65	5	30.0	0.91	13.3	0.39	43.3
3.27	0.085	16.65	5	30.9	1.08	—	—	—
2.13	0.073	9.36	5	—	—	8.6	0.19	—
3.62	0.043	9.36	5	—	—	9.0	0.34	—
4.40	0.036	9.36	5	18.0	0.83	7.8	0.34	25.8
6.95	0.023	9.60	5	4.5	0.33	3.5	0.25	8.0

effect of the quench distance on the production of the tantalum carbides is dramatic. In the first case where the quenching distance was 0.5 inch TaC was produced in very high yield, and in the second case where the quenching distance was 5 inches a peak was again noted. The amount of Ta_2C formed was not appreciably different in either case. The quencher may be freezing the equilibrium obtained at the high temperatures of the plasma jet. Generally yields are lower when quenching rates are lower. The preparation of TaC from

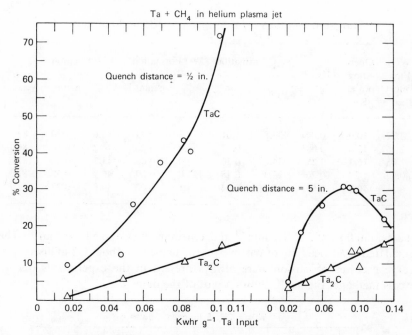

Figure 9 Preparation of tantalum carbide from tantalum and methane. (2)

Ta_2O_5 and methane shows that more complicated inorganic reactions that involve several steps can be carried out in good yields using a plasma jet.

C. THE PREPARATION OF BORON CARBIDE.   The preparation of boron carbide has been reported by Bosch and deVynck (31), using a hydrogen-argon plasma arc, $1.4 \, m^3 \, hr^{-1} \, H_2 - 1 \, m^3 \, hr^{-1}$ Ar at 15 Kw, and admixing powdered boron metal carried in a propane-butane mixture, flow $3.6 \, m^3 \, hr^{-1}$, which acted as the carbon source. The product of the reaction was boron carbide, B_4C.

6. *The Reaction of Methane with Metal Oxides.*

a. TUNGSTEN CARBIDE PREPARATION FROM TUNGSTEN OXIDE AND METHANE (2, 4). Tungsten trioxide powder was carried in a methane stream and fed through the feeding ring into the flame of a helium plasma jet.

Since about 95% of the methane is decomposed into its elements in the plasma jet (16), this decomposition provides both the carbon supply and the hydrogen necessary for the oxide reduction. The copper cold finger was placed about 5 inches below the feeding ring. Table 21 gives the experimental data and results obtained in these experiments. All these reactions were carried out

TABLE 21
Tungsten carbides from tungsten oxide and methane

WO_3 Flow, g min^{-1}	Operating power, Kw	Kwhr g^{-1}	W$_2$C Formation %	g min^{-1}	WC Formation %	g min^{-1}	W Formation %	g min^{-1}	% Total conversion
3.77	10.0	0.044	32.8	1.01	7.3	0.23	43.6	1.30	83.7
2.46	12.6	0.085	33.1	0.67	9.4	0.20	44.2	0.86	86.7
1.05	16.3	0.25	34.6	0.30	5.0	0.04	43.2	0.36	82.8
0.94	14.8	0.26	23.3	0.18	11.0	0.09	46.9	0.35	81.2
0.51	10.3	0.33	9.2	0.04	4.1	0.02	80.8	0.33	94.1

at a helium flow of 34 liters min^{-1} and a methane flow of 6.5 liters min^{-1}. The calculated residence time of particles in the flame was about 0.3 milliseconds. Large excesses of carbon were always present in the experiments due to excess methane. Figure 10 shows a plot of the data.

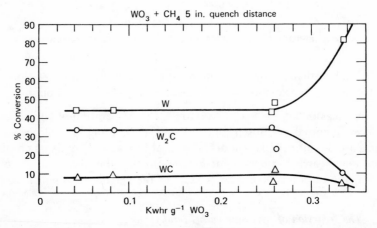

Figure 10   Preparation of tungsten carbide from tungsten trioxide and methane. (2) (5 in. quench distance.)

The three products of the reaction, tungsten (43 to 81% conversion), tungsten carbide (4 to 11% conversion), and ditungsten carbide (9 to 35% conversion) are formed in a total conversion of from 81 to 94%. The major product is tungsten, which is favored at higher Kwhr g^{-1} WO$_3$ inputs (higher temperatures). The formation of W, W$_2$C, and WC is reasonably constant up to an input level of 0.25 Kwhr g^{-1} WO_3. At this point tungsten formation rapidly increases at the expense of W_2C and, to a lesser extent, WC.

b. PREPARATION OF TANTALUM CARBIDE FROM TANTALUM PENTOXIDE AND METHANE (2, 4). Tantalum pentoxide powder was carried in a methane stream into the flame of a helium plasma jet. The pyrolysis of the methane provides the hydrogen necessary for the oxide reduction and the carbon required for the carbide formation.

The results obtained in these experiments are given in Table 22. All reactions were carried out at a helium flow of 34 liters min^{-1} and a methane flow

TABLE 22

Preparation of the tantalum carbides from tantalum pentoxide and methane

Ta_2O_5 Flow, g min^{-1}	Kwhr g^{-1}, Input	Operating power Kw	Cold finger quench, inches	TaC Formation		Ta_2C Formation		Ta Formation		% Total conversion
				%	g min^{-1}	%	g min^{-1}	%	g min^{-1}	
0.20	1.38	16.65	0.5	23.6	0.04	14.2	0.02	5.6	0.01	43.4
0.56	0.497	16.65	0.5	19.7	0.10	14.1	0.07	7.0	0.03	40.8
2.10	0.126	16.65	0.5	18.0	0.33	13.5	0.24	14.7	0.25	46.2
0.38	0.412	9.36	0.5	18.8	0.06	—	—	9.3	0.03	—
1.07	0.145	9.36	0.5	—	—	12.5	0.11	12.5	0.11	—
1.43	0.109	9.36	0.5	—	—	13.1	0.16	8.2	0.11	—
0.33	0.845	16.65	5	19.3	0.06	5.6	0.02	17.4	0.05	42.3
0.62	0.445	16.65	5	20.4	0.11	—	—	18.3	0.09	—
0.36	0.435	9.36	5	—	—	15.4	0.05	—	—	—
0.63	0.248	9.36	5	—	—	—	—	12.7	0.07	—
1.46	0.191	16.65	5	8.3	0.11	16.7	0.21	8.3	0.10	33.3
1.92	0.145	16.65	5	13.3	0.22	14.9	0.24	12.0	0.19	40.2
1.68	0.093	9.36	5	6.8	0.10	2.6	0.04	8.2	0.11	17.6
1.83	0.085	9.36	5	—	—	—	—	9.1	0.14	—

of 6.5 liters min (25 to 240 times in excess of that needed for the reduction of Ta_2O_5).

The products of the reaction TaC, Ta_2C, and Ta are plotted in Fig. 11. The effect of the quenching distance is dramatic. In the case where the quencher was 0.5 inch below the jet, the product TaC goes up linearly with the Kwhr g^{-1} input. Where the quenching distance was 5 inches, a peak was obtained which shows that adequate quenching does not take place when the Kwhr g^{-1} is increased beyong 0.4. Note that in the second case the formation of Ta_2C also peaks and then falls off rapidly in contrast to the 0.5 inch distance. The

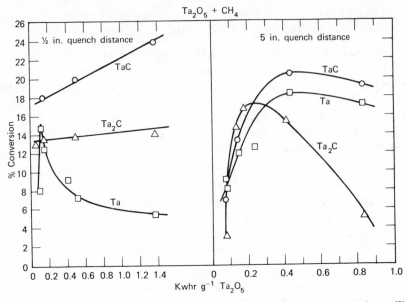

Figure 11   Preparation of tantalum carbide from tantalum pentoxide and methane. (2)

production of tantalum metal is favored in the 5 inch case and not in the 0.5 inch quencher distance at higher Kwhr g^{-1} inputs.

7. *Plasma Jet Synthesis of Hydrogen Sulfide.*   Hydrogen sulfide has been successfully synthesized from its elements in a helium plasma jet. Sulfur powder has been carried in a hydrogen stream into the flame of a helium plasma jet (2, 4). Conversions as high as 37% based on sulfur input have been obtained.

Sulfur powder was fed into the helium plasma by a water-cooled feeding ring. The powder, carried in a hydrogen stream, was fed perpendicularly to the axis of the jet flame. A water-cooled stainless steel chamber $2\frac{1}{4}$ inches in diameter and $13\frac{1}{2}$ inches long was used for quenching the reaction products.

Table 23 shows the experimental conditions and results. All the runs were carried out at a helium flow rate of 17.7. liters min^{-1} and a hydrogen flow rate of 4 liters min^{-1}.

The maximum yield obtained was 36% as shown in Fig. 12. This graph plots both % conversion and grams of H_2S formed per Kwhr versus Kwhr g^{-1} of sulfur input. It can be seen from this plot that the maximum conversion point does not occur at the maximum g H_2S $Kwhr^{-1}$. In fact, a nearly linear plot is obtained for the g H_2S $Kwhr^{-1}$ versus Kwhr g^{-1} S input. This shows that operation at the maximum yield point does not necessarily mean that the maximum production rate per Kwhr has been reached.

TABLE 23
Hydrogen sulfide synthesis runs

Sulfur powder rate, g min^{-1}	Power input, Kw	Power/ powder rate, Kw min g^{-1}S	Kwhr g^{-1}	% Conversion based on sulfur input	Formation rate, g min^{-1}	g Kwhr^{-1} H$_2$S
1.220	7.50	6.1	0.0101	26.4	0.342	2.733
0.683	7.50	10.98	0.0183	25.7	0.186	1.488
0.568	9.00	15.8	0.0263	36.6	0.221	1.473
0.470	7.75	16.5	0.0275	30.7	0.153	1.180
0.430	7.75	18.0	0.030	31.1	0.142	1.100
0.330	7.50	22.7	0.038	13.2	0.046	0.370
0.310	7.75	25.0	0.041	12.6	0.041	0.320
0.490	14.50	29.6	0.048	18.4	0.096	0.397
0.250	7.59	30.3	0.0505	16.5	0.044	0.347

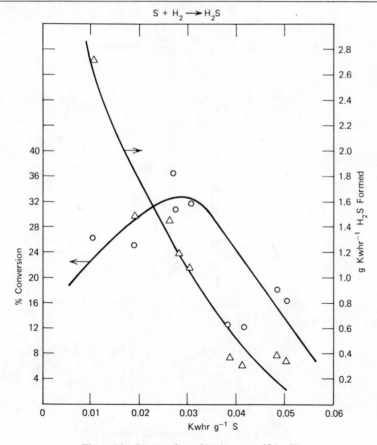

$$S + H_2 \longrightarrow H_2S$$

Figure 12 Preparation of hydrogen sulfide. (2)

E. Liquid Reactions

1. *Production of Ozone.*   The preparation of ozone using a plasma jet (32) was carried out by passing liquid oxygen into an inert gas plasma. Figure 13 shows the schematic of the experimental set-up. The apparatus had a liquid oxygen feeding ring attached to the plasma jet and thence to a reaction chamber. The liquid oxygen flowed fast enough through the ring to be collected in a dewar flask attached to the bottom of the reaction chamber. Ozone in concentrations up to 0.4 wt% was collected in the oxygen found in the liquid

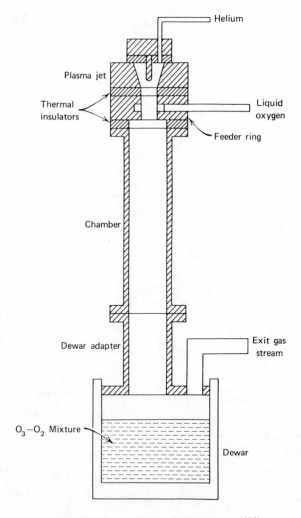

Figure 13   Ozone production apparatus. (32)

TABLE 24
Production of ozone in the plasma jet

Arc characteristics

Voltage	27	27	29	29	28	26.8	26.8
Amperage	340	340	320	310	320	345	345
Kilowatts	9.2	9.2	9.3	9.0	8.95	9.25	9.25
Helium flow, liters min^{-1}	16	16	15.2	15.2	18.0	16	16
Kcal mole^{-1} He	111	111	119	115	97	111	111

LOX flow

liters min^{-1}	1.25	2	3	3	3	4	5

Ozone yield

Weight, %	0.23	0.23	0.46	0.38	0.35	0.21	0.20
lb hr^{-1}, collected	0.35	0.63	1.13	1.17	1.07	1.04	1.01
lb hr^{-1}, LOX flow	0.44	0.70	2.06	1.70	1.58	1.24	1.35

in the dewar flask. Table 24 gives the experimental results of the investigations and Figs. 14 and 15 show the production of ozone versus power input and ozone production versus liquid oxygen flow.

2. **Liquid Hydrocarbon Studies.**   Thermal Dynamics Corp. (33) reported the production of acetylene by allowing a nitrogen plasma jet to operate in kerosene. The results of two experiments are given in Table 25.

Pedoseev and Shteiner (34) produced 29% acetylene and 10% ethylene by directing an argon plasma jet into the surface of liquid kerosene.

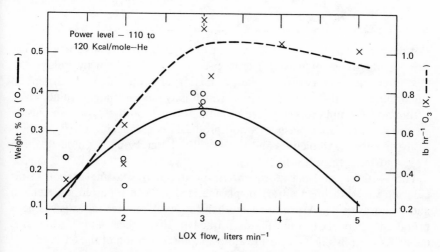

Figure 14   Production of ozone versus liquid oxygen flow. (32)

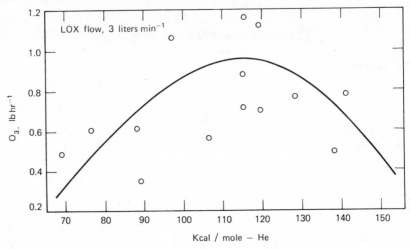

Figure 15   Production of ozone versus enthalpy input. (32)

TABLE 25
Kerosene experiments

	I	II
Power Kw	5.4	6.1
Nitrogen flow, CFH	26	26
$\% \ C_2H_2$	18.4	18
$\% \ CH_4$	2.7	2.6
$\% \ H_2$	27.2	27.9
Net Kw $lb^{-1} \ C_2H_2$	3.55	3.94

A comprehensive study of the cracking of lower hydrocarbons and gasolines with various types of plasma jets is given in a book edited by Polak (35). One interesting observation is the production of propylene and ethylene in equal quantities to that of acetylene, which may have economic value.

Illin and Eremin (36,37) passed gasoline through both a hydrogen plasma jet and a water vapor plasma jet and produced 6% and 11% C_2H_2, respectively, together with olefines and parafins, the latter being 9% and 9% and 19% and 16%, respectively.

The synthesis of hexachlorobenzene produced by passing carbon tetrachloride vapor through an argon plasma jet has been reported by Kanaan and Margrave (38). A proposed mechanism involving free radicals has been proposed where $CCl\cdot$ radical was formed in the highest temperature zone (6000°K) by splitting off chlorine atoms. Upon formation of the $CCl\cdot$ radical polymerization occurred producing C_6Cl_6, hexachlorobenzene.

3. **Production of Terpenes.**   Using nitrogen or a noble-gas-type plasma generator, the reactions of terpene chemicals have been experimentally investigated (2, 39). The experimental set-up consisted of a perpendicular feed ring attached to a water-cooled quenchirtg chamber and thence to a liquid receiver, as shown in Fig. 16. The terpenes were fed as liquid through the feeding ring, which was situated between the plasma generator and the quenching chamber.

The results obtained in several of the investigations are tabulated in Tables 26 and 27.

As is shown in Table 26, recycling the liquid under the same conditions of flow rate and power input more than doubles the percentage of conversion. Increasing the power also increases considerably the percentage of conversion.

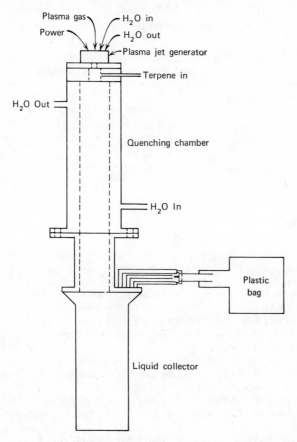

Figure 16   Apparatus for studying reactions of terpenes. (2)

TABLE 26
β-pinene pyrolysis

Liquid flow,[a] cc min^{-1}	Power, Kw	% Conversion into myrcene
260	18.30	26.0
225[b]	6.30	12.8
75[b]	6.24	12.3
295	14.96	11.4
208	6.40	5.4

[a]Helium gas fed below liquid feeding.
[b]recycled.

TABLE 27
α-terpinene pyrolysis

Liquid flow, cc min^{-1}	Power, Kw	% Conversion into para-cymene	% Conversion into α-pinene	Total Conversion
100	6.46	1.63	2.37	4.00
125	5.67	2.49	0.94	3.43
120	5.30	1.91	1.47	3.38
190	6.24	1.39	1.12	2.51
590	6.63	1.26	0.40	1.66
560	6.65	1.49	—	1.49

REFERENCES

1. H. L. Gilles and C. W. Clump, *Ind. Eng. Chem., Process Design and Develop.*, **9**, 194(1970).
2. C. S. Stokes, *Advan. Chem. Series*, **80**, 390(1969).
3. C. S. Stokes, J. A. Cahill, J. J. Correa, and A. V. Grosse, *Plasma Jet Chemistry, Final Report*. Air Force Office of Scientific Research, Grant 62–196, The Research Institute of Temple University, Philadelphia, Pa., December 1964.
4. C. S. Stokes and J. A. Cahill, *Plasma Jet Chemistry, Final Report*. Air Force Office of Scientific Research Grant 775–65, The Research Institute of Temple University, Philadelphia, Pa., December 1965.
5. A. V. Grosse, H. W. Leutner, and C. S. Stokes, *Plasma Jet Chemistry, First Annual Report*. Office of Naval Research Contract NONR–3085(02), The Research Institute of Temple University, Philadelphia, Pa., December 31, 1961.
6. J. O. Gibson and R. Weidman, *Chem. Eng. Progr.*, **59**, 53 (1963).
7. J. E. Anderson and L. K. Case, *Ind. Eng. Chem., Process Design and Develop.*, **1**, 161 (1962).
8. H. W. Leutner and C. S. Stokes, *Ind. Eng. Chem.*, **53**, 341 (1961).

9. *Chemical Week*, January 18, 1964, p. 64.
10. G. V. Gulyaev, G. I. Kozlov, L. S. Polak, L. N. Khitrin, and G. N. Khudyakov, *Dokl. Akad. Nauk SSSR, Him. Tekh.*, **148** (3), 641 (1963).
11. C. S. Stokes and E. W. Smith, private communication.
12. W. K. Maniero, P. F. Kienst, and C. Hirayama, *Westinghouse Engr.*, **26**, 66 (1966).
13. C. Hirayama and W. K. Maniero, *Am. Chem. Soc.*, Div. Fuel Chem., Preprints, **11**, 470 (1967).
14. J. L. Blanchet and H. C. Lavalee, *Calibration of an Argon Plasma Jet and Its Application to the Production of Oxygen by the Carbon Dioxide Reduction.* Paper Presented at the 15th Chem. Inst., Canada Chem. Eng. Conf. University of Laval, Quebec, October 1965.
15. M. P. Freeman and J. P. Skrivan, *A.I.Ch.E.J.*, **8**, 450 (1962).
16. H. W. Leutner, *Ind. Eng. Chem., Process Design and Develop.*, **2**, 315 (1963).
17. M. P. Freeman, "Chemical Reactions in Electrical Discharges." *Amer. Chem. Soc. Advan. Chem. Ser.*, **80**, 406 (1969).
18. R. A. Damon and D. H. White, *Typical Inorganic and Inorganic High Temperature Plasma Jet Reactions, Report No. PLR–119.* Santa Ana, Calif.: Plasmadyne Corp., September 20, 1962.
19. R. F. Baddour and D. R. Bronfin, *Ind. Eng. Chem., Prod. Res. and Develop.*, **4**, 162 (1965).
20. D. R. Bronfin and R. N. Hazlett, *Ind. Eng. Chem., Fundamentals*, **5**, 472 (1966).
21. A. V. Grosse, C. S. Stokes, J. A. Cahill, and J. J. Correa, *Plasma Jet Chemistry, Final Report.* Office of Naval Research Contract NONR–3085 (02), The Research Institute of Temple University, Philadelphia, Pa., June 30, 1963.
22. H. Harnisch, G. Meymer, and E. Schallus, *Angew. Chem.*, **2**, 238 (1963).
23. C. S. Stokes and W. W. Knipe, *Ind. Eng. Chem.*, **52**, 287 (1960).
24. T. B. Selover, *A.I.Ch.E.J.*, **10**, 79 (1964).
25. R. F. Baddour and J. M. Iwasyk, *Ind. Eng. Chem., Prod. Res. and Develop.*, **1**, 169 (1962).
26. R. F. Baddour and J. L. Blanchet, *Ind. Eng. Chem., Prod. Res. and Develop.*, **3**, 259 (1964).
27. R. D. Graves, W. Kawa, and R. W. Kiteshue, *Ind. Eng. Chem., Process Design and Develop*, **5**, 59 (1966).
28. R. L. Bond, I. F. Galbraith, W. R. Ladner, and G. I. T. McConnell, *Nature*, **200**, 1313 (1963).
29. Y. Kawana, M. Makino, and T. Kimura, *Intern. Chem. Eng.*, **7**, 359 (1967).
30. H. W. Leutner, *Ind. Eng. Chem., Process Design and Develop.*, **1**, 166 (1962).
31. F. M. Bosch and I. A. de Vynck, *Silicate Ind.*, **27**, 587 (1962).
32. C. S. Stokes and L. A. Streng, *Ind. Eng. Chem., Prod. Res. and Develop.*, **4**, 36 (1965).
33. *Plasma Flame Used in Formation of Acetylene from Kerosene.* Plasma-Fax Bulletin PF-2, Thermal Dynamics Corp., Lebanon, N. H., October 1960.
34. S. D. Fedoseev and E. V. Shteiner, *Tr. Mosk. Khim-Teknol. Inst.*, **48**, 172 (1965).
35. L. S. Polak, ed., *Kinetika i. Termodinamika Khemicheskikh Reaktsii v. Nizko Temperaturna*, Akad. Nauk SSSR, 1965.
36. D. T. Illin and E. N. Eremin, *Intern. Chem. Eng.*, **2**, 524 (1962).
37. D. T. Illin and E. N. Eremin, *Intern. Chem. Eng.*, **3**, 229 (1963).
38. A. S. Kanaan and J. L. Margrave, *Intern. Sci. Technol.*, **75** (1962).
39. C. S. Stokes and J. J. Correa, *Terpene Reactions in a Plasma Jet, Final Report.* The Glidden Company, The Research Institute of Temple University, Philadelphia, Pa., December 1964.

General

1. R. F. Baddour, and R. S. Timmins, eds., *The Application of Plasmas to Chemical Processing*. Cambridge, Mass.: M.I.T. Press, 1967.
2. *Carbon-Black Formation Using the Plasma Flame in Micro-Chemical Reactions*. Plasma-Fax Bulletin PF-3. Thermal Dynamics Corp., Lebanon, N. H., October 1960.
3. R. A. Damon and D. H. White, *Proposed Plasma Chemical Processes of Interest to the Petroleum Industry*. Report No. PLR-115. Plasmadyne Corp., Santa Ana, Calif., February 8, 1962.
4. P. R. Dennis, C. R. Smith, D. W. Gates, and J. B. Bond, *Plasma Jet Technology*. NASA SP-5033, October 1965.
5. *Development and Possible Applications of Plasma and Related High Temperature Generating Devices*. Report MAB-167-M. Division of Engineering and Industrial Research, National Academy of Sciences, National Research Council, Washington, D.C., August 30, 1960.
6. R. E. Greenlee, *The Plasma Jet in Chemical Processing*. Clyde Williams and Co., Columbus, Ohio (March 1, 1963); R. E. Greenlee and W. H. Bickley, *Potential Applications for Plasma Jet Processing in the Petrochemical Industry*. Clyde Williams and Co., Columbus, Ohio (April 30, 1963).
7. H. M. Hulburt and M. P. Freeman, "Chemical Reactions in the Plasma Jet." *Trans. N.Y. Acad. of Sciences*, **25**, 770 (1963).
8. R. R. John and W. L. Bade, "Recent Advances in Electric Arc Plasma Generator Technology." *ARS Journal*, January 1961.
9. G. R. Kubanek and W. H. Gauvrn, "Recent Developments in Plasma Jet Technology," *Can. J. Chem. Eng.*, **45**, 251 (1967).
10. C. W. Marynawski, R. C. Phillips, J. R. Phillips, and N. K. Hiester, "Thermodynamics of Selected Chemical Systems Potentially Applicable to Plasma Jet Synthesis." *I&EC Fundamentals*, **1**, 52 (1962).
11. T. B. Reed, "Plasma Torches." *International Science and Technology*, June 1962, p. 42.
12. Staff Feature, "Plasma—Fourth State of Matter." *I&EC*, **55**, 16 (1963).
13. C. S. Stokes, "Chemical Reaction with the Plasma Jet." *Chem. Eng.*, April 12, 1965, p. 191.
14. C. S. Stokes, "Chemical Reactions in Electrical Discharges." *Am. Chem. Soc. Advan. Chem. Ser.*, **80**, 390 (1969).
15. F. B. Vursel and L. S. Polak, "Plasma Chemical Technology," *Ind. Eng. Chem.*, **62** (6), 8(1970).

CHAPTER SIXTEEN

Plasma Chemical Processing

F. VURSEL and L. POLAK

I. INTRODUCTION

The ever-growing use of operating conditions with extremes of temperatures, velocities, reaction times, and so forth, is one of the main trends in the development of present-day chemical processing and technology. The development of radically new technological and economically efficient methods for obtaining chemical products and for producing new materials with specific properties requires the study of physical and chemical processes proceeding at temperatures of 10^3 to 1.5×10^4 °K, at reaction times ranging from 10^{-5} to 10^{-2} sec, and under pressures ranging from fractions of a millimeter of mercury to tens of atmospheres. The problems mentioned above have given rise to a new trend in physical chemistry and chemical technology: investigations of chemical processes in a low-temperature plasma—"plasma chemistry" (1).

The low-temperature plasma is characterized by a partial or complete ionization of atoms and molecules; naturally, such a plasma is quasi-neutral. Great opportunities for obtaining such a plasma (which from a chemist's viewpoint is high-temperature) have arisen during the last few years as a result of the development of engines of different types for rocketry and space technology, as well as for studies in the field of nuclear synthesis; gas dynamics with chemical reactions; gas-discharge techniques; and plasma metallurgy. Because of these developments, the problem of chemical reactions in a plasma was found to be realizable at a substantially new technological level than was possible 30–60 years ago when the first rather timid and technically imperfect attempts were undertaken in this field (2).

Plasma chemical processes hold particular promise for the industrial realization of chemical reactions possessing the following characteristics: (1) equilibrium is shifted to high temperatures; (2) reaction rates are sharply increased with a temperature increase; (3) high yields are obtained under substantially nonequilibrium conditions; (4) widely accessible and low-cost raw materials, unstable in composition, are used. There are great promises in the field of obtaining pure and super-pure (e.g., semi-conductors) materials, since purity of products during plasma chemical processes in high-frequency and microwave plasmas is determined by the purity of source materials only and even it can be increased during the process without any additional expenses.

At present, the low-temperature plasma affords the possibility of conducting chemical processes at temperatures up to 20,000°K, at pressures ranging from 10^{-4} to 10^4 atm, under both equilibrium and nonequilibrium conditions.

Low-temperature plasma can be used in chemical reactions as:

1. A source of extremely concentrated specific energy, in other words, of high heat content at high temperatures;

2. a source of positive and negative ions, potential precursors for ion and ion-molecule reactions;

3. a source of luminous radiation for photochemical reactions.

Low-temperature plasma can be generated in DC and AC plasmatrons with the industrial frequency (with efficiency up to 95%), hf and microwave generators, as well as in glow and corona discharges, in adiabatical piston compressors and shock tubes, and by means of powerful lasers.

Of particular industrial interest at present are DC and AC electrode plasmatrons and plasma generators with high-intensity arcs as the sources of low-temperature plasmas. Plasma temperature should be high to insure rather high dissociation of reagent molecules, but the new compounds were produced in marked quantities at temperatures the threshold of which was determined by thermodynamic and kinetic factors. The quenching seems to play a significant, if not deciding, part in the technology of quasi-equilibrium-type plasma chemical processes.

The character of chemical conversions that occur at temperatures of the order of several thousand degrees is largely determined by thermodynamic properties of substances which take part in a reaction at one or another of its stages. Given reliable thermodynamic constants it should be possible to determine, in most cases, optimal temperature conditions for reactions, values of product yields expected, and energy indices of the process.

At the same time, the course of reaction depends, as a rule, not only on the thermodynamic properties of a reacting system. Prior to converting to equilibrium state, determined by the thermodynamics of reaction, the system experiences a series of intermediate stages. The rate at which the system goes through these stages is determined by the kinetics of the process. That is, the rate of achieving equilibrium energy distribution according to degrees of freedom is determined by physical kinetics and the rate of achieving equilibrium chemical composition is determined by chemical kinetics. In this case, the plasma chemical reactions are characterized by the strong mutual effects of the factors of the physical and chemical kinetics. The terminal rate of setting up equilibrium energy distribution according to different degrees of freedom in some cases limits the possibility of using the classical methods of chemical kinetics based on an assumption about Maxwell-Boltzmann energy distribution in the reacting system.

But in the cases when the methods of chemical kinetics can be thought to be applicable, the studies on chemical kinetics of the system present difficulties in that the rather high velocities of chemical reactions at the temperatures under consideration can depend to a considerable extent on velocity of physical processes such as the diffusion (molecular) and turbulent transfer, the microscopic mixing of the reacting system's components.

The investigation of a plasma chemical process suggests, in the general case, a study on the elementary act of collisions at $kT \sim E_{act} \sim E_{bond}$, thermodynamics, physical and chemical kinetics of the process as well as on the problems of gas dynamics of mixing flows of reacting substances, taking into account that the mutual complicating effects of the factors act on each other. The complexity of the task put in such manner is obvious. Therefore, it is right to adopt some physically sensible simplification of individual sides of the problem, differentiation of individual factors, and their mutual effects.

Special theoretical and experimental investigation on the problem of quenching, playing a deciding role in most quasi-equilibrium plasma chemical processes, has a dominant role in plasma chemical technology.

There are two types of reactions in a plasma jet where composition of products depends on quenching conditions. The first type includes reactions which produce in succession a number of intermediate products, some of which should be frozen. As an example of such reactions is a conversion of methane into acetylene, a detailed description of which is given in Section II. It is natural that not only the quenching velocity, but also the moment when temperature starts to decrease, is of prime importance for such reactions. It is important not to be late with the quenching.

A peculiarity of reactions of the second type lies in the fact that the desired compounds are final products of a reaction which proceeds only at high temperatures; the product molecules are sufficiently stable at room temperature. The purpose of quenching, in this case, is to cool a product of reaction as soon as possible so that the product has no time to decompose within the intermediate range of temperatures. This type of reaction includes, for example, thermal formation of nitric oxide in air. In this case, it is necessary to insure the required rate of quenching, which should not start too early in the reaction sequence when equilibrium composition is not reached.

The selection of required quenching conditions greatly affects the product yield in plasma chemical reactions. For example, in the conversion of methane to acetylene even 2×10^{-3} seconds delay in quenching leads to a decrease in the acetylene concentration from 15.5 to 10% (3). The decrease in the rate of the product gas quenching in the synthesis of nitrogen oxides from 10^8 to 10^7 deg sec^{-1} leads to a decrease in the nitrogen oxide concentration from 9.6 to 6.4% (4).

Moreover, it is necessary not only to provide an average quenching rate in a certain temperature range but also to observe a definite law $dT/dt = f(T)$ (4). The violation of this law in any temperature range cannot be offset by an increase in the quenching rate in another range. It is often, however insufficient to provide the necessary quenching rate and high yield of a product. In some cases, it is important not only to remove heat rapidly from a system but also to utilize as much of it as possible.

Let us now consider the main methods of quenching (4, 40). The method most extensively employed is the cooling of hot gases in a water-cooled pipe, which is used to cool gases having temperatures up to 4000°K. When diameter of the pipe is ~ 3 mm, the quenching rate will be $\sim 10^6$ deg sec^{-1} at 3000°K.

The method of quenching by injection of water is also widespread. The process of interaction between water streams and hot gas flow was considered in some detail in Ref. 5. The estimates show that the quenching rate amounts to $\sim 10^8$ deg sec^{-1}, when pressure is 10 atm, ratio of water and gas flows is 1 : 1, and initial gas temperature is about 3000°K.

The same rates of quenching can be obtained when the products of plasma chemical process are mixed with cold gas and in a fluidized bed reactor (6). The quenching of hot gases can also be performed in the Laval nozzle. The quenching rate amounts to $\sim 10^8$ deg sec^{-1} at an initial gas temperature of 4000°K and with nozzle diameter of 1 mm. However, the rate of cooling decreases with the temperature increase while, in some cases, it should be maximum close to $T_{initial}$. Besides, since in the ultimate stagnation region of supersonic flow its temperature again takes on the initial value, the Laval nozzle should be coupled with other methods of heat removal.

If the chemical reactions proceed in nonequilibrium plasma the quenching of products may not be required, since the heavy particles temperature is low (up to 1000°K); but, if quenching is required all the same, the requirements for it will be considerably moderate.

II. PLASMA CHEMICAL PROCESSES

The advantages of plasma chemical processes are as follows:

1. High specific enthalpies and high temperatures, high rates of processes (reaction time $\sim 10^{-3}$–10^{-5} sec). These advantages generated a need for making miniature technical equipment [e.g., a plasma chemical reactor for methane pyrolysis having a capacity of 25,000 t year^{-1} is about 65 cm long and ~ 15 cm in diameter (7)].

2. The great majority of plasma chemical processes of practical interest are one-stage processes.

3. Plasma chemical processes are not sensitive to impurities of the raw materials (e.g., in the plasma chemical pyrolysis of natural gas the impurities in methane amount to 20–25 %; when pure metals are produced from minerals, the composition of the latter is of no significance).

4. One can use raw materials which are difficult to process but which are rather widely accessible (natural gas, air, infusible metal-containing minerals, etc.).

5. Plasma chemical processes are perfectly simulated, optimized, and controlled.

6. Because of the character of low-temperature plasma, it is possible to control it by means of a magnetic field which in turn results in sharp reduction of the requirements imposed upon heat resistance of materials.

It is quite reasonable to divide plasma chemical processes into two groups: quasi-equilibrium and nonequilibrium.

The problems springing from the studies of plasma chemical processes under quasi-equilibrium conditions, that is, of high-temperature chemical processes, are described in detail in Ref. 1 and we shall consider some of them.

In the described reactions of this type, where $E_{act} > kT$, a chemical reaction, which is itself a nonequilibrium process, does not introduce considerable changes into the equilibrium energy distribution of particles. Therefore, the main principles of chemical kinetics may be used for the description of quasi-equilibrium plasma chemical processes. To conduct such processes under optimal conditions it is necessary to know their thermodynamic and kinetic peculiarities and to properly solve problems connected with the quenching of reaction products.

When describing chemical processes conducted under nonequilibrium conditions the familiar concepts and chemical kinetics cannot be used, because a theory of chemical kinetics of non-equilibrium processes does not exist.

To give a description of such processes it is necessary to know the energy distributions of the particles, evolution of these distributions with time, cross-sections of different reactions, and their energy dependence.

III. PLASMA CHEMICAL PROCESSES UNDER QUASI-EQUILIBRIUM CONDITIONS

To determine some of the characteristics of such processes, several suggestions have been made (8–10). In the present paper we shall follow the classification suggested in Ref. 10, that is, we shall divide all plasma chemical processes according to the following technological criterion: whether end products of the process are final or intermediate products of a chemical process.

A. Processes in which End Products are Final at High Temperatures and Thermodynamically Allowed under Equilibrium Conditions

When investigating processes of this type it is necessary to determine properly the equilibrium concentrations of the end products.

Problems of thermodynamics of high temperature processes have been worked out rather thoroughly (11,12). As it is, it follows from equations for changing isobaric potential that the role of the entropy factor increases with temperature increase. Therefore, with increase in temperature (pressure remaining constant) the processes of decomposition and dissociation, should prevail. At the same time, as the experimental investigations show, at temperatures of ~ 3000–$10,000°K$ concurrent with the processes of dissociation of complex substances there are other processes which give rise to formation of compounds nonexistent at usual temperatures (e.g., particles C_3, C_9 from hydrocarbons, Al_2O, AlO, Na_2, Ba_2O_3). Equilibrium compositions have been calculated for several multicomponent systems such as rocket fuel combustion products (13) as well as for the systems composed of carbon and hydrogen (14), nitrogen and fluorine (15), silicon, chlorine, and hydrogen (16).

The most important problem that arose from studies of processes of that type is the quenching problem described in Section I.

Among processes of that type are the processes intended for reducing oxides and chlorides to elements and for obtaining nitrides, carbides, nitric oxides, and so forth.

Reduction of oxides and chlorides to elements is commonly carried out in the high-intensity arc by using anode of oxide pressed with carbon powder or in a hydrogen plasma jet.

For example, the reduction of Fe_2O_3, SiO_2, Al_2O_3, MgO, and B_2O_3 described in (17) was conducted in a high intensity arc on a laboratory installation. Solid products obtained were collected on a metal surface being cooled. The author has obtained rather high yields of products (up to 83% Fe, 73% Si, and 17% Mg).

Described in Ref. 18 is a process for obtaining uranium carbide and tantalate also in the high-intensity arc conducted on a semi-industrial installation (with a capacity of 600 kW). Products with purity of 99.95% were produced with such an installation.

The process of production of boron from boron trifluoride and trichloride in a hydrogen plasma jet was investigated. In the first case the conversion degree of reagents amounted to $\sim 30\%$, but in the second case to $\sim 60\%$ (19).

The authors of this article have been engaged in research on the process to produce pure silicon powder from tetrachlorosilane in DC electrode plasma jet and in high-frequency electrodeless plasmatrons. Kinetic investigations conducted on decomposition of tetrachlorosilane (20) and thermodynamic calculations of equilibrium compositions of products of $SiCl_4$ decomposition made it possible to determine optimal conditions for carrying out the processes.

An investigation of the kinetics of tetrachlorosilane decomposition was carried out within the temperature range of 3000–6000°K. The initial stage of $SiCl_4$ decomposition was studied in an adiabatical piston, but the decomposition to silicon in a plasma jet. It was found that the tetrachlorosilane decomposition occurs by successive separation of chlorine atoms, via $SiCl_2$, and yielding silicon as a stable product; that is, decomposition of $SiCl_4$ takes place in stages:

$$\text{1st stage:} \quad SiCl_4 \longrightarrow SiCl_3 \longrightarrow SiCl_2$$
$$\text{2nd stage:} \quad SiCl_2 \longrightarrow SiCl \longrightarrow Si$$

The second stage of $SiCl_4$ decomposition is rate controlling. Rate constants of the mentioned stages of tetrachlorosilane decomposition have been determined:

$$K_1 = 5 \times 10^8 \exp\left(-\frac{88,000 \pm 5000}{RT}\right) \sec^{-1}$$

$$K_2 = 5 \times 10^7 \exp\left(-\frac{126,000 \pm 10,000}{RT}\right) \sec^{-1}$$

The results obtained from thermodynamic calculation of the process of tetrachlorosilane decomposition in neutral and reducing atmosphere, performed by the authors, show that the silicon production is favored in reducing atmosphere at a temperature of $\sim 4500°K$ (at a pressure of 1 atm). In some experiments, the silicon yield obtained was near that possible thermodynamically. Purity of silicon obtained in high-frequency plasmatron without electrode depends only on purity of reagents.

The production of titanium nitride from titanium tetrachloride in the plasma jet of ammonia or nitrogen hydrogen mixture has also been studied (9). The powder obtained consisted of 95% titanium nitride and some titanium imide, which could be easily removed by means of diluted hydrochloric acid.

The process of the production of titanium dioxide by oxidation of titanium tetrachloride in a plasma jet was commercialised in some countries. A thermodynamic estimate of the process $TiCl_4 + O_2 \rightarrow TiO_2 + 2Cl_2$ shows that the displacement of equilibrium to desirable products occurred even at room temperature; but rate of reaction was extremely low. When temperatures amount to 1000–1500°K the rate of the reaction sharply increases and the process proceeds within $\sim 10^{-2}$–10^{-3} sec.

One of the possible ways to realize the process is as follows (21): vapors of titanium tetrachloride are introduced into a plasma jet of oxygen created by an electrodeless hf plasmatron. Powder of titanium dioxide is collected in the filters; chlorine and oxygen (up to 85% by volume) are subsequently separated.

The same situation, in terms of the thermodynamics of the process, occurs in the case of the oxidation of hydrogen chloride during production of chlorine and water, the rate of which is low at low temperatures. This process is conducted in a plasma jet of water vapor at temperatures of 1500–3000°K (22). The degree of hydrogen chloride conversion amounts to 45% for one run. Many investigators were engaged in research on oxidation of atmospheric nitrogen, but the most comprehensive description of this process is given in the report (14) as well as in the proceedings published during the last few years (23). The experiments showed the influence of plasma temperature, pressure, and nitrogen-to-oxygen ratio on the process of formation of nitric oxide (Fig.1).

An investigation of the temperature-dependent quenching process enabled us to establish the law, $dT/dt = f(T)$ required to freeze 95% of the amount of nitric oxide produced. During the experiments, under the best conditions, gas mixtures containing up to 8% of NO were produced. This yield is considered to be of industrial significance. Based on the authors' assessments (4), optimal conditions for conducting this process are as follows: range of pressures, 20–30 atm; temperatures, 3000–3300°K. The quenching should be performed by cold nitrous gases up to temperatures of ~1800°K followed by the recovery of the heat from waste gases. In this case, the nitrogen fixation in the plasma jet is characterized by electric energy consumption of 8 kwh per 1 kg of NO, which establishes the plasma route as economically more attractive than the present ammonia route for nitrogen fixation.

During the processes described above, reagents were introduced into a plasma in the gas phase, wherein gas-phase reactions proceeded and, in some cases, condensed-phase products were formed.

In many plasma chemical processes, powders are used as reagents. In such cases, chemical processes follow physical processes such as heating of particles in the plasma jet and evaporation of solid particles. Therefore, it is very important to study the behavior of solid particles in plasma jets (24).

Solid particles can be flowed around by plasma jet at atmospheric pressure under conditions of continuous flowing, flowing with sliding, and free-molecular movement, depending on the value of Reynold's number for the plasma

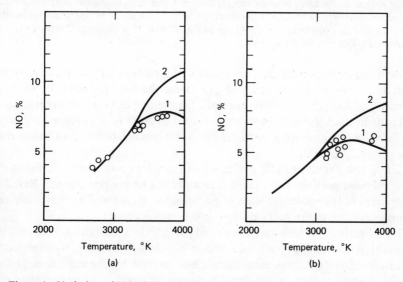

Figure 1   Variation of NO yield with temperature of N_2–O_2 mixture. (a) O_2:N_2 = 1:1; (b) O_2:N_2 = 1:4. Curve 1, equilibrium NO concentration for 1 atm pressure; Curve 2, equilibrium NO concentration for 10 atm pressure. Open circles, experimental points for 5–10 atm pressure.

jet (24). It was shown that presence of a powder in plasma involves a decrease in gas temperature and a more uniform distribution of its properties. Besides, the author (24) has pointed to the fact that a powder turbulates a jet in the case of a laminar flow and decreases turbulence in the case of an initial turbulent flow (see Fig. 2).

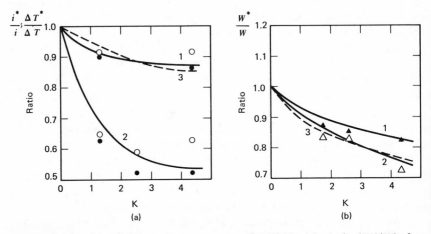

Figure 2   Ratios of enthalpy $(i*/i)$, temperature $(\Delta T*/\Delta T)$, and velocity $(W*/W)$ of one phase system to those of two phase system as functions of the degree of approximation (K) of the system to the two phase system. (a) Curves 1 and 2, experimental temperature and enthalpy ratios for 10–15 kwh, respectively; Curve 3, calculated temperature ratios. (b) Curves 1 and 2, experimental velocity ratios for 10 and 15 kwh, respectively; Curve 3, calculated velocity ratios for 15 kwh.

By using experimental data on velocity and particle temperature values as well as on plasma properties, one can assess the time required for melting particles of different sizes. For example, the melting of tungsten particles of 5 microns in diameter at plasma temperature of 5000°K requires $\sim 10^{-5}$ sec, an increase in diameters of particles up to 100 microns involves an increase in the necessary time up to ~ 1 sec.

The results of the solution of a set of equations indicating the behavior of condensed particles introduced into a plasma jet are presented in Ref. 25. Dynamics of the relative motion of particles and gas as well as phase conversions occurring in the particles were taken into account.

Investigations of the behavior of solid particles in a plasma have enabled us to develop methods for the production of powders of tungsten, molybdenum, titanium, vanadium, zirconium metals, and so forth by the reduction of the corresponding oxides in a hydrogen plasma jet, as well as to research the technological parameters of processes with laboratory installations and to design a larger plasma installation (26).

Of practical interest are the studies on processing of phosphate raw materials in a plasma. Reference 27 shows that the crystal lattice of fluorapatite is shattered in a plasma jet of nitrogen in the range of temperatures from 2000° to 6000°K and that it is defluorinated up to 96%. Addition of silicon dioxide into raw materials brings the degree of defluorination to 99%. Phosphorus, entering into the composition of solid fluorapatite, is thus converted into a soluble form in citric acid. Phosphorus pentoxide, present in the solid products, is dissolved in weak hydrochloric acid.

B. Processes in which End Products are Intermediate Products of Chemical Reactions

For processes of this type, a study of the reaction kinetics, as well as the determination of reaction time, are of great importance: quenching requirements follow from the kinetic process. Not only the quenching rate, but also the time at which the quenching is imposed, is of decisive importance.

Among the processes of this type are processes for the production of acetylene and unsaturated compounds from hydrocarbons, tetrafluoroethylene from tetrafluoromethane, nitrogen fluorides, cyanogen, hydrazine, hydrocyanic acid, hydroxylamine, formaldehyde, and so forth.

A great number of papers have been devoted to a plasma chemical process for the production of acetylene from natural gas. The process of feeding natural gas directly into an electrical discharge (known as electrocracking) is the most highly developed industrial process and it was first realized in Germany in 1940. At present, industrial installations with capacities of 10^3 kW are in operation in Germany, Rumania, the USSR, and the USA (6–8). The best electrocracking results for natural gas are as follows (28): total degree of conversion, $\sim 70\%$; conversion into acetylene, $\sim 5\%$; content of acetylene in products up to 14.6% by volume with energy consumption amounting to 13.6 kwh per cubic meter under normal conditions. But the products contain substantial amounts of carbon black and acetylene homologs; the process is poorly controlled and optimized.

A series of American companies, such as DuPont (29) and Westinghouse (30), have developed their own version of electrocracking using a plasmatron with a magnetic stabilization arc forming a cone as it were a solid one, instead of the long arc (about 1 m) given in Ref. 28. In these processes the conversion of methane into acetylene amounts to 80% and acetylene concentration to 20% by volume, with an electric energy consumption of 12.5–13.3 kwh kg^{-1} of acetylene. So high a concentration of acetylene in the pyrolysis products is created because the process is performed in two stages (cracking of natural gas is performed in the arc, and pyrolysis of heavy hydrocarbons in the gas cracking jet when quenching petroleum). The above results for the process were obtained on an industrial installation (capacity of which was 25,000 tons of acetylene a year).

Some investigators have studied the pyrolysis of natural gas in a plasma jet (28, 31). Calculations of the kinetics of the production of acetylene from methane (31) have enabled us to determine the reaction time, temperature range, starting time, and rate of quenching of the reaction products. A set of equations of chemical kinetics (Kassel's scheme was used) and of hydrodynamics of a plasma jet was integrated by an electronic computer. Maximum concentration of acetylene is accomplished during $\sim 10^{-3}$–10^{-4} seconds (Fig. 3). The maxima of ethylene and acetylene concentrations are separated

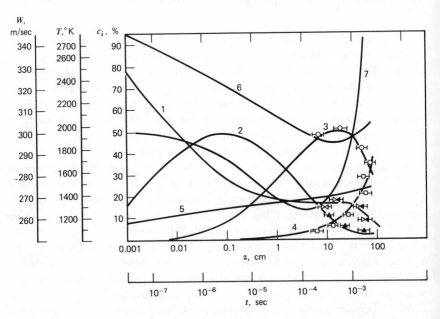

Figure 3 Relations between the concentrations, c_i, of methane pyrolysis products (Curves 1–5 for CH_4, C_2H_4, C_2H_2, C, and H_2, respectively) and the distance z (cm) [or time t (sec)] over which the reaction occurred, temperature T, and time t (Curve 6), and plasma jet (gas) velocity W (m/sec) and time t (Curve 7).

— with time, relative to the plasma jet separated in space. It should be noted that the spatial separation of sections of plasma jet concentrated with different substances is one of the characteristics of plasma chemical processes.

The quenching of acetylene should start in $\sim 10^{-3}$ sec because that is the time at which the process of acetylene decomposition starts, due to the temperature increase caused by heat evolution when carbon is produced.

Experiments on methane pyrolysis on a laboratory scale (7) and on an industrial installation in a hydrogen plasma jet confirmed the results of calculations. Under energy optimal conditions the methane conversion amounted to 90–95%, conversion of methane into acetylene 80%, acetylene concentration in the pyrolysis products 16% by volume; energy consumption was 9 kwh kg^{-1} of acetylene.

It should be noted that 45% of the total energy is consumed directly by a chemical reaction as against 30–35% of that in the case of methane oxidation pyrolysis. Practically, the gases of plasma chemical pyrolysis are free from carbon black; content of acetylene homologs is low and they decrease proportionately with the installation capacity; CO and CO_2 are not present; hydrogen is a commercial product.

When arranging the second stage, C_2H_2 yield increases up to 23% by volume and, in addition, ethylene is produced.

The characteristics of different methods used at present for producing acetylene are compared in Table 1 (32).

TABLE 1

Comparison of the characteristics of methods for acetylene production

Characteristics of processes	Methane, pyrolysis in plasma jet	Electric arc cracking of methane (Hüls)	Electric arc cracking of methane (DuPont)	Oxidizing pyrolysis of methane (Badische Anilin und Soda-Fabrik)
Total conversion of methane, %	90	70	90	90[a]
Degree of methane conversion into acetylene, %	80	50	80	30
Acetylene concentration, % by volume	16 / 23[e]	14 / —	— / 20[e]	9
Degree of useful application of energy, %	45	35	30	35
Purity of byproduct (hydrogen), %	95[b]	75[c]	80[c]	65[d]
Yield of acetylene homologs, amu	60	200	—	100
Yield of aromatic compounds, amu	5	120	—	100
Production cost of acetylene, amu	65	110	110	100
Energy consumption per 1 kg of acetylene, kwh	9	12	15	4
Capital expenditures, amu	60	70	70	100

[a]Main portion of methane is consumed by combustion.
[b]Technical hydrogen.
[c]Hydrogen-methane mixture.
[d]Hydrogen-carbon oxide mixture.
[e]With the second stage.

Industrial realization of any process relating to hydrocarbon processing calls for the solution of problems on the effects of variations in feed composition and on the process results. Some conclusions about the sensitivity of the process of hydrocarbon pyrolysis in a plasma jet in relation to the variations in feed compositions can be obtained from analysis of the work given in Ref. 33.

Analysis of the results of thermodynamic calculations for the C–H systems (33) showed that the basic results of a pyrolysis process, including conversion into acetylene, reaction temperature, and energy expenditure, depend on "energy" criterion representing the relationship between the energy consumed by pyrolysis and the heat effect of complete decomposition of raw materials to acetylene and hydrogen at the standard temperature (Fig. 4). The results of experiments on pyrolysis of methane, propane, and their

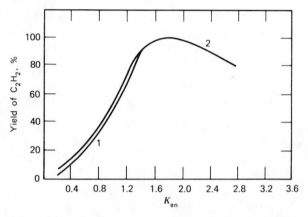

Figure 4 Conversion (%) into acetylene as a function of "energy" criterion K_{en}. Curve 1 for CH_4; Curve 2 for C_2H_6, C_3H_8, C_4H_{10}, and C_5H_{12}.

mixtures in a hydrogen plasma jet as well as the results of plasma chemical pyrolysis of different hydrocarbons have confirmed the conclusions mentioned above. Thus, it is practically possible to obtain constant composition of pyrolysis gases even when changes in the composition of raw materials under pyrolysis occurred, by making corresponding changes in the energy imparted to the plasma. The results of these calculations, obtained by economists, are in agreement with an assessment of this process which is considered the most economic process among those available at present. Such conclusions were drawn by Westinghouse and MHD companies in the USA and by economists from the USSR (34).

The production of acetylene and olefins (ethylene and propylene) during the pyrolysis of liquid hydrocarbons in a plasma jet was investigated on an installation of capacity up to 4000 kw (35). The kinetic and thermodynamic analysis of hydrocarbon decompositions have dictated the conditions under which the process should be conducted (36). Conversion of raw materials (low-octane gasoline) into acetylene and olefins accounted for 75 % of the decomposition during which the acetylene-to-ethylene ratio was changed depending on temperature. Energy consumption amounted to 3–3.5 kwh kg^{-1} of the sum of unsaturated compounds.

A correlation of the results between pyrolysis of straightrun gasoline, which finishes boiling at 150°C in a plasma jet, and oxidizing pyrolysis is shown in Table 2 (32).

Because of the high yield of acetylene in the plasma chemical pyrolysis of natural gas and the high yield of acetylene and ethylene in the plasma pyrolysis

TABLE 2

Correlation of the results between gasoline pyrolysis in plasma jet and oxidizing pyrolysis

Name of components of pyrolysis products	Pyrolysis in hydrogen plasma jet		Oxidizing pyrolysis	
	Composition of pyrolysis products, wt %	Yield per 1 g of raw materials, wt %	Composition of pyrolysis products, wt %	Yield per 1 g of raw materials, wt %
Hydrogen	7.1	0.7	2.2	
Nitrogen	none	none	1.95	0.62
Carbon monoxide	none	none	29.8	
Carbon dioxide	none	none	10.5	0.15
Methane	10.4	8.9	8.5	12.3
Ethane	2.1	1.8	0.4	
Propane	none	none	0.9	1.9
Ethylene	21.9	18.6	22	32.1
Acetylene	30.5	26.0	9.6	13.9
Propylene	23.2	19.7	3.3	4.8
Butenes	none	none	0.40	0.6
Acetylene homologs	$\lesssim 4.0$	$\lesssim 3.8$	5.0	7.2
Gasoline + toluene in liquid products	15	3.1	5.5	0.08
Sum of unsaturated hydrocarbons C_2–C_3	75.6	64.3	34.9	50.8
Energy consumption kwh per 1 kg of unsaturated hydrocarbons C_2–C_3		3.5	not given	
Degree of conversion into gas, wt %		79	75	

of liquid hydrocarbons, direct hydrochlorination and chlorination of these products are possible without their removal. This permits a sharp decrease in the price of vinyl chloride (37).

Plasma chemical pyrolysis of other oil refinery products as well as pyrolysis of crude oil were also performed (38). The results obtained were of the same character as in the case of the plasma chemical pyrolysis of gasoline.

The amount of impurities, not easily separable (e.g., acetylene homologs or higher olefins) strongly affects the cost of acetylene and olefin production via hydrocarbon pyrolysis. In this respect, of some interest is the work (39) in which effects of temperature conditions on composition of higher acetylene and olefin hydrocarbons during gasoline pyrolysis in a hydrogen plasma jet have been studied. The report (39) shows that increase in the reaction temperature from 1300 to $1650°K$ involves a decrease in higher acetylene and olefin hydrocarbons by 3–5 times with high C_2H_2 and C_2H_4 yields being maintained. The possibility of decreasing the amounts of acetylene homologs and higher olefins obtained during hydrocarbon pyrolysis is one of the advantages of plasma chemical methods.

The process of production of tetrafluoroethylene from tetrafluoromethane by a high-intensive arc device with carbon electrodes has been studied in some works reviewed in Ref. 40. The authors have found that C_2F_4 yield increases with increasing capacity and decreasing pressure. Maximum value of the yield (75 mole%) was achieved at a power of 20 kw and pressure of 0.1 atm. The results of thermodynamic calculations of the product compounds for the C–F system given in Ref. 40 show that the basic equilibrium product over the temperature range 2000–3500° is C_2F_2, and at $4000°K$ F. The end product C_2F_4 is produced during the quench as a result of the following reactions: $C_2F_2 + F \rightarrow C_2F_3 + F \rightarrow C_2F_4$. But the radicals are produced in the arc $(CF_4 \xrightarrow{c} C_2F_2)$.

The production of nitrogen fluorides in a nitrogen plasma jet was investigated with CF_4 and SF_6 introduced into it (15,40). The yield of the products containing combined nitrogen (mainly NF_3 and CF_3NF_2) amounted to 1% of nitrogen introduced and increased as power (temperature) and F : N ratio increased. The quenching was performed in a heat exchanger at the rate of 10^6 deg sec^{-1}. In this process, too, the end products are produced during quenching.

Of industrial interest is the process of cyanogen production. In the works (9,41), the process was performed in a nitrogen plasma jet (reagent, carbon tetrachloride). The analysis of the results of thermodynamic calculations for the C–N system and of the kinetic constants of possible reactions for producing and decomposing C_2N_2, performed in (23), shows that the temperature range of 3600–4400°K is considered optimal to carry out the process. It is possible to obtain up to 50% of C_2N_2 in the pyrolysis gas, and in this case, energy consumption will amount to 4.5–5 kwh lb^{-1} of cyanogen. According to the calculations obtained by American investigators (41), this process can be economically competitive.

Some papers (23,41–48) are devoted to studies of the production of hydrocyanic acid in a plasma jet. Analysis of the results of thermodynamic calculations of the H–C–N systems, given in (23,41), shows that the HCN yield and specific energy consumption are dependent on the H : C : N ratio. For example, it is possible to obtain pyrolysis gases, containing 14% by volume of C_2H_2 and 12% by volume of HCN, at a pressure of 1 atm. and a ratio of H : C : N = 4 : 1 : 1, in the temperature range of 1500–2500°K. The experimental results obtained for hydrocyanic acid and acetylene production are given in Refs. 23 and 41–45.

In Refs. 42 and 43 methane and ethylene were introduced into a nitrogen plasma jet. In the first case, conversion to hydrocyanic acid and acetylene amounted to ~75% (per carbon introduced). Increase of quenching velocity causes the acetylene formation. In Refs. 41–45 this process was investigated in a plasmatron provided with an expendable carbon electrode. If a mixture of hydrogen and nitrogen was used as the plasma-forming gas, degree of conversion to hydrocyanic acid was as great as 50% (per carbon consumed), and in this case, the gas was 13–14% acetylene. If the plasmatron operated on ammonia, the degree of conversion was as great as 40%.

The possibility of chlorosilane production was studied (9). Silicon tetrachloride was introduced into a hydrogen plasma jet. A mixture of products generally obtained included compounds of SiH_xCl_{4-x} composition, of chlorosilanes with chains of 3–4 atoms of Si, as well as of $SiCl_4$, unreacted. The purpose of these studies was to obtain trichlorosilane. Under the best conditions the 70% conversion of tetrachlorosilane to trichlorosilane occurred at an energy consumption of 4 kwh kg^{-1} of trichlorosilane.

A process for oxidizing methane by air in an argon plasma jet has also been studied (46). The authors have studied the effects of temperature on the product yields (H_2, HCHO, CO, CO_2, H_2O, H_2O_2). As it was shown, the maximum yield of formaldehyde amounted to 3.5% only for methane at a temperature of 1600–1700°K.

IV. PLASMA CHEMICAL REACTIONS UNDER NONEQUILIBRIUM CONDITIONS

Investigations of chemical processes have been performed in the different zones of glow discharges, in silent discharges, in pulse discharges (we do not dwell upon the radiation-and-chemical processes described in many studies in some detail), under laser radiation, and so forth.

Analysis of chemical processes taking place under nonequilibrium conditions shows that by using the requisite operating conditions:

1. Radically new compounds can be obtained (O_2F_2, O_3F_2, O_4F_2, XeF_4, XeF_2).
2. High yields of the end products can be achieved (C_2F_4 from CF_4, etc).
3. Since marked concentrations of radicals can be obtained, it is possible to use them for performing chemical reactions, the equilibrium of which is shifted to the end products, but the reaction speeds are slow (production of chlorine by oxidizing hydrogen chloride).
4. The quenching of the reaction products can prove to be unnecessary and some processes can be economically competitive.

To study the mechanism and kinetics of a chemical reaction under nonequilibrium conditions, it is necessary to know cross-sections of all the processes, their dependence on energy of the reacting particles, energy distribution of these particles, and evolution of such distributions with time. Reactions with electrons and ions can play a large part.

Unfortunately, there are no such complex investigations of chemical processes in literature, though at present such investigations can be performed.

However, analysis of the data now available from literature permits a determination of the effects of some factors listed on the kinetics of chemical reactions.

We shall consider the conditions resulting from a course of chemical reactions at such initial temperatures when $E_{act} \cong kT$, and the course of chemical reactions in the systems with stationary distribution of reacting particles with energies. In the latter case, average energies of different particles can differ by an order of magnitude.

When $E_{act} \sim kT$, even if a chemical reaction started under quasi-equilibrium conditions, the reaction itself disturbs the initial equilibrium distribution of reacting particles with energies. The point is that the rate at which molecules decrease with energy, exceeding E_{act}, during a chemical reaction is higher than the rate at which they flow from the main part of distribution.

By using the method of mathematical experiment (the Monte-Carlo method) the authors showed in (47) that just such a situation occurred during decomposition of methane and tetrachlorosilane at an initial temperature of 15,000°K.

In glow discharges (in the region of the positive column) the following conditions are realized: stationary distributions of electrons and heavy particles with energies are set, but in this case average energies of electrons exceed by one order of magnitude that of the heavy particles (48).

The effect of electron energy distribution on the velocity of a chemical reaction can be obtained from the analysis of results obtained during studies of some processes in the cathode area [synthesis of ammonia (2), oxidation of nitrogen (49)]. As found, the production velocity of reaction products in the cathode area considerably exceeds the velocity of their formation in the positive column of a glow discharge. It is well known that the energy distribution of electrons differs in the different zones of a discharge.

It is possible to obtain "active" gases, containing considerable concentrations of atoms from glow discharges in molecular gases.

The active gases obtained are often used to perform reactions on the surface of solid or in the liquid phase, for depositing a film and so on. For example, the method of surface activations of some polymers was suggested (50). Partially dissociated oxygen (3–4%), produced in a glow discharge, passed around a specimen surface with the result that the weight of it decreased and some of its properties were changed (wettability, ability to adhere with coatings applied to the specimen after such treatment). Such properties were not observed when specimens were blown on with cold oxygen. The process was performed when discharge power was 200–300 w; pressure, several mm Hg; oxygen consumption, 5×10^{-3} mole $\sec^{-1}$; temperature of specimen, $80°$; time of treatment, 15 min. Specimens of polypropylene, polyethylene, polytetrafluoroethylene, and polyvinylchloride were subjected to such treatment.

The mechanism of the activation process, in the authors' opinion, is as follows: Atoms of oxygen oxidize molecules of a polymer. The polymer radicals obtained produce the products having lower molecular weight as a result of chain reactions, which volatilize and, due to high pressure of vapors, protect the active surface of the polymer after the activation process.

The method for producing amorphous films on different base layers (metallic and nonmetallic) from reactions in gas phase of metal organic compounds of the type $R_x M$ or $(RO)_x M$, where $R = C_2 H_5$, $C_3 H_7$, and so forth, with "active" gases generated in a microwave discharge, is described in Ref. 51. By using oxygen plasma, films of oxides of silicon, germanium, boron, tin, and titanium were produced. The base layers were positioned outside the discharge zone. If heating of the base layers exceeds a certain critical temperature, the value of which is determined by the velocity of the reagent flow, the discharge governing the conditions, and the films which are free from admixtures of other decomposition products—reagent. The effects of temperature, pressure, flow rate, and electrical parameters of a plasma on the velocity of growth of films have also been studied. To produce nitride or oxynitride films, it was suggested that a plasma of nitrogen or nitrogen oxide be used.

Under nonequilibrium conditions radical reactions are also obtained, the equilibrium of such reactions being shifted in the direction required to produce the necessary products. For example, report (52) describes the oxidation of hydrogen chloride by means of oxygen, carried out in a microwave discharge at pressures ranging from 5 to 50 mm Hg and plasma power of 200–350 w. The maximum degree of hydrogen chloride conversion, amounting to 50%, was noted at a pressure of 20 mm Hg, specific energy of 20 w cm^{-3}, and a gas temperature of $\sim 700°$K (Fig. 5). It is expected that the reaction proceeds by a free-radical mechanism with radicals of O and H.

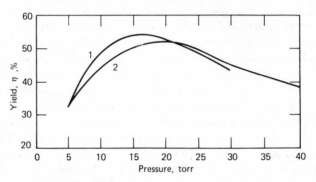

Figure 5   Conversion of HCl into Cl$_2$ (η, %) as a function of pressure. Curves 1 and 2 for 208 and 342 w, respectively, of absorbed power. Feed rates: O$_2$, 0.341 $\times$ 10^{-4} mole sec^{-1}; HCl, 1.37 $\times$ 10^{-4} mole sec^{-1}.

It is well known that the end products can be produced by recombination of radicals generated in a plasma. The end products can be decomposed during prolonged residence in the discharge zone. A decrease in the residence time in a plasma is achieved in different ways. One of these methods is the use of pulsed operating conditions. Another possible way, in case of the production of hydrazine from ammonia, involves the adsorption of an end product in jets of one or another of the adsorbents introduced into the discharge zone (53).

Of some interest, from the scientific viewpoint, are the processes of production of inert gas compounds (xenon tetrafluoride, xenon hexafluoride, etc.) (54). The above compounds are formed only in nonequilibrium plasmas, in the positive column of glow discharges, when pressure is 1–15 mm Hg and the reactor is cooled to 78°K. But, for the present, nobody can say anything about the mechanism of such compound formations.

One of the most important characteristics of nonequilibrium plasma chemical processes is the fact that due to the low temperature of heavy particles (molecules), the quenching process is unnecessary in most cases, and this reduces the expenditures considerably.

With the advent of the laser many investigators have attempted to perform chemical processes by irradiation. They used powerful lasers to initiate a dense plasma. A detailed description of studies on plasma production by means of laser, properties of plasmas thus produced, and the interaction between laser radiation and surface is given in Ref. 55.

In this report, we shall consider only the interaction between laser radiation and solid surfaces. Under intense laser irradiation, the surface emits electrons (with current density of up to 10^5 amp cm^{-2}) and is heated up to a temperature of $\sim 10,000°K$. Using laser pulses, the blow-off of material can occur. The rate of material blow-off can amount to 10^6 cm sec^{-1}. In the case of a high power laser, the ionization of a substance being carried off takes place, and the energy of the ions formed can amount to several keV. In experiments carried out on irradiation of solids suspended between electrodes, ions of high energies, ionized repeatedly, have been obtained. By using spectral methods it is now possible to obtain new data on the properties of many substances. A chemical reaction under a low-power laser radiation was studied in Ref. 56. These authors have studied the action of ruby laser radiation on diluted aqueous solutions of Mohr's salts (oxidation from Fe^{2+} to Fe^{3+}). Radiation intensity was selected so as to avoid a breakdown in the solution; in this case, there were no thermal reactions under test conditions. The analysis of relationship between amount of Fe^{2+} oxidized and radiation dose, as well as of relationship between rate of Fe^{3+} formation and intensity of radiation, made it possible to establish a photochemical mechanism for the oxidation of Fe^{2+} ions.

In the opinion of the author (53), the processes of the production of nitrogen from air, hydrogen peroxide, and so on are more economically efficient.

The basic results of chemical processes under nonequilibrium conditions described in the literature are summarized in Table 3.

TABLE 3
Chemical processes under nonequilibrium conditions[a]

Process	Experimental conditions and results	Reference
Synthesis of ammonia from nitrogen and hydrogen	(1) Silent discharge in stoichiometric mixture of N_2 and H_2 at 1 absolute atm. Yield of NH_3 amounts to 0.3×10^{-4} mole per coulomb.	2
	(2) Glow discharge at a pressure of 1–4 mm Hg. Conversion, 98%.	2
Production of hydrazine from ammonia	(1) Arc under 4 mm Hg. Conversion up to 50% of NH_3 decomposed. Relationships	2, 57

TABLE (*Continued*)

Process	Experimental conditions and results	Reference
	between dissociation degree of NH_3 and N_2H_4 yield, and (UP/V) were obtained.	
	(2) Glow discharge in ammonia at 0.6–11 mm Hg. Production of hydrazine occurs in positive column.	58
	(3) Discharge at 50 cycles sec^{-1}. Hydrazine yield, 11 g kwh^{-1}. In pulse discharge the yield amounts to ~ 47 g kwh^{-1}. Hydrazine concentration in gases, 0.01–0.02%.	54
Oxidation of nitrogen	(1) Glow discharge in mixtures of N_2 and O_2, oxides being produced in negative glow region. Pressure, 0.7–4 mm Hg. Maximum yield when $N_2 : O_2 = 62:38$.	2
	(2) Hf electrode discharge in air at frequency of 270 kilocycles sec^{-1}, and pressure of 180 mm Hg. Content of NO in the gas is 5% at 65 w. This is three times more than that found in a low-frequency discharge of the same power.	59
	(3) Hf electrodeless discharge in air at frequency of 27.5 megacycle and at 110 mm Hg. Content of NO in plasma at 375 w is 2%.	60
	(4) Glow discharge in air. Products formed in positive column. Pressure, 50–300 mm Hg. Relationships between NO content in gas and i, ip are given. Maximum concentration of NO, 5–6%.	61
	(5) Glow discharge in air. Products formed in cathode region. Pressure, 50–400 mm Hg. Relationships between NO content and i were given. Initial section of the curve	49

	is same (61). Then NO content increases linearly up to 8%, with growth of initial section.	
	(6) Glow discharge in mixtures of N_2 and O_2. Products formed in cathode region. Effect of N_2-and-O_2 ratio on NO content in gas was studied. Maximum content of NO when $N_2:O_2 = 1:1$; then 1:4 and 4:1.	62
	(7) Pulse discharge in air at pressures of 20–500 mm Hg. Power in pulse, 20 megaW when pulse duration is 2 msec. NO content, 2.5%.	63
	(8) Microwave discharge in air. Relationships between NO yield and $\beta = PZ/E^2\tau$ were given. Maximum yield of NO, 0.8 mole kwh^{-1}.	64
Dissociation of carbon dioxide	(1) Glow discharge in CO_2 at pressure of 30–100 mm Hg. Degree of dissociation depended upon pressure, amounting to 40% below 50 mm Hg, and increased with increasing current density.	2
	(2) Silent discharge in CO_2. Degree of dissociation amounted to 30%.	2
Dissociation of CO	Microwave discharge in CO, at pressures of 1–8 mm Hg. When power in discharge was 400 w, layers of carbon black deposit on discharge tube walls were noted; CO_2 and O_2 were produced. When power in discharge was 120 w, C_3O_2 was deposited instead of carbon black.	54
Decomposition of nitrous oxide	Silent discharge in N_2O at pressures of 200–800 mm Hg. Degree of N_2O decomposition was maximum at 200 mm Hg ($\sim 90\%$).	2
Oxidation of hydrogen	Glow discharge	2
Oxidation of CO	Glow discharge	2
Cracking of methane	Glow discharge in methane at pressures of 40–50 mm Hg. Conversion into C_2H_2 was up to 80%. C_2H_2 content, 9%.	2

TABLE (*Continued*)

Process	Experimental conditions and results	Reference
Decomposition of ethylene	Energy consumption, 13 kwh per 1 cu.m of C_2H_2. Glow discharge in ethylene at pressures of 0.7–1.7 mm Hg. Mechanism and kinetics were studied.	65
Conversion of methane with carbon dioxide and water vapor	Glow discharge in mixtures of CH_4 with CO_2 and CH_4 with H_2O at a pressure of 50 mm Hg. Degree of methane conversion, 98%. When current densities were high, CO and H_2 were produced; when current densities were low, C_2H_2, CO, and H_2 were produced.	2
Production of hydrocarbons from carbon oxides and hydrogen	(1) Glow discharge in mixtures of CO and H_2 at pressure of 10 mm Hg. Yields of C_2H_2 and CH_4 were low.	2
	(2) Microwave discharge in mixtures of CO and H_2 at pressures of 10–50 mm Hg. CH_4, C_2H_2, and H_2O were produced when residence time in discharge zone was 1 min approximately. Conversion of CO to CH_4 was 80%.	54
Synthesis of hydrocyanic acid from nitrogen and methane	Glow discharge in mixtures of N_2 and CH_4 at pressures of 10–15 mm Hg. Conversion of methane to hydrocyanic acid depended on current density and on composition of mixture. Conversion was 80% when concentration of methane in mixture was 15%. C_2H_2 was produced simultaneously with HCN. C_2H_2:HCN ratio varied according to current density used.	2
Decomposition of acetone	Silent discharge in acetone vapor at pressures up to 100 mm Hg. CO_2, CO, C_2H_2, C_2H_6, H_2 were produced.	2
Decomposition of benzene	Silent discharge in benzene vapor. H_2, CH_4, C_2H_2, C_2H_4, and biphenyl were produced.	2

Production of ozone	Glow discharge in oxygen at pressure of 0.5 mm Hg.	2, 66
Reduction of titanium tetrachloride by hydrogen	Glow discharge in mixture of $TiCl_4$ and H_2. Products contained 90% Ti (purity 99.6%) and 10% lower chlorides.	67, 68
Reduction of zirconium halides	Glow discharge at pressures of 3–4 mm Hg in mixtures of zirconium halide and hydrogen. $ZrCl_3$, $ZrBr_3$, ZrI_3, ZrF_3 were produced.	69
Reduction of boron trichloride	Discharge in mixtures of BCl_3 and H_2 at pressures of 30–200 mm Hg. Optimum yield was achieved when ratio $BCl_3 : H_2$ = 1:5. Purity of boron was 99.9%.	70
Production of hydrides	Discharge in H_2 inside a reaction tube, walls of which were coated with elements such as phosphorous, sulfur, arsenic, and so on.	54
Production of boranes	Discharge in mixtures of H_2 and BCl_3 taken in ratio 12:1, at 20 mm Hg. Quenching of products was performed using liquid nitrogen. Compounds of composition B_2H_6, $B_{10}H_{16}$, and B_2H_{16} were produced.	54
Production of oxygen and fluorine compounds	(1) Discharge between copper electrodes in mixtures of $O_2 : F_2$ = 1:2 at a pressure of 12 mm Hg (2000 V, 25 ma). Dark red liquid of O_3F_2 compound was produced at 77°K. It decomposed into O_2F_2 at 115°K.	71
	(2) Discharge in mixture of $O_2 : F_2$ = 2:1 at 5–15 mm Hg (840–130 V, 4.5 ma). Dark red deposit of O_4F_2 was formed on walls at $T < 90°K$. At $T \sim 90$–110°K O_4F_2 was decomposed into O_3F_2 and O_2.	71
Production of compounds of inert gases (a) Production of xenon tetrafluoride	Discharge in mixture of Xe:F_2 = 1:2 at 2–15 mm Hg, between copper electrodes. ($V \simeq$ 1100–2800 V, i $\simeq$ 10–30 ma). Reactor was cooled to temperature of 78°K. Consumption of mixture of Xe and F_2 was 136 cu. cm h^{-1}.	54

TABLE (*Continued*)

Process	Experimental conditions and results	Reference
(b) Production of xenon hexafluoride	Practically, all the reagents introduced were converted into XeF_4. Discharge in mixture of $Xe:F_2 = 1:3$, at 2–15 mm Hg, in reactor under conditions described in (54).	54
Production of chlorine by the oxidation of hydrogen chloride	Microwave discharge in mixture of HCl and O_2 at 10–50 mm Hg; power in plasma was 200–300 w. Fifty % conversion of HCl occurred at 20 mm Hg.	52
Production of fluorocarbon compounds	Arc between carbon electrodes in CF_4, CF_3Cl, C_2F_5Cl, and so on. at 1–50 mm Hg. C_2F_4, C_2F_6, and C_3F_6 were found in the products.	40

[a]U, power of discharge; V, gas consumption; P, pressure; i, current density; Z, impedance; E, field intensity in plasma; τ, residence time in the discharge zone.

V. CONCLUDING REMARKS

Below, we list some processes in nonequilibrium low-temperature plasma, the development of which are of commercial interest:

1. Oxidation of nitrogen contained in air in microwave generated plasmas.
2. Production of C_2F_4 in glow discharge.
3. Decomposition of nitrous oxide in silent discharge.
4. Synthesis of hydrocyanic acid in nitrogen-methane mixture.
5. Reduction of titanium tetrachloride by means of hydrogen.
6. Reduction of zirconium halides.
7. Production of boranes (B_2H_6, $B_{10}H_{16}$, etc.).

Plasma chemical technology is the technology of tomorrow; today we have only a vague idea of the boundless possibilities for the use of low-temperature plasmas in chemical and other branches of the industry.

REFERENCES

1. *Kinetics and Thermodynamics of Chemical Reactions in Low-Temperature Plasma.* Moscow: Nauka, 1965.
2. A. B. Shekhter, *Chemical Reactions in Electrical Discharge.* Moscow-Leningrad: Department of Scientific and Technical Information, 1935.

3. F. A. Bukhman, G. V. Guliaev, V. G. Melamed, L. S. Polak, and Yu. L. Khait, *Kinetics and Thermodynamics of Chemical Reactions in Low-Temperature Plasma*. Moscow: Nauka, 1965, p. 60.

4. L. S. Polak and V. S. Sthchipatchev, see Ref. 3, p. 151.

5. Yu. L. Khait, see Ref. 3, p. 167.

6. W. M. Goldberger, *Brit. Chem. Eng.*, **8**, 610 (1963).

7. G. V. Guliaev and L. S. Polak, *Kinetics and Thermodynamics of Chemical Reactions in Low-Temperature Plasma*. Moscow: Nauka, 1965, p. 72.

8. M. P. Freeman and J. E. Skrivan, *Petroleum Refiner*, **41**, 124 (1962).

9. H. Harmish, G. Heimer, and E. Shalus, *Chem. Ing. Techn.*, **35**, 7 (1963).

10. F. B. Vursel and L. S. Polak, *Kinetics and Thermodynamics of Chemical Reactions in Low-Temperature Plasma*. Moscow: Nauka, 1965, p. 238.

11. J. Drowart and P. Goldfinger, *Ann. Rev. Phys. Chem.*, **13**, 459 (1962).

12. V. A. Kireev, *Uspekhy Khimii (USSR)*, **33**, 707 (1964).

13. *Kinetics, Equilibria and Performance of High-Temperature Systems*. Proceedings of the 1st Conference, Los Angeles, California, 1959. New York: Gordon and Breach Sci. Publishers, 1960; Proceedings of the 2nd Conference, Los Angeles, California, 1962. New York: Gordon and Breach Sci. Publishers, 1963.

14. R. F. Duff and S. H. Bauer, *J. Chem. Phys.*, **36**, 1754 (1962).

15. B. R. Bronfin and R. N. Hazlett, *Ind. Eng. Chem.*, *Fundamentals*, **5**, 472 (1966).

16. I. Niederkorn and A. Wohl, *Rev. Roumaine Chim.*, **11**, 85 (1960).

17. H. J. Kusch, *Chem. Ing. Techn.*, **65**, 448 (1963).

18. J. O. Gibson and R. Weidman, *Chem. Eng. Progr.*, **59**, 53 (1963).

19. G. E. Biggerstaff, W. R. Golliher, R. Z. Harris, and W. R. Rossmasler, U.S. Atomic Energy Comm., KY–453, 1964, p. 38; *Chem. Abstr.*, **61**, 1531e (1964).

20. F. B. Vursel and L. S. Polak, *Khimia Visokich Energii (USSR)*, **1**, 268 (1967).

21. I. V. Antipov, A. B. Gugnjak, S. N. Dmitriev, I. D. Kulagin, Ja. M. Lipkes, A. B. Loginov, S. V. Ogurtzov, N. N. Rikalin, L. M. Sorokin, and T. P. Sushko, *Fisika i Khimia Obrabotki Materialov (USSR)*, No. 4, 146 (1968).

22. J. B. Margeloff. U.S. Pat. No. 3254958, September 17, 1962.

23. R. S. Timmins and P. R. Amman, *The Application of Plasmas to Chemical Processing*. Cambridge, Mass.: MIT Press, 1967, p. 99.

24. N. S. Surov and L. S. Polak, *Fisika i Khimia Obrabotki Materialov (USSR)*, **19**, No. 2 (1969).

25. I. K. Tagirov, I. Ja. Basieva, and Yu. V. Zvetkov, *Physical Chemical Processes in Metallurgy of Colored and Rare Metals*. Moscow: Nauka, to be published.

26. D. M. Chizhikov, Yu. V. Zvetkov, S. S. Deineka, I. K. Tagirov, and I. Ja. Basieva, *New Techniques in Powder Metallurgy*. Moscow: Nauka, 1968, p. 143.

27. V. V. Pechkovsky, A. L. Mosse, A. I. Teterevkov, A. A. Chesnokov and A. I. Davidenko, *Ingenerno-Fisitcheskii Zhurnal (USSR)*, **14**, No. 6 (1968).

28. M. Gladisch, *Chem. Ind.*, **88**, 471 (1962).

29. *Chemical Week*. **94**, No. 3, 65 (1964).

30. D. A. Maniero, P. P. Kienast, and C. Hirayama, *Westinghouse Eng.*, **26**, No. 3, 65 (1964).

31. V. G. Melamed, T. A. Mukhtarova, L. S. Polak, and Yu. L. Khait, *Kinetics and Thermodynamics of Chemical Reactions in Low-Temperature Plasma*. Moscow: Nauka, 1965, p. 12.

32. L. S. Polak, *Neftekhimia (USSR)*, **7**, No. 3, 463 (1967); Proceedings of the 7th World Petroleum Congress, 1967, p. 283.

33. A. L. Suris and S. N. Shorin, *Khimia Visokich Energii (USSR)*, **3**, 99 (1969).

34. *Chem. Eng.*, **71**, No. 3, 29 (1964).

35. K. Sennewald, E. Shallus, and F. Pohl, *Chem. Ing. Techn.*, **35**, 1 (1963).
36. F. B. Vursel and L. S. Polak, *Kinetics and Thermodynamics of Chemical Reactions in Low-Temperature Plasma.* Moscow: Nauka, 1965, p. 100.
37. Sh. Gomi, *Petroleum Refiner*, **43**, No. 11 (1964).
38. L. S. Polak, P. N. Endjuskin, V. N. Uglev, and N. L. Volodin, *Khimia Visokich Energii* (*USSR*), **3**, 184 (1969).
39. L. S. Polak, V. N. Uglev, S. N. Chernikh, and P. N. Endjuskin, *Proceedings of the 3rd Conference on Generators of Low-Temperature Plasmas.* Minsk, 1967.
40. B. Bronfin, *The Application of Plasmas to Chemical Processing.* Cambridge, Mass.: MIT Press, 1967, p. 157.
41. H. W. Leutner, *Ind. Eng. Chem.*, Process Design and Development, **1**, 166 (1962).
42. P. W. Young and N. Levy, Brit. Pat. No. 890414. September 28, 1962.
43. G. A. Mannela, *J. Chem. Phys.*, **37**, 678 (1962).
44. H. W. Leutner, *Ind. Eng. Chem.*, Process Design and Development, **2**, 315, 1963.
45. A. V. Grosse, H. W. Leutner, and C. S. Stokes, 1st Annual Report of Research Institute of Temple Univ., Philadelphia, 1961, p. 16.
46. A. A. Ovsjannikov and L. S. Polak, *Kinetics and Thermodynamics of Chemical Reactions in Low-Temperature Plasma.* Moscow: Nauka, 1965, p. 118.
47. S. A. Denicik, S. N. Lebedev, Yu. G. Malama, and L. S. Polak, *Khimia Visokich Energii* (*USSR*), **1**, 500 (1967).
48. A. von Engel, *Ionized Gases*, 2nd ed. London: Oxford University Press, 1965.
49. G. A. Mironov, A. N. Maltzev, and E. N. Eremin, *Zh. Fiz. Khim.*, **37**, 36 (1963).
50. R. M. Mantell and W. L. Ormand, *Ind. Eng. Chem.*, Process Design and Development, **3**, 300 (1964).
51. D. R. Secrist and J. D. MacKenzie, *Am. Chem. Soc.*, Div. Fuel Chem. Preprints. Part **1**, 1, 112, 203 (1967).
52. R. F. Baddour and P. H. Dundas, *The Application of Plasmas to Chemical Processing.* Cambridge, Mass.: MIT Press, 1967, p. 87.
53. P. L. Spedling, *Nature*, **214**, No. 5084, 124 (1967).
54. F. K. McTaggart, *Plasma Chemistry in Electrical Discharges.* Amsterdam: Elsevier Publ. Co., 1967.
55. R. G. Meyerand, *AIAA J.*, **5**, No. 10, 3 (1967).
56. A. V. Egunov and V. V. Korobkin, *Khimia Visokich Energii* (*USSR*), **1**, 202 (1967).
57. I. I. Skorokhodov, L. I. Nekrasov, N. I. Kobozev, and A. D. Philonova, *Zh. Fiz. Khim.*, **35**, 1026 (1961).
58. J. C. Devins and M. Burton, *J. Am. Chem. Soc.*, **76**, 2618 (1954).
59. E. N. Eremin, S. S. Vasiljev, and N. I. Kobozev, *Zh. Fiz. Khim.*, **8**, 814 (1936).
60. C. S. Stokes, J. J. Korea, L. A. Streng, and H. W. Leutner, *Am. Inst. Chem. Eng. J.*, **11**, 370 (1965).
61. E. N. Eremin and A. N. Maltzev, *Zh. Fiz. Khim.*, **30**, 1615 (1956).
62. L. M. Krichtina, A. N. Maltzev, and E. N. Eremin, *Zh. Fiz. Khim.*, **40**, 2784 (1966).
63. M. M. Bogorodskaja and E. N. Eremin, *Zh. Fiz. Khim.*, **38**, 1849 (1964).
64. R. L. McCarthy, *J. Chem. Phys.*, **22**, 1360 (1954).
65. E. N. Borisova and E. N. Eremin, *Zh. Fiz. Khim.*, **40**, 2713 (1966).
66. L. I. Nekrasov, I. I. Skorokhodov, and N. I. Kobozev, *Zh. Fiz. Khim.*, **40**, 2361 (1966)
67. I. K. Ingraham, K. W. Downes, and P. Marier, *Can. J. Chem.*, **35**, 850 (1957).
68. K. Ishisuka, U.S. Pat. No. 2860094, 1958; *Chem. Abstr.*, **53**, 8894 (1959).
69. I. E. Neuman and J. A. Watts, *J. Am. Chem. Soc.*, **82**, 2113 (1960).
70. L. Yu. Markovsky, V. I. Lvova, and Yu. D. Kondrashov, *Proceedings of the Conference on Chemistry of Boron and its Compounds.* 1958, p. 36.
71. A. V. Grosse and A. D. Kirshenbaum, *J. Am. Chem. Soc.*, **81**, 1277 (1959); **83**, 1004 (1961).

CHAPTER SEVENTEEN

Chemical Reactions in Flame Plasmas

H. F. CALCOTE and W. J. MILLER

I. INTRODUCTION

Ions can be produced in combustion flame plasmas by two mechanisms: collisional ionization and chemi-ionization. In collisional ionization (sometimes loosely referred to as "thermal ionization"), the kinetic energy of the colliding species is sufficient to ionize one of the collision partners, for example, in the ionization of sodium:

$$Na + M \longrightarrow Na^+ + M + e$$

where M is another molecule. Such reactions are significant for low ionization potential elements, as in the alkali metals and alkaline earths, and become increasingly significant as the temperature is increased.

A chemi-ionization reaction is one in which the energy released in the formation of new chemical bonds is sufficient to ionize a product of the reaction,

$$CH + O \longrightarrow CHO^+ + e$$

When chemi-ionization occurs, as in a hydrocarbon flame, the degree of ionization usually exceeds the equilibrium value. Chemi-ionization may, however, also be the mechanism by which equilibrium ion concentrations are attained: this is the case in the ionization of alkaline earths.

Electron attachment, ion-molecule, and ion recombination reactions all occur in flames, producing an abundance of both positive and negative ions. Flames thus offer a useful medium in which to study plasma reactions over a broad range of temperature (ambient in the case of atomic flames to 4800°K for C_2N_2/O_2 flames) and pressure (< 1 torr to > 760 torr). Flame ionization is of practical significance in analytical chemistry (flame-ionization detectors), in radar interference effects in rocket exhausts (free electrons in the exhaust plume alter the dielectric constant and interfere with the propagation of electromagnetic waves), in re-entry phenomena (oxidation of ablation products to produce ionization), and in MHD power generation (combustion gases are used as the working fluid for which high-electron densities are desirable).

This chapter deals with the reactions involving the production of ions and their subsequent fate in flames; the practical aspects of the phenomena of flame ionization will not be covered. Only the most recent results and interpretations will be treated; the historical development will not be traced. The interested reader is referred to previously published reviews (1–3) for accounts of the early work, dating back to the first scientific experiments with flames. For detailed discussions of reactions of neutral species occurring in flames, the reader is referred to several good reviews and recent papers (4,5).

II. EXPERIMENTAL TECHNIQUES

Much of the instrumentation used in plasma diagnostics has been successfully employed in flames. The most notable exceptions are the optical spectroscopic methods such as Doppler and Stark line broadening, which are applicable only at very high ($\geq \sim 10^{14}$ cm^{-3}) charged species concentrations. In general, the ion and/or electron concentrations in flames do not exceed 10^{13} cm^{-3} and are frequently many orders of magnitude lower (concentrations of 10^5 cm^{-3} are not unusual). The techniques which have proved to be of most value in flame-ionization studies are electrostatic probes, microwave and rf techniques, and mass spectrometry. Space limits a complete review here, but brief descriptions of the more useful techniques, as well as some indication of the problems peculiar to each will be given, to provide the reader with the experimental background behind the bulk of the data in subsequent sections.

A. Electrostatic Probe

Basically, an electrostatic probe is a piece of electrically conducting material which, when inserted into a plasma and biased at an appropriate voltage, is used to measure charged species concentrations. In practice, the voltage is swept through a wide range, from positive to negative voltages and the current is recorded. The current-voltage characteristic thus obtained can, in principle, be interpreted to yield both positive ion and electron (or negative ion) concentrations and electron temperatures. Probes have a major disadvantage in that they must be inserted into the flame and thereby disturb it. However, they can afford a high degree of spatial resolution and have been used for concentration measurements over an extremely large charged species concentration range—10^5–10^{14} cm^{-3}.

The equations for the calculation of charged species number densities for the practical case of a cylindrical probe have been developed by Calcote (6,7) from the theory of Bohm, Burhop and Massey (8). More recently, the theory has been refined by Jensen and Kurzius (9) to include the effects of gas-flow velocity. For other probe theories applicable to flames, see Refs. 10–14. The resulting equation for subsonic laminar flames is

$$[n_+] = j_{+p} \left\{ \frac{4}{v_+} + \frac{d}{Sh.D_a} \right\} \tag{1}$$

where, for a long ($L \gg d$) cylinder in cross-flow with $Re < 2000$,

$$Sh = Sh_0 + 0.55\ Re^{1/2}Sc^{1/3} \tag{2}$$

and

$$Sh_0 = \cfrac{2}{\left\{ \ln \left[\cfrac{2(L + 2\lambda_+)}{d + 2\lambda_+} \right] \right\}} \qquad [3]$$

In these equations, $[n_+]$ is the positive ion concentration in the flame, j_{+p} the positive ion current flux at the plasma potential, v_+ is the positive ion mean thermal velocity, d the probe diameter, L the probe length, Sh the perimeter-mean Sherwood number, D_a the ambipolar diffusivity, λ_+ the positive ion mean free path, Re the bulk flow Reynolds number based on the probe diameter and Sc the corresponding Schmidt number. Equation [2] stems from reinterpretation in terms of eq. [3] of existing correlations of data (15), relating to transfer of heat and mass to and from cylinders in cross flow.

Experimentally, probe measurements in flames are complicated by high gas temperatures. Water-cooled probes have been successfully employed (7), but great care must be exercised to eliminate leakage currents from the probes to the cooling systems which constitute part of the ground or reference electrode. Because the mobility of the electron is so much greater than that of the positive ion, the ground area must be very much larger than the probe collection area to obtain "saturation" electron currents. The adequacy of the ground should be tested by varying its area; usually a metal burner top will suffice, but additional grounded screens are often necessary in the vicinity of the probe.

When the reference and collection electrodes are of equal or nearly equal size, the apparatus is referred to as a "double probe" (see Ref. 10). The current-voltage characteristics in this case are symmetrical and only the concentration of the species with the lowest mobility can be measured. In principle, it is possible to determine the electron temperature with either single or double probes from the shape of the current-voltage characteristic curve near the plasma potential.

The withdrawal of charged species by the probe may severely perturb the plasma in the vicinity of the probe. However, if the probe collection area is made very small and the biasing voltages are kept low, one may reasonably assume that the probe perturbation is insignificant and the currents collected are an accurate indication of the bulk plasma properties. By increasing the potential on the probe to several hundreds of volts and shielding the rest of the plasma, it is possible to totally withdraw all of the ions between the electrodes. This method is of particular advantage in studies of ion formation rates in which ions are withdrawn as soon after their formation as possible. Flame ionization detectors used in gas chromatography are operated in this way for the quantitative detection of hydrocarbon and hydrocarbon-like materials (16,17).

B. Microwave and Radio-Frequency Methods

Microwave techniques for flame plasma investigations are numerous and varied; they include cyclotron resonance (18), microwave scattering (19), microwave absorption (20,21), and microwave cavity resonance (22,23). High-frequency resonance methods employing both condensers (24) and coils (25,26) have also been used to measure electron concentrations. In general, these techniques are not applicable over as wide a range of charged species concentrations as electrostatic probes, nor do they afford the high degree of spatial resolution attainable with probes. On the other hand, they do not disturb the flame and they are the most dependable tools available for the measurement of electron concentrations.

Few differences exist between experimental procedures for microwave flame diagnostics and those for the study of other plasmas. One must be careful, of course, to prevent the highly reactive, hot flame gases from damaging expensive waveguides and other electronic apparatus, but this problem is no more severe, in general, than those associated with other plasmas. Too many variations of these techniques have been used for flame plasma studies to be even briefly described here. However, very little laboratory flame work has been done with any microwave methods recently, with the notable exception of the resonant cavity. Of all microwave techniques, this method seems most lasting and, therefore, a qualitative description of its function follows.

A section of the flame to be studied is passed through the center of a cylindrical cavity resonating in a mode (usually TM_{010}) in which the resonance frequency—typically 3000 MHz—is independent of the cylinder length. In such a mode, the cavity may be made quite short for greater spatial resolution (22,23). Microwave power is fed from a tunable klystron through the cavity and an appropriate load to a detector. Normally, the microwave output from the cavity is rectified and measured as a DC current. A schematic of a typical apparatus is given in Fig. 1. The shield flame is very important, because it minimizes temperature and concentration gradients in the inner test flame.

When electrons are introduced into the flame, the "Q-factor" of the cavity is lowered, and the rectified current falls. Under typical experimental conditions, currents in the presence and absence of electrons in the flame, I and I_0, respectively, are related to the corresponding Q's through the expression

$$\frac{I}{I_0} = \left[\frac{Q}{Q_0}\right]^2 \qquad [4]$$

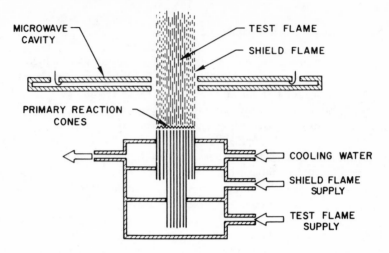

Figure 1   Burner and microwave cavity.

The equation for the calculation of the electron concentration from the observed current ratio is

$$[e] = R_c \left[\left(\frac{I_0}{I} \right)^{0.5} - 1 \right]$$ [5]

where R_c is the cavity constant, a function of the electron-molecule collision frequency. As with nearly all other plasma diagnostic methods used in flames, except the electrostatic probe, a calibration procedure is used in quantitative work; the equilibrium ionization produced by the addition of small concentrations of cesium salts to 1 atm flames has been frequently employed.

C. Mass Spectrometry

Mass spectrometers are now widely employed in studies of transient species in reacting gas mixtures. Techniques have been developed for the investigation of both neutral molecules and ions; the facilities involved share the advantages and problems common to mass spectrometry and, to a large extent, the difficulties encountered in sampling system design. In general, reactive species at a relatively high pressure are expanded into an instrument in a manner designed to "freeze" the chemistry and thus maintain the individual species identities and concentrations prevalent immediately upstream of the sampling system. The extent to which this is possible has been the subject of a number of recent investigations categorized as "molecular beam" studies (27).

Instruments, such as the one shown in Fig. 2, which have been specifically designed (28) for the detection and identification of flame ions, have two distinct advantages over neutral or molecular beam systems: (1) no ion source is required within the mass spectrometer and (2) since the sampled species are charged, they may be separated immediately after sampling from the accompanying neutrals with electrostatic lenses.

A typical sampling system consists of a small orifice in a cone tip. The cone angle chosen constitutes a compromise between the degree of flow perturbation caused by the cone and requirements for rapid pumping downstream of the sampling orifice. The ion mean-free-path in the first evacuated (lens) section should be as large as possible, but in practice one usually settles for a mean free path equal to, or slightly greater than, the distance from orifice to mass analyzer inlet, that is, something on the order of a few centimeters at a pressure of $\leqslant 10^{-4}$ torr. Under these conditions, molecular flow prevails from the lens section into the mass analyzer housing and differential pumping can be employed to maintain the much lower pressures required there. Each of these sections is indicated in the apparatus of Fig. 2, which is a typical system employed in flame plasma investigations.

Flames have been studied at pressures from about 1 torr (29) up to 1 atm (30,31). Thus, the gas flow through the sampling orifice is in the continuum

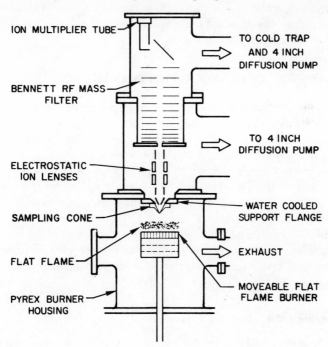

Figure 2   Low pressure burner and flame ion mass spectrometer.

or transition flow regimes with a free jet expansion dowstream of the orifice. In this phase of the flow history, the analysis of neutrals via molecular beam formation and charged species studies have common problems. Collisions with the inside walls of the sampling cone during the expansion change neutral species energy and composition distributions and destroy charged species. A skimmer, or second sampling cone, is installed downstream of the initial sampling orifice in molecular beam systems, to allow only those molecules in the central portion of the expanding jet to enter the mass analyzer. This excludes, as far as possible, the molecules which have undergone collisions with the walls or with other molecules whose energies are not representative of the desired distribution. Thus, another stage of pumping between the skimmer and the mass analyzer is required. Electrostatic lenses to focus and accelerate charged species out of the expanding jet perform essentially the same function in ion sampling as the skimmer in molecular beam systems, that is, the separation of the species to be studied from those not representative of the reacting gas mixture being sampled.

It has been found (32) that free radicals such as OH disappear from the sampled gas stream if the sampling cone angle is reduced much below 90°. Apparently, the radicals or ions are destroyed by wall reactions which occur with increasing frequency as the angle is reduced. Cones with angles larger than 90° increase the sensitivity, but also increase the likelihood of disturbing the flow in the reacting gas mixture.

III. IONIZATION IN HYDROCARBON FLAMES

The equilibrium composition of hydrocarbon combustion products consists of a mixture of molecules and atoms with very high ionization potentials. To explain the observations of ion production in these systems, one must therefore invoke nonequilibrium or kinetic considerations. Historically, nearly all of the excited species known to exist in hydrocarbon flames have been considered as ionization precursors. Whenever these species failed to provide an adequate explanation, other species, whose existence in flames had only been postulated, were proposed.

The following discussion summarizes the most salient observations which, when considered collectively, have led to our present level of understanding of the nonequilibrium (chemi-)ionization processes which accompany hydrocarbon combustion.

A. Mechanism of Positive Ion Formation

It has been observed that the ion concentrations in uncontaminated hydrogen and carbon monoxide flames are $< 10^6$ cm^{-3}; in fact, the low level of ionization in H_2/air flames now provides the basis for hydrocarbon detection in gas chromatographic flame-ionization detectors (16,17). Hydrocarbon flames, on the other hand, exhibit ion concentrations as high as 10^{13} cm^{-3}. These and other observations (33) have led to the conclusion that the reaction(s) responsible for ion formation apparently involves some species containing both carbon and hydrogen. Moreover, all hydrocarbon combustion flames contain chemi-ions. Compared to the ionization in flames of paraffin hydrocarbon (alkanes) fuels, the concentrations of ions and electrons are higher in flames of unsaturated fuels and lower in flames of oxygenated fuels, such as acetone, alcohols, and esters. These observations have been made by a number of workers, most notably Bulewicz and Padley (18) and Sternberg (17). It has also been noted that the number of ions produced per nonoxygenated carbon atom is approximately constant. The numbers given in Ref. 17 lead to a value of 2.5×10^{-6} ions per carbon atom for small amounts of paraffin hydrocarbons in an H_2/air flame. The same value of about 10^{-6} ions (or electrons) per carbon atom or C_2H_2 molecule (the numbers are not as precise here as in the work on flame ionization detectors) has been reported by Hand and Kistiakowsky (34) in shock tube measurements of C_2H_2 oxidation. Peeters and Van Tiggelen (35) have found the ion yield in $CH_4/O_2/N_2$ flames to vary as a function of flame composition. The values obtained range from 1.3 to 3.6×10^{-6} ions per carbon atom with the maximum occurring at an equivalence ratio of 1.3 (equivalence ratio is defined as ϕ = actual fuel to oxidizer ratio/stoichiometric fuel to oxidizer ratio).

Plots of steady-state ion concentration or of ion production rate vs. number of carbon atoms in the fuel molecule yield straight lines of nearly unit slope. Figure 3 from the data of Sternberg et al. (17) shows two such plots. Analytical chemists have observed this to occur with such regularity that an "effective carbon number" is now frequently cited to indicate the particular response expected from a compound in a flame ionization detector; the presence of various functional groups in the molecule may be taken into account with the correction factors given in Table 1. A carbonyl carbon atom does not contribute to ionization; once the carbon-oxygen double bond is formed, the reactions leading to chemi-ionization cannot occur. In further support of this point, as noted previously, CO/O_2 flames do not produce chemi-ionization.

Since all the paraffins, including methane, produce the same number of chemi-ions per carbon atom, it has been reasoned that the ionization precursor is a species containing a single carbon atom and each carbon atom in the molecule participates in the ionization process to the same extent. Most investigators now agree that this species is CH.

The ion production rate varies linearly with the number of carbon atoms for a fixed number of molecules and is directly proportional to the concentration

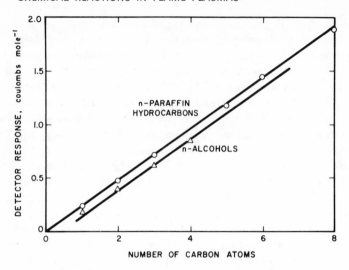

Figure 3 Gas chromatographic flame ionization detector response for paraffin hydrocarbons and alcohols (17).

TABLE 1
Contributions to effective carbon number[a]

Atom	Type	Effective carbon number contribution
C	Aliphatic[b]	1.0
C	Aromatic	1.0
C	Olefinic	0.95
C	Acetylenic	1.30
C	Carbonyl	0.0
C	Nitrile	0.3
O	Primary alcohol	−0.6
O	Secondary alcohol	−0.75
O	Tertiary alcohols, esters	−0.25
O	Ether	−1.0
Cl	Two or more on aliphatic C	−0.12 each
Cl	On olefinic C	0.05

[a]Source: Sternberg et al., Ref. 17.
[b]An aliphatic C atom produces 0.25 coulombs g-atom^{-1}.

of hydrocarbon. This proportionality has been found to exist (17) over a range of seven orders of magnitude for any given hydrocarbon added to H_2/air flames. At a constant mole fraction of fuel, the ion-mole fraction is also approximately a constant over a range of pressure from 10 to 760 torr (6). It has therefore been concluded that the ion-producing reaction is first order in hydrocarbon and second order overall. The other reaction partner in this bimolecular process must be oxygen or an oxygen-containing species; ionization maximizes in nearly stoichiometric flames and decreases in rich flames where hydrocarbon species maximize. Figure 4 shows results typical of those obtained by many experimenters who have determined ion or electron concentrations as a function of fuel-to-oxygen ratio. Bulewicz and Padley (18) have demonstrated that the oxygen-containing species participating in the elementary ionization reaction cannot be H_2O, OH, CO, CO_2, or O_2. They did this by diluting stoichiometric flames or various fuels with inert diluents, as well as with H_2 and O_2, and determining the effect on relative

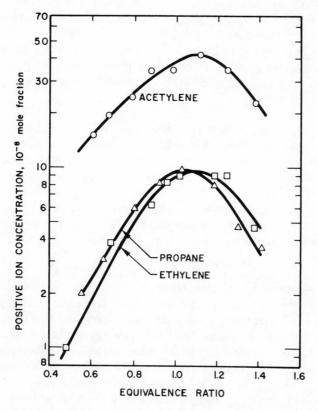

Figure 4   Effect of equivalence ratio on maximum ion concentration ($p = 35$ torr) (6).

electron concentrations. They confirmed (via a process of elimination) that the oxygen atom is the species responsible. Fontijn and coworkers (36,37) and Arrington et al. (38) provide more direct evidence for the dominant role of the oxygen atom in the ion-forming reaction. Both sets of investigators studied the reactions of hydrocarbons with O_2-free streams of oxygen atoms (usually in an inert gas) at low pressure. Large ion concentrations and/or ion-production rates were observed; addition of O_2 diminished the ion-production rate. Arrington et al. (38) found the ion production to be first order in both oxygen atoms and C_2H_2. The rates of ion formation inferred in all of these " atomic flame " studies are considerably higher than those in hot flames. In two of these studies (37,38), the authors report that at least one ion (some disagreement exists as to the exact number) is produced for each 10^3 C_2H_2 molecules consumed; this is to be compared to about 1 ion per 10^6 fuel molecules reported above for hot flames.

Since high temperature flames also contain appreciable concentrations of oxygen atoms, particularly in the flame front where atom and radical concentrations frequently overshoot their equilibrium values, the elementary ionization reaction in flames almost certainly involves this species. It has already been noted that the CH radical is considered the most likely fuel derivative participating in the reaction; therefore, the process most widely accepted as responsible for chemi-ionization in hydrocarbon combustion is

$$CH + O \longrightarrow CHO^+ + e \qquad [6]$$

The electronic state of the CH radical in this reaction has been the subject of considerable controversy. Excited CH is a well known species in hydrocarbon combustion systems; its spectrum has been extensively studied in both absorption and emission. The suggestion that one of the excited states might be involved in reaction [6] or other ionization reactions arose first from thermodynamic considerations and then from observations of apparent parallelisms between light emission and ion formation rates in shock tubes (39) and flames (40). It was also proposed (41) that the reaction

$$CH^* + C_2H_2 \longrightarrow C_3H_3^+ + e \qquad [7]$$

might be a source of chemi-ionization. Subsequently, however, when these hypotheses were tested more rigorously, they were found lacking by several investigators: Miller (29) found that in low-pressure H_2/O_2 flames, the emission from CH was second order (see Table 2) in added C_2H_4 or C_2H_2, whereas the ion concentration was first order; Bulewicz (42) has reported that CH emission is proportional to pressure to the 2–2.5 power over the pressure range of 30–93 torr, in which ion and electron concentrations are directly proportional to pressure; Arrington et al. (43), in an extension of their low-temperature flow tube studies of the $O-C_2H_2$ reaction, have reported a

TABLE 2

Dependence of observed concentrations on hydrocarbon additives in hydrogen/air or oxygen flames[a]

Additive	C_2H_2	C_2H_2	C_2H_4
Oxidizer	Air	Oxygen	Oxygen
Pressure, torr	760	4	4
	Order of dependence[b]		
Total ions	0.5	1.0	1.0
CH*	—	2.0	2.0
$C_2H_2^{c}$	—	—	1.0
H_3O^+	0.5	1.0	1.0
CHO^+	1.0	1.0	—
CH_3O^+	1.5	2.5	3.5
CH_5O^+	—	2.0	2.5
$C_3H_3^+$	2.0	2.0	3.5
$C_2H_3O^+$	—	1.0	1.5
$C_2H_5O^+$	—	—	2.0

[a]Source: Green and Sugden, Ref. 62, and Miller, Ref. 29.
[b]From slope log $[n_{max}]$ versus log [hydrocarbon added]. Uncertainty in slopes is ± 0.1.
[c]From small gas sampling probe experiments.

discrepancy between the rates of ion formation and CH chemiluminescence as well as an ion-formation rate too high to be supported by the measured concentrations of O atoms and excited radicals–CH, C_2, or OH. It is important to note that the aim of all of these studies was to ascertain the role of excited CH radicals in the *main* ion-producing reaction. If reaction [6] involving ground state CH is indeed reponsible for the bulk of chemi-ionization, it is probable that excited CH also makes a contribution.

Until recently, the heat of formation of CHO^+ and therefore also the thermochemistry of reaction [6] has been quite uncertain. The heat of formation of CHO^+ has recently been established as 204 $(+3, -12)$ kcal mole^{-1}. Thus reaction [6] involving ground state CH is nearly thermoneutral (≈ 2 kcal endothermic). For the convenience of the reader, this and other important thermochemical data used in this chapter are given in Table 3.

The apparent activation energy for reaction [6] should not be confused with the various determinations of global activation energies for the entire ionization process which have appeared in the literature. Several investigators have attempted to determine the temperature dependence of the ion-forming reactions (35,56,57) and have measured inferred "activation energies" ranging from 23 to 77 kcal. These measurements probably pertain to a series

TABLE 3
Thermochemical data

Species	ΔH_f, kcal mole^{-1}	References	Species	ΔH_f, kcal mole^{-1}	References
O	60	44	CNO$^+$	207	Estimate
CH	142	44	H$_3$O$^+$	141	50
NO	22	44	NH$_4$$^+$	152	51
HNO	24	44	CH$_3$O$^+$	212	52
NO(A$^2\Sigma^+$)	148	45	CH$_5$O$^+$	136	53
NH (A^3 II)	166	45	C$_2$H$_3$O$^+$	172	52
CN (B$^2\Sigma^+$)	185	45	C$_2$H$_5$O$^+$	202	52
CN (A^2 II)	137	45	C$_3$H$_3$$^+$	265	52
NCN (A^3 II$_u$)	188	46	O$^-$	26	44
O$_2$$^+$	279	52	O$_2$$^-$	-10	44
NO$^+$	235	44	OH$^-$	-33	44
HNO$^+$	200	Estimate	CN$^-$	37	54
CHO$^+$	204	49	C$_2$$^-$	107	55

of reactions which ultimately produce chemi-ionization and not to the elementary ion formation reaction.

Some recent work of Niki et al. (58), although not conducted in flames, is especially pertinent to the question of the identity of the primary ion: when C_3O_2 is reacted with H and O atoms in a low-temperature, low-pressure flow system, the *only* positive ion observed is CHO$^+$ and this only when H and O atoms are both present. Details of the experiments are consistent with ion formation via reaction [6]. Moreover, since the reaction proceeds rapidly at room temperature, there is apparently no significant activation energy involved.

Perhaps the most direct and convincing confirmation of the proposed mechanism would be the experimental measurement of [CH], [O], and total ion-concentration profiles in a variety of flames; the product [CH] [O] should be proportional to the rate of formation of CHO$^+$ at every point in the flames. Unfortunately, measurements of both [CH] and [O] are extremely difficult and have only recently been attempted. Spatially resolved profiles for ions, [CH] and [O], are available (59) only in two low-pressure hydrocarbon flames and the accuracy of this data has been questioned (60).

Thus, through the process of elimination (no alternative is consistent with the observations) and a series of inductive arguments (convincing collectively, but none stand alone), reaction [6] has come to be accepted as the reaction responsible for ionization in hydrocarbon combustion systems.

The mechanism for ion formation is thus generally well understood—this is not true of the rate at which it proceeds. Direct measurements of the ion-formation rate are complicated by the difficulty of measuring the volume within the flame in which the reaction occurs.

The reaction rate coefficient for reaction [6] has been variously estimated from 10^{-13} to 10^{-11} cm^3 sec^{-1}. The high value is a theoretical estimate based on absolute reaction rate theory for zero activation energy processes (61). A somewhat lower value has been estimated (62) from the reverse of the iso-electronic reaction

$$NO^+ + e \longrightarrow N + O \qquad [8]$$

The lower estimates (62–64) are from experimental observations in flames in which a steady state is assumed between rates of ion formation and rates of ion decay. The steady-state hypothesis is based on several unrealistic assumptions which tend to make values of k_6 thus derived, lower limits.

B. Positive Ion-Molecule Reactions

Instead of a simple ion spectrum consisting of one or two species, as might have been hoped for, mass spectrometric examination of hydrocarbon flames has revealed a wide variety of ions, the most important of which are shown in Fig. 5. The proposed "primary" ion, CHO$^+$, is present in the flame front as well as downstream, but its maximum concentration is quite low, reflecting its very rapid rate of reaction to produce other species.

Table 4 is a compilation of some of the positive ions observed in high

TABLE 4
Positive ions identified in hydrocarbon flames

		1-atm flames		Low-pressure flames
Mass	Identity	Ref. 41	Ref. 65	Ref. 40
15	CH_3^+	X	X	X
19	H_3O^+	X	X	X
26	$C_2H_2^+$	X	—	—
29	CHO^+	X	X	X
31	CH_3O^+	X	X	X
33	CH_5O^+	X	X	X
39	$C_3H_3^+$	X	X	X
43	$C_2H_3O^+$	X	X	X
45	$C_2H_5O^+$, CHO_2^+	X	X	X
47	$C_2H_7O^+$, $CH_3O_2^+$	X	X	—
49	$CH_5O_2^+$	X	X	X
53	C_3HO^+	X	—	X
61	$C_2H_5O_2^+$	X	—	—

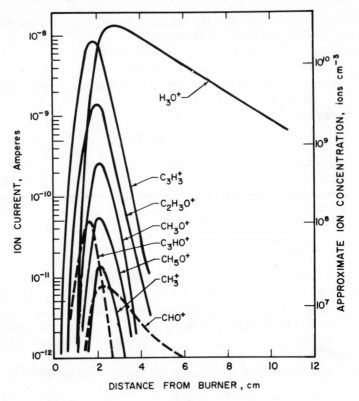

Figure 5   Positive ion profiles in an acetylene/oxygen flame (40). (Pressure = 2 torr, total flow = 70 cm³ (STP) sec⁻¹, equivalence ratio = 1.0, burner diam. = 15 cm.)

temperature combustion systems by various workers. In general, the work of Calcote et al. (40) is concerned with low-pressure (1 to 10 torr) hydrocarbon flames, that of Sugden et al. (41,62) with 1-atm $H_2/O_2/N_2$ flames containing small amounts of hydrocarbon, and that of Van Tiggelen et al. (65) with hydrocarbon flames at 40 torr. The ions present in greatest abundance in the reaction zones of combustion flames are $C_3H_3^+$, $C_2H_3O^+$, CH_3O^+, CH_5O^+, and $C_2H_5O^+$.

The reactions proposed for the formation of these ions are indicated in the diagram of Fig. 6. Many of the neutral reactants cited are known (66) to be present in cool flames, and CH_2O has been detected in high temperature combustion systems (4). The plausibility of several of the suggested reactions has been demonstrated (37) in low-temperature O atom/C_2H_2 experiments, in which the addition of the neutral organic species indicated caused an increase in the concentration of the corresponding protonated species (for example, addition of CH_2O gave rise to increased quantities of CH_3O^+). Subsequent to their formation via the various proton-transfer processes indicated in Fig. 6, the flame-front ions must react to produce H_3O^+; the decay curves in Fig. 5 are much too sharp to be accounted for by a diffusional loss mechanism or ion recombination. The parallelism of these curves and those taken in H_2/O_2 flames containing small amounts of hydrocarbons suggests the existence of rapidly shifting pseudo equilibria among a large number of neutral combustion intermediates and the flame-front ions. There are two routes to H_3O^+ consistent with this equilibrium hypothesis. One route is demonstrated in Fig. 6 in which a proton is transferred to H_2O from only two of the flame-front ions; the other ions disappear via rapid ion-molecule reactions which involve, as products, the species capable of producing H_3O^+ directly. In the other route, an oxidative ion-molecule reaction of one or more of the flame-front ions produces H_3O^+; the other ions disappear via ion-molecule reactions as before. The rate constant for the oxidative reaction producing H_3O^+ in such a scheme has been deduced (29) as 3×10^{-11} cm^3 sec^{-1}.

In either case, the very large rate constants associated with many of the ion-molecule reactions enable the ion concentrations to be in "equilibrium" with each other and with the neutral combustion intermediates, despite the fact that the latter species are themselves present at concentrations far above their equilibrium values. It is impossible to decide at present which mechanism prevails.

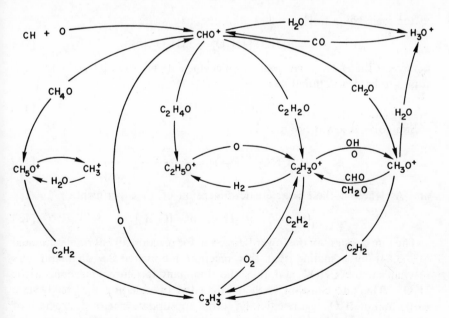

Figure 6   Representative ion-molecule reaction scheme in hydrocarbon flames.

The addition of small amounts of hydrocarbons to H_2/O_2 or $H_2/O_2/N_2$ flames provides a potentially effective technique for the study of ion-molecule reactions. Equilibrium composition calculations show that addition of up to $1\% \, C_2H_2$ to an H_2/O_2 flame at 5 torr changes the H atom concentration by less than 10%, and the concentrations of OH, O_2, O, and H_2O remain essentially constant. Experimental measurements (62) reveal similar constancy in 1-atm flames. Variations in individual ion concentrations or other observed quantities with hydrocarbon concentration may therefore be used to infer kinetic information concerning the specific ion formation mechanism. Green and Sugden (62) have conducted such a study in 1-atm flames and similar experiments have been done (29) in flames at 4 torr (see Table 2). In both studies, straight-line plots of $\log[n]$ vs. $\log$[hydrocarbon added] were obtained for a variety of ions and for CH emission. The concentration measurements are always made at the maximum concentration of the observable in question, and, in all cases, the deviations from multiples of $\frac{1}{2}$ were small. Since H_3O^+ is the dominant ion in all the flames studied, the dependence of total ion concentration on added hydrocarbon in each case is the same as that for H_3O^+, that is, at 1 atm $[H_3O^+] \cong [n_+] \propto [C_2H_2]_0^{1/2}$ and at reduced pressure $[H_3O^+] \cong [n_+] \propto [C_2H_2]_0$ or $[C_2H_4]_0$. The results are consistent with the overall mechanism set forth earlier, since, for example, assuming reaction

$$CHO^+ + H_2O \; \rightleftharpoons \; CO + H_3O^+ \qquad [9]$$

as the main route to H_3O^+ at 1 atm, one may write:

$$k_9[CHO^+]\,[H_2O] = \alpha\,[H_3O^+]^2 \qquad [10]$$

where α is the H_3O^+/e recombination coefficient and, since $[CHO^+]$ has been found to be proportional to $[C_2H_2]_0$,

$$[H_3O^+] \propto [C_2H_2]_0^{1/2} \qquad [11]$$

Similarly, at low pressures:

$$k_9[CHO^+][H_2O] = \frac{D_+}{\Lambda^2[H_3O^+]} \qquad [12]$$

and Λ^2 where is the characteristic dimension of the experiment.

$$[H_3O^+] \propto [C_2H_2]_0 \quad \text{or} \quad [C_2H_4]_0 \qquad [13]$$

The rate constant in the foward direction for reaction [9] has been estimated (33,63,64) by assuming that this reaction represents the dominant loss mechanism for CHO^+ and thus the dominant formation mechanism for H_3O^+. The rate constant is then calculated by equating the steady-state formation of H_3O^+ via reaction [9] to the appropriate rate of destruction of H_3O^+, that is, eq. [12] at low pressures and eq. [10] at high pressures. The ion data from Fig. 5, together with the equilibrium H_2O concentration $(7 \times 10^{14}$ cm$^{-3})$, gives a value of $k_9 = 8 \times 10^{-9}$ cm^3 sec^{-1}. Green and Sugden's data in an atmospheric-pressure flame (62) gives $k_9 = 4 \times 10^{-8}$ cm^3 sec^{-1}, in fair agreement with the measurements at low pressure. Green and Sugden estimated k_9, by a much less direct technique, to be 7×10^{-9} cm^3 sec^{-1}. Recent measurements (47) in the ion source of a medium-pressure mass spectrometer lead to a value of $k_9 = 3 \times 10^{-9}$ cm^3 sec^{-1}.

It should be noted, however, that the assumption that reaction [9] is the dominant path from CHO^+ to H_3O^+ neglects the fact that any one of the other ions observed may be capable of producing H_3O^+ directly.

The origin of $C_3H_3^+$ has been the subject of considerable discussion. As noted previously, it was proposed that this ion was the product of the primary ionization reaction [7]. However, since excited CH is not an important ionization precursor and $C_3H_3^+$ is nevertheless the predominant flame-front ion, ion-molecule reactions (Fig. 6) are responsible for its formation; for example,

$$CH_3O^+ + C_2H_2 \longrightarrow C_3H_3^+ + H_2O \qquad [14]$$

In further support of this contention, Niki et al. (58) found that the addition of C_2H_2 to the $C_3O_2/H/O$ system gave rise to $C_3H_3^+$ without increasing the overall level of ionization.

Slightly downstream of the visible reaction zone of a typical hydrocarbon flame, the only significant ionic species present are CHO^+ and H_3O^+. The process responsible for the formation of these ions can be represented by the proton exchange (33) of reaction [9]. Beyond the maximum in the H_3O^+ profile in Fig. 5, it may be seen that H_3O^+ and CHO^+ are present in an approximately constant concentration ratio; that is, reaction [9] has apparently reached equilibrium. The value of the equilibrium constant, K_9, may be determined from the ratio $[H_3O^+]/[CHO^+]$ and calculated equilibrium values for [CO] and $[H_2O]$. In Fig. 5, $[H_3O^+]/[CHO^+] = 3 \times 10^3$ and $[CO]/[H_2O] = 4$; thus $k_9 = 1.9 \times 10^4$, and the free energy change for the reaction is -40 kcal mole^{-1}. At a flame temperature of 2200°K, the corresponding free energy change based on JANAF (44) thermochemical data (corrected for the recent adjustments in the heat of formation of CHO^+) is ≈ -35 kcal mole^{-1}.

C. Negative Ion Chemistry

The bulk of the negative charge in hydrocarbon combustion flames is carried by the electron. Negative ion concentrations have been estimated to vary from $[n_-] \cong [n_+]$ to $[n_-] \cong 10^{-3} [n_+]$. The negative ions which have been identified in hydrocarbon flames are summarized in Table 5.

In hydrocarbon flames at 1 atm, negative ions are most abundant in the flame front and the total maximum negative-ion concentration has been reported

TABLE 5
Negative ions identified in hydrocarbon flames

		Acetylene Flames			Methane stoic.	Neopentane stoic.
	Identity	Stoic. O_2 Ref. 40	Stoic. $O_2/70\%$ N_2 Ref. 31	2.8% in H_2/O_2 Ref. 69	O_2/N_2 Ref. 31	O_2/N_2 Ref. 31
Pressure, torr		1	760	760	760	760
Mass						
12	C^-	X	—	—	—	—
15	CH_3^-	—	X	—	X	—
16	O^-	X	X	—	X	X
17	OH^-	X	X	X	X	X
24	C_2^-	X	X	X	—	—
25	C_2H^-	—	X	X	—	X
26	CN^-	—	X	—	—	X
32	O_2^-	X	X	X	X	X
36	C_3^-	X	—	X	—	—
41	C_2HO^-	—	X	—	—	—
42	$C_2H_2O^-$	—	X	—	—	X
43	$C_2H_3O^-$	—	X	—	X	X
45	CHO_2^-	—	—	X	—	—
46	$CH_2O_2^-$	—	X	—	X	X
47	$CH_3O_2^-$	—	X	—	—	X

to approach that of the positive ions (31,67). The electron attachment process in hydrocarbon flames thus occurs in the flame front and, as discussed next, involves some nonequilibrium species. Figure 7a shows the overall positive and negative ion profiles in a C_2H_2/O_2 flame at 1 atm; Fig. 7b is for a $H_2/O_2/N_2$ flame containing a small amount of KCl to produce ions. The attachment mechanisms in these two flames are quite different. The high negative-ion concentrations attained in the hydrocarbon flame front decay to their equilibrium value downstream, whereas in the $H_2/O_2/N_2$ flame, electron attachment is slow and in the early stages of the flame, the negative-ion concentrations are far below equilibrium.

Three-body attachment reactions such as

$$OH + e + M \longrightarrow OH^- + M \qquad [15]$$

$$O_2 + e + M \longrightarrow O_2^- + M \qquad [16]$$

have been suggested (69) as an explanation for the observations in both cases, but, although they seem to account fairly well for the OH^- formation in

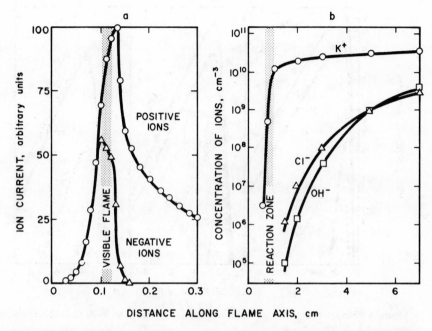

Figure 7 Comparative negative ion profiles in hydrocarbon and K-seeded hydrogen flames at 1 atm. (Note linear and logarithmic scales.) (a) C_2H_2/O_2 Flame (67); (b) $H_2/O_2/N_2/KCl$ (4:1:4:10^{-7}) Flame (68).

Fig. 7b, they cannot be responsible in both flames. Although there are considerable differences in the concentrations of these species in the two flames cited, these differences are far too small to account for the large differences in observed attachment rates. Similarly, the dissociative attachment

$$e + H_2O \longrightarrow OH^- + H \qquad [17]$$

can be demonstrated to be far too slow to account for the results in either flame (63).

Consistent with these observations are those of Green (69), who found that the maximum negative-ion concentration in 1-atm $H_2/O_2/N_2$ flames containing 2.8 % C_2H_2 is obtained in or near the flame front. The ion concentration in his system was somewhat lower than in flames burning hydrocarbon fuel only. Green reports a maximum $[n_-] \cong 10^{-2} [n_+]$. Low-pressure flames also contain negative ions (40) to the extent of about $10^{-2} [n_+]$. The profiles of the most important ions in several stoichiometric hydrocarbon/oxygen flames at 2.5 torr are given in Fig. 8. The dominant ions in each case are O^- and OH^-. Total negative ion concentrations reach their maxima very near

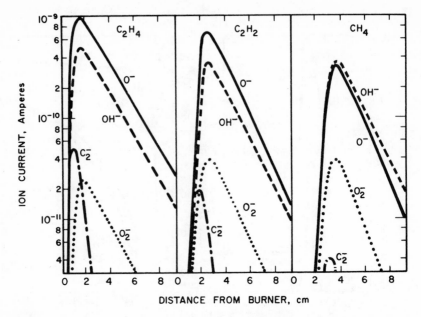

Figure 8 Negative ion profiles in low pressure stoichiometric hydrocarbon/oxygen flames ($p = 2.5$ torr).

the visible reaction zone. The ion C_2^- is present only in the flame front; downstream O^-, OH^-, and O_2^- predominate. As is the case with positive ions downstream of the flame front, equilibrium is apparently established among the negative ions. The reactions dominating the negative ion equilibria may be considered to be those paralleling the H/O neutral species equilibria,

$$H + O_2^- \rightleftharpoons OH + O^- \qquad \Delta H = -7 \text{ kcal} \qquad [18]$$

$$O^- + H_2 \rightleftharpoons OH^- + H \qquad \Delta H = -5 \text{ kcal.} \qquad [19]$$

These ion-molecule reactions are exothermic in the forward direction and, by analogy to other exothermic ion-molecule reactions, can be expected to be very rapid, with rate constants on the order of 10^{-9} cm^3 sec^{-1}. The equilibrium constants for reaction [18], in the temperature range 2000–2500°K, lie between 27 and 42; those for reaction [19] between 3 and 5. Thus, even the rate constants for the reverse reactions will be $> 10^{-11}$ cm^3 sec^{-1}. Comparison of these rate coefficients with those for neutral species (H, O, H$_2$, O$_2$, and OH) reactions reveals that even the slowest ion-molecule processes involved are much faster than those governing neutral species concentrations. The ions, then, are in equilibrium with the neutral species, whether the overall equilibria are established or not. A detailed examination of the negative-ion content downstream of the flame front should be an accurate indication of neutral free radical concentrations.

For example, the [OH]/[H] ratios in the flames of Fig. 8 may be calculated from observed negative ion ratios and the equilibrium constants for reaction [18] at the appropriate flame temperatures

$$\frac{[OH]}{[H]} = \frac{K_{eq}[O_2^-]}{[O^-]} \qquad [20]$$

Similarly, the observed ratio of $[OH^-]/[O^-]$ together with the equilibrium constants for reaction [19] will give $[H]/[H_2]$. The results of these calculations for the flames of Fig. 8 are given in Table 6. Comparison of the concentration

TABLE 6
Equilibrium and negative-ion inferred [H] and [OH] in low-pressure flames[a]

Flame	T, °K	Observed ion ratio		$[H]/[H_2]$		$[OH]/[H]$	
		$[OH^-]/[O^-]$	$[O^-]/[O_2^-]$	Exp.	Equil.	Exp.	Equil.
C_2H_2/O_2	2500	0.5	43	8.8	1.83	0.64	0.69
C_2H_4/O_2	2300	0.7	22	5.4	0.72	1.5	1.5
CH_4/O_2	2000	0.2	11	2.2	0.25	4.1	3.6

[a]Pressure = 2.5 torr

ratios thus derived from the experimental data with those calculated assuming complete equilibrium reveals that, although the [OH]/[H] ratios appear to be well equilibrated, the [H] in every case is appreciably above equilibrium. Thus, in these low-pressure flames, H and OH both appear to be present at concentrations above equilibrium to about the same extent—a factor of from 5 to 10. Moreover, the degree of neutral species disequilibrium is greater in the low-temperature flames.

At present, the most perplexing negative-ion problem concerns the identification of the reaction producing the initial negative ion in hydrocarbon flames. From the evidence already given, the three-body reactions, [15] and [16], cannot be important in hydrocarbon flames at 1 atm; they must be even less important then at low pressures. Because of the observations in the flame front of C_2^- at low pressures (40) and C_2H^- at high pressures (31), dissociative attachment reactions producing these species have been sought. The most likely mechanism proposed (40) to date is:

$$C_2H_2 + O \longrightarrow C_2H_2O^* \qquad [21]$$

$$C_2H_2O^* + e \longrightarrow C_2^- + H_2O \qquad [22]$$

Thermodynamic considerations for this mechanism require that much of the energy of reaction [21] be retained in the product until collision with an electron. Analogous reactions may be written (64) involving the ketyl radical (C_2HO). The exothermic reaction

$$C_2^- + H + M \rightleftharpoons C_2H^- + M \qquad [23]$$

would then account for C_2H^-.

Direct three-body attachment to C_2,

$$C_2 + e + M \longrightarrow C_2^- + M \qquad [24]$$

has also been proposed (63), but the rate constant for such processes are generally not large enough to account for the observations at low pressures.

Either of these proposals is supported by the observations that: (1) Fuel-rich flames contain more negative ions than lean flames and CH, CH_2, and CO, (the precursors of C_2H_2O or CH_2O) are expected to be more abundant in fuel-rich systems. (2) Electron attachment does not occur upstream of the flame front where fuel molecules would attach were they responsible. There-fore, the participation of some reaction intermediate is indicated. (3) The ion profile of C_2^- exhibits a very rapid decay and it must have a correspond-ingly rapid rate of formation in the flame front in order to attain the high concentration observed. Whether C_2HO or C_2H_2O is involved or not, the evidence nevertheless strongly indicates that C_2H^- or C_2^- is the first ion formed.

Since the profiles for C_2^- and C_2H^- in flames at low pressure and 1 atm, respectively, both exhibit rapid decay, it appears that these ions undergo ion-molecule reactions resulting in the OH^-, O^-, and O_2^- ions observed downstream. The reactions responsible are probably analogous to those which participate in the oxygenation of neutral C_n species. For example:

$$C_2^- + O_2 \longrightarrow C_2O + O^- \qquad [25]$$

$$C_2^- + H_2O \longrightarrow C_2H + OH^- \qquad [26]$$

$$C_2H^- + O_2 \longrightarrow C_2O + OH^- \qquad [27]$$

These reactions produce O^- and/or OH^- directly; since all of the downstream ions appear to undergo rapid reactions producing pseudo equilibrium, the formation of any one of them from C_2^- or C_2H^- is sufficient to account for the observation of all three.

D. Ion Decay Processes

Ions produced in the flame-front decay downstream of the flame by two processes: recombination and diffusion. At high pressures (near 1 atm), recombination dominates and at low pressures (less than about 30 torr), diffusion dominates. The relative importance of the two processes depends upon the dimensions of the flame. When the rate of ion decay in the direction of flow is great, it is also necessary to include diffusion in the direction of flow to accurately account for ion decay behind the combustion zone (6). When only a single ion is involved—the usual situation because of ion-molecule charge transfer reactions—the decay of ion concentration is defined by the equation

$$D_a \nabla^2[n_+] - v \frac{dn_+}{dx} - \alpha[n_+]^2 + q = 0 \qquad [28]$$

where D_a = ambipolar diffusion coefficient
v = linear flow velocity
α = ion recombination coefficient
q = rate of ion formation
x = distance along a flow line

Simplified forms of this equation have been used to determine ion recombination coefficients and diffusion coefficients in flames (see Refs. 6, 25, and 40). The very simple process of plotting $1/n_+$ versus t (obtained from the flow velocity) is often used to compute α from the slope.

Table 7 summarizes a rather large number of measurements of the

TABLE 7
Natural flame ion recombination[a] $H_3O^+ + e \rightarrow$ products

Flame[b]		Pressure, torr	Temperature, °K	Recombination Coefficient, 10^{-7} cm^3 sec^{-1}	References
Propane/air,	0.86	33–760	~2000	2.2 ± 0.4	70
	0.88	66	2090	2.4	6
		33	2080	1.6	6
	0.93	40	1740–2130	2.4	40
	1.0	200–1500	—	2.2 ± 1	71
	1.2	55	—	2.9	72
Methane/air,	0.51	760	1500	1.1	73
	1.1	66	—	2.5	72
Methane/oxygen/nitrogen 2% CH$_4$/85.5% CO/1%		760	—	1.9	35
H$_2$/11.5% O$_2$		76	1630	1.3	74
Acetylene/air, 0.94		—	—	1.2	75
	1.2	20	—	2.8	72
Hydrogen/air/1% acetylene		760	2300	2.2 ± 1	62
			Average	2.1	

[a]Measurements in all cases made with electrostatic probes except Ref. 62 (mass spectrometer) and Ref. 35 (total ion collection in strong electric fields).
[b]The number is the equivalence ratio.

recombination coefficient in various hydrocarbon flames, at various equivalence ratios, pressures, and temperatures and by various experimental techniques. The agreement is astounding in view of the manner in which most of the data was collected and interpreted. From the mass spectrometer observations that H_3O^+ is the dominant ion downstream of the flame front, the independence of the measured recombination coefficient on pressure, and its absolute magnitude, it is concluded that the dissociative recombination

$$H_3O^+ + e \quad \longrightarrow \quad \text{products} \qquad [29]$$

is being observed. Similar values for this reaction rate have been obtained in shock tubes (76). The use of flames to measure ion-recombination coefficients at high temperatures and over a broad temperature and pressure range represents a fruitful area of research. For this purpose, positive and negative ions other than the naturally occurring ions may be made to dominate through the use of additives.

There have been several attempts to ascertain the temperature dependence of ion/electron recombination coefficients in flames. Calcote et al. (40) found $\alpha(H_3O^+)$ to be temperature-independent over the range 1740–2130°K. King (77) has reported that $\alpha(H_3O^+)$ increases slightly with temperature, but the increase amounts to only 30% in flames between 1620 and 2010°K; thus, it could be called temperature-independent in this case as well, particularly in view of the uncertainties in the data in Table 7 even at constant temperature. At present, then, there is simply not sufficient data available to conclusively assign a temperature dependence to reaction [29], but for most practical purposes one may assume $\alpha(H_3O^+) = 2 \times 10^{-7}$ cm^3 sec^{-1} over the range 1600–2300°K.

At higher temperatures, $\alpha(H_3O^+)$ appears to adhere to $T^{-3/2}$ to T^{-2} dependence; Wilson and Evans (76) measured electron disappearance rates in shock tube studies of oxygen/hydrocarbon mixtures over a temperature range of 2500–5500°K. The values of α at the temperature extremes are given as $1.8 \pm 0.5 \times 10^{-7}$ and 4×10^{-8} cm^3 sec^{-1} at 2500 and 5500°K, respectively.

At low pressures where diffusion out of the flame is the dominant decay mechanism, the diffusive loss of positive ions may be represented (70) by

$$\frac{d[n_+]}{dt} = \frac{D_a}{\Lambda^2} [n_+] \qquad [30]$$

where Λ^2 is the "characteristic dimension" of the experiment. The cylindrical approximation

$$\left(\frac{1}{\Lambda^2}\right) = \left(\frac{\pi}{h}\right)^2 + \left(\frac{2.4}{R}\right)^2 \qquad [31]$$

has been used for flat flames (71); R is the radius and h the height of the flame. The ambipolar diffusion coefficient for H_3O^+ has been estimated with this equation (40) at 2000°K and 40 torr to be 27 cm^2 sec^{-1}. Assuming $D_a \propto T^{3/2} p^{-1}$, this would give 60 cm^2 sec^{-1} at 298°K and 1 torr.

IV. IONIZATION IN NONHYDROCARBON FLAMES

The level of ionization in nonhydrocarbon flames is generally very low; at 1 atm, there are less than 10^6 ions cm^{-3} in CO, H_2, CS_2, H_2S, CH_2O, or C_2F_4 flames in air or oxygen (78–80). Ionization is occasionally observed in these flames due to trace concentrations of hydrocarbon or minute concentrations of alkali metals. Impurities can be very important because the ion mole fractions may be as low as 10^{-12}. Thus, the concentration of sodium typically present (81) in the atmosphere at 1×10^{11} cm^{-3} becomes significant.

Ammonia/oxygen flames have been reported (79) to contain about 10^9 ions cm^{-3} at 1 atm and ammonia/nitric oxide flames about 10^7 ions cm^{-3} at 1 atm. DeJaegere, Deckers, and Van Tiggelen (65) have confirmed the small concentration of ions in NH_3/O_2 flames and have identified the principal ions as NO$^+$ (dominant) and NH$_4^+$. The ion NO$^+$ has also been observed in H_2/N_2O flames (80).

The following reactions might be expected to be important in ammonia flames:

$$NH\,(^3\Pi) + O \longrightarrow HNO^+ + e \qquad \Delta H \approx -26 \text{ kcal mole}^{-1}$$

$$HNO^+ + OH \longrightarrow NO^+ + H_2O \qquad \Delta H \approx -22 \text{ kcal mole}^{-1}$$

$$HNO^+ + NH_3 \longrightarrow NH_4^+ + NO \qquad \Delta H \approx -15 \text{ kcal mole}^{-1}$$

Cyanogen/oxygen flames produce the highest temperatures obtainable in laboratory flames, 4800°K at 1 atm, Fig. 9 (see Thomas et al. (85) for flame temperature measurements, and Schexnayder (82) for adiabatic flame temperature and equilibrium concentration calculations, including ions). The maximum temperatures of hydrocarbon and hydrogen flames are ≈ 3400 and 3100°K, respectively. Maximum equilibrium adiabatic electron concentrations in cyanogen/oxygen flames vary from 1.6×10^{11} cm^{-3} at 0.01 atm to 4×10^{14} cm^{-3} at 100 atm (82). In hydrocarbon flames, on the other hand, "equilibrium" ionization is negligible compared to chemi-ionization. The high temperature and wide range of equilibrium ion concentrations make the cyanogen flame a useful tool for studying high-temperature chemical reactions. Such studies cannot be made, however, until the mechanism of ion formation in cyanogen flames is understood. The limited amount of work done on ionization in cyanogen flames is no doubt due in large measure to the high cost of the gas and its toxicity.

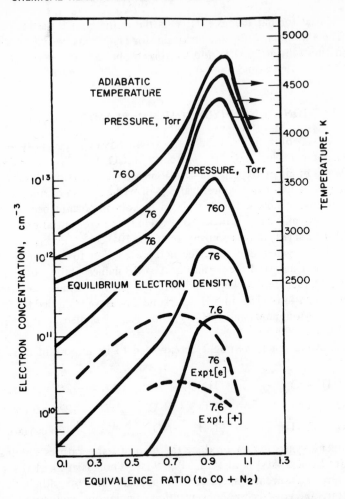

Figure 9   Flame temperature and electron concentration for cyanogen/oxygen flames. Adiabatic values (82), experimental electron concentration at 76 torr (84), and experimental positive ion concentration at 7.6 torr for a 25 cm diameter flat flame (83).

Bulewicz and Padley (84) measured electron concentrations in cyanogen/ oxygen flames by the cyclotron resonance method from 50 to 200 torr on a burner of only 1.0–1.5 cm diameter. In such an intensely luminous flame, radiation losses are often significant and the flame temperature was probably considerably less than adiabatic. Because the flame temperatures and ionization potentials are high, heat losses have a strong effect on the equilibrium electron concentration; for example, at $\phi = 1.0$ and p = 76 torr, $T_b = 4560°\mathrm{K}$ and $n_e = 1.3 \times 10^{12}$ cm^{-3}; if the temperature were reduced to 3600°K by radiation losses, the equilibrium electron concentration would be only 8.4×10^9 cm^{-3}.

The experimental results have been interpreted (84) as indicating nonequilibrium ionization, although the measured concentrations are either close to adiabatic equilibrium values or are smaller by a factor of almost 10 (see Fig. 9). Bulewicz and Padley (84,86) summarized their observations as follows: (1) The electron concentration varies as the pressure squared. (2) The emission intensities of CN, NCN, and NO (for all flame compositions and for dilution with N_2 or Ar) also vary as p^2. (3) The electron concentration reaches a maximum in lean flames but the emission intensities of CN, NCN, and NO all peak in rich flames. (4) Dilution with the same amount of Ar or N_2 reduces the electron concentration to the same extent. (5) The decay of log [e] with distance (time) above the flame is linear.

It is premature to derive a mechanism for ionization in these flames, but a discussion of the possibilities is instructive. The pressure dependence of [e] led Bulewicz and Padley to conclude that the mechanism of ionization is due to a termolecular reaction. However, while they obtain a very smooth straight line of [e] versus p^2, the pressure was varied by a factor of only 4. Moreover, no account was taken of diffusion effects nor of flame temperature changes with pressure. Further work is required to accurately determine the pressure dependence of ionization in these flames.

The linear decay of log [e] with distance above the flame zone is consistent with a loss mechanism dominated by diffusion. Equilibrium electron attachment would not be expected to be important at such a high temperature, although the CN radical has a high electron affinity, 3.2 eV.

Mass spectrometric examination of a cyanogen flame reveals (80) the dominant ion to be NO^+, with smaller concentrations of N^+, CO^+, C^+, and CN^+. When NO (6%) was added to a CO/O_2 flame no ions were detected; the addition of 3% cyanogen produced an abundance of NO^+ ions.

The termolecular reactions suggested (84) for the production of NO^+ are:

$$CN + O + O \longrightarrow CO + NO^+ + e \qquad \Delta H = -6 \text{ kcal mole}^{-1}$$

$$NO + N + N \longrightarrow N_2 + NO^+ + e \qquad \Delta H = -12 \text{ kcal mole}^{-1}$$

$$NO + C + O \longrightarrow CO + NO^+ + e \qquad \Delta H = -42 \text{ kcal mole}^{-1}$$

Similar termolecular reactions were also suggested (86) for excitation of CN and NO. It seems far more probable that, because a fast reaction is required at low pressures, a bimolecular reaction is involved.

The simple bimolecular reaction

$$N + O \longrightarrow NO^+ + e \qquad \qquad [32]$$

is endothermic by 62 kcal mole^{-1}. At the high equilibrium concentrations of

N and O atoms in the flame (stoichiometric at 7.6 torr, $T = 4370°K$), 6×10^{14} and 2×10^{14}, respectively, this reaction would be sufficiently fast if the pre-exponential factor for the rate constant were only 10^{-13} cm^3 sec^{-1}. This compares favorably with 3×10^{-12} cm^3 sec^{-1} derived from shock tube experiments (87,88). Thus, even at temperatures lower than the adiabatic flame temperature, reaction [32] as well as several others with similarly large activation energies could be significant in producing ions.

The reaction

$$\text{CN } (B^2\Sigma^+) + \text{O} \longrightarrow \text{CNO}^+ + e \qquad [33]$$

would be expected to be nearly thermoneutral and might thus play a role. Because of the large concentrations of excited species in the cyanogen flame (86), reactions of excited species such as

$$\text{NCN*} + \text{O} \longrightarrow \text{NO}^+ + \text{CN}^- \qquad \Delta H \approx +24 \text{ kcal mole}^{-1}$$
$$\text{NO*} + \text{CN*} \longrightarrow \text{NO}^+ + \text{CN}^- \qquad \Delta H \approx -61 \text{ for CN } (B^2\Sigma)$$
$$+13 \text{ for CN}(A^2\Pi)$$

may also be important. Thus, there appears to be no difficulty in accounting for adiabatic equilibrium ionization levels in high-temperature cyanogen flames, in contrast to hydrocarbon flames where the ionization level is far greater than anticipated by equilibrium.

The cyanogen flame seems to be an example in which chemi-ionization is the path by which equilibrium or thermal ionization is attained.

V. ADDITIVES

The addition of small concentrations of a substance into a flame in quantities such that the gross flame properties (temperature, burning velocity, and concentration of major constituents) are not changed, enables one to study thermodynamics and chemical kinetics at relatively high temperatures. The special case of the addition of hydrocarbons to hydrogen/air flames has already been discussed in Section III. In this section, we will review some of the work on alkali and alkaline earth metal addition to flames and briefly indicate some work which has been done with other additives. Alkali and alkaline earth ionization have received much attention because of their importance in flame spectroscopic analytical procedures, the augmentation of flame ionization for MHD applications and their significance in exhaust plume ionization in rocket communications problems. Other additive work has been motivated by the hope of reducing the level of ionization in rocket exhaust plumes and by the wish to clarify an apparent correlation between additives which inhibit combustion and reduce the extent of flame ionization.

A. Alkali Metals

When small concentrations of alkali metal are added to non-ionized flames of carbon monoxide or hydrogen, electrons are produced by collisional reactions of the type

$$A + M \rightleftharpoons A^+ + e + M \qquad [34]$$

where A is the metal atom, A^+ the ion and M any molecule in the system. At high flame temperatures, M can contain large amounts of internal energy (vibration and rotation) which may become available for ionization. The possible importance of this sort of energy exchange is indicated by the observation that replacing nitrogen in a CO/O_2 flame by argon (at the same temperature) reduced the rate of ionization significantly (89). The cross-sections for ionization observed by Hollander, Kalff, and Alkemade (89) for Na, K, and Cs in $CO/O_2/N_2$ flames and by Jensen and Padley (90) for alkali metals in $H_2/O_2/N_2$ flames at 2400°K are very large (22,90):

$$
\begin{array}{ll}
\text{Li} & 7 \times 10^{-12} \text{ cm}^2 \\
\text{Na} & 9 \\
\text{K} & 8 \\
\text{Rb} & 7 \\
\text{Cs} & 11 \\
\end{array}
$$

These very high cross-sections have been interpreted as indicating the participation of excited electronic states of alkali-metal atoms in the overall ionization process (22,89,91).

Hollander (91) and Hollander, Kalff, and Alkemade (89) photometrically (emission) determined the variation of atomic metal content with height (equivalent to time) in a carbon monoxide flame and compared the results with the calculated equilibrium (Saha's equation) concentration, based on the measured variation of temperature above the flame. The difference between the concentration of alkali metal added and that observed represented the alkali-metal ion concentration, because alkali-metal compound formation was negligible. The results reported in Fig. 10 were thus obtained. The fact that the measured ion concentration lags behind the equilibrium concentration indicates that, under the experimental conditions, the ionization reactions are slow with respect to the time scale of the experiment. The rate of the forward reaction [34], was thus measured as a function of temperature and the activation energy for ionization was found to be equal to the ionization potential of the alkali metal, within 5%. Jensen and Padley (22,90) obtained similar results in $H_2/O_2/N_2$ flames.

Recombination coefficients for the three-body recombination of alkali-metal ions (and, for comparison, for several other metal ions) and electrons—

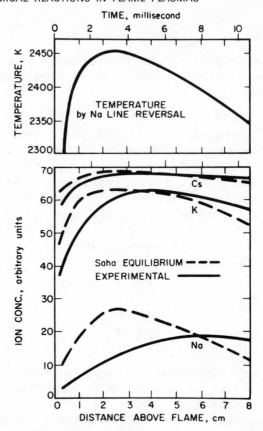

Figure 10 Alkali metal ionization in $CO/O_2/N_2$ flame at 1 atm (89,91).

TABLE 8
Recombination coefficients[a] for metal ions in flames

Flame	Temperature °K	$A^+ + e \xrightarrow{M} A$ 10^{-9} cm^3 molecule sec^{-1}								References
		Li	Na	K	Rb	Cs	Cr	Mn	Pb	
Propane/air	1970	9	3	0.4	0.3	0.2	—	—	—	77
$CO/O_2/N_2$	2400	—	9	3	—	0.7	—	—	—	89
$H_2/O_2/N_2$	2530	—	4	3	—	—	—	—	—	93
	2400	6	—	—	—	—	—	—	—	92
	2370	15	—	—	—	—	20	25	9	94
	2270	—	6	4	—	5	—	—	6	95
	2250	9	9	7	6	9	25	8	7	22

[a]As a second order reaction.

the reverse of reaction [34]—are summarized in Table 8. The various investigators used completely different flames and several different techniques to obtain these values.

When alkali metals are added to hydrocarbon flames or flames containing hydrocarbons, the ion concentration may be observed to exceed both the equilibrium alkali metal ion concentration and the concentration of ions produced by chemi-ionization (see Fig. 11). The enhanced ionization is due to the rapidity of the dissociative charge transfer reaction:

$$H_3O^+ + A \longrightarrow A^+ + H_2O + H \qquad [35]$$

coupled with a decreased rate of ion recombination for metals compared with that for the molecular ion, H_3O^+, normally present (see Tables 7 and 8).

From a plot of log $[H_3O^+]$ against time downstream of the reaction zone (a straight line), Hayhurst and Sugden (68) derive a reaction rate coefficient for reaction [35], when A is sodium, of 1.1×10^{-8} cm^3 sec^{-1} at 2000°K.

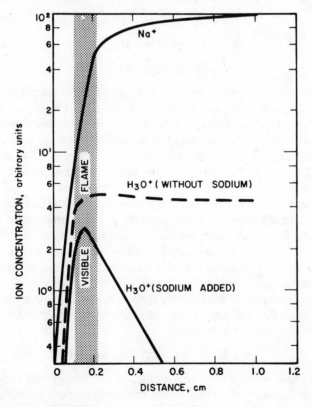

Figure 11 Effect of sodium addition to H_2/O_2 flame containing trace concentrations of hydrocarbon, $T = 2000°K$ (68).

Van Tiggelen and DeJaegere (96) deduce a reaction rate coefficient for charge transfer from H_3O^+ to potassium of 5×10^{-8} cm^3 sec^{-1} at 2500°K.

The continuous increase in $[Na^+]$ well downstream of the visible zone (refer again to Fig. 11), is probably due to reaction [34], that is, the alkalimetal ionization continues slowly until equilibrium is reached. Because these flames were so small (2 mm burner diameter) one must be cautious in interpreting the data quantitatively.

The presence of halogen atoms may also cause the alkali metal ion concentration to attain a value in excess of thermodynamic equilibrium (97,98). The halogen atom acts as a catalyst in promoting the steady state:

$$A + 2H \rightleftharpoons A^+ + e + H_2 \qquad [36]$$

A^+ exceeds the Saha equilibrium concentration because the slow rate of three-body atom recombination permits above-equilibrium concentrations of atomic hydrogen to persist downstream from the flame front. The mechanism is accounted for by the three reactions:

$$A + X \rightleftharpoons A^+ + X^- \qquad [37]$$

$$X^- + H \rightleftharpoons HX + e \qquad [38]$$

$$HX + H \rightleftharpoons H_2 + X \qquad [39]$$

The sum of these reactions gives reaction [36]. Typical results obtained by Hayhurst and Sugden (97) are shown in Fig. 12. In this work, an $H_2/O_2/N_2$ flame with 0.8 % C_2H_2 (added to increase the rate of alkali-metal ion equilibration when no halogen was present) was burned on a Meker burner with an outer shield flame; the electron concentration was measured with a microwave resonant cavity. The concentrations of free electrons with and without bromine present are given as $[e]_{Br}$ and $[e]$, respectively. Of course, large halogen concentrations decrease the electron concentration by electron attachment and alkali-metal halide formation. From analysis of the data, Hayhurst and Sugden deduced the recombination coefficients for the reverse of reaction [37]; these are presented in Table 9. Cesium did not show a maximum with any of the halogens and the ionization of lithium was too small to determine because of hydroxide formation.

Recent experiments by Jensen (99) further demonstrate the use of flame ionization to study high temperature chemistry—in this example, chemical equilibrium involved alkali metaborates:

$$A + HBO_2 \rightleftharpoons ABO_2 + H \qquad [40]$$

Because of the complexity of the system, several independent experimental techniques were used: microwave cavity resonance to determine the electron concentration; electrostatic probes to determine the total positive ion con-

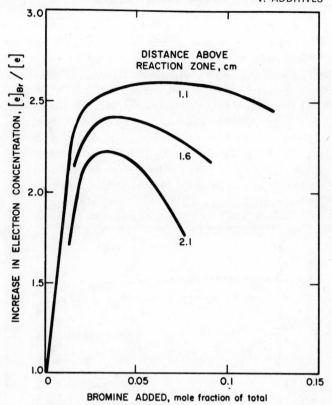

Figure 12 Enhancement of alkali metal ionization by bromine $H_2/O_2/N_2$ flame containing $4 \times 10^{-5}\%$ sodium at $2000°K$ (97).

TABLE 9
Recombination coefficients for alkali metal ions and halogen ions at $1800°K^a$

| | $A^+ + X^- \rightarrow A + X$ | |
| | 10^{-10} cm^3 sec^{-1} | |
Halogen, X^-	Na$^+$	K$^+$
Cl	6.0	1.6
Br	3.5	2.3
I	4.0	2.5

^{a}Source: Hayhurst and Sugden, Ref. 97.

centration; mass spectrometry to identify the specific ions involved; and absorption and emission spectroscopy to determine the alkali-metal atom concentrations. Boron was added to atmospheric pressure fuel-rich $H_2/N_2/O_2$ flames seeded with the alkali metal to be studied. A Meker burner flame shielded from entrained air by a concentric annular flame of the same composition and linear flow rate was employed. A typical experimental result is shown in Fig. 13. A self-consistent interpretation of the results is given in terms of reaction [40]. The enthalpy changes and equilibrium constants deduced are reported in Table 10. Note that, in this example, measurements of ionization were used to obtain information on neutral species. Attachment of electrons was also observed in these experiments (see Fig. 13), which provided (99) the equilibrium constant for the reaction

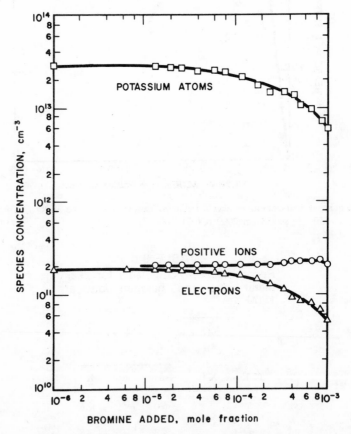

Figure 13   Effect of boron on alkali metal ionization. Measurements made 2.5 cm above reaction zone of a fuel-rich $H_2/O_2/N_2$ flame at 1 atm containing small concentrations of potassium atoms, $T = 2055°K$ (99).

TABLE 10
Enthalpy and equilibrium constants for metaborates derived
from ionization measurements[a]

$A + HBO_2 \rightleftharpoons ABO_2 + H$		
Alkali metal, A	ΔH_0^0, kcal mole^{-1}	Equilibrium constant, K
Li	-5 ± 5	$15 \exp \left(\dfrac{+2300}{T} \right)$
Na	$+5 \pm 5$	$12 \exp \left(\dfrac{-3000}{T} \right)$
K	$+2 \pm 5$	$37 \exp \left(\dfrac{-2500}{T} \right)$

[a]Source: Jensen, Ref. 99.

$$HBO_2 + e \;\rightleftharpoons\; BO_2^- + H \qquad [41]$$

$K = 1.5 \times 10^3 \exp(-10,000/T)$ and the electron affinity for BO_2, $EA = 93 \pm 5$ kcal mole^{-1}.

B. Alkaline Earth Metals

Flames containing alkaline earth metals have been studied much less extensively than flames containing alkali metals. The ionization potentials of the alkaline earths are somewhat larger than the ionization potentials of the corresponding alkali metal; compare the values for Ca, Sr, and Ba, 6.09, 5.65, and 5.19 eV respectively, with those for K, Rb, and Cs, 4.32, 4.16, and 3.85, respectively. At the same temperature and metal atom concentration, then, the ion concentration should be much smaller for the alkaline earths than for the alkali metals. However, experimentally it is observed that the electron concentrations for flames containing alkaline earths can greatly exceed the expected equilibrium concentration based on metal atom ionization (93,100). This has been explained by chemi-ionization:

$$A + OH \;\rightleftharpoons\; AOH^+ + e \qquad [42]$$

which is not distinguishable from:

$$AO + H \;\rightleftharpoons\; AOH^+ + e \qquad [43]$$

because

$$AO + H \;\rightleftharpoons\; A + OH \qquad [44]$$

is in equilibrium. The suggested pre-exponentials in the rate constants for reactions [42] and [43] are about 2×10^{-10} cm^3 molecules^{-1} at 2000°K. Reaction [42] or [43] can be followed by the ion-molecule reaction:

$$A\text{OH}^+ + \text{H} \rightleftharpoons A^+ + \text{H}_2\text{O} \qquad [45]$$

Equilibrium constants for reaction [42] have been deduced from microwave cavity measurements of electron concentrations of $\text{H}_2/\text{N}_2/\text{O}_2$ flames at 1 atm containing alkaline earths (see Table 11).

TABLE 11

Equilibrium constants for alkaline earth hydroxide ions[a]

$A + \text{OH} \rightleftharpoons A\text{OH}^+ + e$	
Alkaline earth, A	Equilibrium constant, K
Ca	$1.8 \times 10^{-3} \exp\left(-\dfrac{18 \pm 5}{T}\right)$
Sr	$2.0 \times 10^{-3} \exp\left(-\dfrac{13 \pm 4}{T}\right)$
Ba	$1.7 \times 10^{-3} \exp\left(-\dfrac{3 \pm 5}{T}\right)$

[a]Source: Jensen, Ref. 100.

The ionization mechanisms for alkaline earth metals and alkali metals are thus different. For the alkaline earths, chemi-ionization involving hydroxyl radicals or hydrogen atoms (both of which may be present in excess of equilibrium) may rapidly produce high ion concentrations; for the alkali metals, the ionization reaction involves transfer of internal energy and the equilibrium condition is approached more slowly. It is thus not surprising that Schofield and Sugden (93) observed that alkaline earths are capable of catalyzing the ionization of alkali metals via the reaction

$$\text{SrOH}^+ + \text{Na} \longrightarrow \text{SrOH} + \text{Na}^+ \qquad [46]$$

C. Halogens

Because halogens have large electron affinities, for example, 3.6 eV for chlorine, one might expect that the addition of halogen to a flame containing electrons would produce negative ions. Such is the case; however, the reaction is very slow. Hayhurst and Sugden (68) added potassium chloride to a small premixed hydrogen flame and observed K$^+$, Cl$^-$, and OH$^-$ (see Fig. 7b).

The K^+ reached its steady-state value very quickly while the Cl^- and OH^- concentration rose slowly. Because the H atom concentration decreases downstream of the flame front the observations were considered to be consistent with the mechanism

$$HCl + e \longrightarrow Cl^- + H \qquad [47]$$

rather than

$$Cl + e + M \longrightarrow Cl^- + M \qquad [48]$$

The rate constant for Reaction [47] has been estimated (63) to be 10^{-10} $\exp(-20{,}000/RT)$, based on the collision cross-section data of Buchel'nikova (101).

Chlorine has been added in the form of CCl_4 to low-pressure C_2H_2/O_2 diffusion flames, with the observation that the negative ion concentration is increased by several orders of magnitude (102). The negative ions Cl_2^-, Cl^-, $ClOH^-$, and C_2Cl^- were observed. Since attachment apparently occurred only in regions containing CCl_4, the attachment reaction evidently involved CCl_4 itself or a decomposition fragment and not reaction [47] or [48]. Of even more interest was the observation that, with the addition of CCl_4, copious quantities of heavy positive hydrocarbon ions ranging in mass from 63 to greater than 150 were observed (Fig. 14) simultaneously with the formation

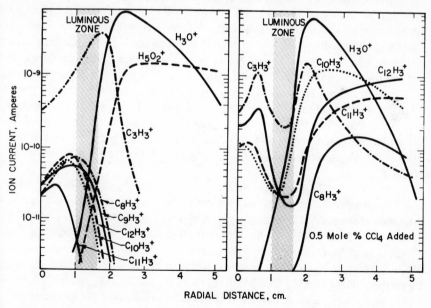

Figure 14 Effect of carbon tetrachloride on some positive ion profiles in a low pressure spherical diffusion flame, acetylene/oxygen; fuel inlet tube diam $= 0.6$ cm, $p = 4$ torr (102).

of soot. These ions differed from each other by about 12 mass units, indicating the successive addition of a carbon atom to the ion. This observation supports the various theories which have suggested that an ionic mechanism (103,104) is important in soot formation in flames.

The addition of chlorine to a stoichiometric C_2H_4/O_2 flame at 2 torr in the form of PCl_3 had essentially no effect on the total positive ion concentration (102). However, the ion PO^+ was identified and observed to exceed the H_3O^+ concentration downstream of the flame front. The PO^+ ion was apparently produced in charge-transfer reactions.

VI. ELECTRON TEMPERATURES

Some electrostatic probe measurements in flames (7,12,74,105,106) have indicated electron temperatures exceeding the gas temperature by several thousand degrees (see Fig. 15), while other measurements (10) have shown the electron temperature to be equal to the gas temperature. There are also discrepancies in the observations of temperature profiles. For example, Bradley and Matthews (74) observed T_e to peak behind the peak in $[n_+]$ (Fig. 15), while Calcote (7) observed T_e to generally peak at the same position in the flame as $[n_+]$ and Attard (105) in a torch flame observed T_e to increase downstream and then level off. Because of the complications involved in probe measurements (especially at high pressures), the lack of a clear pattern in the results of various investigators who have observed excess electron temperatures, and the rapidity with which electron temperatures are expected to approach the gas temperature (70), the subject of excess electron temperatures must be approached warily. An independent observation of excess electron temperature by a technique other than probes would be desirable. The only alternative measurement is one given in the review by von Engel (106), in which an electron noise measurement of Attard is quoted, indicating excess T_e.

Electrons might be produced with an excess of energy if the chemi-ionization reaction producing them is exothermic; they might also be produced in collisions of the second kind as proposed by von Engel and Cozens (106,107). Bradley and Matthews (74) have presented evidence which supports the "second kind" collision theory: they made double probe measurements in flames burning at 76 torr. Methane was added to both a carbon monoxide and a hydrogen flame (85.5% CO, 2% CH_4, 1% H_2, 11.5% O_2, and 2% CH_4, 17.5% H_2, 80.5% air). An electron temperature exceeding the gas temperature was observed in the carbon monoxide flame (Fig. 15), but not in the hydrogen flame. They suggested the following reaction of the second kind as the source of hot electrons:

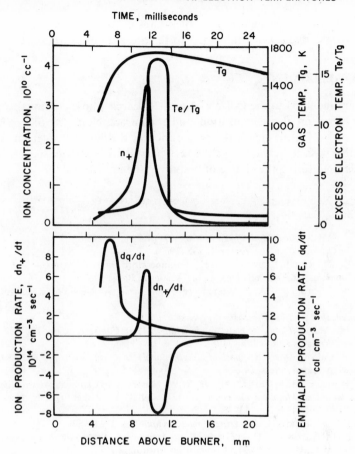

Figure 15   Excess electron temperatures and related quantities in a carbon monoxide/oxygen/methane flame. Unburned gas composition: 85.5% CO, 2% CH_4, 1% H_2, 11.5% O_2 (74).

$$CO_2^* + e \longrightarrow CO_2 + e^* \qquad [49]$$

von Engel and Cozens (106,107,108) hold that the main source of excess flame ionization is the heating of the few stray electrons (always present) by collisions of the second kind to sufficient energies to ionize the combustion gases. If this were the primary mechanism of flame ionization, we would expect nonequilibrium ionization in carbon monoxide flames to be the same as in hydrocarbon flames, but this is not observed. The argument also suffers on quantitative grounds; even with maximizing assumptions (106), the electron energies are calculated to be less than 1 eV.

The subject of excess electron temperatures in flames requires more study to remove the questions with respect to the present observations.

ACKNOWLEDGMENT

We are indebted to the Office of Naval Research whose continual support of our work on flame ionization under contract Nonr-3809(00) NR092–515/7–26–68 (473) has made the preparation of this book chapter possible. We also wish to acknowledge the very helpful criticism and suggestions of D. E. Jensen during the course of preparing the manuscript.

REFERENCES

1. H. A. Wilson, *Rev. Mod. Phys.*, **3**, 156 (1931).
2. H. F. Calcote, *Combust. Flame*, **1**, 385 (1957).
3. K. E. Schuler, ed., "Ionization in High Temperature Gases." *Progress in Astronautics and Aeronautics*, Vol. XII. New York: Academic Press, 1963.
4. R. M. Fristrom and A. A. Westenberg, *Flame Structure*. New York: McGraw-Hill, 1965.
5. *Combustion Institute Symposia Proceedings*, I–XII.
6. H. F. Calcote, *Eighth Symposium (International) on Combustion*, pp. 184–199. Baltimore: Williams and Wilkins, 1962.
7. H. F. Calcote, *Ninth Symposium (International) on Combustion*, pp. 622–633. New York: Academic Press, 1963.
8. D. Bohm, E. H. S. Burhop, and H. S. W. Massey, *The Characteristics of Electrical Discharges in Magnetic Fields*, A. Guthrie and R. K. Wakerling, eds. New York: McGraw-Hill, 1949, pp. 13–76.
9. D. E. Jensen and S. C. Kurzius, *Combust. Flame*, **13**, 219 (1969).
10. B. E. L. Travers and H. Williams, *Tenth Symposium (International) on Combustion*, pp. 657–672. Pittsburgh: The Combustion Institute, 1965.
11. J. R. Cozens and A. von Engel, *Electronics*, **19**, 61 (1965).
12. R. Carabetta and R. P. Porter, *Twelfth Symposium (International) on Combustion*, pp. 423–435. Pittsburgh: The Combustion Institute, 1969.
13. S. H. Lam, *AIAA J.*, **2**, 256 (1964).
14. G. Maise and A. J. Sabadell, *AIAA J.*, **8**, 895 (1970).
15. E. R. G. Eckert and R. M. Drake, *Heat and Mass Transfer*, 2nd ed. New York: McGraw-Hill, 1959.
16. A. B. Littlewood, in *Gas Chromatography*, edited by N. Brenner, J. E. Cullen, and M. D. Weiss. London: Academic Press, 1962, pp. 288–294.
17. J. C. Sternberg, W. S. Galloway, and D. T. L. Jones, in *Gas Chromatography*, edited by N. Brenner, J. E. Cullen, and M. D. Weiss. London: Academic Press, 1962, pp. 231–267.
18. E. M. Bulewicz and P. J. Padley, *Ninth Symposium (International) on Combustion*, pp. 638–646. New York: Academic Press, 1963.
19. V. L. Granatstein and S. J. Buchshaum, "Microwave Scattering from Turbulent Plasma " in *Turbulence in Fluids and Plasma*, edited by J. Fox. New York : Brooklyn Polytechnic Press, 1969, pp. 231–249.

20. H. Belcher and T. M. Sugden, *Proc. Roy. Soc., Ser. A*, **202**, 17 (1950).
21. W. W. Balwanz, *Tenth Symposium (International) on Combustion*, pp. 685–697. Pittsburgh: The Combustion Institute, 1965.
22. D. E. Jensen and P. J. Padley, *Eleventh Symposium (International) on Combustion*, pp. 351–358. Pittsburgh: The Combustion Institute, 1967.
23. P. J. Padley and T. M. Sugden, *Eighth Symposium (International) on Combustion*, pp. 164–179. Baltimore: Williams and Wilkins, 1962.
24. A. J. Borgers, *Tenth Symposium (International) on Combustion*, pp. 627–637. Pittsburgh: The Combustion Institute, 1965.
25. H. Williams, *Seventh Symposium (International) on Combustion*, p. 269–276. London: Butterworths, 1959.
26. H. Smith and T. M. Sugden, *Proc. Roy. Soc., Ser. A*, **211**, 31 (1952).
27. *Molecular Beams, Advances in Chemical Physics*, Vol. X, edited by J. Ross. New York: Interscience Publishers, 1966.
28. H. F. Calcote and J. L. Reuter, *J. Chem. Phys.*, **38**, 310 (1963).
29. W. J. Miller, *Eleventh Symposium (International) on Combustion*, pp. 311–320. Pittsburgh: The Combustion Institute, 1967.
30. I. R. Hurle, T. M. Sugden, and G. B. Nutt, *Twelfth Symposium (International) on Combustion*, pp. 387–394. Pittsburgh: The Combustion Institute, 1969.
31. A. Feugier and A. Van Tiggelen, *Tenth Symposium (International) on Combustion*, pp. 621–624. Pittsburgh: The Combustion Institute, 1965.
32. F. T. Green and T. A. Milne, "Mass Spectrometric Sampling of High Pressure-High Temperature Sources." In *Advances in Mass Spectrometry*, Vol. III, pp. 841–850, edited by W. L. Mead. London: The Institute of Petroleum, 1966.
33. H. F. Calcote, "Ionization in Hydrocarbon Flames." In *Fundamental Studies of Ions and Plasmas*, Vol. I, pp. 1–42, edited by H. D. Wilsted. AGARD Special Publication No. 8, September 1965.
34. C. W. Hand and G. B. Kistiakowsky, *J. Chem. Phys.*, **37**, 1239 (1962).
35. A Peeters and A. Van Tiggelen, *Twelfth Symposium (International) on Combustion*, pp. 437–446. Pittsburgh: The Combustion Institute, 1969.
36. A. Fontijn and G. L. Baughman, *J. Chem. Phys.*, **38**, 1784 (1963).
37. A. Fontijn, W. J. Miller, and J. M. Hogan, *Tenth Symposium (International) on Combustion*, pp. 545–557. Pittsburgh: The Combustion Institute, 1965.
38. C. A. Arrington, W. Brennen, G. P. Glass, J. V. Michael, and H. Niki, *J. Chem. Phys.*, **43**, 525 (1965).
39. G. P. Glass, G. B. Kistiakowsky, J. V. Michael, and H. Niki, *J. Chem. Phys.*, **42**, 608 (1965).
40. H. F. Calcote, S. C. Kurzius, and W. J. Miller, *Tenth Symposium (International) on Combustion*, pp. 605–618. Pittsburgh: The Combustion Institute, 1965.
41. P. F. Knewstubb and T. M. Sugden, *Seventh Symposium (International) on Combustion*, pp. 356–362. London: Butterworths, 1959.
42. E. M. Bulewicz, *Combust. Flame*, **11**, 297 (1967).
43. C. A. Arrington, W. Brennen, G. P. Glass, J. V. Michael, and H. Niki, *J. Chem. Phys.*, **43**, 1489 (1965).
44. *JANAF Thermochemical Data*. Midland, Michigan: The Dow Chemical Company (continuously updated).
45. G. Herzberg, *Molecular Spectra and Molecular Structure*, Vol. I, 2nd ed. New York: Van Nostrand, 1951.
46. G. Herzberg, *Molecular Spectra and Molecular Structure*, Vol. III. New York: Van Nostrand, 1966.

47. H. Pritchard and G. Harrison, *J. Chem. Phys.*, **48**, 5623 (1968).
48. F. H. Dorman, *J. Chem. Phys.*, **50**, 1042 (1969).
49. A. G. Harrison, *J. Chem. Phys.* **50**, 1043 (1969).
50. J. L. Beauchamp and S. E. Buttrill, *J. Chem. Phys.*, **48**, 1783 (1968).
51. A. P. Altshuler, *J. Am. Chem. Soc.*, **77**, 3480 (1955).
52. R. R. Bernecker and F. A. Long, *J. Phys. Chem.*, **65**, 1565 (1962).
53. E. Lindholm and P. Wilmenius, *Ark. Kemi*, **20**, 255 (1963).
54. J. T. Herron and V. H. Dibeler, *J. Am. Chem. Soc.*, **82**, 1555 (1960).
55. R. E. Honig, *J. Chem. Phys.*, **22**, 126 (1954).
56. T. Fueno, N. R. Mukherjee, T. Ree, and H. Eyring, *Eighth Symposium* (*International*) *on Combustion*, pp. 222–230. Baltimore: Williams and Wilkins, 1962.
57. D. Boothman, J. Lawton, S. J. Melinek, and F. J. Weinberg, *Twelfth Symposium* (*International*) *on Combustion*, pp. 969–978. Pittsburgh: The Combustion Institute, 1969.
58. H. Niki, E. E. Daby, and B. Weinstock, " Chemi-Ionization in the Room Temperature Reaction of Carbonsuboxide with Atomic Hydrogen and Oxygen." Presented at the 156th National Meeting of the American Chemical Society, Atlantic City, September 1968.
59. R. P. Porter, A. H. Clark, W. E. Kaskan, and W. E. Brown, *Eleventh Symposium* (*International*) *on Combustion*, pp. 907–915. Pittsburgh: The Combustion Institute, 1967.
60. A. Fontijn and D. E. Jensen, comments following above reference.
61. S. C. Kurzius and M. Boudart, *Combust. Flame*, **12**, 477 (1968).
62. J. A. Green and T. M. Sugden, *Ninth Symposium* (*International*) *on Combustion*, pp. 607–621. New York: Academic Press, 1963.
63. H. F. Calcote and D. E. Jensen, in *Ion Molecule Reactions in the Gas Phase. Advances in Chemistry Series No. 58*, pp. 291–314. Washington: American Chemical Society, 1966.
64. W. J. Miller, *Oxidation and Combustion Reviews*, **3**, 97 (1968).
65. S. DeJaegere, J. Deckers, and A. Van Tiggelen, *Eighth Symposium* (*International*) *on Combustion*, pp. 155–160. Baltimore: Williams and Wilkins, 1962.
66. C. E. Boord, " Cool Flames and the Organic Reaction Mechanisms Involved in Their Formation." *Literature of the Combustion of Petroleum. Advances in Chemistry Series No. 20.* pp. 5–14. Washington: The American Chemical Society, 1958.
67. P. F. Knewstubb, *Tenth Symposium* (*International*) *on Combustion*, p. 624. Pittsburgh: The Combustion Institute, 1965.
68. A. N. Hayhurst and T. M. Sugden, *Proc. Roy. Soc.*, *Ser. A*, **293**, 36 (1966).
69. J. A. Green, "Observations on Negative Ions in Hydrocarbon Flames." In *Fundamental Studies of Ions and Plasmas*, Vol. I, pp. 191–214, edited by H. D. Wilsted AGARD Special Publication No. 8, 1965.
70. H. F. Calcote, in *Dynamics of Conducting Gases, Proceedings of the Third Biennial Gas-Dynamics Symposium*, pp. 36–47. Evanston: Northwestern University Press, 1960.
71. E. S. Semenov and A. S. Sokolik, *Zhur. Tekhn. Fiz.* (*USSR*), **32**, 1074 (1962).
72. I. R. King, *J. Chem. Phys.*, **37**, 74 (1962).
73. G. Wortberg, *Tenth Symposium* (*International*) *on Combustion*, pp. 651–655. Pittsburgh: The Combustion Institute, 1965.
74. D. Bradley and K. J. Matthews, *Eleventh Symposium* (*International*) *on Combustion*, pp. 359–368. Pittsburgh: The Combustion Institute, 1967.
75. E. N. Taran and V. I. Tverdokhlebov, *High Temperature*, **4**, 160 (1966).
76. L. N. Wilson and E. W. Evans, *J. Chem. Phys.*, **46**, 859 (1967).

77. I. R. King, *J. Chem. Phys.*, **36**, 553 (1962).
78. H. F. Calcote and I. R. King, *Fifth Symposium (International) on Combustion*, p. 423. New York: Reinhold, 1955.
79. I. R. King, *J. Chem. Phys.*, **31**, 855 (1959).
80. A. Van Tiggelen, in *Ionization in High-Temperature Gases. Progress in Astronautics and Aeronautics*, Vol. XII, pp. 165–196. New York: Academic Press, 1963.
81. R. M. Moyerman and K. E. Shuler, *Science*, **118**, 612 (1953).
82. C. J. Schexneyder, Jr., *The Composition and Thermodynamic Properties of the Products of Cyanogen/Oxygen Combustion*. NASA TND-2422, August 1964.
83. S. C. Kurzius and F. H. Raab, Princeton: AeroChem Research Laboratories, Inc. (unpublished data).
84. E. M. Bulewicz and P. J. Padley, *Ninth Symposium (International) on Combustion*, pp. 647–658. New York: Academic Press, 1963.
85. N. Thomas, A. G. Gayden, and L. Brewer, *J. Chem. Phys.*, **20**, 369 (1952).
86. E. M. Bulewicz, *Twelfth Symposium (International) on Combustion*, pp. 957–967. Pittsburgh: The Combustion Institute, 1969.
87. Shao-Chi Lin and J. D. Teare, *Phys. Fluids*, **6**, 355 (1963).
88. A. Frohn and P. C. T. Deboer, *AIAA J*, **5**, 261 (1967).
89. Tj. Hollander, P. J. Kalff, and C. T. J. Alkemade, *J. Chem. Phys.*, **39**, 2558 (1963).
90. D. E. Jensen and P. J. Padley, *Trans. Faraday Soc.*, **62**, 2140 (1966).
91. Tj. Hollander, *AIAA J.*, **6**, 385 (1968).
92. P. F. Knewstubb and T. M. Sugden, *Trans. Faraday Soc.*, **54**, 372 (1958).
93. K. Schofield and T. M. Sugden, *Tenth Symposium (International) on Combustion*, pp. 589–604. Pittsburgh: The Combustion Institute, 1965.
94. R. G. Soundy and H. Williams, "A Simple Electrostatic Probe for the Measurement of Ion Densities in Atmospheric Pressure Flames and Its Application to a Study of Charge Exchange Reactions in Hydrocarbon Flame Gases." In *Fundamental Studies of Ions and Plasmas*, Vol. I, pp. 161–189, edited by H. D. Wilsted. AGARD Special Publication No. 8, September 1965.
95. A. N. Hayhurst and T. M. Sugden, "The Ionization Processes Associated with Metallic Additives in Flame Gases," presented at the 20th International Symposium on Properties and Applications of Low Temperature Plasmas, I.U.P.A.C., Moscow, 1965.
96. A. Van Tiggelen and S. DeJaegere, "Experimental Study of Chemi-Ionization." Final Report, AF-EOAR-65-82. Louvain, Belgium: University of Louvain, May 1967.
97. A. N. Hayhurst and T. M. Sugden, *Trans. Faraday Soc.*, **63**, 1375 (1967).
98. P. J. Padley, F. M. Page, and T. M. Sugden, *Trans. Faraday Soc.*, **57**, 1552 (1961).
99. D. E. Jensen, *Trans. Faraday Soc.*, **65**, 2123 (1969).
100. D. E. Jensen, *Combust. Flame*, **12**, 261 (1968).
101. I. S. Buchel'nikova, *J. Exp. Theor. Phys.*, **35**, 1119 (1958).
102. W. J. Miller, Princeton: AeroChem Research Laboratories (unpublished data).
103. J. B. Howard, *Twelfth Symposium (International) on Combustion*, pp. 877–887. Pittsburgh: The Combustion Institute, 1969.
104. E. R. Place and F. J. Weinberg, *Eleventh Symposium (International) on Combustion*, pp. 245–255. Pittsburgh: The Combustion Institute, 1967.
105. M. C. Attard, in *Magnetohydrodynamic Electrical Power Generation*, Vol. I, pp. 21–30. European Nuclear Energy Agency, 1965.
106. A. von Engel, *Brit. J. Appl. Phys.*, **18**, 1661 (1967).
107. A. von Engel and J. R. Cozens, *Nature*, **202**, 480 (1964).
108. A. von Engel and J. R. Cozens, "Flame Plasmas." *Advances in Electronics*, Vol. 20, pp. 99–146. London: Academic Press, 1964.

CHAPTER EIGHTEEN

Chemical Reactions in Shock Wave Generated Plasmas

W. C. GARDINER, JR.

I. INTRODUCTION

The use of shock tubes for generation and study of plasmas has engaged the attention of physicists, chemists and engineers for a number of years. A substantial body of information on the elementary chemical reactions that occur in shock-wave generated plasmas has accumulated. In this chapter a survey and a discussion of the results published through 1968 are given. As far as we are aware, this is the first general review of the subject of chemistry in ionizing shock waves since the early paper of Blackman and Niblett (1). Comprehensive discussions of the chemistry of air ionized in shock waves have been given by Lin and Teare (2) and by Stupochenko, Losev, and Osipov (3). The latter authors also present a fairly detailed account of shock propagation theory taking ionization into consideration, and discuss many of the observations in shock-ionized rare gases.

The experimental methods used in shock tube research on plasmas are discussed elsewhere in this book (4). We shall therefore confine ourselves to brief mention of the methods used to obtain specific results. In a few cases where the interpretation originally given to the measurements required revision in light of subsequent discoveries about measurement techniques, the difficulties with the methods will be discussed in greater detail.

The field of research on shock-wave generated plasmas actually covers a substantially larger area than will be treated here. We omit those studies in which the primary emphasis is on the physics and technology of electromagnetic shock drivers, even though much of the research in this area is intended for ultimate use in physical studies of plasmas themselves. We also forego discussing observations in the dense, very hot plasmas created by shock waves in annular magnetohydrodynamic devices. Very little chemistry is involved in such experiments, since atomization is complete on a space/time scale that is small compared to the usual diagnostics used to study plasmas. Shock waves generated by sparks and high-energy pulsed lasers will likewise be omitted from our survey, since such experiments do not give well-defined shock waves and so far have not provided fundamental information on the physics or chemistry of plasmas. Finally, we shall not consider the phenomena that are observed in astrophysical studies of shock waves generated far out in the cosmos. These topics do not lend themselves to study of chemical reactions occurring under plasma conditions.

A note concerning the literature surveyed and the bibliographic references is in order. Most of the literature of this subject was first published in report form rather than in the open literature. Where reports have been superceded by articles in the open literature, only the article is cited. Where the article does not contain all of the material in the report, the report is also cited providing that copies of the report are readily available. Reports that are not readily available have been considered nonexistent, even though some of them contain first-rate contributions to the field and are occasionally cited elsewhere.

A number of erudite theoretical papers describing the gas dynamics of shock propagation in presence of intense radiation and ionization have appeared. Only those papers which have a direct bearing on the analysis of experimental data giving information on the chemical reactions important in the ionization are mentioned. Most of them have been directed toward understanding the propagation of extremely strong ionizing shock waves or toward an understanding of energy-transfer mechanisms important in the heating and ablation of surfaces exposed to the ionized air surrounding re-entering space vehicles.

II. THE SHOCK TUBE AS A MEANS OF GENERATING AND STUDYING PLASMAS

The simplest description of a shock tube is that it is a thermostat in which a gas sample can be taken by a rapid shock compression from a low temperature, say room temperature, to a high temperature, say 5000°K, and kept hot for a sufficient length of time to carry out physical or chemical experiments (5). In the common pressure-driven shock-tube apparatus, the gas is initially at a pressure of some 0.01 atm and reaches a shock pressure of perhaps 1–10 atm. The available testing time in the hot gas would be typically about 0.1–1 msec. An elementary description of applying the shock tube to plasma research would say that the gas temperature can be so hot behind a strong shock wave that ionization occurs. The degree of ionization, the identity of the ions, and the time history of the ion and electron profiles behind the shock-wave would be the obvious first goals of research on shock wave generated plasmas. Interpretation of these results in terms of the physical and chemical processes responsible for ion creation and destruction would follow.

Before discussing the considerations that force shock-tube researchers to take account of substantial deviations of actual shock-tube performance from this simple description, we shall give an outline of the experimental conditions which have been used for plasma studies in shock tubes. For the special topic of chemi-ionization, which occurs at temperatures far below those required to induce measurable thermal ionization, the upper temperature limit is determined by the rate of the ionization and recombination processes that are to be studied rather than by ionization potentials or structural limitations of the shock tube. Such studies have spanned the temperature range 1400–2800°K. The low end of the temperature range of most thermal ionization studies is determined by the ionization potential of the most easily ionized species in the sample under investigation (Table 1) and at the high end by the driving capability of the shock tube used. The driving capability is determined by three factors. The first has to do with whether one is able to use a reflected rather than an incident shock wave; reflected shock waves are typically about twice as hot as incident shock waves. The second has to do with the construction of the shock tube. The temperature of a pressure-driven shock wave depends upon the pressure ratio across the diaphragm separating the driver

TABLE 1
Ionization potentials and sound speeds of various gases

Gas	IP, (eV)	a_0, meters sec^{-1}
Argon	15.8	333
Neon	21.6	454
Helium	24.6	1008
Krypton	14.0	—
Xenon	12.1	184
Hydrogen (H_2)	15.4	1326
Hydrogen (H)	13.6	—
Nitrogen (N_2)	15.6	349
Nitrogen (N)	14.5	—
Oxygen (O_2)	12.2	331
Oxygen (O)	13.6	—
Nitric oxide	9.3	334
Air	—	347
Sodium	5.1	—
Potassium	4.3	336
Cesium	3.9	183
Mercury	10.4	—
Chromium	6.8	—
Titanium	6.8	—
Silicon	8.1	—
Calcium	6.1	—
Water	12.6	—
Aluminum	6.0	—
C_3H_3	6.7(?)	—
CHO	7.7	—

gas from the experimental gas. Stronger materials of construction allow higher driving pressures to be used, larger tube diameters allow lower experimental gas pressure to be used, and special construction techniques allow more efficient utilization of the driver to obtain stronger shocks from given driving pressure ratios. The third factor influencing the upper temperature limit is the nature of the experimental gas, in particular its molecular weight and its heat capacity. The shock heating of the experimental gas is essentially a conversion of the PV work done originally in compressing the driver gas into heating of the shocked gas; the greater the heat capacity of the experimental gas, the more difficult it is to attain high shock temperature. Studies in monatomic gases are therefore favored, and high temperatures in diatomic and polyatomic gases are more easily attained if they are mixed with a large percentage of a monatomic gas such as argon. High molecular weights also favor attainment of high temperatures.

It is of interest to have an overview of the range of experimental conditions which may be studied in shock-wave generated plasmas (6). For this purpose it is convenient to consider the parameters for shock-heated argon. Since ionization increases the number of particles in a gas, the degree of ionization is dependent on the pressure of the plasma. To achieve a high degree of thermal ionization it is therefore expedient to work at low pressures. On the other hand, shock flow becomes difficult to characterize if large amounts of shocked gas are lost to the boundary layer of the shock tube, which implies a lower pressure limit for successful operation of a shock tube of given geometry. In a typical shock tube of about 10 cm diameter, the preshock pressure cannot be made less than about 1 torr without encountering severe boundary-layer effects. With this condition on the pressure satisfied, achieving a substantial degree of ionization depends only on obtaining a high shock velocity. The velocity is usually given in shock tube research as the shock Mach number, defined as the ratio of the shock propagation velocity to the velocity of sound in the unshocked gas. In Fig. 1 the equilibrium degree of ionization is plotted as a function of the shock Mach number for argon. If 1% is taken as a minimum degree of ionization for observation by most plasma diagnostics, then we can see from Fig. 1 that shocks of Mach number greater than about 10 are required. The corresponding temperature at ionization equilibrium is seen in Fig. 2 to be about $9000°K$, once again depending somewhat on the pressure of the unshocked gas. The dependence of the achievable ionization on the ionization potential of the gas is shown in Fig. 3 for each of the noble gases. It is clear that the heavier noble gases, having lower ionization potentials, show much greater degrees of ionization for a given shock Mach number. It is also easier to achieve high shock speeds in the heavier noble gases due to the increasing efficiency of shock drivers for shocking high

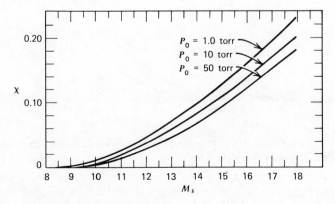

Figure 1   Equilibrium degree of ionization χ for argon at three different starting pressures as function of shock Mach number (1).

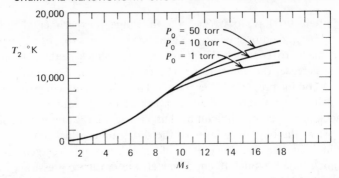

Figure 2 Temperature at ionization equilibrium in argon at three different starting pressures as function of shock Mach number (1).

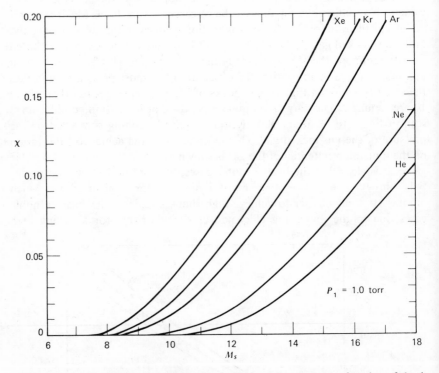

Figure 3 Equilibrium degree of ionization χ for the noble gases as a function of shock Mach number. The starting pressure is 1.0 torr in each case (1).

molecular weight (low sound speed) gases. For a rough orientation on the degree of ionization obtainable in other gases, the sound speed and ionization potential data in Table 1 can be compared with the noble gas curves in Figs. 1 to 3.

The fundamental theory governing the operation of shock tubes is to be found in standard reference works (5). For the purposes of some of the experiments discussed here, the operation of the shock tube is described with sufficient accuracy by a set of four coupled algebraic equations embodying the conservation equations of steady one-dimensional shock flow. Frequently, however, it is necessary in strong shock studies to take account of non-ideal (two-dimensional) shock flow, or to consider flow including radiative energy transfer, or to use numerical integration procedures in interpreting the observed profiles. A brief description of these topics with references to the appropriate literature is given here.

In most shock-tube practice it is sufficient to assume that the shock wave is a one-dimensional disturbance propagating in the shock tube at constant velocity. Calculating the temperature and pressure behind the shock wave (either the incident shock wave or the shock wave reflected from the end wall of the shock tube) then requires measurement of a single parameter, usually the incident shock velocity, and solution of the set of four equations. The range of experimental conditions needed to produce thermal ionization can be attained, however, only by pushing the capabilities of most shock tubes to their limits, and it is therefore not surprising that the simple one-dimensional steady-flow equations may begin to break down. The first complication is that the velocity of the wave fails to be constant. At first the velocity increases, as the driver gas finds an increasing area to flow through the expanding diaphragm opening, and then it decreases due to viscous losses at the wall of the shock tube. The former effect has been the subject of several experimental and theoretical studies (5), which gave the general conclusion that the rate of diaphragm opening is strongly dependent upon the experimental arrangement used and can be improved by appropriate design of the apparatus. The attenuation effect, however, is of more importance for plasma studies in pressure driven shock tubes. The theory and experiment of this effect have been subjected to quite detailed investigation, and the equations describing the effects of the attenuation have developed in several degrees of approximation (7).

Another consequence of operating a shock tube at very high temperature is that the density of the experimental gas is likely to have been made so low that the loss of shocked gas to the thermal boundary layer at the shock-tube wall (or at the surface of any probes within the tube) may be quite significant. This has two effects on the interpretation of experimental observations. The first is that the observations themselves may be perturbed by the cold gas in the boundary layer. A Langmuir probe, for example, will not measure the true electron or ion concentration in flowing shocked gas (8). Likewise, optical measurements of emission intensity from the shocked gas may be affected by absorption in the cold boundary layer. Boundary layer effects of this kind are highly dependent upon the circumstances and must be evaluated separately for each particular experiment.

The second effect of severe boundary-layer growth is that the usual relationship between the distance of a gas element from the shock front and the time that has elapsed since it passed through the shock front no longer holds (9).

The nonideal shock-tube behavior mentioned so far has not involved the fact that we are dealing with plasmas. Two special effects arise from the fact that the shocked gas is a plasma. The first has to do with the energy balance in the shocked gas. A significant fraction of the energy contained in a plasma may consist of radiation, and in computing the energy content and the energy loss rate in ionized shocked gas, radiation energy must be added to the usual enthalpy and kinetic energy terms considered in shock flow. Several authors have considered the mathematical treatment of this problem in detail (10). One important effect of radiation from the plasma is its interaction with both the unshocked gas and the shock-tube wall ahead of the shock wave to generate precursor species, for example electronically excited atoms or even photoelectrons. Precursor effects have been studied by many investigators and will be discussed in detail in later sections (11).

The second effect of ionization upon shock wave structure has to do with the small mass of electrons. The small mass of electrons means that their mobility is so high that they may be able to diffuse a significant distance ahead of the density discontinuity of the atoms which is normally taken as the definition of the shock front. In the second place, one must consider in shock-tube experiments the usual circumstance in plasma experiments that inefficient energy transfer between electrons and atoms allows very large differences to arise between the electron and the atom temperatures, including, of course, all temperatures defined by populations of atomic electronic states. Problems of this nature were recognized in the earliest papers on ionization in shock waves and have been a recurrent theme throughout the history of shock-tube research on plasmas. The electron temperature problem plays a central role in interpretation of chemical reactions in shock-wave generated plasmas.

All of the discussion so far has implicitly assumed that the shock tube is of the pressure-driven variety, in which the shock wave is generated by expansion of a high-pressure gas (generally hydrogen or helium) into the experimental gas. Many important plasma studies, however, have been with shock tubes incorporating an electromagnetic driver, in which the shock wave is generated by expansion of a dense, high-pressure plasma created by an energetic discharge. In many versions of the electromagnetic shock tube the main coupling of energy into the driver is through electromagnetic coupling of the conducting driver gas to the discharge circuit. Electromagnetic shock tubes possess some advantages for studies of shock-wave generated plasmas. In the first place, very high shock strengths are readily achieved, enabling plasma studies to be made in light gases, in particular helium and hydrogen, which could not otherwise be raised to plasma temperature in a shock tube (except by high explosive drivers). Secondly, they have the advantage that the shock tube need not be opened to the atmosphere between experiments, which means that experiments can be performed more rapidly, and to some extent more cleanly, than with pressure-driven shock tubes. Electromagnetic shock tubes have, however, some serious drawbacks also. The shock velocity is usually not at all constant down the length of the tube, and the shock temperature is therefore not constant. Perhaps more serious is the fact that the driver gas is a hotter and denser plasma than the experimental gas. This means that the difficulties caused by interactions of the ionized shocked gas with the pre-shock gas and shock-tube walls are intensified in the electromagnetic shock tube.

III. NOBLE GASES

Noble gas plasmas generated in shock waves have been more thoroughly studied, both theoretically and experimentally, than any other kind of shock-wave generated plasma; in fact, the number of publications on noble gas plasmas is greater than the number of publications on all other types of shock-wave generated plasmas combined. The reason for this lies partly in the fact that noble gases, having no internal degrees of freedom (besides electronic excitation), are more easily shocked to high temperatures, partly in the fact that the noble gases can be more readily obtained in highly pure form than other gases, and partly in the historical accident that noble gas plasmas were studied early in the history of shock-tube research, found quite interesting, and subsequently pursued by many authors looking for simple but rewarding systems to study. On the theoretical side one has the advantages that all of the atomic energy states are well known, that the time dependence of the populations (or at least the relative populations) of various electronic states can be followed readily by spectroscopic experiments, that the absorptivities of the rare gases to radiation emitted by the plasma are known, and again that the role of impurities can be reduced to a greater degree in the noble gases than in other systems, allowing their contributions to the ionization processes to be studied accurately. Countering these advantages, one has the circumstance that the ionization potentials of the noble gases are higher than the ionization potentials of other monatomic gases (for example, gases of alkali metals) which one might be able to study at lower temperatures and with lesser contributions from disturbing effects that will be discussed presently.

The chemical reactions that can occur in noble gas plasmas are far more limited in extent than the chemical reactions which can occur in the plasmas of other gases or gas mixtures. We shall find, however, that most of the typical processes which occur in other plasmas also occur in noble gas plasmas, and in more readily interpretable experimental situations. Shock-wave generated plasmas in the noble gases are therefore a good starting point for describing shock-wave generated plasmas. It will not be appropriate to trace the historical development of our understanding of the processes that occur in noble gas plasmas, because the historical development was rather complex and also error-prone. We shall instead consider the elementary processes which might be expected to occur in noble gas plasmas generated in shock waves, ignoring the difficulty that shock-tube researchers had in identifying these processes in the first place, and then recount the evidence underlying them and the nature of the theoretical interpretations that have been proposed to provide unified descriptions of strong shock waves in noble gases.

The least energetic process that can occur as a result of shock heating of a noble gas is excitation of the upper atomic electronic levels. There are a great many of these levels even in helium, hence a complete description of the relaxation in the excited atomic states would have to be very extensive. Fortunately, it turns out that all of the excited atomic states relax together subsequent to shock heating. The characteristic activation energies for exciting the atomic states appear to be about equal to the energies of the first excited states. For describing the excitation, therefore, we shall lump the excited atomic states together and write the chemical equation

$$A = A^*   \qquad [1]$$

assuming for chemical kinetics purposes that the energy required for this step is the first excitation energy of the noble gas concerned.

(The first excited electronic states of all of the noble gases are actually metastable states not connected by electric dipole transitions to the ground states. If A^* is taken to be the lowest excited state of a noble gas atom, then it will automatically have a radiative lifetime sufficiently long that A^* persists until it can participate in collisional processes. On the other hand, there are excited electronic states of noble gas atoms that do have dipole transitions to the ground states; these states are just slightly more energetic than the metastable states. Since atoms in these states have very short radiative lifetimes, they will generally decay radiatively before undergoing collisional processes. However, the emitted radiation is "resonance radiation" (12) and will be absorbed by another atom before travelling far through the gas; it is said to be "trapped" or "imprisoned" in the gas. The trapping of this radiation has the same effect kinetically as the trapping of electronic excitation in a metastable atom, namely, that the electronically excited atom A^* will be able to undergo collisional processes before the excitation energy escapes as radiation from the gas. The accuracy of energy measurements by shock-tube methods is not sufficient to distinguish between the different types of excitation. We shall therefore omit the distinction in our discussion and assume that A* represents whichever of the lowest lying states actually participates in the subsequent collisional processes.)

The next least energetic process is ionization by formation of the diatomic molecule ion

$$A + A^* = A_2^+ + e^- \qquad [2]$$

Since the dissociation energy of noble gas molecule ions is rather low, they will be expected to dissociate rapidly compared to their rate of formation

$$A_2^+ + M = A + A^+ + M \qquad [3]$$

Once a few electrons are produced in the gas, they will also be able to undergo collisional excitation and ionization processes.

$$e^- + A = A^* + e^- \qquad [4]$$

$$e^- + A^* = A^+ + 2e^- \qquad [5]$$

The direct formation of ions is of course also possible for energetic electron-atom collisions

$$e^- + A = A^+ + 2e^- \qquad [6]$$

Reactions [4] and [6] are particularly important in the study of noble gas plasmas, not only because they turn out to be rather important in the ionization process, but also because they can be studied in other types of experiments.

Reactions of impurities are another thermal source of electrons in a noble gas. Even the most rigorous methods of purification and the most careful execution of experiments usually leave a few parts per million of impurities in a noble gas. Since the ionization potentials of the expected impurities are several volts lower than the ionization potentials of the noble gases themselves, formation of ions from the impurities would be expected to be much more rapid than ionization of the noble gas atoms. The molecular identity of trace impurities is difficult to establish, and it is therefore customary to regard the impurities simply as unknowns and to consider that collisional processes can lead to their rapid ionization at the shock front.

$$Imp + M = Imp^+ + M + e^- \qquad [7]$$

Plasmas are very bright; it has been found that photoexcitation and photoionization processes can be quite important in shock-wave generated plasmas. A number of different types of photochemical processes can be envisaged.

First, there are the interactions of the plasma light with the noble gas atoms themselves.

$$hv + A = A^*$$ [8]

$$hv + A^* = A^+ + e^-$$ [9]

$$hv + A = A^+ + e^-$$ [10]

The wavelengths needed for these processes are well known from spectroscopic investigations. For the most part, the corresponding absorptivities are also known. Less well known are the photo-ionization processes for the impurities, although it is certain that they occur as supplements to the collisional ionization process

$$hv + Imp = Imp^+ + e^-$$ [11]

The photoelectric effect can also be responsible for supplying electrons to the gas from the walls of the shock tube, once again with uncertain efficiency

$$hv + Wall = Wall^+ + e^-$$ [12]

Radiation from the plasma can occur from the reverses of reactions [8] through [11] and also as continuum emission from free-free bremsstrahlung due mostly to

$$A^+ + e^- = A^+ + e^- + hv$$ [13]

Regardless of the origin of the electrons, they have at first very low kinetic energy compared with the noble gas atoms. Owing to the very large difference in mass between electrons and atoms, the collisional transfer of energy required to raise the distribution of electron kinetic energies to the distribution characteristic of the translational temperature of the gas is very inefficient. Heating of the electrons is therefore one of the rate limiting processes in shock-generated noble gas plasmas. When it is important to distinguish between hot (thermalized) and cold electrons, one can so note, and write the thermalization reaction as

$$e^-(cold) + M = e^-(hot) + M$$ [14]

considering that the actual process does not occur in a single collision but rather as a result of a large number of thermalizing collisions.

The electron thermalization problem is but one part of a larger difficulty in describing energy relaxation in shock-generated plasmas. Passage of an element of gas through a shock front results first in imparting energy to the translational motion of the noble gas atoms. As the gas relaxes to equilibrium, a very large fraction of this translational energy is transferred to supplying the ionization and excitation energies needed for the previous reactions, and in very hot shocks a substantial part of the energy may also be in the form of radiation. It is therefore a nontrivial problem to write the energy conservation equation for shock flow in an ionizing gas. This is complicated also by the energy escape route from the plasma afforded by radiation. Radiation from the plasma acts not only as a plasma cooling mechanism, but also as an energy transfer mechanism which can heat and photolyse gas far ahead of the shock wave. Each of these effects will be shown later to complicate not only the theoretical analysis of strong shocks in the noble gases, but also the practical understanding of the operation of the diagnostic methods used to observe the process of ionization.

The high mobility of electrons creates another problem that is otherwise absent in shock-tube research. Since strong shock waves are often studied at low pressures, electron diffusion can affect the concentration gradients of electrons in a manner similar to the effect of hydrogen atom diffusion upon the profiles of laminar flames. This effect is enmeshed with the electron-thermalization rate, (that is, reaction [14]) and for accurate results the final extraction of electron reaction rates (rates of reactions [4–6]) can only be done by computer analysis of the observed ionization profiles.

The foregoing remarks suffice to indicate the type of processes that one may expect to occur in the ionization of noble gases in shock waves. We turn now to the experiments that have been done to investigate these processes. Let us note first that the lighter noble gases, helium and neon, have not been given much attention in shock-tube research. Their low atomic weights and high ionization potentials imply that extraordinary shock drivers are required to produce ionization in these gases. Argon is heavy enough to be shocked conveniently to ionizing temperatures, and has been studied most extensively. Krypton and xenon have been the subject of a sufficient number of studies that comparisons can be made between the results of several workers.

Let us consider first the work of Harwell and Jahn (13) on the earliest stages of ionization in argon, krypton, and xenon. These authors studied relatively weak shock waves (M_s from 7 to 10) by a microwave technique that was sensitive to electron concentrations 10^{11}–10^{13} cm^{-3}. The impurity level in the experimental gases used was extraordinarily low, less than 1 ppm. After correcting the observed microwave data for the characteristics of the detectors and for attenuation of the shock waves, it was found that the initial growth of electron concentration was linear in time (Fig. 4). When the ionization rates were plotted on Arrhenius graphs, linear plots were obtained (Fig. 5). The energies of activation were far below the ionization potentials of the respective gases. For argon, (IP = 15.8 eV) Harwell and Jahn obtained $E_A = 11.9$ eV; for krypton (IP = 14.0 eV), E_A was found to be 10.4 eV; and for xenon (IP = 12.1 eV), E_A was found to be 8.6 eV. These activation energies compare quite well with the first excitation energies of the noble gas atoms which are 11.6, 9.9, and 8.3 eV, respectively. On this basis, Harwell and Jahn concluded

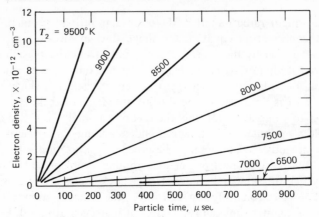

Figure 4   Rate of initial ionization in argon ($P_0 = 5$ torr) at various temperatures. At electron concentrations greater than 10^{13} cm^{-3} the microwave method for measuring electron concentration no longer works (13).

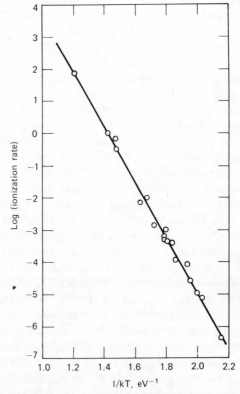

Figure 5   Arrhenius graph for the initial ionization rate in argon ($P_0 = 5$ torr). The slope corresponds to an activation energy of 11.9 eV, compared to the ionization potential of 15.8 eV (13).

that the ionization they observed was due to the atomic excitation process reaction [1] as the rate-limiting step, followed by ionization in a faster atom-atom process

$$Ar + Ar^* = Ar^+ + Ar + e^- \qquad [15]$$

This atom-atom process is indistinguishable kinetically from the combination of reactions [2] and [3] if [3] is much faster than [2]. Harwell and Jahn attempted to demonstrate that the ionization process they observed was second order in the argon density, but were only partly successful due to the small range of conditions which could be studied by their methods. They also investigated the role of impurities, and found that impurity levels of a few parts per million made substantial changes in the ionization rates and activation energies.

Two main conclusions are to be drawn from the work of Harwell and Jahn. First, if the initial ionization process is to be studied without complications due to impurities, then the impurity concentration must be less than 1 ppm. Second, the activation energy for the initial ionization process appears to correspond to the first excitation energy of the noble gas atom, indicating that the rate-limiting step is excitation of the atom in reaction [1]. It should be remembered that these conclusions refer only to the initial ionization; other processes will be found to predominate in later stages.

Kelly (14) continued the work of Harwell and Jahn using improved techniques and also studied ionization in argon-xenon mixtures (15). Arrhenius graphs of the initial rates were used as in the work of Harwell and Jahn to obtain activation energies. Since Kelly was able to obtain an accurate calibration of the sensitivity of his instrument for electron concentration measurements, he obtained reliable rate constants for reaction [1] for argon, krypton, and xenon. Kelly expressed the rates in terms of excitation cross-sections in the form

$$Q = C(E - E_0)$$

where E is the center-of-mass relative energy, E_0 is the threshold energy for excitation, which Kelly took to be the first excitation energy, and C was determined from the experiments to be 1.2×10^{-19} cm^2 eV^{-1} for Ar, 1.4×10^{-19} cm^2 eV^{-1} for Kr, and 1.8×10^{-20} cm^2 eV^{-1} for Xe. These values proved to be able to reproduce the experimental ionization-rate data within $\pm 15\%$ over a factor 3 variation in starting pressure, which may be taken as a satisfactory verification that the process is second order in the noble gas concentration. The values of the relative cross-sections are quite surprising, there being no ready explanation either for the argon and krypton cross-sections being approximately equal to one another or for the xenon cross-section being an order of magnitude smaller than the other two. Another unusual effect noticed in xenon was that in low temperature runs there was a rapid increase in ionization to about 2×10^{11} electrons cm^{-3} at the shock front, followed by a slower rise that correlated well with the atom-atom rate expected from higher temperature measurements. This level of ionization is plausibly attributable to full ionization of the impurities in the shock tube, but there is no ready explanation for it to be present in xenon runs, but absent in argon and krypton runs.

In xenon-argon mixtures the main ionization is of the xenon atoms, since the ionization potential of xenon is far lower than that of argon. Both argon atoms and xenon atoms, however, are available as collision partners for reaction [1]. By separating the xenon-xenon ionization rate from the rate in the argon-xenon mixture, Kelly was able to measure the cross-section slope constant C for argon-xenon excitation collisions, obtaining the value 1.8×10^{-20} cm^2 eV^{-1}. Since this is the same as the xenon-xenon cross-section, one may conclude that excitation cross-sections in the energy ranges studied here are independent of the collision partner.

It should be noted that the relative rates of the initial ionization process would be in the same ratios as the cross-section slope constants given here regardless of the shape of the cross-section function which actually pertains to atom-atom ionization processes. Kelly's choice was based on his theoretical preference, and not upon experimental measurement of the cross-section function.

Another demonstration of the importance of impurities at the parts-per-million level is provided by the probe experiments of Frohn (16). Frohn employed a shock tube capable of ultra-high vacuum operation and measured electron concentrations in argon shocks with a probe technique. Whereas a linear increase in ionization was observed when the impurity concentration was reduced to 10 ppm, a parabolic increase was observed when the impurity concentration was reduced below 1 ppm, as shown in Fig. 6. These preliminary results are not in accord with the results obtained by Kelly, who observed a linear increase in ionization at the same stated impurity concentration, and over the same range of electron concentration (14). Kelly and Frohn both employed sophisticated methods, yet their results are not in agreement; clearly we must be cautious in accepting the conclusions of other authors using less stringent precautions to suppress impurities in the test gas.

The papers of Harwell and Jahn and of Kelly were taken as a starting point in this section because of the apparent reliability of their results and the care which they took in the execution of their experiments and in the interpretation of the microwave data. These authors were not the first, however, to conclude that reaction [1] was the rate-limiting process for the initial ionization of shocked noble gases. This conclusion was reached by several earlier authors also. The earlier investigators, however, were, in most cases, using indirect plasma diagnostics and gases with impurity levels well above the parts per million level. Johnston and Kornegay (17), for example, using gases with

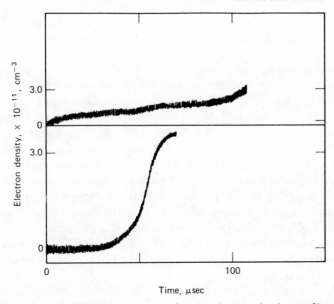

Figure 6 Influence of impurity concentration on electron density profiles in argon shocks. The Mach number was 8 and the starting pressure 8 torr for both shock waves. The upper trace corresponds to [Imp] $10 <$ ppm, while the lower trace corresponds to [Imp] < 1 ppm (16).

impurity levels in the parts per thousand range, interpreted their microwave data in much the same terms as did Harwell and Jahn and Kelly. They also obtained an activation energy equal to the first excitation energy in xenon. In view of the high sensitivity to impurities demonstrated by Harwell and Jahn, it might seem at first sight that the results of Johnston and Kornegay, and other authors to be discussed later, would give the correct activation energy only by coincidence. Although this may be partly true for some of the diagnostics for ionization rate that were used, many of the processes that involve impurities are also initiated by reaction [1], and will also have the apparent activation energy of [1]. If the initial ionization mechanism is correct, therefore, any observations which depend on the concentration change of A* might give the temperature dependence of the ionization as well. It is possible, however, to draw quite different conclusions from apparently similar experimental studies when the impurity level is high. An example would be the study of Hacker and Bloomberg (18), who monitored the visible emission intensity from the shock front as well as microwave attenuation by the electrons. The conclusions drawn by these authors do not resemble those of the other authors mentioned so far.

We shall return to the subject of the initial ionization, considering in particular the processes that can supplement the atom-atom process at higher shock strengths, after considering the reactions that ensue after the electron concentration has reached a sufficiently high level that the consequences of electron-atom processes are important.

It is a well known fact of plasma physics that the cross-sections for excitation and ionization of atoms by electron impact are much larger than the corresponding cross-sections for equally energetic atomic collisions. (A simple explanation is that relative velocity is much greater in an electron-atom interaction than in an equally energetic atom-atom interaction, so that the former is a much more effective quantum-mechanical perturbation and consequently more likely to lead to a change in quantum state or to ionization.) On this basis we would expect that as soon as atom-atom processes (reactions [1] and [2], or processes involving impurities) have introduced enough electrons, electron-atom processes will become much more important than the atom-atom processes, and that the former will completely dominate the subsequent ionization history. As previously mentioned, we would also expect that the electron-atom processes will be retarded by inefficient energy transfer between atoms and electrons.

The earliest investigators of ionizing shock waves in noble gases were guided by just these considerations in interpreting their results. After the existence of a dense plasma in strong argon shocks had been quantitatively proved by spectroscopic (19) and electrical (12) measurements, Petschek and Byron (20) undertook to investigate the kinetics of the ionization process by probe and radiation measurements. They observed the latter stages of the approach to ionization equilibrium in argon shocks with $11 < M_s < 18$ by probe and continuum emission measurements. They considered the rates of electron heating, that is, reaction [14], and the rate of electron impact excitation and ionization, that is, the rates of reactions [4] and [5], in their interpretation of the results. The rate of ionization was shown to depend only on the rate of electron heating, the calculated ionization-growth rate being essentially independent of the assumed cross-sections for electron-impact excitation and ionization. In order to assess the contribution to the ionization from processes preceding the dominance of electron-impact processes, Petschek and Byron extrapolated their ionization growth rate back to the shock front and concluded that other processes were contributing about 10% of the total ionization. Since probe and emission measurements are far less sensitive than the microwave measurements which were later used to study the initial ionization, Petschek and Byron were unable to observe this process directly and had to base their conclusions on indirect arguments and on theory. They rejected atom-atom processes as probably being too inefficient to contribute significantly, calculated the absorption of plasma radiation by argon and found that it would cause insufficient ionization, and then considered thermal and photochemical ionization of impurities. Both of these processes were considered to be possible, but Petschek and Byron were not able to account for the total initial ionization they estimated on the basis of the impurity level they calculated for their experiments.

The basic difficulty with Petschek and Byron's analysis turned out to be that they considerably underestimated the cross-section for the atom-atom excitation process, and were incorrect in dismissing its contribution as unimportant. Several later authors, building upon the Harwell and Jahn measurements of the initial ionization rate, developed theoretical descriptions of the entire ionization profiles in argon which were in moderately good agreement with the data of Petschek and Byron, and also with later observations of the latter stages of ionization (21–25). It will not be necessary for us to consider any of these theoretical investigations in detail; suffice it to say that each of the papers cited has a different theoretical formalism for handling the algebra of calculating ionization profiles, but that all of them come quite close to predicting quantitatively the Petschek and Byron results as well as later results.

The use of radiation profiles or probe measurements to define ionization profiles in shock-wave generated plasmas is not highly recommended for definitive experiments, since they are not in agreement with one another (20,21) and only connected to the ionization profile through indirect theoretical models. A far better procedure is dual wavelength interferometry, a technique first suggested and used for study of shock-wave generated plasmas by Alpher and White (26). The range of usefulness of the conventional Mach-Zehnder interferometer is such that electron concentrations within an order of magnitude of 10^{17} cm^{-3} can be measured with microsecond or submicrosecond resolution, which is admirably suited to study of the later stages of ionization in strong noble gas shocks. (An elegant modern version of this technique is described in the following section.) Experimental investigations of argon shocks using this method were reported by Wong and Bershader (22) and Oettinger and Bershader (24), the former also reporting emission observations. These authors were able to show that the transition from predominantly atom impact ionization to predominantly electron impact ionization occurs at a degree of ionization between 10^{-4} and 10^{-3} for shock Mach numbers between 12 and 18. After the electron impact takeover, the ionization growth becomes approximately exponential until ionization is virtually complete and recombination reactions begin to be important. Oettinger and Bershader give a particularly complete (except for the role of impurities) theoretical treatment of the ionization process in shocks in the Mach number range they studied. Their treatment includes the main effects of radiation from the plasma. They obtained ionization profiles in good agreement with experiment both in the ionization region and in the radiative cooling region, which we discuss in more detail later. A comparison of their theoretical calculations with experiment is shown in Fig. 7. The electron and atom temperatures calculated from a Mach 18 shock in argon using their theoretical formalism is shown in Fig. 8. In criticism of their work, it must be said that they were not able to find a consistent atom-atom cross-section which would explain the ionization delay times in all of their runs. Similarly, Wong and Bershader (22) had to reduce the Harwell and Jahn cross-section by a factor of 2.5 to obtain agreement with the ionization delay times observed by them. These difficulties may be connected with impurity effects, which may have been of some importance in their experiments. Another possibility is that the linear excitation cross-section formula used by Kelly (14) is not suitable for higher temperature experiments.

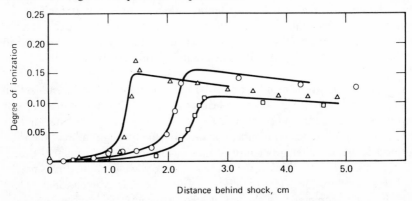

Figure 7 Comparison of calculated and observed ionization profiles behind argon shocks. In this figure (and in Fig. 8) distance rather than particle time is shown as the independent variable. $\bigcirc$: $M_s = 16.3$, $P_0 = 3$ torr; $\triangle$: $M_s = 16.3$, $P_0 = 5$ torr; $\square$: $M_s = 15.0$, $P_0 = 5$ torr (24).

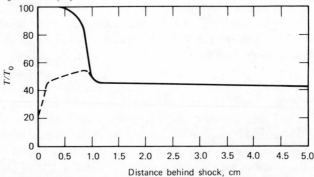

Figure 8 Temperature profiles calculated for a Mach 18 shock in argon, with $P_0 = 3$ torr, $T_0 = 296.5°K$. Atom and ion temperature (solid line); electron temperature (dashed line). The electronic temperature of the atoms and ions would be expected to follow the electron temperature (24).

We turn now to a consideration of the more physical rather than chemical consequences of electrons being present in strong noble gas shocks. Several early investigators noticed that electrical and optical signals could be detected at large distances ahead of the shock front, and the term " precursor " signals was coined to designate the observations. In experiments with electromagnetic shock tubes these signals are very strong and are connected with the behavior of the driver plasma; we shall ignore the experiments with electromagnetic shock tubes in this connection, since these studies were mostly concerned with very strong shocks where chemical reactions are not of interest. Precursor signals in pressure-driven glass shock tubes were first studied systematically by Weymann (27) and Gloersen (28). Weymann used electrostatic and magnetic probes to study precursor electrical signals in argon shocks with $8 < M_s < 12$. The electron density was found to be about 10^7 cm^{-3} one meter ahead of the shock front. Gloersen measured electrical signals on external rings in shocks of comparable strength in xenon. Although the electrical precursors must have been a surprise to the first investigators, there are, in retrospect, at least three processes which one might reasonably expect could lead to large electron concentrations ahead of ionizing shocks, namely photoelectric emission from the shock-tube walls, photo-ionization of the test gas or impurities from plasma radiation, or electron diffusion. It might be thought that diffusion could be ruled out because it would lead to charge separation and therefore large retarding fields. This was in fact the assumption of Petschek and Byron (20). More detailed consideration, however, shows that the possibility of electron diffusion can not be dismissed so easily. In the first place, the thermal velocities of electrons behind the shock front are very large, typically some 300 times the thermal velocities of argon atoms in ionizing shocks. The mean free paths of electrons in argon are unusually long due to the Ramsauer-Townsend effect (27). Finally, the actual electrical field in a shock tube is a three-dimensional field, rather than a simple gradient along the tube axis which acts to reduce the retarding effect of charge separation. These three effects have made the possibility of significant diffusion of electrons seem plausible enough that extensive theoretical investigations of the magnitude of electron diffusion under shock-tube conditions were carried out (29–31). Pipkin developed the consequences of a simple model that succeeded in reproducing the main features of Weymann's observations. Wetzel (30), on the other hand, found that a more detailed theoretical model was inconsistent with the proposal that electron diffusion could be responsible for the observed electron concentrations. Appleton (31) investigated the behavior of the electron concentration profile at the shock wave and found electron concentration which were not inconsistent with Pipkin's analysis.

The question of the origin of the precursor electrons was resolved experimentally (32,33). Weymann and Holmes (33) measured both the ion and the electron profiles upstream of ionizing argon shocks with probes and found that the positive and negative currents were proportional to one another. The only process which one would expect to produce equal numbers of ions and electrons in the gas is photo-ionization. They confirmed this by imposing an axial magnetic field of sufficient strength to retard radial electron diffusion almost completely, and found the expected loss of probe signal. Photoelectric emission from the walls is also eliminated by these results, although it was already known from the polarity of the signals in Weymann's original work (27) that photoelectric emission was not the source of the precursor electrons.

Knowing that the precursor ionization is due to photo-ionization ought to be sufficient to allow identification of the relevant photo-ionization processes and quantitative measurement of photo-ionization cross-sections, but this has in fact proved to be a rather difficult problem. In the first place, the degrees of ionization measured by different later workers do not seem to be consistent (34–37). The theoretical considerations based upon these studies are also divergent in respect to the conclusions drawn with regard to the relative importances of impurity and noble gas ionization, and the relative contributions of line and continuum plasma radiation. It seems clear, however, that very small impurity concentrations are sufficient to contribute measureably to the precursor ionization at long distances from the shock front (31).

The radiation from noble gas shocks has been the subject of numerous experimental studies, many of which have been directed toward discovering the elementary reactions responsible for it. A number of theoretical studies have also been undertaken, primarily with a view toward understanding the effects of radiative energy transfer. One effect of this energy transfer is a contribution to the excitation and ionization processes that we have discussed heretofore. A second effect is to cool the plasma. Whereas there are large measures of disagreement concerning the proper way to handle the theory of the first effect, the second one seems to be well understood and in good agreement with the experimental observations. Since the radiative cooling is also concerned with chemical reactions in the plasma, we shall consider it briefly here (34–41). The reactions that occur during the initial excitation and ionization continue to occur later in the ionized gas flow, but there the reverse reactions become significant. Accounting for the later stages of the flow therefore involves finding out which of the reverse reactions [–1] to [–15] dominate in the equilibration and cooling mechanisms. The reaction kinetics problem is severely complicated by the presence of photons again, just as it was in the initial stages of the flow (34–41).

We have already alluded to the fact that the binding energies of the noble gas molecules and molecule ions are too small for these species to have anything more than a transient existence in shock-wave generated plasmas. They have nonetheless been held to contribute to the emission processes in shocked xenon (28,42–45). The arguments used to support this suggestion were based primarily on the observation that the activation energy associated with the continuum emission from xenon shocks was found to be the same as the energy of the first excited atomic state, which could form an excited Xe_2^* molecule capable of continuum emission. In view of the success of other authors in correlating the behavior of the continuum emission with the behavior of "free-bound" emission predicted by the Kramers-Unsöld theory (46), as well as the finding that the ionization of the noble gases itself is characterized by an activation energy equal to the energy of the first excited atomic state, it is probably safe to conclude that molecular continuum radiation does not contribute significantly to the radiation from noble gas plasmas in shock waves.

Free-bound emission is emitted in what is essentially the reverse of reaction [9]

$$e^- + A^+ = A^* \qquad [-9']$$

where the asterisk now denotes the entire manifold of excited atomic states, rather than only the first one. Since most of the relevant excited states are characterized by very large principal quantum numbers, it is a good approximation to use hydrogenic wave functions to describe these states and to consider the free-bound emission in noble gas plasmas in terms of the theory of free-bound emission in a hydrogen plasma. The predictions of the theory that can be tested experimentally are the brightness, the quadratic dependence upon the degree of ionization, the temperature dependence, and the spectrum. All of these have been thoroughly investigated for shock-wave generated plasmas in argon, krypton, and xenon (47–55). Although there are some details that are not in complete accord with the theory, it is clear from the overall good agreement that the continuum emission is predominantly due to the reverse of reaction [9] in all shock-wave generated noble gas plasmas.

The line emission from the noble gas atoms and atomic ions has also been studied with a view either toward measuring the line shape and brightness to determine whether the atomic states were in local thermodynamic equilibrium with the plasma or in attempts to derive kinetic information to determine the contributions of radiative energy transfer to the several stages of the ionization process (19,43,49). It appears that the local thermodynamic equilibrium assumption is valid for the resonance states, and that the line profiles are in accord with expectations for the plasma conditions investigated. Due to the large number of lines with unknown radiative lifetimes, calculating the kinetic effects and cooling effects of line radiation is a less certain matter (36,50). As far as the resonance states are concerned, the trapping effect mentioned previously limits the radiative effects to such short ranges that they may be neglected for kinetics purposes. Most of the line emission, however, is not resonance radiation, and can escape the plasma to provide both cooling and photolysis. The uncertain photolytic consequences of the line emission have been mentioned previously in connection with the contribution of impurity ionization to the initial ionization process in noble gas shocks.

Direct identification of the ionic species present in noble gas shocks has been achieved by mass spectrometric sampling of the plasma (56–59). The sampling is accomplished by allowing gas to escape from the plasma through a pinhole in the end plate of the shock tube. Theoretical calculations show that even though the ions must diffuse through a rather thick boundary layer before they enter the mass spectrometer, the resulting ion spectra give valid ion profiles of the plasma created in the reflected shock wave. Sturtevant and Wang (56,57,59) used very low starting pressures in their studies, so that the pressure in the plasma was of the order of 0.1 atm or less. The Xe^+ profile they found in a xenon shock is shown in Fig. 9. It shows just the behavior we would expect from the interferometric studies of the electron concentration profiles. When the mass spectrometer was set to observe the profiles of other

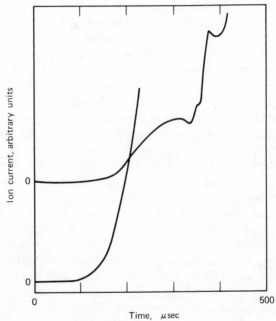

Figure 9   Concentration of Xe^+ as function of time after shock reflection. The shock temperature before ionization was 7700°K, and the equilibrium degree of ionization was 12%. The lower oscilloscope trace has four times the sensitivity of the upper one. At 300 μsec a secondary wave arrives at the end plate to terminate the experiment just after ionization equilibrium has been attained (56).

ions in the plasma, however, quite startling results were obtained. (Fig. 10) A large number of different ions appear, and two of them, H^+ and O^+, are clearly more important in the early stages of ionization than the noble gas ion, in this case Ar^+. Whether or not this behavior should be compared with other studies of the initial ionization (for instance, Refs. 13 or 14) is not certain, for the impurity level in these experiments was relatively high to start with, due to the unusually low starting pressures employed, and it is also likely that the arrival of the shock wave at the end plate of the shock tube removed substantial amounts of impurities from the wall right in front of the sampling inlet. In a subsequent study (59) in which the impurity level was reduced to

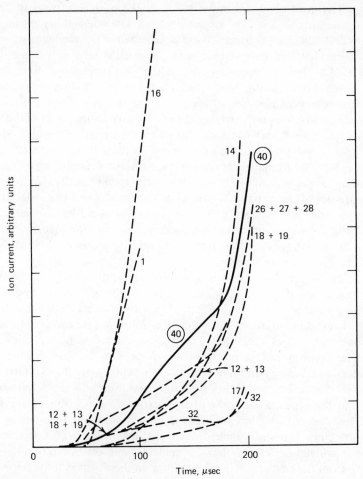

Figure 10 Ion currents for various m/e ratios for reflected shocks in argon. The temperature before ionization was 16,600°K (56).

about 50 ppm, the temperature dependence of the initial ionization rate in argon was studied between 10,000 and 14,300°K and found to correspond to an activation energy of 12.4 eV, just as was found in the high purity microwave experiments of Kelly (14). The implications of this result are uncertain again in light of the large impurity concentration.

Creswell, Di Valentin, and Dove (58) used more conventional starting pressures (about 5 torr) in their experiments, using a similar technique for mass sampling but a time-of-flight rather than a magnetic mass analyzer. They found that the noble gas atoms (Kr^+ or Xe^+) were the principal species after long times, but that many other ions appeared early in the ionization history. The most abundant impurity ion at the start was found to be K^+, with smaller amounts of Na^+ appearing also. The other abundant impurity ion was NO^+, which was formed more slowly than K^+. Among the other ions which were identified were H_2O^+, H_3O^+, and many ions with masses in the range 25–32. These authors suggest that the alkali metal ions were formed from material removed by the shock wave from the sampling orifice, or perhaps from colloidal particles suspended in the test gas. These authors also searched for precursor ions arriving at the sampling orifice ahead of the shock wave. Finding none, they conclude that under their relatively mild conditions ($T = 5000°K$) the precursor ions concentration must be less than 10^7 cm^{-3}.

It is indeed unfortunate that the mass spectrometric studies have not been carried out as yet with noble gases of the purity used by Kelly (14) for microwaves studies of the initial ionization, or with shocks strong enough to give detectable precursor ionization. Such experiments would be very valuable in identifying the photo-ionization processes responsible for precursor ionization and in separating the atom-atom and impurity processes dominating the initial ionization in noble gases.

In concluding this section, it is of interest to mention that some work has been done on shock ionization of helium. Due to its high sound speed, helium cannot be ionized in conventional pressure-driven shock tubes, but the required shock strength can be achieved with high explosive drivers (60) or with electromagnetic shock tubes (61). The studies reported so far have done little more than confirm that the shock waves generated in these devices behave in an understandable way and that plasmas sufficiently dense for detailed study can be produced. The complications of the electromagnetic shock tube experiment and the expense and noise of high explosive shock tubes have so far precluded study of chemical reactions in helium plasmas generated by these methods. Since helium (with hydrogen, discussed in the next section) is a system in which one believes that the elementary processes can be interpreted starting from the fundamentals of quantum mechanics, it is to be hoped that research on ionizing shock waves in helium will continue.

IV. DIATOMIC GASES OTHER THAN AIR

Strong shock waves in diatomic gases show five types of relaxation leading to thermal and chemical equilibrium. Two of them, vibrational and rotational relaxation, are thermal only and do not involve chemical reactions. The other three—dissociation into atoms, excitation of electronic degrees of freedom, and ionization—have reaction mechanisms susceptible to kinetics studies. Vibrational relaxation and the rates of dissociation of diatomic molecules have been studied extensively in shock-tubes experiments, and numerous emission studies on relaxation of molecular electronic states have been done. Relatively few papers on the kinetics of rotational relaxation or ionization have appeared in the literature, however. The paucity of rotational relaxation studies is basically due to the fact that rotational relaxation is too fast for convenient study in shock tubes, and can only be observed by difficult reflection methods (62) or by working at very low pressures (63). The paucity of mechanism studies on ionization of diatomic molecules, however, is only due to relative lack of interest. In this section we present the few results that have been reported for nitrogen and hydrogen. A study of ionization in nitric oxide is described in Section V.

The only direct observations of shock-wave generated ionization in nitrogen are due to measurements by Valentin and Cottereau (64). They used a probe technique to measure the conductivity behind incident nitrogen shocks from 4 to 6 km sec^{-1}, and concluded that the equilibrium conductivity was attained. They did not report kinetic results.

Many primarily spectroscopic studies of the equilibrium radiation from ionizing shocks in nitrogen have been reported, most of them directed toward detailed understanding of the radiation from hot air. The radiation consists of atomic and ionic line emission, molecular band emission, and a strong continuum. In the ir spectrum, the continuum is Kramers' radiation due to free-free interactions (65–69)

$$e^- + N, N_2 = e^- + N, N_2 \qquad [16]$$

In the vacuum uv, the continuum is principally due to atomic ion free-bound transitions

$$e^- + N^+ = N^* \qquad [17]$$

The visible emission was found to be due to atomic free-free transitions, reaction [16], and also to the free-bound process (67):

$$e^- + N = N^{-*} \qquad [18]$$

Virtually all of the spectral studies are in excellent accord with theory.

[For an outstanding example of agreement see Buttrey, McChesney, and Hooker (70); for an observation of lack of thermal equilibration in the (B–X) molecular band emission from N_2^+, see Allen (71).] The spectral properties of hot nitrogen are discussed in connection with air radiation in detailed reviews (72).

The only paper dealing explicitly with the kinetics of ionization in nitrogen shocks is that of Wray (73), who monitored the emission profiles of the first positive system (B–A) of N_2 and the first negative system (B–X) of N_2^+ in incident shocks over the temperature range 7000–18,000°K. Wray's apparatus included a pulsed discharge which permitted him to convert the test gas partially to nitrogen atoms, in yields up to 20%, just prior to shock heating. By comparing the profiles of the two emission intensities over a range of preshock atom concentrations and temperatures, Wray was able to separate the contributions from molecular and atomic processes. He proposed that the ionization process involves the mechanism

$$N_2 + N_2 = N + N + N_2 \tag{19}$$

$$N + N = N_2^+(X) + e^- \tag{20}$$

$$N_2^+(X) = N_2^+(A) = N_2^+(B) \tag{21}$$

$$N_2^+ + N = N_2 + N^+ \tag{22}$$

with reaction [20] being the rate limiting step for ionization, while reactions [21] and [22] are essentially in equilibrium under his conditions. On theoretical grounds, he argued that reaction [20] would not be expected to proceed from the ground state atoms, and that reaction [20] is actually

$$N^* + N = N_2^+ + e^- \tag{23}$$

the asterisk denoting nitrogen atoms in one of the two excited electronic states ^2D or ^2P. Since no evidence was available on the rates of excitation of ground state N atoms to the ^2D or ^2P states, Wray simply assumed that the excited states would be in local equilibrium with ground-state atoms. The initial slopes of the N_2^+(B–X) emission profiles were in reasonable agreement with theoretical slopes calculated for the mechanism (reactions [19–22]) using the rate constant for reaction [20] given by Lin and Teare (2). Quantitative agreement was not obtained, however. The role of atom excitation processes in nitrogen shocks deserves further study. The direct molecular process

$$N_2 + N_2 = N_2 + N_2^+ + e^- \tag{24}$$

contributed, again according to calculations made with the rate constants of Lin and Teare, only at the highest temperatures studied.

Hydrogen presents a severe problem for shock-tube research, because its very high sound speed implies that extraordinary driving methods are required in order to achieve strong shock waves. At the same time, hydrogen is the one gas in which we expect behavior which we would like to believe can be understood a priori on a quantum mechanical basis. It is therefore very gratifying that a successful experimental study of ionization in shock-heated hydrogen was carried out by Belozerov (74). To obtain the necessary high velocity waves, Belozerov used a Phillipov pinch (75) as the driver. The ionization process was monitored by an elegant double-frequency interferometer, which used a ruby laser and a KDP second harmonic generator as the light source.

Since the double-frequency interferometer affords an accurate and reliable method of monitoring the density and the ionization simultaneously, the dissociation relaxation and the ionization relaxation could be followed independently. It was found in preliminary experiments that in the shock speed range from 28 to 34 km sec^{-1} the two processes could be separated from one another. It was also found, unfortunately, that the Phillipov pinch driver gave "blast waves", rather than steady shock waves, in this speed range (5). This effect had to be taken into account in reducing the interferometric data.

In a gas of hydrogen atoms, the electron temperature is only slightly different from the atom temperature. This fact permitted substantial simplification of the theoretical analysis compared with the noble gas cases considered in Section III. It was further found on theoretical grounds that radiative ionization processes were negligible compared to collisional ones for the conditions studied. This reduced the data analysis to consideration of impurity ionization, atom-atom processes, and electron-atom processes. It was assumed that the 5 ppm of impurities were ionized at the shock front and that the subsequent ionization was due to a combination of atom-atom and electron-atom processes. Since the cross-sections for excitation and ionization of hydrogen atoms by electrons are known (76), the only uncertainties are the atom-atom excitation and ionization cross-sections. Belozerov assumed these excitation and ionization cross-sections to be equal, and then used the ratio of atom-atom to electron-atom excitation cross-sections as the single adjustable parameter to bring the calculated and observed experimental results into agreement. It was found that good agreement was obtained assuming the atom-atom cross-section to be about 1/50 of the known electron-atom value, $\sigma_e = 5 \times 10^{-17} (10.2 - E)$ cm^2. (76)

It is unfortunate that only a single study of ionization relaxation in hydrogen is available. In view of the extreme difficulty of doing the experiment, however, it is fortunate that the results obtained by Belozerov provide such a clear picture of the processes. Summarizing them in terms of chemical reactions, then, we have

$$\text{Imp} + H_2 = e^- + \text{Imp}^+ + H_2 \qquad [25]$$

$$H_2 = 2H \qquad [26]$$

$$H + H = H^* + H \qquad [27]$$

$$H^* + H = H + e^- + p^+ \qquad [28]$$

$$e^- + H = H^* + e^- \qquad [29]$$

$$e^- + H^* = H + e^- \qquad [30]$$

Transitory formation of H_2^+ is of course possible, as in the noble gas plasmas considered in Section III.

V. AIR

Plasmas in air are the most important of all shock-wave generated plasmas from a practical point of view, since they are generated as a consequence of supersonic flow past meteors and space vehicles returning to the earth's atmosphere and also in strong explosions. The rates of ionization and de-ionization in strong air shock waves determine the effectiveness of communications and of radar tracking in critical situations, and it is therefore not surprising that fundamental research has been done on this topic by many investigators. As far as moderately strong ionizing shock waves are concerned ($M_s < 27$, or 9 km sec^{-1}, corresponding to $< 1\%$ ionization), the observations seem to be well described by a straightforward reaction mechanism with quite well known rate constants. In very strong shock waves ($M_s > 27$), which are beyond the range of the aforementioned practical interests, there arise complications due to electron-atom collisions and to radiation coupling to the shock wave, and the theoretical and experimental situations become less clear. Three extensive reviews of the moderate strength situation have been published (2,77,78); see also (72,79). The present review modifies the viewpoints expressed in Refs. 77 and 2 only to the extent of incorporating some later results which indicate a few quantitative adjustments to the rate constants of these references and define more clearly the transition to very strong shock behavior.

We consider air to be composed of nitrogen and oxygen only; the role of trace constituents in ionizing shock waves in air has not been considered in enough theoretical or experimental detail to warrant our discussing it here.

A strong shock wave in air has five different types of relaxation processes, all of which must be considered simultaneously for a complete description of the approach to equilibrium. We can simplify matters somewhat by assuming that the thermal relaxation, that is, vibrational and rotational equilibration, is essentially complete before dissociation and ionization commence. Obtaining an adequate description of the chemical relaxation then amounts to determining the contributions of several elementary processes to the approach to chemical and ionization equilibrium. This problem was first solved in detail by Lin and Teare (2). Subsequent refinements of their procedures and assumed rate constants have done very little to alter their picture of ionization relaxation in air. Their paper should be consulted for references to the earlier experimental papers on air ionization.

The chemical history of the neutral species in shocked air was assumed by Lin and Teare to be determined by the elementary reactions

$$O_2 + M = O + O + M \tag{31}$$

$$N_2 + M = N + N + M \tag{32}$$

$$NO + M = N + O + M \tag{33}$$

$$O + N_2 = NO + N \tag{34}$$

$$N + O_2 = NO + O \tag{35}$$

$$N_2 + O_2 = NO + NO \tag{36}$$

The initial atomization is governed by the rate of reaction [31], since the dissociation energy of O_2 (5.1 eV) is much less than that of N_2 (9.8 eV). Formation of the equilibrium concentrations of N and NO then follows from reactions [34] and [35], and later from reaction [33]. Reaction [36] was at one time thought to be fast enough to be important (80); subsequent work (81) showed that this was not the case. The resulting neutral species concentration profiles are shown in Fig. 11.

Lin and Teare then considered in detail the possible rates of all types of processes which could affect the ionization profile, including electron and ion impact processes, photo-ionization, charge exchange, electron attachment, and ionization in neutral atom and molecule collisions. The rates of these processes were taken from experimental data where possible and supplemented by theoretical estimates. For the conditions which they studied only the atom-atom reactions turned out to be really significant. At the highest shock speed they considered, 9 km sec^{-1}, photo-ionization and electron impact still contributed less than one-third to the total ionization rate. The relative contributions for a typical air shock are indicated in Fig. 12.

Of all possible atom-atom processes, the chemi-ionization reaction

$$N + O = NO^+ + e^- \tag{37}$$

was found to be the most important, owing essentially to its low endoergicity (2.8 eV) compared with the next most favorable reaction

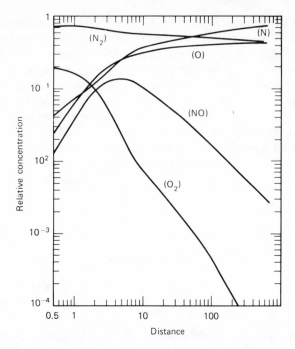

Figure 11 Computed relative atom and molecule concentrations for a relatively weak ($M_s = 20$) ionizing shock in air. The equilibrium relative concentrations depend on the pressure. In this calculation the starting pressure was 0.02 torr (2).

$$N + N = N_2^+ + e^-$$ [38]

for which $\Delta H = 5.8$ eV. Thus ionization relaxation in air shocks is governed by one of the best known and best understood of all atom-atom processes (82).

The description given in the preceding paragraphs was supplemented, but not basically altered, by subsequent experimental work. One of the uncertainties in the analysis was the rate of reaction [36]. Measurements of the decomposition rate of nitric oxide (77,80) had been interpreted in terms of a rate-constant expression for the reverse reaction that would imply a significant forward reaction rate in shocked air. A subsequent investigation by Camac and Feinberg (81) showed, however, that nitric oxide is formed in air shocks only by the reactions [31], [34], and [35].

In a shock-tube mass spectrometer study of ionization of 2% NO in Kr, Creswell, DiValentin, and Dove (83) confirmed that NO^+ was the dominant ion formed, but were unable to explain their results in terms of the rate of reaction [37] found by others, their ionization rates being too high to be accounted for by reaction [37] alone. They consider that another process must be operative in NO ionization, probably involving intermediate excitation of

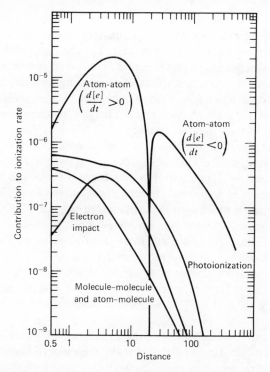

Figure 12 Computed contributions of various ionization processes to the ionization profile of the shock wave of Fig. 10. Most of the atom-atom rate is due to reaction [28]. Note that in contrast to noble gas shocks, electron impact contributes only a minor amount to the total ionization (2).

NO to an excited electronic state

$$NO + M = NO^* + M \qquad [39]$$

$$NO^* + M = NO^+ + e^- + M \qquad [40]$$

The contribution of reactions [39] and [40] to the ionization process in air shocks would be expected to be small, since by the time NO is generated, N and O atoms are also present in high concentrations. Impurity ions found to be present in low concentration included H_2O^+, H_3O^+, Na^+, and K^+.

Air ionization was studied by a probe method in an ultra-clean (ultimate vacuum 7×10^{-8} torr) shock tube by Frohn and de Boer (84). They obtained an ionization rate compatible with Lin and Teare's rate constant expressions (2), and hence with the microwave reflection measurements of Lin, Neal, and Fyfe (47). From their work it can be concluded that impurities do not play a major role in air ionization.

In a primarily instrumental paper, Koch and König (85) measured the velocity of ionizing shock waves in air as a function of distance from the diaphragm of their shock tube. The profile they found was the expected one, namely an increase followed by a decrease. The changes, however, were rather larger than expected, corresponding to differences of several hundred degrees in shock temperature over a distance of three meters. Experimenters studying ionization profiles over longer periods of time clearly should measure the attenuation of their shock waves and take the temperature variation into consideration in their data analysis (8).

Two subsequent investigations of air ionization in essentially the same low-temperature range as the work of Lin, Neal, and Fyfe (47) have indicated that the rate of reaction [37] used by Lin and Teare (17) was too low. Thompson (86), who monitored nitric oxide by its ir emission and ionization by a hollow-collector Langmuir probe over the temperature range 3000–5000°K, suggested a factor 3 increase. A factor 3 increase was also suggested by Taylor, Scharfman, and Morita (87), who used probe measurements of ionization for air shocks with $8 < M_s < 26$. In a rather different type of experiment, involving rapid expansion of air ionized in a reflected shock wave, Stein et al. (88) concluded that their value for the reverse rate at 2900°K is in agreement with the Lin and Teare value if a $T^{-3/2}$ temperature dependence for the reverse rate is assumed.

The high- and low-temperature data for reaction [37] were examined critically by Hansen (82). He concluded that the theory of dissociative recombination and all of the experimental data were in accord with the expression (for the reverse rate) $\alpha = 4.8 \times 10^{-8} (kT)^{-1/2} (1 - e^{-0.27/kT})$ cm^3 sec^{-1}, where kT is expressed in eV. This value for the rate of reaction [37], together with the rates of the other reactions given by Wray (77) and Camac and Feinberg (81), probably represent the best available values for the reaction rates pertinent to hot air. Three limitations of this set of reactions should be noted. First, electron attachment becomes important for lower strength shock waves due to the relatively high (~ 0.5 eV) electron affinities of species such as NO_2, O, O_2, and O_3; therefore, reactions forming and among their negative ions then need to be considered. Second, it has been found in purely theoretical studies (89) that electron attachment to NO^+ (reaction [28]) actually results in production of excited nitrogen atoms in high yield. Therefore, it may be necessary to consider the excited atomic states for some purposes. Finally, air actually contains other elements besides nitrogen and oxygen; at high altitudes in particular, reactions of species not considered here may play important roles.

An extension of air studies to higher shock strengths was carried out by Wilson (90), who used the diagnostic method of monitoring the degree of ionization by following the ir bremsstrahlung emission at 6 microns. He confirmed that reaction [37] dominates the ionization mechanism for shock speeds below 9.5 km sec^{-1}, but found that electron impact was the dominant mechanism at higher shock speeds. As may be expected, shock structure in air at very high shock speeds becomes complex, and cannot be fully described without considering the effects of radiation. The Kramers' radiation is intense enough to provide efficient radiative cooling, and radiative coupling to the shock front can also occur in a manner quite analogous to the noble gas cases considered in Section III.

An extension of air studies to lower shock strengths was undertaken by Sutton (91). The results were in accord with the earlier work of Lin, Neal and Fyfe (47).

An opportunity to investigate deionization processes directly is afforded by the shock tunnel technique, in which a test gas sample is heated to a high "reservoir" temperature in a reflected shock wave and then expanded rapidly in a nozzle. If ionization equilibrium has been established in the reservoir, then the subsequent nozzle expansion to lower temperature and density must lead to lower degrees of ionization down the nozzle. Following the decrease in ionization with emission observations, microwave methods, and probes yields direct rate information on the processes which dominate the ionization. This technique was used by Dunn and Lordi to measure the rate of [–37] in expanding air flows (92); to measure the rate of [–38] in expanding nitrogen flows (93); and to measure the rate of [–41] in expanding oxygen flows (94)

$$O + O = O_2^+ + e^- \qquad [41]$$

These measurements are particularly important for the opportunity they give to compare shock tube data directly with room temperature dissociative recombination experiments. Reasonable agreement was found for all cases, using the theoretical analysis introduced by Hansen (82).

Many shock-tube experiments have been concerned with the equilibrium spectroscopic properties of hot air. These have been treated in extensive review articles (72).

VI. CHEMI-IONIZATION

Chemi-ionization refers in principle to any chemical reaction leading to ionization in excess of the thermal equilibrium value. Although this might seem to include a wide range of possible reactions, the phenomenon seems to be restricted almost entirely to the reactions of oxygen with organic compounds. As far as shock-tube studies are concerned, chemi-ionization has been observed only in the reactions of oxygen with acetylene, methane, ethane, propane, ethylene, benzene, and formaldehyde and, to a far smaller degree, in the reaction of iodoform with acetylene. By implication from flame experiments, for example by the observed universal applicability of the flame ionization detector in gas chromatography, chemi-ionization would be observed under similar conditions regardless of the nature of the organic compound.

The fact that combustion can give rise to ionization has been known for a very long time indeed, having been essentially discovered by Faraday (95). Studies of the reaction mechanisms leading to ionization in flames (96,97) were already numerous at the time shock-tube studies of combustion began, and it is not at all surprising that combustion initiated by shock waves also produces ions. As it turned out, however, the first indication that elementary reactions energetic enough to cause ionization were occurring in shock waves was in a study of ultraviolet chemiluminescence by Kistiakowsky and Richards (98). They observed pulses of vacuum ultraviolet chemiluminescence in the wavelength range 1500–1770Å, corresponding to photon energies of 160–200 kcal, in the shock-initiated combustion of acetylene. Noting that this energy is also sufficient to produce ions, Hand and Kistiakowsky (99) looked for and found ionization in similar shock waves by a probe technique.

The conditions studied by Hand and Kistiakowsky are quite typical of those studied by later workers. They used small concentrations of oxygen and acetylene in a large excess of argon (97%), and shocked the mixture to a temperature in the range 1400–2500°K. Their starting pressure was 1 torr, whereas later investigators of the reaction used somewhat higher pressures. (Unstable shock waves, tending to turn into self-sustaining detonations, occur if starting pressures of 10 torr or higher of such acetylene/oxygen/argon mixtures are used.) Their plasma diagnostic was intended to be a Langmuir probe, but after encountering difficulties similar to those of Petschek and Byron (20), they treated the probe operation as a conductivity measurement in the manner previously used by Basu and Fay (100) in a study of ionization in detonation waves in acetylene-oxygen mixtures.

The ionization was found to behave in a manner quite analogous to the vacuum ultraviolet and also the blue $CH(^2\Delta)(^2\Sigma-^2\Pi)$ chemiluminescence. After an induction period of some 10 μsec, the ionization increased exponentially, peaked, and then decayed slowly. (Fig. 13) Quantitative study of the behavior of the exponential growth constants with temperature showed that they behaved just as the chemiluminescence growth constants, suggesting that the intermediate species responsible for the chemiluminescence were closely related to the ones responsible for the chemi-ionization. Hand and Kistiakowsky suggested that the ionization proceeded by the reaction already suggested by several flame studies.

$$CH^* + O = CHO^+ + e^- \qquad [42]$$

where the asterisk indicates a CH radical in the $A(^2\Delta)$ or $B(^2\Sigma)$ excited electronic states. Since these are the same states responsible for the blue chemiluminescence, the parallel behavior of the ionization and the blue emission is

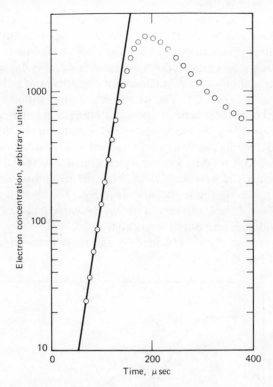

Figure 13 Dependence of probe current on time in an acetylene-oxygen ($C_2H_2/O_2/Ar =$ 1.2/1.8/97) shock at 2575°K. The initial pressure was 1.0 torr. The straight line demonstrates that the ionization is produced in reactions of closely coupled to the branched chain reactions of the acetylene-oxygen explosion. The decay of the ionization is due to second order dissociative recombination processes (99).

explained. They attributed the vacuum ultraviolet emission to CO ($A^1\Pi$) formed in the reaction

$$CH^* + O = CO(A^1\Pi) + H \qquad [43]$$

which in turn explains the parallel behavior of the ionization and the vacuum ultraviolet emission. The source of CH^* was considered to be

$$C_2H + O_2 = CO_2 + CH^* \qquad [44]$$

or

$$C_2H + O = CO + CH^* \qquad [45]$$

which again were previously suggested by studies in flames. (Later experiments, however, led to reconsideration of all of these conclusions.)

The acetylene oxidation experiments were continued by Glass, Kistiakowsky, Michael and Niki (101–104) using two complementary experimental techniques. The first was an extension of the work of Hand and Kistiakowsky in incident shock waves using a probe to measure electron density and photomultiplier/filter stations for a simultaneous measurement of emission intensity either from CH* or from C_2^*. The second was a time-of-flight mass spectrometer arranged to analyze samples taken from the gas in reflected shock waves by a small nozzle. The mass spectrometer was operated in two different modes. In the first, no ionizing electron beam was used and the detector was sensitive only to positive ions produced in the shock-heated gas. In the second mode, the ions from the gas were kept away from the mass analysis section by a repeller grid while the bulk gas was analyzed. The overall array of four diagnostics allowed these workers to obtain a complete picture of the evolution of the oxidation and of the ionization.

A typical reaction profile obtained by the mass spectrometer method is shown in Fig. 14.

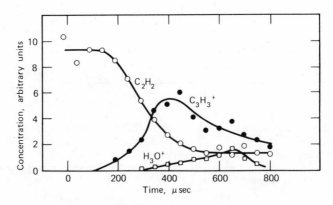

Figure 14 Concentration profiles for C_2H_2, $C_3H_3^+$ and H_3O^+ in a reflected shock wave with $T = 1600°K$, $C_2H_2/O_2/Kr = 2/3/95$ (103).

Their experimental observations may be summarized as follows:

1. The main reaction appears to be a typical branched chain explosion, the principal products H_2O, CO, and CO_2 rising rapidly to their equilibrium values after C_2H_2 and O_2 begin to disappear.

2. The exponential growth constants for the CH* emission and the ionization are identical.

3. The exponential growth constant for ionization is approximately twice that for the production of CO, H_2O, and CO_2.

4. The first chemi-ion observed is $C_3H_3^+$, which remains an abundant

species; other ions, the most prominent of which is H_3O^+, appear later and are clearly the result of ion-molecule reactions.

5.   Study of the temperature and composition dependence of the ratio of ionization to chemiluminescence shows that the two are not intimately related, despite their identical time constants. In the case of $C_2H_2/O_2 = 2$ mixtures near $1900°K$, the exponential rise of ionization continues long after luminescence entirely disappears.

6.   When CO is added to the reactant gas, $C_3H_3^+$ showed a rather different profile; its normal rapid decay is replaced by a slow decay and later by a final slow increase.

7.   The absolute yield of $C_3H_3^+$ is about 10^{-6} of the yield of CO.

The authors considered that the bulk chemistry of the oxidation is adequately interpreted by the following mechanism.

$$H + O_2 = OH + O$$
$$O + C_2H_2 = OH + C_2H$$
$$OH + C_2H_2 = H_2O + C_2H$$
$$C_2H + O_2 = 2CO + H$$
$$C_2H + O_2 = CH + CO_2$$
$$C_2H + C_2H_2 = C_4H_2 + H$$
$$C_4H_2 = ?$$
$$CO + OH = CO_2 + H$$
$$H + C_2H_2 = H_2 + C_2H$$
$$O + H_2 = OH + H$$
$$O + C_2H_2 = CO + CH_2$$
$$CH_2 = ?$$

The mechanism of chemiluminescence was proposed to be the same as previously suggested by Hand and Kistiakowsky. The behavior of the $C_3H_3^+$ ion, however, suggested that the traditional assumption from flame experiments that it was a secondary ion produced by ion-molecule reactions was incorrect. They suggested the single elementary step

$$CH + C_2H_2 = C_3H_3^+ + e^- \qquad [46]$$

The thermochemical consequences of postulating this step were considered by Kistiakowsky and Michael (102) to be in accord with theoretical expectations.

Support for the assumption that this reaction is responsible for chemi-ionization in the acetylene-oxygen reaction was provided by iodoform-acetylene experiments undertaken by Glass and Kistiakowsky (101). They found that acetylene/argon mixtures and iodoform/argon mixtures gave probe currents for positive ions that were orders of magnitude smaller than in acetylene-oxygen shocks, whereas a mixture containing both iodoform and acetylene (7.5 torr Ar, 0.027 torr CHI_3, 0.075 torr C_2H_2) gave maximum ionization about 1/50 as large as in a typical acetylene-oxygen shock at the same temperature. The mechanism assumed to account for the ionization is

$$CHI_3 = CHI_2, CHI, CH + I$$
$$CH + C_2H_2 = C_3H_3$$
$$CHI + C_2H_2 = C_3H_3I$$
$$C_3H_3I = C_3H_3{}^+ + I^-$$
$$C_3H_3 + I = C_3H_3^+ + I^-$$
$$CHI + C_2H_2 = C_3H_3^+ + I^-$$

Thermochemical analysis of the data indicated that the heat of formation of $C_3H_3^+$ was probably lower than the value of 11.7 eV suggested by mass spectrometry (105); it was therefore concluded (101,102) that in acetylene-oxygen mixtures reaction [46] could account for the chemi-ionization. Reaction [42] was simultaneously eliminated from consideration due to the observed differences between the CH emission profiles and the ionization profiles.

The conclusion of these workers that $C_3H_3^+$ was the major if not the only primary ion produced under their experimental conditions was subjected to some criticism based on flame and room temperature flow system results (106). The essence of the defense of reaction [46] as opposed to reaction [42] is that CHO^+ ions were not detected in the shock-tube mass spectrometer experiments and would have to react with acetylene by a reaction such as

$$CHO^+ + C_2H_2 = C_3H_3^+ + O \qquad [47]$$

at a rate corresponding to 5 times faster than gas kinetic collisions in order to account for their absence from the experimental spectra. Such high reaction rates are well known in ion-molecule chemistry, but it would appear unlikely that this particular one would have anything like the Langevin cross-section.

The intensive experimental study given to the acetylene-oxygen reaction was followed by extensive studies of the oxygen and chemi-ionization of methane, formaldehyde, and ethylene using the same experimental techniques (103,107,108). The oxidation of methane in shock waves proves to have a complicated mechanism under most experimental conditions. The ionization profiles of methane oxidation in shock waves were qualitatively similar to, but quantitatively different from the profiles in acetylene oxidation (103). The complexity of the observations was such that mechanistic interpretation was not attempted. It can be surmised that the mechanism is probably similar to the mechanism of methane oxidation in flames. Recent experiments on the main course of the reaction indicate that the degenerate chain character of methane oxidation in shock waves can be avoided by working at very high pressure (109). It is possible that the ionization mechanism could also be studied in high-pressure shock-tube experiments.

The chemi-ionization yield in the oxidation of formaldehyde was found to be about one order of magnitude less than in the oxidation of acetylene (107). The only ions detected were CH_3O^+ and H_3O^+. The latter was found to be the major species, but CH_3O^+ appeared at the same time as H_3O^+. The probe current was found to rise exponentially in time with an exponential growth constant about three times larger than the growth constants measured in the mass spectrometer for H_2O. The total ionization appeared to have a very small dependence upon temperature. Finally, no CH chemiluminescence could be detected. This set of facts would appear to be a good foundation for postulation of a chemi-ionization mechanism. Unfortunately, this is frustrated by the fact that the mechanism of the oxidation itself does not fit into the conventional branched-chain category, as do the oxidations of acetylene and hydrogen. Instead, the oxidation of formaldehyde under the conditions of these experiments appeared to be first a decomposition to form among other things hydrogen, which then underwent its usual branching-chain reaction with oxygen to produce the eventual explosion. The uncertain nature of the reactions of the atoms and radicals with formaldehyde and its decomposition products prevented drawing any conclusions about the likely reactions leading to chemiluminescence. One could regard the essential difficulty as residing in the fact that in formaldehyde there is already a carbon-oxygen bond; most elementary steps which one would like to propose for liberating sufficient energy to cause ionization involve initial formation of a carbon-oxygen bond. Perhaps a trade-off reaction of the type suggested by these investigators (107)

$$CHO + CHO = CH_2 + CO_2 \qquad [48]$$

is effective in producing species energetic enough to lead to ionization.

The oxidation of ethylene (108) was the last reaction in which mass spectrometer and probe measurements were used to investigate chemi-ionization. In following the course of the main reaction, it was found that a major part of the reaction leads to formation and then to subsequent oxidation of acetylene. Not surprisingly, then, the ionization was found to proceed in a manner very similar to the ionization accompanying the oxidation of acetylene. All of the observations were consistent with the supposition that the mechanism of chemi-ionization in the oxidation of ethylene was identical to the mechanism of chemi-ionization in the oxidation of acetylene.

An interesting alternative pathway for ion production is suggested by room-temperature flow experiments on the reaction of O atoms with carbon suboxide radicals. Emission from the (A-X) transition of CO was found by Bayes (110) to show positive intensity perturbations at rotational lines having accidental near-degeneracy with the metastable $I'\Sigma^-$ state, thus indicating that one of the products of the $C_2O + O$ reaction is $CO(I'\Sigma^-)$. Reaction of

$CO (I'\Sigma^-)$ with H atoms would be energetic enough to lead to production of $CHO^+ + e^-$. The following mechanism might therefore be operative in producing chemiions in the acetylene-oxygen reaction.

$$O + C_2H_2 = C_2O + H_2$$
$$C_2O + O = CO + CO(A'\pi \text{ or } I'\Sigma)$$
$$CO(A) = CO(X) + hv$$
$$CO(I) + H = CHO^+ + e^-$$
$$CHO^+ + C_2H_2 = C_3H_3^+ + O$$

Subsequent investigations of chemiionization in the acetylene—oxygen reaction brought several new features to light, some of which are in substantial disagreement with the results of Kistiakowsky and coworkers.

Burke, Dove, and Kane (111) studied the reaction in reflected shock waves using a dynamic sampling technique and a quadrupole mass filter. Their observations covered a much wider range of composition than the earlier studies. The findings were in general agreement with the earlier ones, with an important exception. The exception is that $m/e = 29$ (CHO^+) was a prominent ion, present in all but the richest mixture experiments. The difference between this finding and the absence of $m/e = 29$ in the earlier results (101–104) is so far unexplained. Acceptance of the Burke, Dove, and Kane result would have the effect of removing the large discrepancy between the flame results on the initial ionization process (96–97) and the shock tube results.

Matsuda and Gutman (112) investigated ionization and CH* emission growth rates in reflected shock waves in $C_2H_2/O_2/Ar$ mixtures using techniques that allowed them to make measurements much earlier in the reaction than was possible with the techniques used previously. They used a total collection technique for electrons, rather than a Langmuir probe, and observed the emission intensity from the end wall of the shock tube rather than from the side. The increased sensitivity led to totally different findings about the growth constants for ionization and CH* emission than were obtained earlier. In particular, it was found that the growth constants for CH* emission were equal to the growth constants for major species, but 1/2 of the growth constants for ionization. This means that two chain centers react to form the primary chemiion, rather than one as in reaction [46]. This does not, however, establish the traditional reaction [42] as the primary ion source, since there is still no obvious way that CH* can be produced in a reaction involving only one chain center. Matsuda and Gutman offer a calculation showing that the concentration of $C_3H_3^+$ could exceed the concentration of CHO^+ by factors of 100 or larger during the induction period, even if the latter is the primary ion.

In view of the apparent impossibility of finding a reaction mechanism that can account for what appear to be the major observations of chemiionization rates in shock waves, we must conclude that the initial ionization process is unknown. It is clear that new and different experiments are needed if this question is to be settled.

In all of the investigations mentioned so far the primary emphasis has been on discovering the elementary reactions which are responsible for producing ions. It is also observed in these experiments, however, that the ionization eventually decays, and it is appropriate to consider the possible ways in which this decay occurs. This question was investigated by Wilson and Evans (113). These workers studied the rate of recombination of electrons with ions behind hot (2500–5500°K) incident shock waves in lean hydrocarbon/oxygen/argon mixtures using a microwave phase-shift technique to monitor the electron density. The spatial resolution of their apparatus was insufficient to follow the rapid jump in ionization at the end of the induction period, but it was able to follow more accurately than the probe measurements of Hand and Kistiakowsky (99) the absolute value of the ionization during the slow decay.

In reducing the experimental data, the reasonable assumptions were made that the concentrations of negative ions were negligible and that ion-molecule reactions were so much faster than the de-ionization reactions that the relative positive ion concentrations do not change. Since most of the mixtures studied were lean ones, the predominant ion is H_3O^+ and it could be assumed that $[e^-] = [H_3O^+]$. The electron decay would then follow second-order kinetics if the reaction responsible for decay of ionization is the expected dissociative recombination. This was indeed found to be the case. (Fig. 15) From the experimental records for ionization decay in acetylene/oxygen and methane/oxygen shocks, second-order rate constants ("recombination coefficients") were obtained over the temperature range 2500–5500°K. The temperature dependence of the recombination coefficient taking the acetylene/oxygen and the methane/oxygen mixtures together was found to be given by the expression $\alpha = 1.08T^{-1.98}$ cm^3 sec^{-1} ± 8%. Extrapolated to room temperature, this expression yields $\alpha = 1.3 \times 10^{-5}$ cm^3 sec^{-1}. This value is considerably higher than the values typical of dissociative recombination of diatomic molecules, for which numerous room temperature experiments yield $\alpha \cong 10^{-7}$ cm^3 sec^{-1}. If the temperature dependence can indeed be extrapolated down to room temperature using the expression obtained by Wilson and Evans, then it is reasonable to conclude that the reaction responsible for the recombination involves the polyatomic H_3O^+ ion

$$e^- + H_3O^+ = H_2O + H \text{ (or other neutrals)} \qquad [49]$$

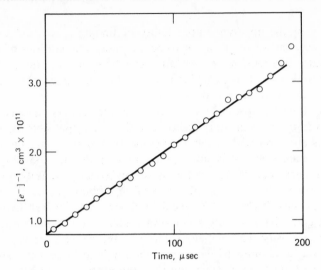

Figure 15 Second order electron density decay plot observed by a microwave method. The test gas composition was $C_2H_2/O_2/Ar = 1/5/94$. The shock temperature was $3030°K$ (113).

There is some doubt about the validity of the extrapolation, however. The available measurements of the temperature dependence of dissociative recombination processes following pulsed discharges all indicate that a T^{-1} dependence is followed. Furthermore, 1.3×10^{-5} cm^3 sec^{-1} seems to be too high in comparison for example with dissociative recombination of electrons with $N_2O_2^+$ or N_4^+, both of which have recombination coefficients of 2×10^{-6} at room temperature and also follow a T^{-1} dependence (114). The identification of H_3O^+ as the recombining ion must therefore be regarded as tentative.

The results for methane and acetylene oxidation were compared with mixtures of oxygen with ethane, ethylene, propane and benzene in shocks near $3800°K$. The recombination coefficients appear to be the same as for acetylene and methane fuels within the scatter of the data. In some of the mixtures studied it would be expected that ions other than H_3O^+ were present in large concentrations. The recombination rate is however apparently unaffected. The recombination coefficients were in good agreement with the available values from flame studies.

The work of Wilson and Evans shows clearly that the mechanistic complexity of the processes leading to chemi-ionization in shock waves is balanced by mechanistic simplicity of the process (or processes) responsible for ionization decay in the same shock waves. While it is unfortunate that the identity of the recombining ion is not as clearly established as one would wish, the apparent lack of dependence of the recombination rate on ion composition indicated that the identity of the recombining ion is not important for any practical purpose. The T^{-1} dependence of the recombination coefficient is not in accord with theoretical expectation or experimental findings on other recombinations, and deserves further investigation.

VII. METALS, ALKALI HALIDES, AND RELATED SYSTEMS

One of the uses of a shock tube is as a spectroscopic light source for ultraviolet and visible emission studies of atomic and atomic ion spectra. Since the conditions of excitation in a shock wave are more similar to the conditions of thermal excitation in the outer layers of stars than any other laboratory spectral source, astrophysicists turned to the shock tube for information on atomic spectra, in particular on absolute emissivities or f-numbers of metal atoms and metal ions. In the course of this research it was noted that chemistry as well as physics is involved in establishment of thermal equilibrium radiation, and it subsequently turned out that this chemistry is quite interesting in its own right. Our interest now is in plasmas containing metal ions, in particular alkali metal ions. Since alkali metal atoms have the lowest ionization potentials of all the elements, they are the most easily ionized thermally, and their study in the shock tube would be of interest on that account alone.

The principal experimental difficulty in studying metals in the shock tube is the obvious one of getting them into the gas phase. Except for mercury, cesium, and potassium, which have substantial vapor pressures at low temperatures, all of the metals studied had to be introduced into the shock tube in some form of aerosol, usually an aerosol of a compound of the metal, or in the form of some compound which has a high vapor pressure, such as tetraethyl lead or hexacarbonyl chromium. Since the aerosol must first evaporate before gas phase reactions leading to atomic excitation and ionization can occur, the analysis of experimental results on shock waves through aerosols is complicated by the presence of a poorly understood preceding physical process.

The first report on ionizing shock waves in metal vapors was the work of Haught (115) on argon-cesium mixtures. Haught shocked mixtures of 0.5–3% Cs in about 5 torr of Ar to temperatures in the range 4000–10,000°K, and observed the radiation emitted from the plasma. In time-integrated experiments he found that the luminosity was mostly due to atomic lines of cesium. In time-resolved experiments he found that the total luminosity showed a slow rise, followed by a pulse and then a decay to the equilibrium value (see Fig. 16). Haught defined characteristic times for the pulse delay and the pulse duration, and from their temperature dependence showed that the activation energy for the ionization was 1.4 eV, compared to the ionization potential for

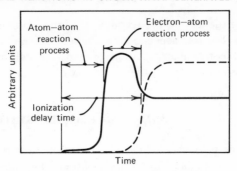

Figure 16 Luminosity profile (observed, solid line) and ionization profile (estimated, dashed line) for shock waves in argon–cesium mixtures. The profiles shown are qualitative only. The indicated ionization delay time was used as a quantitative measure of the ionization rate (115).

cesium of 3.89 eV. The luminosity delay times appeared to be independent of the argon concentration and proportional to the -0.6 and 0.0 powers of the cesium concentration; the pulse duration was found to be independent of both the cesium and the argon concentration. Haught proposed an ionization mechanism quite similar to the conventional noble gas mechanism

$$Cs + M \ (Ar, Cs) = Cs^+ + e^- + M \qquad [50]$$

$$Cs + e^- = Cs^+ + 2e^- \qquad [51]$$

The role of impurities in these experiments is not entirely clear. On the one hand, from the inert gas results one would expect that the initial electrons would be from ionization of impurities. Cesium is so reactive, however, that it might have gettered the unshocked gas so thoroughly before the shock wave that the concentration of impurities was effectively zero.

In this mechanism the origin of the luminosity overshoots lies in the accumulation of Cs in excited atomic states in greater than equilibrium concentrations prior to ionization of the excited atoms. While this is plausible enough, it remains to be seen whether the relative cross-sections for excitation and ionization are actually far enough different that this simple mechanism proposed by Haught is capable of explaining the luminosity profiles quantitatively.

Further experiments on cesium ionization kinetics were described by Louis (116), who used a cesium aerosol in 50 torr of argon as the test gas. The temperature range studied was 2000–5000°K. The ionization rate was measured by monitoring the free-bound continuum radiation intensity. The conclusion reached was that the ionization rate was limited by the rate of electron heating, reaction [14]. The situation appears to be quite similar to the argon situation as described originally by Petschek and Byron (20).

The ionization process in pure potassium vapor was investigated by Hill and Capp (117). They followed the progress of ionization by measuring the current drawn by probes flush with the shock tube wall, obtaining signals such as shown in Fig. 17. Over the shock speed range $3.2 < M_s < 4.6$ they

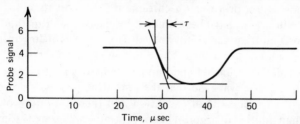

Figure 17 Ionization profile for a shock wave in potassium vapor. The initial slope of the conductivity was used as shown to define ionization times τ, which served as data points for studying the temperature dependence of the ionization rate (117).

found that the rate of ionization appeared to increase with temperature in a way that suggested an activation energy of 1.9 ± 0.3 eV. Since the ionization potential of potassium is 4.3 eV, these authors interpreted the temperature dependence as again indicating a two-step ionization process involving the first excited state at 1.6 eV. The analogy to the inert gas mechanism is pleasing, but in view of the limited accuracy of their results it can only be taken as suggestive.

Shock-wave generated plasmas in sodium vapor were studied spectroscopically by Rothe (118) in reflected shocks over the temperature range 6000–10,000°K. Rothe concluded that the electron-attachment process in the equilibrium plasma was primarily forming sodium atoms in the higher angular-momentum states, that is, that the rate of

$$Na^+ + e^- = Na^*(P, D) \qquad [52]$$

was much greater than the rate of

$$Na^+ + e^- = Na^*(S) \qquad [53]$$

He did not investigate the mechanism of ion production.

Preliminary results on mercury vapor have also been reported (119). The experiments consisted of spectroscopic observations on mercury vapor shocked from $p_0 = 10$ torr to $10 < M_s < 16$. The emission was found to consist of a strong continuum overlaid by the complete arc line spectrum, confirming that the shocks do produce a mercury plasma. No information suggesting the mechanism of ionization was reported, however.

The concentrations of metal atoms and metal ions can be measured simultaneously in hot gases by monitoring the intensity of their emission lines with a multiple wavelength spectrometer. The necessity of an absolute calibration can in principle be circumvented by using the equilibrium emissivities measured in the same apparatus used for kinetic studies; it happens, however, that in the two cases studied so far, the absolute emissivities were also measured. The ionization processes in chromium (120) and titanium (121), each highly dilute in argon, have been studied by the emission method.

Shackleford and Penner (120) studied shock waves in mixtures of hexacarbonyl chromium and argon. The compound $Cr(CO)_6$ is sufficiently unstable that it may be assumed to be completely dissociated to Cr atoms and CO in the incident shock wave, so that the ionization process studied in the reflected shock wave consists of excitation and then ionization of chromium atoms in a high dilution of argon. The concentration of excited atoms Cr(I) was followed by monitoring the intensity of both resonance and nonresonance emission lines. The profiles were similar for both cases. (Fig. 18) The Cr(I)

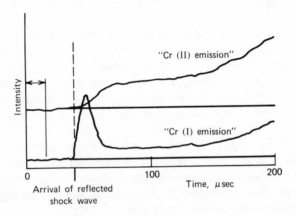

Figure 18 Emission signals from neutral chromium atoms [Cr(I)] and chromium ions [Cr(II)] generated in a reflected shock wave. The slow changes observed after 100 μsec are gasdynamic in origin and are not related to the ionization kinetics (120).

emission began to rise at the reflected shock-wave front, passed through a maximum and decreased to a steady state corresponding to thermal equilibrium, and later began a slow rise due not to any kinetic process but to density and temperature changes related to nonideal reflected shock flow. The profiles of the Cr(II) ion emission also began to rise at the reflected shock front. The rate of Cr(II) formation increased as the Cr(I) profile passed through its maximum, then decreased as the equilibrium ionization was approached asymptotically. The duration of the Cr(I) emission pulse was approximately the same as the time required for the ionization to proceed essentially to completion. The mechanism proposed to account for the results is

$$Cr = Cr^* \qquad [54]$$

$$Cr^* = Cr^+ \qquad [55]$$

where all electronically excited states of the atom are lumped together in
Cr^* and all excited states of the ion are lumped together in Cr^+. The similar
behavior of the Cr(I) emission lines from origins with widely separated energy
(5.6 eV versus 2.9 eV) provides good justification for considering all of the
excited states together, as does the additional finding that the activation
energy of the ionization relaxation time (3.1 eV) is approximately equal to the
energy of the lowest electronic level. Since very small chromium carbonyl
concentrations were used (43–360 ppm), the excitation and ionization processes are limited to Cr-Ar and Cr-e^- collisions, with the latter having a much
larger cross-section. The ionization mechanism would therefore appear to be
quite similar to the inert gas ionization mechanism discussed in Section III.
The level of impurities in the $Cr(CO)_6$ experiments was probably high enough
that impurity ionization provided a sufficient concentration of electrons at the
reflected shock front to allow the excitation and ionization process to be
dominated by electron-atom collisions throughout.

A similar mechanism was postulated by Boni (121) to account for his
experiments on titanium ionization, although the emission profiles observed
were rather different than for chromium ionization. Boni studied shocks in
$TiBr_4/Ar$ mixtures containing about 100 ppm of $TiBr_4$ using essentially the
same apparatus as Shackleford and Penner (120). The Ti(I) emission profiles
were quite similar to the Cr(I) profiles, but the Ti(II) ion profiles did not
approach the equilibrium levels assymptotically, as did the Cr(II) profiles.
Instead, they had maxima very similar to the Ti(I) profiles (Fig. 19). The
activation energy for the time between shock heating and the emission
maximum was found to be 2.1 eV for Ti(I) and 2.5 and 2.7 eV for two lines of
Ti(II), compared with the first excitation energy of 2.4 eV. The maxima in the

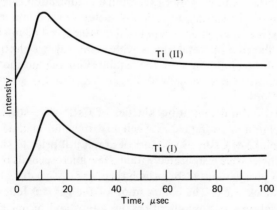

Figure 19 Emission signals from neutral titanium atoms [Ti(I)] and titanium ions
[Ti(II)] generated in a reflected shock wave (121).

Ti(II) profiles were explained as being due to further excitation of Ti(II) to unobserved levels, including multiple ionization. The mechanism postulated is thus

$$TiBr_4 = Ti + 4Br$$
$$Ti = Ti^*$$
$$Ti^* = Ti^+$$
$$Ti^* = Ti^{+*}$$

The possibility of nonadiabatic dissociation to form Ti^+ and Br_x^- ions directly (*vide infra*) was not considered as a possible ionization mechanism.

The overall picture of the state of knowledge on thermal excitation and ionization of metal atoms is unsatisfactory from the viewpoint of a chemical kineticist, and the results quoted in the foregoing paragraphs should be regarded as only suggestive of the underlying mechanisms and indicative of the need for further experiments in this area. The principal shortcomings of the experiments is that they are too few in number and variety of method. The chromium data, for instance, were taken from only seven shock waves. Moreover, the mechanisms postulated do not explain all of the experimental results and are in fact in serious conflict with some of them. For example, the observed order of the chromium ionization rate with respect to chromium is 0.6, while the corresponding order for titanium is 0.2. There is no obvious way to account for these facts with the postulated mechanisms. It is clear that efforts comparable in magnitude to the noble gas studies will be required to achieve a satisfactory interpretation of the observations of thermal ionization of metals. On the experimental side, these studies will be complicated by apparatus difficulties. On the theoretical side, there is no reason to assume that anything other than the lower excitation and ionization energies differentiates the analysis of thermal ionization in metal atoms dilute in noble gases from the analysis of thermal ionization of the noble gases themselves. There is a difficulty in the case of metal atoms with many valence electrons, such as chromium and titanium, in that the equilibrium composition cannot be calculated accurately due to imperfect knowledge of the atomic and ionic partition functions.

The dissociation and ionization kinetics of CsBr were studied by Berry, Cernoch, Coplan and Ewing (122). Their experimental method consisted of dispersing a smoke of CsBr into 50 torr of argon just prior to shock heating; the smoke particles were evaporated within a few microseconds by the incident shock wave to give gaseous CsBr, which then was dissociated and ionized in the reflected shock wave. The composition of the gas was followed by time-resolved absorption spectroscopy of cesium atoms and bromine atomic ions Br^-. The Cs atomic concentration was found to increase almost linearly from

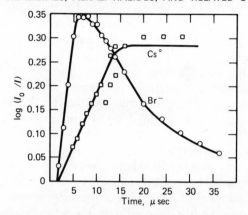

Figure 20 Profiles of cesium atom concentration and bromine atomic ion concentration obtained by time-resolved absorption spectroscopy of a reflected shock wave in argon-cesium bromide test gas (122).

the passage of the reflected shock to the equilibrium value (see Fig. 20). The Br^- concentration, on the other hand, passed through a maximum during the Cs rise and approached an equilibrium concentration far below the maximum value. These results were interpreted with the mechanism

$$CsBr + M = Cs^+ + Br^- + M \qquad [56]$$

$$Br^- + Br = Br_2 \text{ (or } 2 \text{ Br)} + e^- \qquad [57]$$

$$e^- + Br^- = Br + 2e^- \qquad [58]$$

The Cs^+ ions presumably relax to the Cs atoms by the reverses of the processes discussed earlier in connection with thermal ionization of cesium, namely reactions [49] and [50]

Both the initial ionization process and the subsequent relaxation to equilibrium are quite interesting elementary processes. The ionization itself is a violation of the no-crossing rule which in spectroscopy would assert that the adiabatic dissociation of CsBr would be to the atoms rather than to the ions, which are at higher energy than the atoms due to the fact that the ionization potential of cesium is greater than the electron affinity of bromine. The fact that the crossing does occur to allow the initial dissociation to proceed to ions must clearly be due to the fact that the internuclear separation at which the two potential curves cross, 27 Å, is so large that there is insufficient overlap between the 6s valence orbital of Cs and the 3p valence orbital of Br to permit a crossing. The Cs^+ and the Br^- in highly vibrating CsBr have a communication problem in that their only interaction is by the ionic coulomb force, and they can only reach the lower energy atoms by secondary processes.

Electron attachment to Cs^+ must therefore proceed only in subsequent events, that is, by the reverse of the process of thermal ionization studied by Haught (115). The thermal ionization of bromine has not been studied independently; Berry et al. assume that the reverses of the well-studied electron attachment processes participate. The observed overshoots are thus the net result of kinetic violation of the no-crossing rule and the fact that at the equilibrium conditions of these experiments the ratio of atom pairs to ion pairs is about ten.

This work was subsequently extended to a large variety of alkali halides by Ewing, Milstein and Berry (123). They found that the dissociation products were atoms for some of the alkali halides, ions for others, and a mixture of the two for the rest. The criterion developed by these authors for distinguishing between the two dissociation paths is based upon the number of vibrational states of the ionic potential well within the energy band for which a crossing over to the atomic potential curve, and hence into atoms, may occur. This is expressed as the ratio of the width of the energy band in which crossover can occur to the vibrational energy spacing at the energy of dissociation to atoms. This ratio was computed for each of the alkali halides using straightforward theoretical methods. For some cases it is a large number; for NaI, for example, it is about 1000. For other cases the ratio is very small; for RbBr, for example, it is only about 10^{-9}. NaI dissociates into atoms, while RbBr dissociates into ions. When the ratio approaches unity, both processes occur. In addition to the identification of the dissociation process describing the behavior of each of the alkali halides, these experiments provide a wealth of kinetic information, most of which has not yet been analysed. It is clear that the rates of a large number of interesting ionization and deionization processes will be available by kinetic analysis of the data derived from experiments on shock-ionized alkali halides.

Kinetic analysis to provide rate constants for the detachment reactions

$$F^- + Ar = F + Ar + e^- \qquad [59]$$

$$F^- + Cs^+ = F + Cs^+ + e^- \qquad [60]$$

was provided in similar experiments of Mandl, Kivel and Evans (124). The activation energy obtained for reactions [59] and [60] appeared to be equal to the electron affinity of F, and the detachment mechanism seemed to be this set of reactions alone. In view of the difficulty of the experiments and the limited extent of the data analysis, the numerical results must be regarded as tentative.

It can be inferred from the results of Berry et al. that the overshoots observed by Boni (121) in $TiBr_4$ probably have their origin in similar violations of the no-crossing rule for the halide fragments TiBr or $TiBr_2$.

REFERENCES

1. V. H. Blackman and G. B. F. Niblett, "Ionization Processes in Shock Waves." Chapter V of *Fundamental Data Obtained from Shock Tube Experiments*, edited by A. Ferri. New York: Pergamon Press, 1961. A review of air and argon shocks was given by D. Teare, in "Ionization in High Temperature Gases," *Progress in Astronautics and Aeronautics*, Vol. 28, edited by K. E. Schuler. New York: Academic Press, 1963, p. 217. A cursory but more recent review is given by E. Bauer, *J. Quant. Spectrosc. Radiat. Transfer*, **9**, 499 (1969).

2. S.-C. Lin and J. D. Teare, *Phys. Fluids*, **6**, 355 (1963).

3. Ye. V. Stupochenko, S. A. Losev, and A. I. Osipov, *Relaxation in Shock Waves* New York: Springer, 1967.

4. See Volume 1, Chapters 6–10.

5. J. N. Bradley, *Shock Waves in Chemistry and Physics*. New York: Wiley, 1962.

6. The earlier studies concerned with computation and verification of equilibrium conditions in shock wave generated plasmas are discussed by Blackman and Niblett (Ref. 1).

7. R. E. Duff, *Phys. Fluids*, **2**, 207 (1959); H. Mirels, *Phys. Fluids*, **6**, 1201 (1963); J. N. Fox, T. I. McLaren, and R. M. Hobson, *Phys. Fluids*, **9**, 2345 (1966); J. S. Hey, J. T. Pinson, and P. B. Smith, *Nature*, **179**, 1184 (1957); G. Rudinger, *Phys. Fluids*, **4**, 1463 (1961); R. L. Belford and R. Strehlow, *Ann. Rev. Phys. Chem.*, **20**, 247 (1969).

8. E. Locke and K. Plotkin, *AIAA J.*, **5**, 1350 (1967); I. Pollin, *Phys. Fluids*, **7**, 1433 (1964).

9. The effect of attenuation upon ionization rate profiles is discussed by A. J. Kelly, "Atom-Atom Ionization Mechanism and Cross Sections in Noble Gases and Noble Gas Mixtures," Ph.D. Thesis, California Institute of Technology, Pasadena, Calif., 1965. See also Fox et. al., Ref. 7.

10. References to theoretical treatments of shock waves with significant radiation enthalpy are given in Section III.

11. Much of the literature on precursor effects is concerned with electromagnetic shock tubes, in which severe complications from the driver plasma arise. Cf. M. Cloupeau, *Phys. Fluids*, **6**, 679 (1963). Precursor effects in pressure driven shock tubes are discussed in Section III.

12. S. C. Lin, E. L. Resler, and A. Kantrowitz, *J. Appl. Phys.*, **6**, 95 (1955).

13. K. E. Harwell and R. G. Jahn, *Phys. Fluids*, **7**, 214 (1964). The identification of activation energies with excitation energies made in this paper is a persistent theme in shock tube research on ionizing shock waves. An illuminating theoretical analysis of this identification was given by D. L. S. McElwain, L. Wagschal, and H. O. Pritchard, *Phys. Fluids*, **13**, 2200 (1970), based on the argon ionization results of T. I. McLaren and R. Hobson, *Phys. Fluids*, **11**, 2162 (1968). It is shown in this paper that virtually all observations on the temperature dependence of ionizing processes in shock waves may be expected to have activation energies corresponding to the first excitation energies of the atoms concerned.

14. A. J. Kelly, *J. Chem. Phys.*, **45**, 1723 (1966).

15. A. J. Kelly, *J. Chem. Phys.*, **45**, 1733 (1966).

16. A Frohn and P. C. T. de Boer, *Proceedings of the Sixth International Shock Tube Symposium*, Freiburg, 1967 (Ernst-Mach-Institute, 1968) p. 193; *Phys. Fluids*, **12**, I-54 (1969).

17. H. S. Johnston and W. Kornegay, *Trans. Farad. Soc.*, **57**, 1563 (1961). W. M. Kornegay and H. S. Johnston, *J. Chem. Phys.*, **38**, 2242 (1963).
18. D. S. Hacker and H. Bloomberg, *J. Chem. Phys.*, **39**, 3263 (1963).
19. H. E. Petschek, P. H. Rose, H. S. Glick, A. Kane, and A. Kantrowitz, *J. Appl. Phys.*, **26**, 83 (1955).
20. H. Petschek and S. Byron, *Annals of Physics*, **1**, 270 (1957).
21. E. J. Morgan and R. D. Morrison, *Phys. Fluids*, **8**, 1608 (1965); the theoretical method was extended to Kr, Ne, and Xe by M. Merillo and E. J. Morgan, *J. Chem. Phys.*, **52**, 2192 (1970).
22. H. Wong and D. Bershader, *J. Fluid Mech.*, **26**, 459 (1966); K. P. Horn, H. Wong, and D. Bershader, *J. Plasma Phys.*, **1**, 157 (1967).
23. N. R. Jones and M. McChesney, *Nature*, **209**, 1080 (1966).
24. P. E. Oettinger and D. Bershader, *AIAA J.*, **5**, 1625 (1967); P. E. Oettinger, *AIAA J.*, **6**, 150 (1968).
25. M. I. Hoffert and H. Lien, *Phys. Fluids*, **10**, 1769 (1967).
26. R. A. Alpher and D. R. White, *Phys. Fluids*, **2**, 162 (1959).
27. H. D. Weymann, *Phys. Fluids*, **3**, 545 (1960).
28. P. Gloersen, *Phys. Fluids*, **3**, 857 (1960).
29. A. C. Pipkin, *Phys. Fluids*, **6**, 1382 (1963).
30. L. Wetzel, *AIAA J.*, **2**, 1208 (1964).
31. J. P. Appleton, *Phys. Fluids*, **9**, 336 (1966).
32. H. D. Weymann and B. Troy, *Bull. Am. Phys. Soc.*, **6**, 212 (1961).
33. H. D. Weymann and L. B. Holmes, *Proceedings of the Sixth International Conference on Ionization Phenomena in Gases*, Vol IV, Paris, 1962, p. 281; *Phys. Fluids*, **12**, 1193, 1200 (1969).
34. H. K. Sen and A. W. Guess, *Phys. Rev.*, **108**, 560 (1957).
35. J. Pomerantz, *J. Quant. Spectrosc. Radiat. Transfer*, **1**, 185 (1961).
36. L. M. Biberman and I. T. Yakubov, *Sov. Phys. Tech. Phys.*, **8**, 100 (1964).
37. M. McChesney and Z. Al-Attar, *J. Quant. Spectrosc. Radiat. Transfer*, **5**, 553 (1965).
38. R. R. Chow, *AIAA J.*, **3**, 973 (1965).
39. I. M. Cohen and J. H. Clarke, *Phys. Fluids*, **8**, 1278 (1965); J. H. Clarke and C. Ferrari, *Phys. Fluids*, **8**, 2121 (1965).
40. C. E. Chapin, *Nonequilibrium Radiation and Ionization in Shock Waves*, Purdue University School of Aeronautics, Astronautics, and Engineering Sciences, Report AA & ES 67–9, June 1967.
41. A recent, detailed analysis of photoexcitation and photoionization in argon, with extensive references to the earlier literature, was given by R. A. Dobbins, *AIAA J.*, **8**, 407 (1970).
42. W. Roth and P. Gloersen, *J. Chem. Phys.*, **29**, 820 (1958).
43. W. Roth, *J. Chem. Phys.*, **31**, 844 (1959).
44. J. N. Bradley, *J. Chem. Phys.*, **32**, 1875 (1960).
45. W. Roth, *J. Chem. Phys.*, **32**, 1876 (1960).
46. W. Finkelnburg and T. Peters, "Kontinuierliche Spektren." In *Handbuch der Physik*, Vol. 28, edited by S. Flügge. Berlin: Springer-Verlag, 1957, p. 79.
47. S. C. Lin, R. A. Neal, and W. I. Fyfe, *Phys. Fluids*, **5**, 1633 (1962).
48. A. H. Dronov, A. G. Sviridov, and N. N. Sobolev, *Optics and Spec. USSR*, **12**, 383 (1962).
49. F. H. Mies, *J. Chem. Phys.*, **37**, 1101 (1962).
50. V. G. Sevastyanenko and I. T. Yakubov, *Opt. Spectr.*, **16**, 1 (1964).
51. J. Roth, *J. Appl. Phys.*, **35**, 1429 (1964).
52. R. A. Alpher and D. R. White, *Phys. Fluids*, **7**, 1239 (1964).

53. Yu. N. Redkoboradyi and V. I. Fedulov, *Sov. Phys. Tech. Phys.*, **10**, 1275 (1960).
54. P. Valentin and J. C. Leboucher, *Compt. Rend. Acad. Sci.* (*Paris*), **263B**, 17,959 (1966).
55. W. Bötticher, H. Carls, V. Graap, and L. Rehder, *Proceedings of the Sixth International Shock Tube Symposium*, Freiburg, 1967, p. 441.
56. B. Sturtevant, *J. Fluid Mech.*, **25**, 641 (1966).
57. B. Sturtevant and C. P. Wang, in *Recent Advances in Aerothermochemistry*, Vol. II, 7th AGARD Colloquium, Oslo, Norway (May 1966), p. 593.
58. R. Creswell, M. A. DiValentin, and J. E. Dove, *Phys. Fluids*, **9**, 2285 (1966).
59. C. P. Wang, *Phys. Fluids*, **11**, 1865 (1968).
60. R. A. Jeffries, J. B. Seely, and R. G. Fowler, *Phys. Fluids*, **7**, 1390 (1964).
61. E. A. McLean, C. E. Faneuff, and A. C. Kolb, *Phys. Fluids*, **3**, 843 (1960).
62. D. F. Hornig, in *Energy Transfer in Gases*, 12th Solvay Conference. New York: Interscience, 1962, p. 311.
63. M. Camac, in *Fundamental Processes in Hypersonic Flow*, edited by Gordon Hall. Cornell Univ. Press, 1965, p. 195. See also K. L. Wray, *Tenth Symposium* (*International*) *on Combustion*. Cambridge: The Combustion Institute, 1965, p. 523.
64. P. Valentin and M. J. Cottereau, *Compt. Rend. Acad. Sci.*, (Paris) **264B**, 603 (1967). Also *Bull. Am. Phys. Soc.*, **13**, 798 (1968).
65. R. A. Allen, R. L. Taylor, and A. Textoris, *Proceedings of the Sixth International Conference on Ionization Phenomena in Gases*, Paris, 1963, p. 381.
66. R. L. Taylor, *J. Chem. Phys.*, **39**, 2354 (1963).
67. R. A. Allen and A. Textoris, *J. Chem. Phys.*, **40**, 3445 (1964).
68. K. L. Wray and T. J. Connoly, *J. Quant. Spectrosc. Radiat. Transfer*, **5**, 111 (1965).
69. R. A. Allen, A. Textoris, and J. Wilson, *J. Quant. Spectrosc. Radiat. Transfer*, **5**, 95 (1965).
70. D. E. Buttrey, H. R. McChesney, and L. A. Hooker, *J. Quant. Spectrosc. Radiat. Transfer*, **8**, 717 (1968).
71. R. A. Allen, *J. Quant. Spectrosc. Radiat. Transfer*, **5**, 511 (1965). Recent theoretical work by Mnatsakanian and Podlubny, *Teplofizika Vysokik Temperatur*, **8**, 33 (1970), has succeeded in interpreting Allen's results in terms of a plausible set of potential curves for N_2^+.
72. The spectral properties of hot air are reviewed in detail by I. V. Avrilova, L. M. Biberman, V. S. Vorobjev, V. M. Zamalin, G. A. Kobzev, A. N. Lagar'kov, A. Ch. Mnatsakanian, and G. E. Norman, *J. Quant. Spectrosc. Radiat. Transfer*, **9**, 89, 113 (1969). An earlier review of air radiation was given by J. C. Keck, R. A. Allen, and R. L. Taylor, *J. Quant. Spectrosc. Radiat. Transfer*, **3**, 335 (1963).
73. K. L. Wray, *J. Chem. Phys.*, **44**, 623 (1966).
74. A. Belozerov, *Study of the Initial Ionization Process in a Strong Shock Wave*, University of Toronto Institute for Aerospace Studies, Report No. 1313, 1968.
75. V. V. Zhurin and V. A. Sulyeav, *Eng. J. III*, **4**, 645 (1963).
76. W. L. Fite and R. T. Brackman, *Phys. Rev.*, **112**, 1191 (1958); W. Lichten and S. Schultz, *Phys. Rev.*, **116**, 1132 (1959).
77. K. L. Wray, in *Progress in Astronautics and Rocketry*, Vol. 7, edited by R. R. Riddel. New York: Academic Press, 1962, p. 181.
78. Ye. V. Stupochenko, S. A. Losev, and A. I. Osipov, *Relaxation in Shock Waves*. New York: Springer, 1967.
79. E. Bauer, *J. Quant. Spectrosc. Radiat. Transfer*, **9**, 499 (1969).
80. E. Freedman and J. W. Daiber, *J. Chem. Phys.*, **34**, 1271 (1961).
81. M. Camac and R. M. Feinberg, *Eleventh Symposium* (*International*) *on Combustion*. Berkeley: The Combustion Institute, 1967, p. 137.
82. C. F. Hansen, *Phys. Fluids*, **11**, 904 (1968); G. H. Myers and H. W. Young, *J. Chem.*

Phys., **51**, 1597 (1969), show that the electron produced in this process has energy well below the thermal average value, which means that electron thermalization (reaction [14]) must also be taken into account in air ionization.

83. R. A. Creswell, M. A. DiValentin and J. E. Dove, *Proceedings of the Sixth International Shock Tube Symposium*, Freiburg, 1967, p. 149; *Phys. Fluids*, **12**, 1–105 (1969).

84. A. Frohn and P. C. T. de Boer, *AIAA J.*, **5**, 261 (1967); *Rev. Sci. Inst.*, **37**, 775 (1966).

85. B. Koch and M. König, *Proceedings of the Sixth International Shock Tube Symposium*, Freiburg, 1966, p. 540; *Phys. Fluids*, **12**, 1–144 (1969).

86. W. P. Thompson, *Bull. Am. Phys. Soc.*, **10**, 727 (1965).

87. W. C. Taylor, W. E. Scharfman, and T. Morita, *Bull. Am. Phys. Soc.*, **13**, 911 (1968).

88. R. P. Stein, M. Scheibe, M. W. Syverson, T. M. Shaw, and R. C. Gunton, *Phys. Fluids*, **7**, 1641 (1964).

89. J. N. Bardsley, *J. Phys. B* (Proc. Phys. Soc. 2), **1**, 365 (1968).

90. J. Wilson, *Phys. Fluids*, **9**, 1913 (1966); the total ionization times from Wilson's work are not a simple extrapolation of the corresponding low temperature times from Lin, Neal, and Fyfe (47). The graph of total ionization time versus M_s has a sharp maximum near $M_s = 10$. Theoretical explanations of this behavior were given by Biberman and Yakubov, *High Temperature*, **3**, 309 (1965) and Zjelezniak and Mnatsakanian, *ibid.*, **6**, 390 (1968).

91. E. A. Sutton, *AVCO Research Report* RR266, 1967.

92. M. G. Dunn and J. A. Lordi, *AIAA J.*, **7**, 1458, 2099 (1969).

93. M. G. Dunn and J. A. Lordi, *AIAA J.*, **8**, 339 (1970).

94. M. G. Dunn and J. A. Lordi, *AIAA J.*, **8**, 614 (1970).

95. M. Faraday, *Experimental Researches in Electricity*, Vol. 1, par. 272. London: Taylor and Francis, 1839.

96. W. J. Miller, *Oxid. and Combust. Reviews*, **3**, 98 (1968).

97. H. F. Calcote and W. J. Miller, this Volume, Chapter 17.

98. G. B. Kistiakowsky and L. W. Richards, *J. Chem. Phys.*, **36**, 1707 (1962).

99. C. W. Hand and G. B. Kistiakowsky, *J. Chem. Phys.*, **37**, 1239 (1962).

100. S. Basu and J. A. Fay, *Seventh Symposium (International) on Combustion*. London: Butterworths, 1959, p. 277.

101. G. P. Glass and G. B. Kistiakowsky, *J. Chem. Phys.*, **40**, 1448 (1964).

102. G. B. Kistiakowsky and J. V. Michael, *J. Chem. Phys.*, **40**, 1447 (1964).

103. G. P. Glass, G. B. Kistiakowsky, J. V. Michael, and H. Niki, *Tenth Symposium (International) on Combustion*. Cambridge: The Combustion Institute, 1965, p. 513.

104. G. P. Glass, G. B. Kistiakowsky, J. V. Michael, and H. Niki, *J. Chem. Phys.*, **42**, 608 (1965).

105. K. B. Wilberg, W. J. Barthy, and F. P. Lossing, *J. Am. Chem. Soc.*, **84**, 3980 (1962).

106. See discussion following Ref. 103.

107. I. D. Gay, G. P. Glass, G. B. Kistiakowsky, and H. Niki, *J. Chem. Phys.*, **43**, 4017 (1965).

108. I. D. Gay, G. P. Glass, R. D. Kern, and G. B. Kistiakowsky, *J. Chem. Phys.*, **47**, 313 (1967).

109. C. T. Bowman and D. J. Seery, *Comb. and Flame*, **12**, 611 (1968); *ibid.*, **14**, 37 (1970).

110. K. H. Becker and K. D. Bayes, *J. Chem. Phys.*, **48**, 653 (1968); K. D. Bayes, *J. Chem. Phys.*, **52**, 1093 (1970).

111. J. E. Dove, Private communication, 1970.

112. S. Matsuda and D. Gutman, *J. Chem. Phys.*, **53**, 3324 (1970).

113. L. N. Wilson and E. W. Evans, *J. Chem. Phys.*, **46**, 859 (1967).

114. R. Hackam, *Planet. Space Sci.*, **13**, 667 (1965); C. S. Weller and M. Biondi, *Bull. Am. Phys. Soc.*, **13**, 199 (1968); C. S. Weller and M. Biondi, *Phys. Rev.*, to be published.
115. A. F. Haught, *Phys. Fluids*, **5**, 1337 (1962).
116. J. F. Louis, *AVCO Research Report* RR257, 1966.
117. R. M. Hill and B. Capp, *Nature*, **208**, 176 (1965).
118. D. E. Rothe, *J. Quant. Spectrosc. Radiat. Transfer*, **9**, 49 (1969).
119. Y. W. Kim and O. Laporte, *Proceedings of the Sixth International Shock Tube Symposium*, Freiburg, 1967, p. 622; *Bull. Am. Phys. Soc.*, **13**, 791 (1968).
120. W. L. Shackleford and S. S. Penner, *J. Chem. Phys.*, **45**, 1816 (1966); *ibid.*, **49**, 1448 (1968). Earlier spectroscopic studies on chromium emission were reported by G. Charatis and T. D. Wilkerson, *Phys. Fluids*, **2**, 578 (1959); *ibid.*, **5**, 1661 (1962).
121. A. A. Boni, Jr., *J. Chem. Phys.*, **49**, 3885 (1968); *J. Quant. Spectrosc. Radiat. Transfer*, **8**, 1385 (1968).
122. R. S. Berry, T. Cernoch, M. Coplan, and J. J. Ewing, *J. Chem. Phys.*, **49**, 127 (1968).
123. J. J. Ewing, R. Milstein, and R. S. Berry, *Proceedings of the Seventh International Shock Tube Symposium*, Toronto, 1969, p. 591; *J. Chem. Phys.*, to be published.
124. A. Mandl, B. Kivel, and E. W. Evans, *J. Chem. Phys.*, **53**, 2363 (1970).

CHAPTER NINETEEN

Chemical Reactions in Plasmas obtained
by Irradiation with Electromagnetic
Radiations and by Bombardment with
High Energy Particles

M. VENUGOPALAN

I. INTRODUCTION

It is well known that the absorption of electromagnetic radiation by matter will produce chemical effects. Such radiation covers an extremely wide range of wavelengths. For example, standard radio waves have wavelengths of several meters, while the γ rays emitted in radioactive decay have wavelengths of a small fraction of an angström (10^{-8} cm). It may be noted that the γ rays with their large energies are associated with nuclear transformations; X rays with electronic transitions in the lower electronic orbits; ultraviolet and visible radiation with electronic transitions in the outer orbits of atoms and molecules; near infrared radiation with changes in the vibrational energy of molecules; far infrared radiation with changes in the rotational energy of molecules; microwaves and ordinary radio waves with electrical oscillations in specially designed circuits. The type of electromagnetic radiation useful for inducing chemical changes is conveniently selected by subdividing the spectrum into various arbitrary regions as shown in Fig. 1.

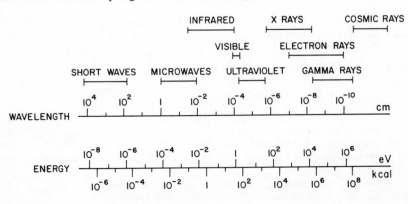

Figure 1   Electromagnetic radiation spectrum.

Although not perhaps of the same charge particle population as is so easily obtainable with electrical discharges, all radiations of high enough energy can contribute to the formation of an ionized medium. If the condition for quasi-neutrality is somewhat relaxed, then these rather exotic states may be accepted as natural extensions of the plasma state. Ionized media or plasma conditions are usually obtained only with radiations of very short wavelength ($< 10^{-5}$ cm) or of energies > 10 eV.

In this chapter we shall be concerned chiefly with the reactions in gases and vapors subjected to irradiation by electromagnetic radiations of wavelength less than 10^{-5} cm (energy > 10 eV). Also included are the reactions in ionized media produced by powerful laser beams. In addition plasmas obtained when a gas is bombarded with high-energy particles such as helium nuclei, protons, deuterons, and so on are briefly reviewed. Finally, there is a discussion of the reactions in some natural plasmas maintained by radiations in the earth's upper atmosphere and in the interstellar outer space.

The plasmas, whose investigation is to be reviewed in this chapter, are essentially of two types which stem from completely different mechanisms, one being mainly photolytic (ultraviolet radiation), the other mainly radiolytic (electron impact). The latter type of plasma has been discussed extensively in Chapter 12 by Tal'rose and Karachevtsev and therefore, our discussions will be concerned only with topics pertinent to natural plasmas.

II. PLASMAS OBTAINED BY PHOTON IRRADIATION

Photons may be absorbed in passing through a gas. In the absorption process the photons disappear, and the absorbed energy goes into excitation and ionization of the particles with which they interact. A number of different mechanisms (1) can participate in the absorption of photons by atoms and molecules: Excitation to upper levels involving resonance transitions without predissociation or pre-ionization; excitation to molecular states adjacent to a dissociation continuum, leading to predissociation; excitation to upper states of atoms or molecules adjacent to an ionization continuum leading to pre-ionization; continuous absorption due (a) to direct excitation into an atomic ionization continuum, (b) to dissociation of molecules into two fragments, each of which may be in the ground state or in an excited state, (c) to direct excitation into one of the molecular ionization continua, without dissociation or pre-ionization, (d) to dissociative ionization into an ion and an atom which may be in an excited state, or (e) to dissociative ionization that produces two ions of opposite sign, one of which is in an excited state. The multiplicity of absorption mechanisms makes the analysis of absorption data difficult. However, information concerning mechanisms can be inferred from the shape of absorption curves and knowledge of the energy levels of the target molecules.

Of all the mechanisms of photo-absorption, photo-ionization is the one of greatest importance for plasmas. It is this topic that we will be discussing in Section A.

A. Photo-ionization Studies

Photo-ionization or continuous absorption is defined as the process in which an atomic or molecular system, neutral or ionic, normal or excited, absorbs a photon and is raised to a state of the electron continuum so that one or more electrons are observed to be emitted. In the particular case of negative ions this process is referred to as *photodetachment*. Electron detachment can also occur through many-electron excitation to a short-lived quasi-discrete state with subsequent decay through a radiationless transition, *auto-ionization*, to an adjacent state of the continuum. This effect is observed as a resonant distortion of the photo-ionization cross-section. Obviously the cross-sections for these reactions and their inverse, continuous emission or radiative attachment and dielectronic recombination, are of fundamental importance for a quantitative understanding of the interaction of radiation and matter, and thus plasmas in general.

The subject has been reviewed during this decade by Ditchburn and Öpik (2), Branscomb (3), McDaniel (4), Samson (5), and Stewart (6). While experimental aspects are discussed in the article by Samson (5), quantal calculations of photo-ionization cross-sections are emphasized in the recent review by Stewart (6). The special case of resonances in photon absorption has been reviewed by Burke (7). More recently Marr (8) has devoted a complete volume to photo-ionization, and Samson (9) a complete volume to vacuum ultra-violet techniques. Thus, in this article only the photo-ionization regions of great interest in laboratory and astrophysical plasmas are discussed. The energy range to be covered here is about 10 to 300 eV, corresponding to the vacuum ultraviolet and x-ray regions. Direct studies of photo-ionization, particularly those involving mass spectrometric analysis of the ionization products, which are evidently of great value for the understanding of reactions in plasmas obtained by photon irradiation, will be emphasized.

1.   General Concepts.   The threshold frequency v_i and the wavelength λ_i for ejection of the least tightly bound electron from an atom or molecule with a first ionization potential V_i is given by the equation

$$h v_i = \frac{hc}{\lambda_i} = e V_i$$

where h is Planck's constant, c the velocity of light in a vacuum, and e the electronic charge. This threshold wavelength expressed in angströms is related to the ionization potential expressed in volts by the equation

$$\lambda_i = \frac{12{,}398}{V_i}$$

Ionization at wavelengths longer than this threshold value can occur in a two-step process involving an atom or molecule that has already been excited. Wavelengths shorter than λ_i are required for ejection of electrons other than the one with the smallest binding energy in the atom.

Most experimental studies (1) of photoabsorption have involved measurements of the attenuation of a beam of photons traversing a gas-filled absorption cell. The radiation absorbed by the gas is defined by the Lambert-Beer law

$$I = I_0 \exp\left(-\sigma_t nL\right)$$

where I_0 is the intensity of the incident radiation, I the intensity after passing through a layer of gas of thickness L, σ_t is the total absorption cross-section, and n is the number density of atoms measured at a pressure p and temperature T and calculated from the relation

$$n = n_0\left(\frac{pT_0}{p_0 T}\right)$$

p_0 and T_0 being, respectively, the pressure and temperature at STP and n_0 the Loschmidt's number equal to 2.69×10^{19} atoms cm^{-3}. The total absorption cross-section is given by

$$\sigma_t = \sigma_s + \sigma_a$$

where σ_s and σ_a are the scattering and true absorption cross-sections, respectively. The scattering of radiation in the vacuum ultraviolet region below 10^{-5} cm is extremely small compared to the true absorption of the radiation and so far has not been calculated for wavelengths above 10 Å and certainly not detected. Therefore,

$$\sigma_t = \sigma_a = \sigma$$

The total absorption coefficient μ is given by $\mu = n_0\sigma$. The units of absorption are sometimes expressed in terms of absorption coefficients μ measured in cm^{-1}, and sometimes in terms of the absorption cross-section σ measured in cm^2 or in megabarns (Mb), where 1 Mb $= 10^{-18}$ cm^2.

The photo-ionization cross-section, σ_i, is that part of the absorption cross-section which represents ionization by absorption of photons of wavelength λ and is given by

$$\sigma_i = \gamma\sigma$$

where γ is the photo-ionization yield, or efficiency, and is defined as the number of ions produced per photon absorbed. Naturally σ_i is expressed in units of cm^2. For atoms the photo-ionization yield is generally considered to be unity at wavelengths shorter than the ionization threshold with the reservation that discrete structure may or may not have yields of unity. Experimental evidence showing that the yields of the rare gases are unity has been given by Samson (10).

2. Experimental Approach.   Apparatus for the direct determination of the cross-sections for photo-ionization has been described by Weissler (1) and more recently by Marr (8). In principle, radiation of known wavelength and intensity is allowed to pass through a gas cell containing parallel-plate ionization chambers which collect the charged particles of both signs produced in ionization events (see Fig. 2). Measurements of these currents yield

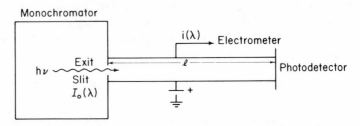

Figure 2   Schematic diagram of a simple ion chamber. The entrance slit of the chamber is the exit slit of the monochromator (11).

the cross-section if the chamber dimensions and gas pressure are known. The magnitude of the ion current, $i(\lambda)$ is given by

$$i(\lambda) = I_0(\lambda)\{1 - \exp [-nl\,\sigma_t(\lambda)]\} \frac{e\sigma_i(\lambda)}{\sigma_t(\lambda)}$$

where λ is the photon wavelength, $I_0(\lambda)$ is the photon flux in photons per second incident on the ion chamber, n is the number of molecules per unit volume, l is the chamber length, e is the electronic charge, and $\sigma_t(\lambda)$ is the cross-section for all processes which absorb photons. One may make comparative or absolute measurements: In the former one obtains the ratio of the ion current from the gas of interest to that from a gas of known photo-ionization efficiency γ $(= \sigma_i(\lambda)/\sigma_t(\lambda))$ under identical conditions of incident flux and absorption in the chamber. Comparison is usually made with a noble gas ($\gamma = 1$), but this comparison is limited to $\lambda < 1023$ Å, that is, 12.127 eV, the ionization threshold of Xe. In the absolute method one must make absolute measurements of the incident photon flux, $I_0(\lambda)$, and the ion current, $i(\lambda)$. Schoen (11) gives an excellent review of both methods and their limitations.

The use of double ion chambers is discussed in detail by Samson (5,10).

If vacuum monochromators are combined with mass spectrometers, measurements can be made of the ion intensity as a function of photon energy for the parent ions and their fragments (12). The onset of ionization* and the structure of the yield curves can be related to energy levels, to photo-ionization cross-sections, and to photodissociation mechanisms.

Another method (13,14) involves the passage of dispersed radiation through a gas and observation of the fluorescence radiation thus induced.

Photo-ionization cross-sections can also be calculated from cross-sections for the inverse process, radiative capture of electrons by positive ions (2).

3. Theoretical Work. A considerable amount of theoretical work has been done in evaluating photo-ionization cross-sections for several neutral atoms and positive and negative ions. Several reviews and summaries describe the calculations in some detail (1–8). The basic concepts and quantal formulas have been well summarized recently by Stewart (6). The theory of photo-ionization and that of photodetachment of electrons from negative ions are similar (3).

Bates (15) writes the formula for the photo-ionization cross-section σ_i

$$\sigma_i(v) = \frac{32\pi^4 m^2 e^2}{3h^3 c} \frac{1}{\Omega_i} \sum_i \sum_f vv C_p \left| \psi_i^* \left(\sum_j \mathbf{r}_j \right) \psi_f(E) \, dT \right|^2 \qquad [1]$$

In this formula $\mathbf{r}_j$ is the position vector of the jth electron, with the sum $\sum_j \mathbf{r}_j$ characterizing the dipole moment, Ω_i is the statistical weight of the initial level, and v is the frequency of the incident radiation; ψ_i is the normalized wave function for the bound initial state, and $\psi_f(E)$ is the normalized wave function for the ion together with the ejected electron, which has velocity v; C_p is a factor, only slightly less than unity, which allows for the distortion of the wave function of the passive electrons, that is, all electrons in the atom except the one that is ejected. The electronic charge and mass are denoted by e and m respectively, and c is the velocity of light in a vacuum. The wave functions for use in these calculations may be obtained from the Hartree-Fock equations (the self-consistent field with exchange) or using the quantum defect method (16).

In deriving the formula Bates (15) assumed that only a single electron is directly involved and also made use of a dipole approximation. This approximation is valid in photo-ionization studies since the wavelength used is large compared with atomic dimensions. The exact application of eq. [1] would surely yield accurate values of σ_i; however, it is not feasible and some approximations have to be made. Bates (17) has pointed out that the integrations in the calculations are particularly sensitive to the form of the wave function employed, since the integrand is positive in some regions of space

---

*The ionization onset potential of an atom is variously referred to as " threshold," " spectral head," or " series limit."

and negative in others, and the exact value of the integral is strongly dependent on the amount of cancellation.

Burgess and Seaton (18) derived a general formula for the calculation of atomic photo-ionization cross-sections based on the model of a single electron moving in a central field. Approximate bound-state radial wave functions which are accurate at large radial distances may be obtained for use in this formula if the effective quantum numbers $v(= n^*)$ are known. Such functions have been used to obtain good estimates for bound-bound transition integrals (19). For bound-free transitions approximate free-state radial functions which have the exact asymptotic form have been used (18). The phases are given by $\delta = \pi\mu$, where μ is the extrapolated quantum defect ($\mu = n - v$). The results of extensive numerical calculations have been summarized by Burgess and Seaton (18) in tables that permit the rapid calculation of transition integrals (for both bound-free and bound-bound transitions) once the energy levels are known. Although the general formula of Burgess and Seaton gave results comparable to those obtained in the best alternative methods of calculation, Moiseiwitsch (20) later argued that Seaton's (15) formulation of the quantum defect method gives inexact phase shifts except at the threshold. A more general formulation may be found in the papers by Moiseiwitsch (20).

Ditchburn and Öpik (2) tabulated the results for many structures, including a number of positive ions. Of particular interest are the results for hydrogen-like structures (H, He^+, and so on), the cross-sections for which were calculated using the equation:

$$\sigma_i(v, n) = \frac{g(32\pi^2 e^6 R Z^4)}{(3^{3/2} h^3 v^3 n^5)} \qquad [2]$$

where R is the Rydberg constant, n is the principal quantum number of the initial state, and g is the Gaunt factor which is a function of the frequency v.

The more recent theoretical developments have been reviewed by Stewart (7). The theory of Burgess and Seaton has been applied also to the rare gases (21); a more comprehensive set of tables from which σ_i can be obtained has been compiled (22) using the same theory. Seaton (23) and his coworkers have considered the general treatment of the many-electron problem using the quantum defect theory (24) to account successfully for series perturbations and resonances, and applied the theory to e-He^+ collisions (25), and to photo-ionization and autoionization studies (26).

At present considerable emphasis is given to developing the formalism of electron-atom scattering and photo-ionization to make use of the speed of digital computers to solve not only the coupled integro-differential equations but to aid in preliminary analysis. Such studies may lead to improved photo-ionization calculations for many atoms and positive and negative ions. The theoretical analysis of stellar and laboratory spectra requires a knowledge of photo-ionization cross-sections for a wide variety of transitions over a comprehensive range of energies. This is a forbidding task using *ab initio* calculations starting from formulas based on a detailed knowledge of wave functions. It is desirable then to have available formulas and tables from which photo-ionization cross-sections can be readily obtained, based on a knowledge of a small number of atomic parameters. It must be noted that autoionization is important for many elements and must always be considered in calculating photo-ionization cross-sections. Also pre-ionization may be important in the case of molecules.

The theoretical work on molecules and molecular ions is much less satisfactory, principally because of the difficulty of obtaining accurate electronic wave functions.

4. Photo-ionization Data For Molecules. A good compilation of photo-ionization data in the optical region for a large number of molecules has been published by the National Bureau of Standards (27) and, more recently, by Marr (8). Table 1 gives the experimental data for molecules which are important constituents of the upper atmosphere plasmas. Photoabsorption cross-sections for molecules such as SO_2 (49), C_2H_2 (50,51), C_2H_4 (51) have also been measured in the vacuum ultraviolet region and the reader is referred to the literature for details.

Schoen (11) has reviewed the measurements of photo-ionization cross-sections of molecules that are of aeronomic interest. His article is also interesting from the point of view of experimental pitfalls, which are not discussed here. Preferred values of the photo-ionization cross-sections of N_2

TABLE 1
Measured photo-ionization data for some molecules of aeronomic interest

Molecule	V_i, eV^a	λ_i, Å^b	λ_m, Å^c	σ_m, Mb^c	References
H_2	15.4	804	780	7.4	28, 29
O_2	16.1	770	550	22	28, 30–33
N_2	15.6	792	750	26	28, 31, 32, 34–36
H_2O	12.5	985	346	100	28, 37, 38
N_2O	12.9	960	700	35	39, 40
NO	9.25	1340	880	20	41–44
CO	14.21	868	600	16.5	45
CO_2	14.4	860	800	18	28, 45
NH_3	10.3	1210	900	10	41, 46, 47
CH_4	12.8	967	960	56	28, 46, 48

$^a V_i$ = ionization potential.
$^b \lambda_i$ = threshold wavelength.
$^c \lambda_m$, σ_m are wavelength and cross-section of maximum absorption associated with the ionization process for which V_i is given.

and O_2 at particular solar lines are given in Table 2. Most of these measurements were made in the laboratory using the comparative method or some

TABLE 2

Absorption and ionization cross-sections^m of O_2, N_2, and O
at solar lines (52)

Solar line, λ, Å	Class	O_2		O	N_2	
		σ	σ_i	$\sigma = \sigma_i$	σ	σ_i
1215.7	H Ly	0.01	0	0	$< 6 \times 10^{-5}$	0
1206.5	Si III	15	0	0	0	0
1175.7^a	C III	1.3	0	0	—	0
1085.7^a	N II	2^b	0	0	—	0
1037.6^a	O VI	0.78	0	0	$< 7 \times 10^{-4}$	0
1031.9	O VI	1.04	0	0	$< 7 \times 10^{-4}$	0
1025.7^j	H Ly B	1.58	0.98	c	$< 10^{-3}$	0
991.6^a	N III	1.75	1.21	0	1.9	0^{b,d}
989.8^a	N III	1.4	0.95^{b,d}	c	1.1	0^d
977.0	C III	4.0	2.5	0	0.7	0^d
972.5	H Ly	32	25^b	0	300	0^{b,d}
949.7	H Ly	6.3	—^{b}	0	5.2	—^{b}
937.8	H Ly	5.0	—	c	10	—^{b}
930.7	H Ly	26	17^b	c	4.8	—^{b}
904	C II	11	6.3^b	3.5	6.3	—
835.3	O III	10	3.7	e	15	—^{b}
835.1	O III	10	3.7	3.2	26	—^{b}
834.5	O II	11	4.0	e	3.3	—^{b}
833.7	O III	13	5.1	3.2	—	—^{b}
832.9 832.7	O III^f	26	10	e	—	—^{b}
790.2	O IV	28	10^b	3.2	24^d	11^{b,d}
790.1	O IV	28	10^b	3.2	26^d	12^{b,d}
787.7^k	O IV	24	13^b	e	9^d	8^d
780.3	Ne VII	28	11^b	3.3	19	—
770.4	Ne VIII	18	11	c	15	—
765.1	N IV	23	12^b	3.3	85^d	66^{b,d}
761.1^k	O V	20	10	e	40	22
703.8	O III	26	23	7	26	—
702.3	O III	24	—	7	26	—
686.3^{k,l}	N III	22	22	c	25^d	24^d
685.8	N III	18	18	7	26^d	25^d
685.5^{k,l}	N III	18	18	c	25^d	24^d
685.0	N III	26	26	7	25^d	24^d
629.7	O V	30	29	12	24^d	24^d
625	Mg X	25	24	12	24	23
610	Mg X	27	25	12	24	24
599.6	O III	28	27	12	23	22

Solar line, λ, Å	Class	O_2		O	N_2	
		σ	σ_i	$\sigma = \sigma_i$	σ	σ_i
584.3	He I	23	23	13	23	23
555.3	O IV	26	25	13	25	24
554.5	O IV	26	26	13	25	23
554.1	O IV	26	25	13	25	24
553.3	O IV	26	24	13	25	24
537.0	He I	21	21	12	25	24
525.8	O III	25	24	12	26	26
522.2	He I	21	21	12	24	23
508.2	O III	24	23	12	22	22
507.7[f] 507.4	O III	23	22	12	24	24
435.0	O III	21	21	12	24	24
430.2[f] 430.0 429.9	O II	18	18	12	21	21
303.8[a]	He I	17	17	9	12	12
247.2[a]		12.3	—[h]	6 —[h]	9.8	—[h]
209.3[a]		9.0	—[h]	4 —[h]	6.5	—[h]
100[a]		1.9	—[h]	0.8 —[h]	0.84	—[h]
68.0[a]		0.9	—	0.2 —	0.50	—
44.6[a]		0.31	—	0.1 —	0.18	—
13.4[a]		0.29	—	0.14[i] —	0.089	—
9.9[a]		0.14	—	0.071[i] —	0.042	—

[a]Blend of several lines observed in solar spectrum.

[b]The absorbing gas has discrete structure at this wavelength and thus the cross-section presently measurable given in the table may not be applicable.

[c]Possible overlap with atomic oxygen ground state (^3P) absorption line.

[d]Considerable variation among measurements.

[e]Possible overlap with atomic oxygen metastable state (^1D) absorption line.

[f]These lines not resolved in laboratory cross-section measurement.

[g]In the wavelength region below 304Å, there are a number of solar lines, but there have been few measurements, and also the cross-section curve appears to be relatively smooth. The wavelengths cited should allow a reasonable estimate to be made.

[h]Although there are no yield measurements, the measured absorption cross-sections (Refs. 6, 72, and 73) may be assumed to be equal to the ionization cross section at least to 100Å.

[i]This value is one-half the O_2 cross-section.

[j]This solar line known to be broad.

[k]The corresponding atomic oxygen (OI) lines (788.18, 761.26, 686.28, and 685.54Å, respectively) broadened by autoionization.

[l]These solar lines are known to overlap OI lines 686.28 and 685.54Å, respectively (Refs. 74 and 75).

[m]Cross-sections in Megabarns (10^{-18} cm^2), taken from data in Refs. 6, 53–55, and 66–75.

variation of it; the findings of rocket spectrophotometry (76) are in substantial agreement with the laboratory studies, that the data compiled by Huffman and Schoen (52) may be used with considerable confidence for aeronomic calculations. Recent measurements of photo-ionization cross-sections of O_2 (53–56), N_2 (53,55,57), NO (54,58–60), CO_2 (61–63), NO_2 (64), H_2O (65,77, 78), and O_3 (79–80) are briefly discussed next.

a. MOLECULAR OXYGEN.   The values given in Table 2 are from Samson and Cairns' work (53) for O_2 and are expected to be accurate to 10% except at those wavelengths at which several lines lay within the monochromator pass band and sharp variation of the cross-section with wavelength was found in the bandpass. The values of Matsunaga and Watanabe (54) agree with those of Samson and Cairns, within experimental error; it should be noted that Matsunaga and Watanabe used both the helium continuum and the hydrogen many-lined source to obtain data in the 600–1020 Å region with resolution of 0.3 Å with the helium source and 0.2 Å with the hydrogen source and their values are recommended at wavelengths between 600 and 1020 Å other than those given in Table 2. On the other hand, the photo-ionization efficiencies of Cook and coworkers (55,56), obtained with a continuum source, are lower than those of Samson and Cairns or Matsunaga and Watanabe over much of the spectral range. In an unstructured continuum such as the O_2 continuum at short wavelengths the photo-ionization efficiencies should approach 1, and since the efficiencies obtained by Samson and Cairns (53) and Matsunaga and Watanabe (54) approach 1 and those of Cook and associates (55,56) do not, it appears that the cross-sections of the former two groups of workers are more likely to be correct.

b. MOLECULAR NITROGEN.   In all but a few cases the values given in Table 2 are taken from Samson and Cairn's data (53); the accuracy is again about 10% except in regions of strong band structure. In the region between 600 and 700 Å the results of Samson and Cairns (53) agree with those of Cook and Metzger (55), although the excellence of the agreement is somewhat fortuitous because the absorption cross-sections of Cook and Metzger are larger and the photo-ionization efficiencies smaller than those of Samson and Cairns. However, in the range 750 to 800 Å the cross-sections of Cook and associates (55,57) do not agree well with those of Samson and Cairns; the differences are probably due to lack of resolution in a region of band structure and to errors in pressure measurements. For wavelengths not given in Table 2 the cross-sections of Cook and Ogawa (57) and of Cook and Metzger (55) for the regions 700–800 Å and 600–700 Å, respectively, are considered reliable within 25% error, except where strong band structure is found.

c. NITRIC OXIDE.   Watanabe, Matsunaga, and Sakai (59) have studied the photo-ionization cross-section of NO in the range 580–1350 Å with the helium continuum (580–950 Å) and the hydrogen many-lined source (860–1350 Å). Their resolution was 0.3 Å in the range 580 to 950 Å; 0.4 Å, 950–1100 Å; and 0.2 Å, 1060–1350 Å. These results supersede those of a previous paper (58) and are the preferred measurements. Absolute intensity measurements were based on a calibrated thermocouple. The photo-ionization cross-section at Lyman α (1215.7 Å) is 2.00 Mb, and the photo-ionization efficiency is 0.81. The cross-section values given by them are probably accurate within 10% below 950 Å and within about 20% at longer wavelengths, except in strong bands where the resolution may not be adequate. Photo-ionization cross-sections obtained by Metzger, Cook, and Ogawa (60) with the helium continuum and about 0.5 Å resolution in the spectral range 600–950 Å appear to be uniformly lower than those discussed previously.

d. CARBON DIOXIDE. Photo-ionization cross-sections of CO_2 have been determined by Cairns and Samson (61), Nakata et al. (62), and Cook et al. (63). Their results do not agree, chiefly due to discrepancies in the measured absorption cross-sections. In the almost structureless spectral region 600–650 Å, the values of the absorption cross-section obtained by Cairns and Samson are 50% higher than those obtained by Nakata et al and 40% higher than those obtained by Cook et al. Cairns and Samson used a double ion-chamber technique to measure the absorption cross-section in the wavelength region of interest here, while the other authors used the measured decrement of photo detector current.

In the spectral region 600–650 Å, the difference between the absorption cross-sections of Cook et al. and those of Nakata et al. lie within their mutual experimental errors, as do the differences between the ionization cross-sections. The same is, however, not true in the spectral range 840–880 Å, a region also without strong bands. Furthermore, we would think that the absorption and ionization cross-sections of CO_2 would be considerably greater than those of O_2 or CO in the spectral region near 600 Å; they appear to be from the work of Cairns and Samson, not from the work of Nakata et al. or Cook et al.

e. NITROGEN DIOXIDE. Watanabe and coworkers (64) have measured the photo-ionization of NO_2. They obtained absorption coefficients in the region 1050–2700 Å and photo-ionization yields in the region 1050–1300 Å, both by photoelectric techniques and with a resolution of 0.2 Å. At 10.83 eV they observed a break in the ionization continuum and ascribed it to dissociative-ionization processes.

f. WATER. Water vapor has been extensively studied. (For a review see Ref. 65). However, data are scarce for the region below 1000 Å. Metzger and Cook (65) found two distinct maxima at 700 and 900 Å, having about equal absorption coefficients of 500 cm^{-1}, and a minimum near 800 Å corresponding to an absorption coefficient of about $400 \, \text{cm}^{-1}$. No band structure was observed in this region. The first maximum in the total cross-section curve at 900 Å probably corresponds to the ionization continuum for the process $H_2O + h\nu \rightarrow H_2O^+ + e^-$. Three other dissociative ionization limits were shown corresponding to the formation of OH^+, O^+, and H^+. The contribution of these ions to the total ionization cross-section is not known. The maximum at 700 Å may be due to the various dissociative ionization processes. The data, in general, are in good agreement with the earlier measurements of Wainfan et al. (28). Data for wavelengths longer than 1000 Å indicate diffuse band structure (77) which becomes continuous to the shorter wavelengths. The data of Astoin et al. (36,78) show many bands below 1000 Å which are evidently absent from the data of Wainfan et al. (28). Metzger and Cook's (65) results are in agreement with those of Wainfan et al. (28) except for the maximum near 900 Å.

g. OZONE. Measurements (79,80) of the atmospheric absorption by ozone show that below 2000 Å the absorption is less than expected. This is attributed to the fact that solar radiation of these wavelengths does not penetrate to the altitudes where ozone is present. Although the Hartley continuum in the 2000–3000 Å region has the larger cross-section (81), the greater solar intensity at wavelengths greater than 3000 Å makes absorption in the weaker Huggins bands also very important. New data in this region has recently been reported (82).

It may be mentioned that the photodissociation products of ozone appear to be one of the most likely sources of excited oxygen atoms and molecules in the earth's atmosphere. At wavelengths below 3100 Å it is energetically possible to have $O_2 \, (^1\Delta_g)$ and $O(^1D)$ as the photolysis products. The threshold for $O(^1D)$ formation is 4100 Å, but the process would also yield a ground state $X^3\sum_g^-$ molecule, which would be a forbidden transition (83). Both flash and steady state photolyses provide evidence that $O(^1D)$ is the primary product (84,85) and not $O_2(^1\Delta_g)$; however, in a recent photolysis experiment (quoted in Ref. 52) at 2537 Å the $^1\Delta_g \rightarrow X^3\sum_g^-$ infrared atmospheric bands of O_2 in emission were observed. This coupled with the observation (70) of intense metastable O_2 absorption bands in the region 830–900 Å supports the presence of metastable $O_2(^1\Delta_g)$, but the efficiency is still unknown.

5. Photo-ionization Data For Atoms.

a. RARE GAS ATOMS. The photo-ionization cross-sections of the rare gases have been measured (86–112) over wide ranges of wavelengths (from their ionization thresholds to 80 Å, and for some atoms from 50 to 0.01 Å) and an essentially complete picture of the continuum absorption of these gas atoms is known. Figure 3 summarizes the photo-ionization cross-sections of the rare gases as a function of wavelength. The vertical lines indicate the positions of the "window"-type discrete absorption lines. The photo-ionization cross-section for some rare gas atoms, for example He, rises abruptly at the photon energies corresponding to the X-ray absorption edge and then decreases gradually as the photon energy is raised above the threshold for the particular shell. On the other hand, for some other atoms, such as Ne, σ_i continues to rise and then falls as the threshold is passed in the direction of increasing photon energy—Fig. 3 shows a distinct, broad maximum for neon.

Samson (5) has compiled both published and unpublished data and tabulated them. In the case of He, Ne, and Ar tabulated data is available (5) for the absorption coefficients continuously from threshold to 0.01 Å; for Kr and Xe cross-section measurements are complete except for the L shell in Kr and the M shell in Xe.

There has been some theoretical work performed on the photo-ionization cross-sections of the rare gases. Helium (113–118) and neon (15,116,119,120) have been studied extensively and the theoretical results are in agreement with the experimental results. In the case of argon (116,121,122) and krypton (116) only order of magnitude agreement is obtained, while no detailed theoretical treatment of xenon has yet been attempted. For a comprehensive comparison between the best experimental and theoretical determinations of σ_i of rare gas atoms, see the articles by Samson (5) and Stewart (6). These articles also

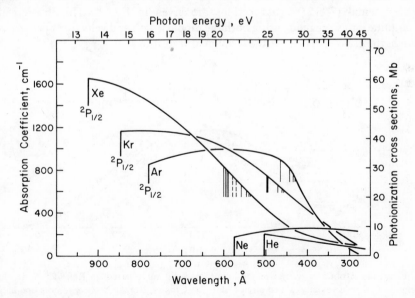

Figure 3   Photo-ionization continuum cross-sections of the rare gases as a function of wavelength. The vertical lines indicate the positions of the discrete "window" type absorption lines in Ar, Kr, and Xe due to (ms–np) type transitions (5).

contain discussions on oscillator strengths for excitations into the photo-ionization continuum, critical absorption energies, and autoionized energy levels.

b. ATOMIC OXYGEN, NITROGEN, AND HYDROGEN. Although an essentially complete picture of the continuum absorption of the rare gas atoms is known, this is not the case for any other atom, partly due to problems associated with the difficulties in dissociating the parent gas molecules to produce atoms and in measuring the atom concentrations, which limit direct measurements to their spectral range. However, cross-sections have been inferred from molecular cross-section data measured from 0.01 to 68 Å and from 200 to 500 Å by considering a molecule to be equivalent to two atoms (5). The photo-ionization cross-sections of atomic oxygen and nitrogen are basic atomic parameters of fundamental importance in the quantitative understanding of the ionosphere.

(1) *Atomic Oxygen* (IP, 910.443 Å). The atomic oxygen spectrum consists of the ionization continuum at wavelengths less than the threshold at 910.4 Å and, in addition, line series converging to limits corresponding to the electronic states of the ion. In the continuum region, there is good reason to believe that the absorption and ionization cross-sections are identical, in analogy with the ionization continua of the rare gases (see above), except for a few nonautoionizing series lines. Most of the absorption lines at wavelengths less than the ionization threshold are autoionized. Theoretical (72) and experimental (74,123) cross-sections are given in Fig. 4. The theoretical computations were made using both the dipole length and velocity approximations, the cross-sections for the individual transitions

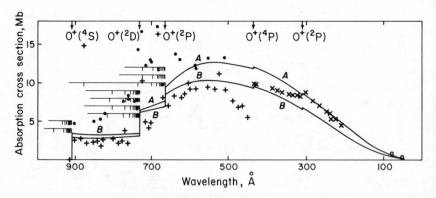

Figure 4 Atomic oxygen cross-sections (52). Solid curve based on Ref. 72: A, dipole length; B, dipole velocity. Filled circles, Ref. 74; Crosses, Ref. 123; × represents one-half O_2 cross-section, based on Ref. 74. Dashed lines beneath point indicate absorption line. Absorption series, based on Ref. 70.

$$O(1s^2 2s^2 2p^4)^3 P + hv \longrightarrow O^+(1s^2 2s^2 2p^3)^4 S°, \,^2D°, \,^2P° + e^-$$
$$O(1s^2 2s^2 2p^4)^3 P + hv \longrightarrow O^+(1s^2 2s 2p^4)^4 P, \,^2P + e^-$$

being over the spectral range from threshold (910.443 Å) to the K edge (23.3 Å). The experimental cross-sections were obtained in two independent measurements, one using discharged oxygen (74), which requires correction for metastable molecules, and the other (123) using a beam technique, which requires calibration against hydrogen atom. The large number of atomic oxygen absorption lines in the ionization continuum has only been realized recently with the measurement and classification of a number of these series by Huffman and coworkers (70). Some of the more intense series members reported by them are shown in Fig. 4. Huffman (75) has pointed out that the lines used in some laboratory measurements may be absorbed by oxygen atom lines, thus leading to the high cross-section values. Recently, some measurements have also been reported (71) on the absorption lines from the metastable $O(^1D)$ and $O(^1S)$ states. Additional calculations have also been published (124).

Acceptable values of the photo-ionization cross-section of atomic oxygen at particular solar lines are given in Table 2.

(2) *Atomic Nitrogen* (IP, 852.188 Å). From their measurements of the relative cross-sections of discharged nitrogen Ehler and Weissler (125) estimated $\sigma_i(N) \simeq 14.4$ Mb at 650 Å, assuming the concentration of N in the discharged nitrogen to be 25%. Samson (5) deduced absorption cross-sections of atomic nitrogen by asuming $\sigma(N) = \frac{1}{2}\sigma(N_2)$, $\sigma(N_2)$ having been experimentally determined (73). These experimental values of $\frac{1}{2}\sigma(N_2)$ from 200 to 500 Å are shown in Fig. 5. There are no theoretical grounds to expect that these cross-sections should be approximately equal to $\sigma(N)$ other than that they are energetic enough to penetrate into the L_1 subshell of the atom. In the absence of reliable experimental data, these values may be useful to give an approximate idea of the magnitude to be expected.

Bates and Seaton (126) calculated the cross-section at the spectral head using both the dipole length and velocity approximations, and obtained 10.8 and 7.7 Mb, respectively. Using a more approximate treatment based on the dipole length formulation they computed the variation in cross-section with wavelength, neglecting the absorption due to the inner shell electrons. Dalgarno and Parkinson (127) modified the approximate treatment described by Bates (15) to include the dipole velocity formulation, and used this treatment to extend the calculations to shorter wavelengths. Their calculations also took into account absorption by the $2s$ electrons. The theoretical cross-sections are reproduced in the inset in Fig. 5. In general, the dipole length approximation is preferred at the spectral head, while the velocity approximation is considered more reliable at shorter wavelengths.

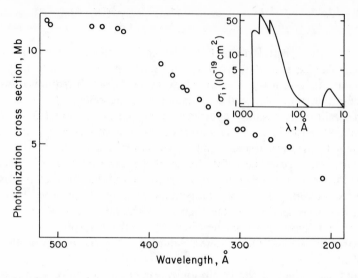

Figure 5   Atomic nitrogen cross-sections. Experimental values (main figure) based on Ref. 73. Theoretical values (inset) based on Ref. 127.

The study of atomic oxygen using the Hartree-Fock approximation by Dalgarno et al. (72) has been followed by an application to nitrogen (and its isoelectronic ions) by Henry (128). The results agree with the earlier calculations of Bates and Seaton (126) at the spectral head.

(3) *Atomic Hydrogen* (IP, 911.754 Å).   The theoretical photo-ionization cross-sections for atomic hydrogen, calculated using Ditchburn and Öpik's (2) formula:

$$\sigma_i(v, n) = \frac{g(32\pi^2 e^6 R Z^4)}{3^{3/2} h^3 v^3 n^5} \qquad [2]$$

and the Gaunt factors (g) given by Karzas and Latter (129), are shown in Fig. 6. The only experimental verification of this formula [2] is the measurement at 850.6 Å by Beynon and Cairns (130), which is also shown in Fig. 6. These authors dissociated approximately 40% (as measured by a Wrede-Harteck gage) of the molecular hydrogen that passed through a 200 W *rf* discharge at 11 Mc sec^{-1}, Their experimental value for $\sigma_i(H)$ of 5.15 Mb is in reasonable agreement with the theoretical value of 5.26 Mb at the same wavelength. Figure 6 also gives the experimental data of Samson and Cairns (73) for molecular hydrogen divided by 2, that is, $\sigma(H) = \frac{1}{2}\sigma(H_2)$. On the average they are about a factor of two greater than the theoretical values; this disagreement is not too surprising since there are no inner shell electrons in hydrogen and the two electrons are involved in the molecular bond.

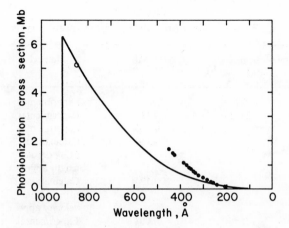

Figure 6 Atomic hydrogen cross-sections. Curve based on theoretical calculations (see Ref. 6). Open circle, experimental work from Ref. 130; closed circles, $\frac{1}{2}\sigma(H_2)$ values from Ref. 73.

c. METAL ATOMS. Photo-ionization cross-sections of the alkali metal atoms (131–137) and the atoms of Ca (138,139), Mg (140), Cd (137), In (141), and Tl (141) have been measured and calculated as well (142–145). Two recent review articles (5,6) and a book (8) give excellent summaries of the experiments and calculations. With the exception of lithium all the alkali metals, characterized by a single electron outside of the closed shells, have a small value for the cross-section at their spectral head, typically of the order of 0.1 Mb or less. The cross-sections then decrease to a minimum at about 1 eV beyond the ionization threshold and then start to increase. As yet no experimental data are available below 1000 Å. Known cross-sections, both experimental and theoretical, are presented in Table 3. New measurements on Cs, Rb, Zn, Hg, Pb, and Mn are in progress and it is expected that in the near future data on the alkali metals will also be extended down to 600 Å.

Because of their low ionization potentials, the alkali and alkaline earth metals have been especially valuable in the production of artificial ion clouds by their photo-ionization in rocketborne experiments. In fact, one of the main interests in the absorption coefficients of these metals arises from the desire to know the rate of ionization if one of them is dispersed as a cloud in the upper atmosphere. If it is assumed that the material is dispersed in a thin layer, the probability per second of photo-ionization at a given wavelength is equal to the product of the photon flux at this wavelength above the atmosphere and the photo-ionization cross-section. For wavelengths below the series limit this cross-section can be taken to be numerically equal to the absorption cross-section.

TABLE 3
Photo-ionization data for some metal atoms

Atom	Ionization threshold, Å	σ_i, Mb	Method	References
Li	2299.5	3.3–3.7	Experimental	134
Na	2412.6	0.13	Experimental	135
		0.116	Experimental	132
		0.136	Calculation using dipole length approx.	145
		0.126	Calculation using dipole velocity approx.	145
K	2856.3	0.008 (at minimum)	Experimental	131
Rb	2968.2	~0.01	Calculation	15
		0.04	Calculation	15
Cs	3184.0	0.03	Calculation	15
Ca	2028.2	0.45	Experimental	139
In	2142.7	~0.1–1.0	Experimental	141
Tl	2029.9	4.5 ± 0.8	Experimental	141

Marmo et al. (146) published a table of photo-ionization rates to be expected for several metal vapors. These rates were obtained by integrating the product of the photon flux and the measured cross-section from the series limit to the lowest wavelength for which values of the cross-section were available at the time. Hudson (147) calculated the photo-ionization rates for some of the alkali and alkali earth atoms in a similar fashion. Some of their results are given in Table 4. Additional discussion is given by Nawrocki and Papa (148).

TABLE 4
Calculated photo-ionization rates in the upper atmosphere for the alkalis and alkaline earths (146–148).

Metal	Probability of photo-ionization, atom sec^{-1}
Li	1.38×10^{-4}
Na	4.0×10^{-6}
K	1.85×10^{-5}
Rb	1.06×10^{-4}
Cs	6.5×10^{-4}
Mg	3.6×10^{-6}
Ca	2.5×10^{-5}

6. Photo-ionization Data For Ions

a. POSITIVE IONS. Photo-ionization cross-sections at the spectral head have been calculated for only a few atomic and molecular ions. Early work by Bates (15) and the more recent work of Burgess and Seaton (18) provide data for C^+, N^+, O^+, F^+, and Ne^+ ions. The cross-section of He^+ has been calculated by a number of workers (149–152) and the cross-section for H_2^+ by Bates et al. (153). These results are given in Table 3 and discussed in a review by Ditchburn and Öpik (2).

TABLE 5
Photo-ionization cross-sections of some positive ions

Ion	V_i, eV	λ_t, Å	σ_t, Mb	References
He^+	54.4	228	1.6	149–152
C^+	24.4	508	3.7	15
N^+	29.6	419	$(6.4)^a$	15
O^+	35.2	353	$(8.1)^a$	15, 18
F^+	35.0	354	2.5	15
Ne^+	41.0	302	4.5	15, 18
H_2^+	16.3	763	0.67	153

^{a}Values in parenthesis at 400 Å (λ_m the wavelength of maximum absorption associated with the ionization process for which V_i is given) and hence the cross-section of maximum absorption.

Little experimental work has been done on photoabsorption by positive ions. Dunn (154) measured the photodissociation cross-section of H_2^+ and N_2^+ ions at a number of wavelengths between 3000 Å and 9000 Å and compared the results with the then available theory. In a recent paper (155) he has described the theory of H_2^+ and D_2^+ photodissociations and calculated their cross-sections for each of the ions 19 and 27 vibrational levels.

b. NEGATIVE IONS (PHOTODETACHMENT). The photo-ionization cross-section of H^- has been the subject of increasingly accurate calculations because of its importance in the analysis of stellar atmospheres (156–158). Although sophisticated continuum wave functions were used in these calculations, there are still considerable differences in the values obtained using the different possible formulations. The calculations, however, demonstrate the sensitivity of the H^- photodetachment cross-section to wave function changes.

Calculations of photodetachment cross-sections for the negative ions C^-, O^-, Ar^-, and F^- have been made by Cooper and Martin (159). Continuous absorption of radiation by C^- in stellar photospheres may be an important source of opacity, especially in stars where the effect is not obscured by an abundance of H^-. For this reason a number of theoretical studies of the photodetachment cross-section of C^- have been carried out, the more recent ones being those done by Myerscough and McDowell (160) and Henry (128). For a discussion of these calculations the reader is referred to the article by Stewart (6).

Numerous experiments have been done on the detachment of electrons from negative ions by photon absorption. In most of this work modulated crossed-beam techniques were used. The technique involved a beam of mass-analyzed negative ions intersecting at right angles in high vacuum by an intense beam of filtered visible light and measuring the current of free electrons produced by photon absorption. Experimental details are available in the reviews by Branscomb (3). The foregoing technique has helped obtain the photo-detachment spectra of H^-, O^-, S^-, C^-, I^-, OH^-, and O_2^-; the photo-detachment cross-sections of H^-, O^-, C^-, and O_2^-; accurate electron affinities for O, S, C, and I. The interpretation of these studies is also discussed at length in the two reviews by Branscomb (3).

Photodetachment spectra in the ultraviolet have been studied by Berry and co-workers (161–164) who made observations of the absorption spectra of atomic halogen negative ions produced in alkali halide vapors which had been heated by shock waves. (They observed thresholds for s-wave capture of electrons by atoms and reported emission spectra produced by radiative capture of low-energy electrons by Cl, Br, and I.) Although the method has much higher optical resolution than the crossed-beam method, it does not lend itself as well to absorption cross-section measurements. Also, it is not possible to take full advantage of this high optical resolution because the plasma ion densities required ($\sim 10^{15}$ cm^{-3}) are such that Stark broadening is substantial.

Branscomb and co-workers (165) have studied the photodetachment thresholds of O^- to form O^3P and O^1D. They point out that the rate of increase of the cross-section above the second threshold is less than calculated, but calibration is very difficult when photon energies exceed 3.7 eV. Branscomb (166) has also measured cross-sections for photodetachment of OH^- and OD^-. These measurements were on a relative basis and made absolute by comparison to the known cross-section for H^-. Woo et al. (167) have measured photodetachment in a drift tube and found the photodetachment rate of O_3^- to be 4.2% that of O^- or 6.0×10^{-2} sec^{-1}.

The angular distributions of photodetached electrons from H^- and O^- have been studied experimentally (168) and theoretically (169). The experimental work was done at the argon laser wavelength, 4880 Å. Several striking facts emerge from the O^- study. The agreement of the theory with the measurements is good; to obtain this agreement, the authors had to calculate the mixing ratio of s to d wave functions in the outgoing electron wave. These authors found a case in which a cylindrical analyzer might have missed a group of electrons entirely. Cooper and Zare (169) showed that the angular distribution varies with the energy of the incident photons. At threshold the distribution is isotropic. It becomes almost $\sin^2 \theta$ (where θ is measured from the vector of the incident light) at photon energies roughly 0.8 eV above threshold and then becomes more isotropic with increasing photon energy. Such a change of angular distribution with energy would be interpreted as a change of cross-section with energy in many electron-energy measurements.

The picture in photodetachment studies has been changed in the last few years by the increased appreciation of the role of ion-molecule reactions. Fehsenfeld et al. (170) have pointed out the importance of NO_2^-, NO_3^-, CO_3^-, and perhaps hydrates of these ions. Photodetachment studies of these ions will require measurements in the near ultraviolet.

B. Dissociative Ionization

Discussions in the previous sections were chiefly involving ion-chamber measurements of photo-ionization cross-sections in which no distinction was made between one ion species and another. In this section we are concerned with measurements of cross-sections for the production of specific ion species by dissociative ionization. Such measurements are made by coupling mass spectrometers to monochromators and for experimental techniques the reader is referred to the literature (12,61). The technique is not free from difficulties and errors.

Comes and Lessman (171) have measured the cross-section for the production of N^+ from N_2 using a vacuum monochromator and quadrupole mass spectrometer. Their results are shown in Fig. 7; these results are pre-

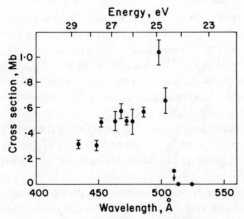

Figure 7 Dissociative ionization cross-section of N_2 measured by Comes and Lessman (171).

ferred to the earlier measurements of Weissler et al. (12) who used a vacuum monochromator coupled to a magnetic mass spectrometer. Comparison of the N_2^+ cross-sections of Comes and Lessman with photo-ionization cross-sections of Samson and Cairns (53) reveals no systematic error in the wavelength range in which N^+ ions were produced, although there is a systematic error in the N_2^+ cross-sections of Comes and Lessman at longer wavelength (~ 500 Å).

Comes and Lessman (172) have also measured using a molecular beam the dissociative photo-ionization cross-section for the production of O^+ from O_2. The cross-sections, which were made absolute by comparison with the photo-ionization cross-section leading to O_2^+, are shown in Fig. 8. The

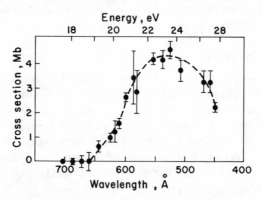

Figure 8 Dissociative ionization cross-section of O_2 measured by Comes and Lessman (172).

accuracy of the results shown is not known, but they are more likely to be low than high and likely to be more in error at shorter wavelengths than at longer, since dissociative ionization of O_2 produces energetic O^+ ions at $\lambda < 584$ Å (see Section C). Dibeler and Walker (173), without making any claim to measure cross-sections, report an O^+ signal 0.03 of their O_2^+ signal at 584 Å. This signal represents a cross-section of about 0.7 Mb, but the relative transmission and counting efficiencies are unknown. Dibeler and Walker also report the formation of O^+ and O^- in the spectral region 718.5 Å to 700 Å with a peak intensity of about 0.03 that of the O_2^+ ion at 718.5 Å. Somewhat earlier Elder (174) had obtained similar information at lower resolution.

Although they make no claim to measure photo-ionization cross sections, Dibeler and co-workers have obtained photo-ionization mass spectra of CO_2 (173), N_2O and NO_2 (175), and H_2O (176).

C. Excitation of Ions and Neutrals

Generally speaking, the states of excitation of ions produced by photo-ionization can be inferred from measurements of the kinetic energies of the charged particles released or from studies of the fluorescence, if any, of the ions. Electron and ion energy distribution measurements are helpful in locating ionic states on energy level diagrams and in determining the relative probabilities of excitation of these states. However, these measurements give no information about neutrals or the classification of electronic states, and occasionally fail to provide information even about the existence of electronic states, because of overlap of two or more vibrational progressions. Studies of fluorescence may give the missing information and may also give more precise results than electron and ion energy measurements do about the relative probabilities of exciting various electronic or vibrational states. Even failure to detect fluorescence when excitation is known to exist may be useful in determining classification when metastable states are possible.

1. Electron and Ion Energies. Energies of charged particles have been studied in cylindrical geometries (177–181), approximately spherical geometries (182,183), and with electron-focusing systems and plane retarding fields (184, 185). In the case of cylindrical geometries, simple retarding potential systems (177–180) and magnetic (181) and electrostatic (186) deflection analyzers have been used. The ion currents measured depend on the angular distributions of the particles, which in turn depend on the final states of the ions and their energies. By attributing to each state a fraction of the photo-ionization cross-section proportional to the electron current associated with it, cross-sections for various states of excitation can be obtained. For experimental details the reader is referred to the literature cited previously.

Table 6 gives relative excitation cross-sections for the various states of N_2^+, O_2^+, and NO^+, which can be excited with 584 Å radiation. Vibrational distributions for the same ions investigated at 584 Å are presented in Table 7 together with some calculated values. Rather large errors (arising from noise proportional to the total current collected and from noise due to scattered low-energy electrons) are quite possible for small transition probabilities to upper vibrational states in retarding potential measurements.

Berkowitz et al. (185) showed that in nitrogen the angular distribution of electrons for the cases in which the ions are left in either the $X^2\Sigma_g^+$ or the $A^2\Pi_u$ state by 584 Å radiation are both spherically symmetric. If in the ionization to the $B^2\Sigma_u$ state the electron angular distribution is also spherically symmetric, as might be expected from the removal of $a\sigma_u$ electron to $a\sigma_g$ state in the continuum, then all methods of electron energy measurements should give the same results. From Table 6 it appears that the relative

TABLE 6
Relative probabilities of exciting various electronic states with 584 Å Radiation

Ion	State	Cylindrical retarding potential systems		Electron lenses and plane retarding potential systems		Spherical retarding potential system	Spherical system with focusing and an electron multiplier
		Ref. 181	Ref. 187	Ref. 185	Ref. 184	Ref. 182	Ref. 183
N_2^+	$X^2\Sigma$	0.34^a	0.35	0.78^b	0.26	0.33	0.32
	$A^2\Pi$	0.51^a	0.45	1.00^b	0.59	0.60	0.55
	$B^2\Sigma$	0.15^a	0.21		0.15	0.08	0.13
O_2^+	$X^2\Pi$	0.24^a				0.18	0.15
	$a^4\Pi + A^2\Pi$	0.35^a				0.37	0.38
	$b^4\Sigma_g$	0.26^a				0.24	0.27
	$B^2\Sigma_g$	0.15^a				0.21	0.20
NO^+	$X^1\Sigma$					0.36^b	
	$a^3\Sigma$					0.06^b	
	$^3\Delta$					1.00^b	
	$A^1\Pi$					0.51^b	

[a]Values estimated from published curves.
[b]Relative values for several but not all states.

cross-sections for the X and the A states are known to 20% and for the B state is known only within about a factor of 2. On the other hand, in Table 7 the agreement is reasonably good both among experiments and between theory and experiments. The spectral region around 584 Å does not have strong autoionization bands, but such bands are present at longer wavelengths and may have a large effect on the energy distribution of the outgoing electrons. However, there exists a difference in the vibrational distribution in nitrogen in the two autoionization bands at 765 and 771 Å (187); in such regions averages of cross-sections for excitation to particular states of the ion over 5 or 10 Å will give misleading answers and investigations with high spectral resolution are required. The only direct information from electron energy experiments concerning the wavelength dependence of the cross-sections for exciting particular states of the N_2^+ ion has been obtained with relatively large band widths and cylindrical analyzers (181,187). These results have been reviewed by Schoen (11).

TABLE 7
Relative vibrational transition probabilities at 584 Å

Ion	State		Lens system and plane retarding potentials	Spherical retarding potential system	Magnetic deflection analysis		Photoionization cross-section data near threshold	Theoretical	
			Ref. 184	Ref. 185	Ref. 182	Ref. 180	Ref. 41	Ref. 188	Ref. 189
N_2^+	$X^2\Sigma_g$	0	1.00	1.0	1.00			1.0	
		1	0.09	>0.2	0.054			0.10	
	$A^2\Pi_u$	0	0.86	0.84	0.85			0.78	
		1	1.00	1.00	1.00			1.00	
		2	0.78	0.73	0.71			0.72	
		3	0.38	0.39	0.46			0.40	
		4	0.16		0.21			0.18	
		5	0.07		0.14			0.08	
		6			0.08				
	$B^2\Sigma_u$	0	1.00			1.00		1.00	
		1	0.18			0.11		0.11	
O_2^+	$X^2\Pi_g$	0	0.50	0.53	0.43				0.60
		1	1.00	1.00	1.00				1.00
		2	0.97	0.98	0.93				0.67
		3	0.57	0.57	0.43				0.24
		4	0.09		0.14				0.05
	$^4\Sigma_g$	0		0.53					1.00
		1		1.00					0.83
		2		0.98					0.40
		3		0.72					0.15
	$^2\Sigma_g$	0				0.75			
		1				1.00			
		2				0.92			
		3				0.67			
		4				0.50			
		5				0.17			
		6				0.13			
NO^+	$X^1\Sigma^1$	0	0.41	0.50	0.59		0.79	0.48	
		1	1.00	0.94	1.00		1.00	1.00	
		2	0.88	1.00	0.81		1.00	0.92	
		3	0.46	0.71	0.40		0.67	0.48	
		4	0.28		0.16			0.16	

At 584 Å the electrons released from O_2 in removal of a Π_g electron to produce the $X^2\Pi_g$ state of the O_2^+ ion have a tendency to come out parallel or antiparallel to the direction of the photon beam (185). Removal of other electrons appears to produce only spherically symmetric distributions. Therefore, the apparent cross-section for the production of the ground state O_2^+ ion will appear to be too small when measured in cylindrical systems. However, Blake and Carver (181), using a cylindrical apparatus, obtained a larger probability for transition to the $X^2\Pi$ state of O_2^+ than did Vroom (182), who used a spherical retarding potential system, and Samson (183), who used a quasi-spherical geometry. Even with resolution of the order of 20 mV (186) no one has been able to resolve the $A^2\Pi_u$ state from the $a^4\Pi_u$ state. At longer wavelengths Blake and Carver (181), who used a helium continuum (~ 10 Å resolution), observed that large deviations from the Franck-Condon principle occur in the autoionization region; this was ascribed by them to the series of events: transition to a superexcited neutral, subsequent radiation of a photon in the red or infrared, and finally autoionization. Schoen and co-workers (187) investigating the same spectral region with a line source (~ 3 Å resolution) and somewhat better energy resolution, also observed strong deviations from the Franck-Condon principle, but no transitions which required the emission of a photon. The difference in results may be due to the differences in light sources used. All these results are summarized in a recent article by Schoen (11).

Other molecules that have been studied in a similar fashion include NO (182,185), CO_2, and N_2O (180), N_2O, and NO_2 (182), and H_2O (181). Angular distribution measurements at 584 Å by Berkowitz et al. (185) in NO have shown that the removal of the Π_g electron, as in the case of O_2, produces an angular distribution peaked along the photon beam. The most surprising fact to emerge from electron energy measurements in NO is that an NO^+ state, $a^3\Sigma$, previously thought to lie 14.22 eV above the ground state of the neutral (190), does not exist there, but that there is a state at about 15.5 eV (178,191), which had not been observed previously. Vroom (182) has reported a state at 14.84 eV, labelled $a^3\Sigma$, but this finding is hitherto unconfirmed by others. The relative transition probabilities to a few, but not all, electronic states and the relative excitation probabilities of various vibrational states of the ground state of NO^+ with 584 Å incident are given in Tables 6 and 7, respectively.

Turner and May (180) have published magnetic energy analyses of electrons from CO_2 and N_2O produced by 584 Å radiation. Vroom (182) using 584 Å radiation and a spherical system, has obtained energy spectra of electrons from N_2O and NO_2. Blake and Carver (181) have measured the electron energy spectrum from H_2O with a cylindrical retarding potential analyzer, from threshold to 584 Å.

Positive ions may be studied by any of the various techniques mentioned in this section. The energy resolution is not nearly as good as it is for electron experiments because the motion of the neutral parent contributes significantly to the velocity of the ion fragment (192). Vroom (182) has measured the energy distribution of O^+ fragments from the photoionization of O_2 at 584 Å, using a spherical retarding potential system. Schoen and co-workers (187) measured the energy distributions from dissociative photoionization of O_2 and N_2 in a cylindrical system at a number of wavelengths between 584 Å and 358 Å. Analysis of these ion-energy distribution measurements reveals that the energies of these ions are great enough to cause significant loss from ion beams in some types of mass spectrometers (with consequent underestimation of the probability of formation of O^+ from O_2), that the $^2\Sigma^-$ state of O_2 predissociates (and other states of the molecular ion may also predissociate), and that some of the energetic neutrals accompanying the energetic ions are in metastable states. No angular distribution measurements have been made.

Schoen and co-workers (187) have measured the dissociative ionization of O_2 in a mass spectrometer very sensitive to ion energies. They found that perhaps all, but not less than half, of the O^+ ions produced by 584 Å radiation had significantly more than thermal energy. At the same wavelength Vroom (182), with a spherical retarding potential analyzer, found that 0.075 of all the ions produced were energetic. Schoen (11,187), with a cylindrical system, found 0.15; the difference may be ascribable to angular distribution effects.

Doolittle, Schoen, and Schubert (187) have found energetic positive ions from the dissociative ionization of N_2 at 358 Å, but not at wavelengths greater than 400 Å. However, these energetic ions constituted only a few percent of the total number of ions produced.

2. Flourescence. In fluorescence experiments radiation of intensity $I_0(\lambda)$ from a monochromator is incident on a gas or vapor contained in a cell (see Fig. 2) and the fluorescence is observed from a side with a photomultiplier. It is preferable to use a second monochromator in conjunction with the photomultiplier. The efficiency F with which fluorescence is detected is a function of the position, x, of the fluorescing molecules in the chamber and of the incident and fluorescent wavelengths λ and λ_f, respectively. If gas quenching, diffusion, or absorption of fluorescent radiation are important, F is also a function of the molecular number density n. Assuming that F is not zero only between the distances L and $L + l$ measured from the entrance to the cell, one gets for the observed fluorescence intensity the relation

$$I_f(\lambda, \lambda_f) = I_0(\lambda) \exp\left[-n\sigma_t(\lambda)L\right] \int_0^l n\sigma_f(\lambda, \lambda_f)$$

$$\exp\left[-n\sigma_t(\lambda)x\right]F(x, \lambda, \lambda_f, n)\, dx$$

Here σ_f is the cross-section for production of the fluorescing state and σ_t is the cross-section for all processes which remove photons from the beam. If $n\sigma_t L \ll l$ and F is independent of λ, x, and n, the equation becomes

$$I_f(\lambda, \lambda_f) = I_0(\lambda)nl\sigma_f(\lambda, \lambda_f)F(\lambda_f)$$

or

$$\sigma_f(\lambda, \lambda_f) = \frac{I_f(\lambda, \lambda_f)}{I_0(\lambda)nlF(\lambda_f)}$$

That is, I_f/I_0 is proportional to the cross-section for excitation of the fluorescing state, under the given conditions. In no experiments in which dispersed vacuum ultraviolet radiation stimulated fluorescence has there been a measurement of $F(\lambda_f)$ which allowed a direct evaluation of $\sigma_f(\lambda, \lambda_f)$. However, in a number of cases the dependence of the cross-section upon incident wavelength has been determined. If the value of the cross-section is taken from electron-energy data at an incident wavelength at which measurement is particularly accurate (584 Å, for instance), then the value is determined at all incident wavelengths from measured wavelength dependence.

It is to be noted that in all fluorescence experiments extreme care should be taken to avoid confusion between the radiation caused by electrons released from the gas or walls and the radiation due to photon absorption processes. Also, confusion can arise if the polarization of the fluorescent radiation changes as a function of incident wavelength; such a change might change the detection efficiency F and be confused with a change in the cross section, σ_f. However, no experimental information about polarization is available.

In the preceding paragraphs we have discussed the principles underlying the methods of obtaining fluorescence information. We shall now consider the results obtained with dispersed, incident radiation, for some molecules of aeronomic interest.

Huffman (14), Cook (55), and their co-workers determined the threshold for the production of a strong visible fluorescence in N_2 to be 661 Å. This wavelength is the energy actually required to excite the $B^2\Sigma_u$ state of N_2^+. Recently, Judge and Weissler (193) have dispersed the radiation, identified the expected first negative bands of N_2^+, and determined the variation of the cross section with wavelength. These authors used the measured value of Frost et al. (182) for the cross section at 584 Å and calculated the cross-section at other wavelengths from their measurements of wavelength dependence. Schoen (11) is of the opinion that this wavelength dependence of the cross section for excitation to the $B^2\Sigma_u$ state of N_2^+ is probably more accurate than that obtained from electron energy data.

Young et al. (194) have found fluorescence from $O('D)$ at 6300 Å when O_2 was photolyzed with 1470 Å radiation. This radiation was expected from photolysis in the Schumann-Runge continuum but had not been found previously because the $O('D)$ state is metastable. Beyer and Welge (195), using magnetic strip multipliers with LiF and CaF_2 windows to detect fluorescence from excited O atoms produced in the dissociation of O_2, observed the direct radiation at 1302, 1304 and 1306 Å from the $O(3s^3S)$ state and the same radiation in cascade from the $O(3p^3P)$ state. Cook and Metzger (55) and Huffman et al. (14) observed a weak fluorescence in O_2 at thresholds which were identified as 736.5 Å and 722 $\pm$ 5 Å, respectively. The onset of this weak fluorescence being gradual the threshold is rather difficult to determine. The fluorescence is probably from the $A^2\Pi_u$ state of O_2^+ and represents detection in a case in which electron-energy measurements have not indicated a state. Recently, Judge and Weissler (193) have detected radiation from the $b^4\Sigma_g^-$ state of O_2^+ and reported several peculiar shifts of vibrational intensity at wavelengths above 600 Å. These shifts are probably related to autoionization.

The relative fluorescence yields from NO have also been measured (195). The atomic oxygen lines at 1302, 1304, and 1306 Å that were observed in the O_2 work (195) were also observed in the NO work; in both these experiments the lines appeared both by direct transition and by cascade. In addition, in the experiments with NO (195), one or more radiations appeared; these radiations were not transmitted by CaF_2 but were transmitted by LiF and have been tentatively attributed to the atomic nitrogen lines at 1200 Å and perhaps 1134 Å. Metzger and co-workers (60) observed radiation in the vacuum ultraviolet and attributed it to the $A^1\Pi \to X^1\Sigma$ transition in NO^+. The threshold for excitation of this radiation was found to be 677.4 Å. However, it is not clear why they did not observe the transitions from the neutral atoms.

D. Laser Ionization

A plasma can be produced by focusing a high-power laser beam on to a material target (196,197) or a gas at moderately high pressure (198–200). Extensive work has been done on the pressure and pulse-width dependence of the breakdown-threshold laser power, on the absorption, scattering, and reflection characteristics of the plasma toward the laser light, on the Doppler-shift of scattered light from the luminous front, and on the expansion of the shock wave which is initiated by the spark. Such work has enabled to estimate electron temperatures (1–10 eV), electron densities (10^{18}–10^{19} cm^{-3}), and heavy particle velocities (10^7 cm sec^{-1}) in many gases. Electron densities greater than 10^{21} cm^{-3} have been reported in argon, for which the spark is most intense (201). Experiments on the blow-off from metal surfaces illuminated by giant-pulsed lasers have indicated similar plasma properties (196). Measurements of the decay of the laser-generated plasma have also been made for the purpose of establishing the mechanism of electron loss and energy loss over several microseconds after the laser pulse (202).

The various processes which have been suggested as the cause of the ionization of gases by laser radiation have been reviewed by Hantzsche, Rompe, and Wolf (203). The breakdown is explained as due to multiple ionization of the atoms (or molecules) of the gas due to the very high field strengths prevailing at the laser focus.

The scope for the application of laser radiation in the field of reactions under plasma conditions is potentially enormous, although as yet comparatively little work has been done. The production of atomic and molecular species in selectively excited electronic states or the production of ions and radicals by laser radiation could initiate certain reactions or radically alter the course of others. Such changes in the course and rates of chemical reactions could also be affected by selectively populating certain vibrational states, for example by absorption of laser radiation. Some preliminary work in this direction has been reported (204,205). The major applications of the laser have been in spectroscopy (206) for obtaining pure rotation and vibration-rotation spectra in gaseous systems (207–210), although lasers have been used for plasma diagnostics (see Vol. 1, Chapter 8) and for plasma confinement in fusion reactors (see Chapter 20). In this section we shall be concerned with the cross-section for laser ionization of gases and solids.

1. Laser Ionization of Gases.   Bebb and Gold (211) have calculated from perturbation theory the ionization cross-section for Xe, Kr, Ar, Ne, He, and H atoms by simultaneous absorption of 7, 8, 9, 13, 14, and 18 ruby laser photons. They found that the cross-section for dipolar transitions in the simplest approximation (plane-wave final state, simplest approximation to the matrix element) is about three orders of magnitude smaller than that for a fairly sophisticated treatment (Coulomb final states, good approximate matrix elements); the value for H was given as $\sigma = 1.4 \times 10^{-244}(\text{flux})^{-7}$ cm^2. Application of the model to rare gases indicated that direct multi-photon ionization can provide the starting electron for observed optical breakdown of gases but that other processes subsequently dominate. Gardner (212) showed that replacing the Poisson distribution by a Polya distribution, which takes account of correlations between coherent photons, leads to correct estimates of the lowest threshold fluxes required to induce ionization breakdown.

Phelps (213) has calculated the rate of growth of ionization by electron impact with atoms and molecules in the presence of an intense laser beam. The excitation and ionization coefficients were calculated using Holstein's formula for the free–free absorption coefficient and using previously determined elastic- and inelastic-scattering cross-sections. Phelps found that the agreement with experimental measurements of the breakdown time is satisfactory if it is assumed that initiating electrons are readily produced by the laser and that some of the atoms or molecules excited by electron impact are immediately photoionized.

Hantzsche et al. (203) suggested that absorption by collision complexes (Ar_6) will likely give a large contribution to ionization since their calculations showed large cross-sections for simultaneous absorption of several photons. The many-photon photoelectric effect was also considered; for Ar with a ruby laser, the many-photon photoelectric effect can be

$$9hv_0 + Ar \longrightarrow Ar^+ + e^-$$

However, this is not likely to be the main contribution and some form of inverse bremsstrahlung plays the largest role.

Litvak and Edwards (197,202) studied the electron recombination in laser-produced hydrogen plasma using time-resolved spectroscopic measurements. Solutions obtained from the rate and energy equations indicated the electron loss to be due to collisional-radiative recombination. They also observed that the absorbed laser energy was at least an order of magnitude greater than could be estimated from the calculated laser absorption coefficient for inverse bremsstrahlung at thermal equilibrium.

2. Blow-Off Plasmas. By focusing an intense laser beam on a solid surface, a small inertially confined plasma is generated near the target surface. Emission of multiply charged ions (214,215), removal of surface adsorbed species (216), as well as the observation of electron thermionic, photoelectric and X-ray emission (217-219) have been reported.

Gregg and David (220) who measured the kinetic energies of ions produced by focusing laser giant pulses on surfaces of Li, LiH, Be, C, Al, S, Zn, and Ag, detected average ion kinetic energies as high as 2000 eV. They also found that the mean-squared ion velocity increased proportionally to approximately the square root of the giant pulse peak intensity for the lower atomic weight materials, and varied with approximately the 0.33 power of the intensity for the higher atomic weight materials. Haught and Polk (221) have studied laser-irradiated single-particle plasmas of LiH and David et al. (222) studied plasma produced from C. Most of these studies, however, were concerned with experimental verification of postulated theoretical models for plasma formation and expansion (223).

E. Photo-ionization as an Aspect of Photochemistry

Photo-ionization as an aspect of photochemistry has been studied to some extent, the literature on the subject was reviewed five years ago by McNesby and Okabe (83) and more recently by Ausloos (224). Since then the construction of light sources emitting a particular wavelength or two, or a narrow wavelength region has led to investigations of the photoionization of a large selection of compounds in an enclosed system. For example, Laufer and McNesby (225) describe an argon resonance lamp emitting only the 1048 Å and 1067 Å lines. Because fragmentation of the parent ion at 1048 Å to 1067 Å will not be as extensive as in a radiolytic system, kinetic studies of certain types of ion-molecule reactions will be facilitated. This coupled with the availability of new optical transmission filters and windows have enabled the discovery of new types of ion-molecule reactions.

Although the mass spectrometer is the most versatile and in many instances the only tool for ion-molecule reactions, in certain systems valuable information on photo-ionization has been obtained by examining the neutral products formed by these reactions (226). When appropriate isotope (deuterium) labelling is used, the neutral products can provide valuable information about the structure of the reacting ions and of the ionic reaction complexes.

Using the Essex technique (227), in which an electric field is applied across two electrodes in the gas or vapor mixture being irradiated, in some cases (228–230) a clear distinction can be made between the products of ion-molecule reactions and those resulting from the decomposition of neutral excited molecules. In the saturation current region the passage of electrons through the mixture does not cause increased ionization, but can augment the number of neutral excited molecules formed. Since the occurrence of fast ion-molecule reactions is unaffected by the presence of electric field, the resulting product yields will be the same as those measured in the absence of an electric field, whereas the yields of products resulting from neutral excited molecule decomposition will show an increase over those measured in field-free experiments. Of course, yields of products resulting from slow ion-molecule reactions may show an actual decrease attributable to the collection of the precursor ions on the electrode (231).

No attempt is made here to list or discuss the individual systems investigated.

F. Photo-ionization in Electrical Discharges

The relative importance of photo-ionization processes, as compared with other atomic collision events, in the spark breakdown of gases at atmospheric pressure, in the corona discharges, and in Townsend "dark" discharges has been discussed at length by several authors, with some variations of opinion (232,233). If photoionization is indeed important in these electrical discharge plasmas, it must necessarily involve vacuum ultraviolet radiation. Quantitative information on the types of processes that have been envisaged (232,233) is, however, difficult to acquire chiefly because of the high absorbability of any effective radiation. Nevertheless, some experimental investigations have been made on the "gas-ionizing" radiations. In the following paragraphs some of these studies with atmospheric gases are briefly discussed.

Bemerl and Fetz (234) studied the pressure dependence of the photoelectric effect at a Cu surface placed in an ionization chamber filled with H_2 or O_2 and exposed to light from a corona discharge between coaxial cylinders in the same gas. They were thus able to measure the absorption coefficient of the gas and the volume ionization resulting from the short-wavelength components of the corona radiation. Przybylski (235) used a similar discharge in O_2 in combination with an ionization chamber which discriminated surface photoelectric effects. At gas pressures above 10mm Hg a monochromatic radiation component lying in the vacuum ultraviolet and having an absorption coefficient of 38 cm^{-1} (STP) was observed; at lower pressures two further components with absorption coefficients of 250 and 550 cm^{-1} were found. The detection of a new component, with a low absorption coefficient (2.5 cm^{-1}, STP), in the radiation from a spark discharge was later reported (236). Experiments with N_2-O_2 mixtures and with air led to the conclusion that the radiation effective in the ionization of air was essentially emitted by N_2 and ionized O_2 with an absorption coefficient of order 5 cm^{-1}. Stroka (237) has followed up these experiments, where no wavelength resolution was attempted, by applying a vacuum photoelectric spectrometer to the radiation from a corona discharge in oxygen at various pressures. It was concluded that the intense radiation component he observed at about 988 Å is identical with the gas-ionizing radiation Przybylski found to have an absorption coefficient of ~ 38 cm^{-1}.

The radiation from a "nonself-sustaining" discharge in oxygen subject to a homogeneous electrical field, that is, a Townsend "dark" discharge, was studied by Teich (238) using an ionization chamber filled with the same gas. The absorption coefficients and the intensity of the ionizing radiation were measured as functions of E/p, where E is the field strength and p the gas pressure. Teich found a radiation component, corresponding to short wavelengths with an absorption coefficient of 38 cm^{-1} which, as mentioned in the preceding paragraph, is also present in the radiation from corona discharges.

Samson and Weissler (239) have used radiation dispersed by a vacuum ultraviolet monochromator to generate ions in O_2 and N_2, respectively, for use in a "mobility tube," that is, for measurements of drift velocities in a uniform field. The apparent advantage of this method, compared with use of the more common ion sources, most of which function by electron impacts, is due to the fact that uncertainties as to the ionic species concerned are avoided. By selecting wavelengths just above the first ionization threshold of the test gas, one can thus be fairly certain that the ions used in the measurement are O_2^+ or N_2^+ in their ground states, whereas electron impact techniques may not only yield ions in metastable or long-lived vibrational states, but also such species as N_3^+.

On the other hand, it may not be amiss to refer here briefly to the effects of external radiations (such as visible light, ultraviolet light, infrared, X and γ rays, etc.) on gas discharges, which have been extensively, but not thoroughly, studied. Loeb (240) has given an excellent critique of the phenomena observed, which in literature are referred to as the positive and negative Joshi effects (photovariation, positive or negative, of the discharge current due to external radiation incident on the discharge tube). The physical mechanism of the Joshi and allied effects (due to magnetic fields, etc.) is still not clear (240), despite numerous studies of the physics of the process, over a time span of 30 years, some of which (241) have shown that even extremely faint light and feeble intensities of electromagnetic radiations falling on miniature-type discharge tubes can cause the negative effect. The interested reader is referred to a recent review and some selected papers (242) for details.

III. IONIZED MEDIA OBTAINED IN RADIOLYTIC SYSTEMS

A. Radiolysis

In radiolytic systems, the high-energy particles (α particles, β particles, and artificially accelerated electrons) or radiations (γ rays and other radioactive emanations) lose their energy in interactions with a molecular system and in the process remove the orbital electrons from the molecules and atoms, thus producing positively charged ions and free electrons (primary ionization). With sufficient kinetic energy, the liberated primary electrons can produce secondary ionization. The essential mechanism of ionization therefore involves the electrons as the major effective energetic species, their energies being greater than ~ 500 keV. In view of the very high energy range involved, something of the order of 10^4 electrons is produced per primary electron involved, which is very unlike the phenomenon observed in electrical discharge plasmas.

Several chemical systems have been investigated radiolytically using both natural and artificial radioactive emanations and high energy particles from nuclear reactors and other high energy machines (243). A technique that has been recently used in such studies for directly observing the transient species is the pulse radiolysis (243), in which an intense pulse of electrons from an accelerator is used in a manner similar to the use of the photoflash in flash spectroscopy. The published literature on the subject is so vast that a detailed discussion of these topics is outside the scope of this article and the reader is referred to the books and reviews cited in Refs. 224 and 243. Most of these investigations have been done at gas pressures much higher than those commonly used in electrical discharges. During the past few years "high" pressure mass spectrometric techniques have been successfully adapted for use with many radiolytic systems and it has been possible to obtain considerable information on the ion chemistry of those systems, especially the primary events. However, studies of radiolytic systems by determination of neutral reaction products have continued unabated and have equally contributed, if not more, to our present knowledge of ion chemistry.

As described in Section II-E, the use of deuterium labelling (226) can yield information about the structure of the reacting ions and of the ionic reaction complexes. Similarly, the application of an electric field across two electrodes in the mixture being irradiated (228–230) makes it possible to distinguish between the products of ion-molecule reactions and those resulting from the decomposition of neutral excited molecules.

B. Ion Chemistry

Investigations of the ion chemistry in radiolytic systems have been chiefly concerned with studies of proton transfer reactions, H^- and H_2^- transfer reactions, charge transfer reactions, and complex rearrangements which involve quite profound changes in structure and bond reorganizations (224, 244). Of particular interest is the occurrence of H_2^- and H^- transfer reactions (245):

$$C_nH_{2n}^+ + RH_2 \longrightarrow C_nH_{2n+2} + R^+$$

$$C_nH_{2n}^+ + RH_2 \longrightarrow C_nH_{2n+1} + RH^+$$

where $C_nH_{2n}^+$ is a lower olefinic ion and RH_2 is a saturated hydrocarbon. The relative rates of H_2^- and H^- transfer reactions to a given olefin ion may be expected to depend on the structure of the hydrocarbon molecule involved. The H_2 transfer reaction has also been reported (246):

$$C_nH_{2n} + RH_2^+ \longrightarrow C_nH_{2n+2} + R^+$$

This reaction is of considerable interest to photoionization and high pressure radiation chemistry (224), because use can be made of this reaction to evaluate the ion pair yield of parent alkane ions, a quantity which is usually rather elusive.

Although the bulk of data obtained from radiolysis work pertains to ions formed as bimolecular reaction products, in the last few years many examples of ions formed with much higher pressure dependence have been observed. To form ions at high pressures in a region from which they can be collected, it is usually necessary to employ electrons of several hundred volts rather than the usual 60–70 volts employed in conventional mass spectroscopy. Kebarle and Hogg (247) have therefore employed alpha particles of high energy to provide primary ions. When ions are formed by high energy massive particles, it is possible to operate at much higher pressures and thus far ions formed at pressures up to about one atmosphere have been studied (247,248). With such a system Kebarle et al. (249) have observed ions having the general formulas $H^+(H_2O)_n$, with n varying from 1 to 7 and $NH_4^+ \cdot nNH_3$ clusters with n as high as 20, and Wexler et al. (248) have observed polymer ions from acetylene having up to 12 carbon atoms. Field and Munson (250) have recently described several high pressure ionic reactions.

The role of charge transfer processes in radiolysis is still not clearly understood, although the occurrence of charge transfer from positively charged inert gas atoms to hydrocarbon molecules has definitely been demonstrated by the increased product yields which, on the basis of isotopic labelling can be shown to be formed by reactions of fragment ions resulting from the charge exchange process (231). A few examples of charge transfer not involving inert gases have also been proposed to occur in gas phase radiolysis (251).

The elucidation of neutralization processes requires a knowledge of the positive ions that will eventually be neutralized by recombination with a thermal electron or negative ion and of the fate of the excited molecule or radical formed in such a neutralization. At the intensities normally used in gas phase radiolysis neutralization is a slow process and therefore, the ions have a higher probability of reacting or diffusing to the wall. In addition, fragmentation of the parent ion may occur (224) and the resulting fragment ions can often initiate a chain reaction of unknown length. Finally, theoretical considerations (252) point to the formation and decomposition of neutral molecules with excitation energies below and above the ionization energy of the molecule.

Ion-molecule reactions of interest in plasma studies are discussed in the next two sections (see IV and V).

IV. IONIZED GASES OBTAINED BY PARTICLE BOMBARDMENT

A. Electron Impact

Studies of ionized gases produced by electron impact on atoms and molecules are of considerable interest in diverse fields of research such as stellar atmospheres, low- and high-temperature laboratory plasmas, atmospheric-physics and chemistry, and mass spectrometry (253). In particular, cross-section data on the ionization of atoms and molecules by electron impact are highly useful in predicting the properties of nonequilibrium plasmas (see Vol. 1, Chapter 3). Such data may be obtained by experimental measurements or by theoretical evaluation (see Chapter 12).

A measurement of an ionization cross-section usually involves the determination of the quantities in the relation

$$\frac{I_i(E)}{I_e(E)} = \rho L \sum_n n\sigma_n(E) = \rho L \sigma_T(E)$$

$I_i(E)$ is the ion current generated by single electron impact, $I_e(E)$ is the current of bombarding electrons of energy E, ρ is the number density of the gas bombarded, L is the collision path length over which the measured ion current is collected, and $\sigma_n(E)$ is the cross-section for producing an ion of nth degree of ionization in the collision, the summation being over the charge states which contribute to the collected ion current. When all charge states are included, the summation is denoted by $\sigma_T(E)$, the total cross-section. Kieffer and Dunn (254) have listed the most important conditions necessary for obtaining accurate measurements of the quantities needed to calculate $\sigma_n(E)$ from the equation.

In general, the apparatus for these measurements can be classified as one of the following: total ionization apparatus, total ionization tube with charge/mass discrimination, mass spectrometer, and crossed-beam apparatus. The apparatus and experimental techniques have been described over and over again in several books. These methods, however, do little to determine final states of ions the knowledge of which are required for understanding plasma phenomena. However, by measuring the light emitted from excited ions formed by electrons of known energy in experiments purporting to measure ionization cross-sections, it is possible to evaluate the cross-sections required in understanding plasma phenomena. Although this method has the difficult problem of absolute radiometry, it has been used in some cases, for example, to observe ionization to the $n = 4$ level (255) of He^+ and to the $v = 0$ level (256) of the $B^2\Sigma_u^+$ state of N_2^+.

Several measurements of the electron impact, ionization cross-section for atoms and diatomic molecules have been reported in the literature. We shall not discuss these here, but refer the reader to a review by Kieffer and Dunn (253) in which the accuracy of the data has been assessed based on conclusions about likely systematic errors. Their discussions show that none of the measured cross-sections are reliable to within 10% at best. In addition to total ionization cross sections, Kieffer and Dunn also discuss individual ionization processes, including dissociative ionization, ionization to a particular final state of an ion, and multiple ionization. Kebarle and Godbole (257) have reported total ionization cross-section data for the rare gases and a few hydrocarbons, extending earlier published results in some cases even up to electron energies as much as 10.5 keV. These high-energy electron impact data are useful in theoretical calculations of ionization cross-sections and stopping power.

The purpose of this section in this chapter is not for discussing the cross-section data, but for emphasizing the importance of electron impact processes in natural plasmas such as the upper atmosphere of the Earth. (A recent discussion of electron impact ionization cross section data is to be found in Chapter 12 of this volume.) Low-energy electrons, moving in the upper atmosphere of the Earth, produce luminosity by electronic excitation of the atmospheric constituents, thus modifying the chemistry of the upper atmosphere through the production of metastable and vibrationally excited species. The low-energy electrons also selectively heat the ambient electron and ion gases so that their temperatures tend to rise above that of the neutral atmosphere.

It is well-known that the upper atmosphere of the Earth selectively absorbs the nonthermal component of the solar radiation in the hard ultraviolet region. The photoelectrons thus produced possess energies far above the energies of most of the other particles and Dalgarno et al. (258) have shown that they exchange energy with other electrons, with ions, and with the kinetic and internal energy states of the neutrals. Recently, Dalgarno (259) has reviewed all the processes by which low energy electrons lose energy in moving through the atmosphere and calculated the cross sections and energy loss rates. An important energy loss mechanism for low energy electrons in the ionosphere is provided by the transfer of momentum in elastic collisions of the low energy electrons with the thermal electrons of the ionospheric plasma, the high efficiency arising from the equal masses and the long range of the Coulomb repulsion. Since the momentum transfer cross section is of the order of 10^{-15} cm^2, energy loss by momentum transfer in collisions with neutral particles is negligible for the ambient electron and neutral particle densities occurring in planetary ionospheres. Slow electrons can also lose energy in a number of modes by excitation of (a) the rotational levels of the molecular atmospheric consitituents, (b) the fine structure levels, for example, of atomic oxygen, (c) vibrational excitation of the molecular species (d) electronic excitation of the low-lying metastable levels. The rotational and vibrational excitations of carbon dioxide are considered to be important energy loss mechanisms in Martian and Venutian atmospheres; the vibrational excitation of N_2 in the F region and of O_2 in and below the E region, both of the earth's ionosphere (see Sec. VB-C for a fuller discussion). The cooling efficiencies for the various mechanisms are listed in Ref. 259.

Finally, Lassettre (260) has recently reviewed the topic of inelastic scattering of high energy electrons by atmospheric gases. In the incident energy range from tens of eV to tens of keV, energy loss measurements are now available for many gases with sufficient resolution to show the vibrational structure, and thus clearly identify the final states produced. Electron impact cross-sections for N_2, O_2, and O are also given in analytic form by Peterson et al. (261), for convenient use in aurora and dayglow studies. In spite of the great increase during the last few years in our knowledge of fast electron collisions, the applications of electron impact data to aeronomic problems attempted so far are few and represent only quite preliminary and approximate work.

B. Proton Impact

Many experimental studies and theoretical calculations have been done on the impact of protons and deuterons (with energies in the range from tens of eV to tens of MeV) with neutral species (262).

For low-energy collisions, the cross-section for direct excitation by proton impact is broadly similar to that by electron impact if the proton and electron have the same velocity. It may be recalled that the electron impact excitation cross-section rises rapidly from threshold to a maximum, which occurs at an impact velocity corresponding to about twice the threshold energy, and then decreases asymptotically as E^{-1} in E for optically allowed transitions, or as E^{-1} for optically forbidden transitions. Thus electron impact excitation is usually far more efficient than proton impact excitation except when the threshold energy is only a small fraction of the thermal energy of the plasma. An example of an excitation process for which proton impact is more efficient than electron impact is

$$H^+ + H(2s_{1/2}) \longrightarrow H^+ + H(2p_{1/2}, 2p_{3/2})$$

the threshold energies for which are 0.0354 and 0.327 cm^{-1}, respectively. The calculated rate coefficients for the process are (262):

$$H^+ + H(2s_{1/2}) \longrightarrow H^+ + H(2p_{1/2}) \quad k = 2.5 \times 10^{-4} \text{ at } 10,000°K$$
$$\text{and } 2.1 \times 10^{-4} \text{ at } 20,000°K$$

$$H^+ + H(2s_{1/2}) \longrightarrow H^+ + H(2p_{3/2})$$
$$k = 2.2 \times 10^{-4} \text{ at } 10,000–20,000°K$$

These values are an order of magnitude larger than those for electrons. The charge transfer process $H^+ + H(2s_{1/2}) \rightarrow H(2p_{1/2}, 2p_{3/2}) + H^+$ is negligible compared to the direct reaction (264).

Collisions which lead merely to a redistribution of angular momentum

$$H^+ + H(nl) \longrightarrow H^+ + H(nl')$$

will usually proceed very rapidly. Similar reactions of astrophysical significance are the proton impact excitation of molecular rotations. The particular case

$$H^+ + CN(j = 0) \longrightarrow H^+ + CN(j = 1)$$

has been investigated (265); the calculations used an approximation analogous to the Bethe form of the Born approximation (266). The derived cross-section for 1 eV protons is about 10^{-12} cm^2, thus suggesting that the process may be important in H II regions (regions near a star).

Low-energy proton collisions may also result in charge transfer processes (267). The symmetrical resonance charge-transfer process

$$H^+ + H \longrightarrow H + H^+$$

does not involve an electronic transition, whereas the asymmetric process

$$H^+ + X \longrightarrow H + X^+$$

does involve an electronic transition. The cross-section of the symmetrical process at 1 eV is about 4×10^{-15} cm^2 (268), this value decreasing slowly with increasing energy. There is no satisfactory theory of asymmetric charge transfer reactions; however, a cross-section of 2×10^{-15} cm^2 has been predicted (269) from analysis of experimental data (267). This value is consistent with the cross-section of 8×10^{-15} cm^2 at 1000°K derived from upper atmosphere data (270).

High energy collisions can, in general, be described by the Born approximation. Because of the occurrence of cosmic rays, high-energy collisions of protons with hydrogen and possibly helium assume special importance in astrophysical plasmas. Several calculations (271) have been performed for the processes

$$H^+ + H(1s) \longrightarrow H^+ + H(2s, 2p, 3s, 3p, 3d)$$

$$H^+ + H \longrightarrow H^+ + H^+ + e^-$$

The ionization cross-section agrees closely with the measurements of Gilbody and Ireland (272) above 40 keV. Studies of the excitation and ionization of He by high energy protons are much less comprehensive than for H. The following processes have been studied:

$$H^+ + He(1^1S) \longrightarrow H^+ + He(1s2p^1P)$$

$$H^+ + He(1^1S) \longrightarrow H^+ + He(1s3p^1P)$$

$$H^+ + He(1^1S) \longrightarrow H^+ + He^+(1s) + e^-$$

$$H^+ + He(1^1S) \longrightarrow H^+ + He^+(nl) + e^-$$

The predicted ionization cross-sections agree well with the experimental measurements at impact energies above 400 keV (273).

A number of experimental measurements of the simple and charge-transfer ionization cross-sections for a variety of molecules have been made with protons varying in energy from keV to MeV (274).

C. Bombardment by Helium Nuclei

Bombardment by He^{2+} particles can lead to processes such as

$$He^{2+} + H \longrightarrow He^+ + H^+ + hv$$

$$He^{2+} + He \longrightarrow He^+ + He^+ + hv$$

The first reaction has a rate coefficient of 1.5×10^{-13} sec^{-1} at $20,000°K$ (275) and the second a rate coefficient of 4×10^{-15} cm^3 sec^{-1} (276). The H + He^{2+} reaction has been studied in detail. McCarroll and McElroy (277) found that for the charge-transfer process

$$H(1s) + He^{2+} \longrightarrow H^+ + He^+(1s)$$

distortion raises the cross-section considerably at moderate energies because the Coulomb repulsion reduces the separation between the initial and final potential energy surfaces. McElroy (278) also considered the process

$$H(1s) + He^{2+} \longrightarrow H^+ + He^+(2s, 2p)$$

which is an example of accidental energy resonance and observed that if no allowance is made for distortion, the cross-sections tend to infinity with decreasing energy. When allowance is made for distortion, the cross-section, on the other hand, tends to zero in the manner determined experimentally by Fite et al. (279).

V. SPACE PLASMAS

A. Interstellar Space

Various reactions involving four and possibly five species have been proposed for the interstellar space plasmas. The interstellar species so far identified are CH, CH^+, CN, and plausibly NaH detected from optical spectra and OH detected by radio methods. The existing information on interstellar lines from optical sources is summarized in Table 8; for details the reader is referred to a recent review by McNally (280). The discovery of OH is much more recent (281–283) than the discovery of the four other species; its initial detection in absorption suggested that it may be associated with the clouds of neutral atomic hydrogen, but later studies (284,285) have indicated that OH may be detected with an abundance of up to 10^{-4} in emission near H II regions (the regions near a star, see Vol. 1, Chapter 1, Section IV-A-1).

It is clear from the data in Table 8 that the optical lines of the molecules identified as interstellar all lie below 4300 Å. Four radio lines have been observed of OH, all lying at 18 cm. Based on an analogy with cometary spectra

TABLE 8
Interstellar molecular lines (280)

Wavelength, Å	Molecule	Classification
3137.53 3143.15 3146.01	CH	$C^2\Sigma^+ - X^2\Pi$
3447.08 3579.02 3745.31	CH$^+$	$A^1\Pi - X^1\Sigma$
3874.00 3874.61 3875.76 3876.30 3876.84	CN	$B^2\Sigma^- - X^2\Pi$
3878.77 3886.41 3890.21	CH	$B^2\Sigma^- - X^2\Pi$
3934.30	NaH (?)	$A^1\Sigma - X^1\Sigma$
3957.70 4232.54	CH$^+$	$A^1\Pi - X^1\Sigma$
4300.30	CH	$A^2\Delta - X^2\Pi$

(286), McNally (280) suggested that interstellar absorption might be divided into (1) absorption in the immediate neighborhood of the exciting star and (2) absorption in space. The radio observations of the OH lines at 18 cm and the optical observations of Muench (287) on the enhancement of CN lines in the neighborhood of H II regions lend support to this hypothesis, although the appearance of interstellar absorption lines in the spectra of certain later-type stars seems to suggest otherwise.

Abundances of these interstellar molecules with respect to hydrogen have been determined (see Table 9): CH, CH$^+$ by Bates and Spitzer (288), OH by Weinreb et al. (281) and Robinson et al. (284), and CN by McNally (280). Clearly the list of interstellar species thus far identified is not exhaustive. For example, in view of the presence of OH, NH may be reasonably expected. Further, H$_2$ may be expected as a molecule whose abundance may be great (289).

Certainly, the formation and destruction of interstellar molecules and their interactions constitute the reactions in interstellar space. Interstellar diatomic molecules may be formed by two body radiative association, by chemical and charge exchange, by surface reactions, by reaction involving negative ions as intermediates, and by degradation of polyatomic molecules formed during the evaporation of grains near hot stars. Available rate data for some of these processes are summarized in Table 10. The rates of chemical exchange reactions

TABLE 9
Abundances of molecular species in interstellar space, with respect to hydrogen

Interstellar molecule	Abundance	References
CH	1.6×10^{-8}	288
CH$^+$	0.8×10^{-8}	288
CN	0.06×10^{-8}	280
OH	10×10^{-8}	281, 284

TABLE 10
Rate data on the formation of interstellar molecules

A. Two-Body radiative association (290)

Process	Rate coefficient, 10^{-18} cm^3 sec^{-1}	Remarks
C $+$ H $\longrightarrow$ CH	$2.0\ (6.0)^a$	Evaluated at 100°K; rate coefficient varies as $T^{1/6}$
C$^+$ $+$ H $\longrightarrow$ CH$^+$	$2.0\ (0)^a$	
N$^+$ $+$ N $\longrightarrow$ N$_2$$^+$	30	Slight variation for $T < 2000$°K
H$^+$ $+$ H $\longrightarrow$ H$_2$$^+$	1.3	Evaluated at 500°K

B. Chemical exchange (291, 292)

Process	T, °K	Cross-section, $\sigma(10^{-16}$ cm$^2)$	Reaction rate, γ(cm^3 sec^{-1})
CH $+$ H $\longrightarrow$ C $+$ H$_2$	100		1.5×10^{-20}
	200	3.94	1.4×10^{-15}
	500		1.7×10^{-12}
	1000		2.2×10^{-11}
NH $+$ H $\longrightarrow$ N $+$ H$_2$	100		1.6×10^{-21}
	200	3.38	4.2×10^{-16}
	500		9.6×10^{-13}
	1000		1.5×10^{-11}
OH $+$ H $\longrightarrow$ O $+$ H$_2$	100		4.1×10^{-23}
	200	2.96	6.8×10^{-17}
	500		4.1×10^{-13}
	1000		9.4×10^{-12}

TABLE 10 (*Continued*)

C. Charge exchange (293)

Reaction		$\sigma(10^{-16}$ cm^2)	$\gamma(10^{-12}$ cm^3 sec^{-1})
CH $+$ H $\longrightarrow$	$C^+ + H_2$	4.02	6.56 $T^{1/2}$
$H_2^+ + C \longrightarrow$	(CH, CH$^+$) $+$ (H$^+$, H)	3.53	4.24 $T^{1/2}$
$H_2^+ + N \longrightarrow$	(NH, NH$^+$) $+$ (H$^+$, H)	3.53	4.20 $T^{1/2}$
$H_2^+ + O \longrightarrow$	(OH, OH$^+$) $+$ (H$^+$, H)	3.53	4.16 $T^{1/2}$

D. Surface reactions (294–296)

Reaction		$\gamma(10^{-17}$ cm^3 sec^{-1})
H $+$ H $\longrightarrow$	H_2	5.9
C $+$ H $\longrightarrow$	CH	3.4 (16)[b]
$C^+ + H \longrightarrow$	CH$^+$	3.4 (0)[b]
N $+$ H $\longrightarrow$	NH	3.2
O $+$ H $\longrightarrow$	OH	3.0

[a]Values in parentheses consider only the ground state of C or C$^+$.
[b]Values in parentheses give rate coefficient for grain negatively charged to -0.03 V.

are temperature dependent, being slow at 100°K but rapid at 1000°K; on the other hand, the rates of charge exchange reactions do not vary rapidly with temperature, being only dependent upon the square root of the kinetic temperature. The rate coefficients for surface reactions were evaluated at a kinetic temperature of 100°K and vary as the square root of the kinetic temperature.

It has been suggested (297) that the negative hydrogen ion may be involved in interstellar space plasma reactions such as:

$$H + e^- \longrightarrow H^- + h\nu \qquad \gamma = 1.5 \times 10^{-17} \text{ cm}^3 \text{ sec}^{-1}$$

$$H^- + H \longrightarrow H_2^- \longrightarrow H_2 + e^-$$

$$\gamma = 1.2 \times 10^{-11} \text{ } T^{1/2} \text{ cm}^3 \text{ sec}^{-1}$$

Clearly, the rate of production of H_2 will be limited by the rate at which the negative hydrogen ion can form.

The evaporation of grains near hot stars can give rise to polyatomic molecules such as CH_4, NH_3, and H_2O in the interstellar space (288); degradation of these species by stepwise removal of H atoms will lead to the formation of diatomic hydrides. Bates and Spitzer (288) suggest that the degradation of a molecule such as CH_4 is more likely to lead to the formation of CH$^+$ than CH since ionization could occur at any stage of the degradation process. Such a mechanism while plausible in the case of CH$^+$ is hindered by the simultaneous occurrence of CH. Muench (287) suggests that the reaction of CH_4 and NH_3 released from solid grains under the action of intense starlight could lead to the formation of CN. Detailed discussions of these processes may be found in Refs. 280 and 298. Stecher and Williams (299) have recently attempted to combine surface and chemical exchange reactions to account for the production of various interstellar species.

Having considered the principal processes of formation of molecules in interstellar space, let us now examine the processes leading to their removal. Evidently these removal processes are photodissociation and photo-ionization occurring in the interstellar space, the rates of both of which have been difficult to determine because of the lack of information on the relevant cross-sections and the interstellar radiation field. Ionized molecules may be removed by rapid dissociative recombination processes. Further, chemical or charge exchange reactions can alter the equilibrium populations of molecular species. Since the reaction

$$CH^+ + H \longrightarrow H_2 + C^+$$

is more rapid than the reverse reaction,

$$H_2 + C^+ \longrightarrow CH^+ + H$$

it is possible that such a reaction could lead to depletion of CH^+. Calculations of the equilibrium densities of interstellar molecules have been made by several authors (288,292,294–296); a discussion of these calculations is to be found in Ref 280

In conclusion, only atomic and diatomic species and grains have been discovered in the interstellar gas, the space abundance of diatomic molecular species is taken as 10^{-8} and that of grains as 10^{-12}. Attempts to assemble the various reaction mechanisms which have been proposed for the interstellar medium have been frustrating because of the lack of systematic observational material and inadequately known molecular data. Hence, different types of reaction are at present required to account for individual species: the presence of interstellar grains is required in order to account for the formation of H_2, CH, and CH^+, while the presence of H_2 is necessary for the formation of OH.

B. The Earth's Atmosphere

1. *General Considerations.* A significant proportion of the solar radiation that is absorbed during the day by the Earth's atmospheric gases (N_2, O_2, CO_2, H_2O, etc) is at sufficiently short wavelengths to produce photo-ionization (see Section II). Thus, there is a region of the atmosphere, known as the ionosphere, in which the gas comprises a " dilute " plasma of ions and electrons. The various regions of the ionosphere are characterized by their altitude and electron density, which ranges from less than 10^4 cm^{-3} in the

D layer, at about 70 km altitude, to 10^6 cm^{-3} in the F_2 layer, at about 300 km (see Fig. 9). Table 11 shows the variation of principal ion species with altitude (300,301). Several features are apparent from the table: atomic positive ions predominate in certain regions and molecular ions in others, the neutral density is sufficiently large to affect recombination rates only in the D region, and the electron temperature appreciably exceeds the ion temperature in certain regions. Also, several of the more abundant ions, notably NO$^+$, are

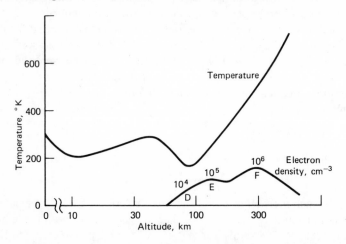

Figure 9   Atmospheric temperature and electron density.

TABLE 11
Approximate ionospheric conditions (quiet, daytime, mid-solar cycle)[a]

Region	Height, km	Principal ions	$\log_{10}[N(\text{cm}^{-3})]$		Temperature, °K		
			Molecular[b]	Atomic[b]	T_e	T_i	T_n
D	60	$H(H_2O)_2^+$, H_3O^+, NO$^+$, NO$_2^-$ (?)	15	10	350	350	35
E	110	NO$^+$, O$_2^+$, e^-	13	11	$\geqslant 250$	250	25
Sporadic E	110	Mg$^+$, Fe$^+$, Si$^+$, Ca$^+$, e^-	13	11	$\geqslant 250$	250	25
F_1	170	NO$^+$, O$_2^+$, O$^+$, e^-	10	10	1100	700	70
F_2	300	O$^+$, (O$_2^+$, NO$^+$), e^-, N$^+$	8	9	2500	1800	150
Magnetosphere[c]	1000	H$^+$, He$^+$ (?)	—	5	1500	1500	150
Protonosphere	2500	H$^+$	—	4	1500	1500	150

[a]Data taken from Ref. 300.
[b]Molecular and Atomic densities [N] are given as $\log_{10}[N(\text{cm}^{-3})]$.
[c]H$^+$ is the principal ion at solar minimum, while He$^+$ is believed to be the principal ion at solar ma mum. Charged particle densities are $< 10^6$ cm^{-3}.

thought not to be formed by direct photo-ionization above 100 km, but rather by fast ion-molecule reactions such as

$$N_2^+ + O \longrightarrow NO^+ + N$$

Recently, evidence has been obtained to suggest that many of the ions in the D region may exist primarily as hydrated clusters of the type $[M(H_2O)_n]^+$.

Because many direct rocket-borne mass spectrometer measurements have been made for atmospheric positive ions (see Vol. 1, Chapter 10), their concentrations are much better established than those of negative ions. The relative importance of NO^+ arises because the low ionization potential of NO (9.3 eV) causes reactions removing NO^+ to be endothermic and therefore slow. Thus its loss is due almost entirely to dissociative recombination rather than ion-molecule reaction (see later). Positive ions not shown in Table 11, but which are also present in the ionosphere, include N_2^+ and the metal ions Na^+, Ni^+, Al^+ observed in the E region by Narcisi (302) and Young et al. (303) from their rocket-flight experiments. (It is presumed that a large fraction of the metal ions arise from ablation of meteors, satellites, etc.) N^+, which has a small number density below 150 km ($< 10^2$ cm^{-3}), becomes one of the more abundant ions around 300 km (304). At night, in the absence of the sun's ionizing radiation, there is a steady decrease in the positive ion and electron densities. The persistence at night of ions such as N_2^+ and O_2^+, however, implies the presence of an ionizing source, the origin and energy of which have yet to be ascertained (305,306).

The presence of negative ions in the ionosphere is a consequence of electron attachment processes and negative ion-molecule reactions. Negative ions that are expected to be important in the D region are NO_2^-, NO_3^-, and CO_3^-, probably with lower concentrations of O^-, O_2^-, and O_3^- (307,308).

Investigations of the reactions in the Earth's upper atmosphere have been made in a variety of ways. These include ground-based observation of airglow emission (see Section B-3), the use of rocket-borne photometers and mass spectrometers, ground observations of "seeding" experiments in which chemicals are released from a rocket at a high altitude, and laboratory studies of the atomic, molecular, and ionic species shown to be present by field experiments. The last type of investigation has been reviewed at the I. A. G. A. Aeronomy Symposia in 1963 and 1968, the proceedings of which have subsequently been published (309,310). Comprehensive accounts of the chemical physics of the various atmospheric processes may be found included in several books (311–315). Undoubtedly, a very interesting topic in plasma chemistry is the study of ion-neutral reactions in ionospheric plasmas.

2. Ion-Molecule Reactions. Reactions between ions and neutral species are considered to be important processes in the ionosphere. Primary positive ions are produced by photo-ionization; primary negative ions by electron attachment. Among the reactions available to primary ions are charge transfer of the type

$$A^\pm + BC \longrightarrow A + BC^\pm$$

and ion-atom interchange

$$A^\pm + BC \longrightarrow AB^\pm + C$$

The measurements in the laboratory of the rates of reactions of the above type in the energy range relevant to ionospheric conditions have largely made use of the flowing afterglow technique which was developed by Ferguson and coworkers (316) and which is described in Vol. 1 (see Chapters 6 and 10). In favorable cases, it is possible to achieve rate constants that are accurate to within $\pm 10\%$ by this method (307). Other methods include the use of mass spectrometer ion sources, drift tubes, crossed beam techniques, and ion cyclotron resonance.

a. POSITIVE ION REACTIONS.   Fite (317) and Paulson (318) have reviewed the positive ion reactions in the energy range from about 0.015 eV to about 0.15 eV; this is the range of temperatures in the ambient natural atmospheres of the Earth and neighboring planets. Initially the attention was focused only on those atmospheric species such as N_2, O_2, and O which are the major

TABLE 12
Positive ion reactions

Reaction	Rate coefficient at 300°K^a, cm^3 sec^{-1}	References
$He^+ + O_2 \longrightarrow He + O + O^+$	$(10 \pm 5) \times 10^{-10}$	319–325
$He^+ + N_2 \begin{cases} \xrightarrow{\sim 65\%} He + N + N^+ \\ \xrightarrow{\sim 35\%} He + N_2{}^+ \end{cases}$	$(12 \pm 5) \times 10^{-10}$ (total)	320–327
$O^+ + N_2 \longrightarrow NO^+ + N$	$(2 \pm 1) \times 10^{-12}$	323, 325, 327–331, 335, 336
$O^+ + O_2 \longrightarrow O + O_2{}^+$	$(2 \pm 1) \times 10^{-11}$	325, 327–330, 332
$N_2{}^+ + O_2 \longrightarrow N_2 + O_2{}^+$	$(1 + 0.5) \times 10^{-10}$	319, 321, 323, 325, 327, 333
$N_2{}^+ + O \longrightarrow NO^+ + N$	2.5×10^{-10}	334
$N_2{}^+ + O \longrightarrow N_2 + O^+$	$< 1 \times 10^{-11}$	334
$O_2{}^+ + NO \longrightarrow NO^+ + O_2$	8×10^{-10}	306, 325
$O_2{}^+ + N_2 \longrightarrow NO^+ + NO$	$< 1 \times 10^{-15}$	306, 325
$O_2{}^+ + N \longrightarrow NO^+ + O$	18×10^{-10}	306

Reaction	Rate coefficient at 300°K[a], cm³ sec⁻¹	References
$N_2^+ + NO \longrightarrow NO^+ + N_2$	5×10^{-10}	306, 325
$N^+ + O_2 \longrightarrow NO^+ + O$	$(3.5 \pm 1.5) \times 10^{-10}$	306, 319, 323, 325, 327
$N^+ + O_2 \longrightarrow N + O_2^+$	$(4.5 \pm 1.5) \times 10^{-10}$	306, 323, 325, 327
$N_2^+ + Na \longrightarrow N_2 + Na^+$	$(5.8 \pm 3.8) \times 10^{-10}$	337
$O_2^+ + Na \longrightarrow O_2 + Na^+$	$(6.7 \pm 2.1) \times 10^{-10}$	337
$O_2^+ + Na \longrightarrow NaO^+ + O$	$(7.7 \pm 2.4) \times 10^{-11}$	338
$NO^+ + Na \longrightarrow NO + Na^+$	$(7 \pm 2) \times 10^{-11}$	337
$Mg^+ + O_3 \longrightarrow MgO^+ + O_2$	2.3×10^{-10}	339
$Ca^+ + O_3 \longrightarrow CaO^+ + O_2$	1.6×10^{-10}	339
$Fe^+ + O_3 \longrightarrow FeO^+ + O_2$	1.5×10^{-10}	339
$Na^+ + O_3 \longrightarrow NaO^+ + O_2$	$< 1 \times 10^{-11}$	339
$MgO^+ + O \longrightarrow Mg^+ + O_2$	$\sim 1 \times 10^{-10}$	340
$H_2O^+ + H_2O \longrightarrow H_3O^+ + OH$	8.5×10^{-10}	341
$H_2O^+ + O_2 \longrightarrow O_2^+ + H_2O$	$\sim 2 \times 10^{-10}$	342
$O^+ + CO_2 \longrightarrow O_2^+ + CO$	1.2×10^{-9}	343
$N^+ + CO_2 \longrightarrow CO_2^+ + N$	1.3×10^{-9}	344
$N_2^+ + CO_2 \longrightarrow CO_2^+ + N_2$	9×10^{-10}	344
$N^+ + CO \longrightarrow CO^+ + N$	5×10^{-10}	344
$N_2^+ + CO \longrightarrow CO^+ + N_2$	7×10^{-11}	344
$C^+ + O_2 \longrightarrow CO^+ + O$	$(1.0 \pm 0.1) \times 10^{-9}$	345, 346
$C^+ + CO_2 \longrightarrow CO^+ + CO$	1.9×10^{-9}	345
$CO^+ + O_2 \longrightarrow O_2^+ + CO$	2.0×10^{-10}	345
$CO^+ + CO_2 \longrightarrow CO_2^+ + CO$	1.1×10^{-9}	345
$CO_2^+ + O_2 \longrightarrow O_2^+ + CO_2$	1.0×10^{-10}	347
$Si^+ + O_2 \longrightarrow SiO^+ + O$	$< 10^{-11}$	348
$SiO^+ + N \longrightarrow Si^+ + NO$	$\sim 1.5 \times 10^{-10}$	348
$SiO^+ + N \longrightarrow NO^+ + Si$	$\sim 1.5 \times 10^{-10}$	348
$SiO^+ + O \longrightarrow Si^+ + O_2$	2×10^{-10}	348

[a]Extrapolated values from high energy data are not included. Where several measurements exist (more than one reference quoted) $\pm$ indicates approximate range of measured value; where single measurements exist $\pm$ indicates estimated experimental uncertainty.

constituents in the atmospheres. Lately, however, it has become increasingly evident that major aeronomic effects involving ions arise through minor atmospheric components such as O_3, NO, OH, CO_2, He, and H. Even the reactions involving metals and other materials of meteoritic origin have drawn considerable interest since Narcisi (302) identified metal ions by mass spectrometric sampling of the D region.

Rate coefficients for several positive ion-molecule reactions of interest in upper atmosphere plasmas are given in Table 12. These rate coefficients were evaluated from laboratory measurements using a variety of methods, the

TABLE 13
Negative ion reactions

	Rate constant, cm³ sec⁻¹			
Reaction	Flowing afterglow experiments at 300°K (308, 351, 355, 358, 359)	Crossed-beam studies above 2 eV ion energy extrapolated to thermal energy, assuming a smooth energy dependence of the cross-section (352, 356)	Mass spectrometer ion source measurements at ~1 eV (353, 354, 357)	Drift tube (360–362)
A. Binary reactions				
$O^- + O_3 \rightarrow O_3^- + O$	$7.0 \times 10^{-10}(308)$			
$O_2^- + O_3 \rightarrow O_3^- + O_2$	$5.3 \times 10^{-10}(351)$ $3.0 \times 10^{-10}(308)$ $4.0 \times 10^{-10}(351)$			
$O^- + NO_2 \rightarrow NO_2^- + O$	$1.2 \times 10^{-9}(351)$	$1.1 \times 10^{-9}(352)$	$\sim 3.0 \times 10^{-9}(353)$	
$O^- + NO_2 \rightarrow O_2^- + NO$			$1.0 \times 10^{-9}(354)$	
$O_2^- + NO_2 \rightarrow NO_2^- + O_2$	$8.0 \times 10^{-10}(351)$	$1.5 \times 10^{-9}(352)$	$1.8 \times 10^{-11}(354)$	
$O_3^- + NO_2 \rightarrow NO_2^- + O_3$		$7.0 \times 10^{-10}(352)$		
$O_3^- + NO_2 \rightarrow ?$ (either NO_3^- or NO_2^- or both)	$1.9 \times 10^{-10}(355)$			
$H^- + NO_2 \rightarrow NO_2^- + H$	$2.9 \times 10^{-9}(351)$	$5.0 \times 10^{-10}(352)$		
$OH^- + NO_2 \rightarrow NO_2^- + OH$	$1.0 \times 10^{-9}(351)$	$1.4 \times 10^{-9}(352)$		
$NH_2^- + NO_2 \rightarrow NO_2^- + NH_2$	$1.0 \times 10^{-9}(351)$			

Reaction			
$F^- + NO_2 \rightarrow NO_2^- + F$	$<2.5 \times 10^{-11}(351)$	$\sim 1.5 \times 10^{-11}$ at 3 eV (356)	
$Cl^- + NO_1 \rightarrow NO_2^- + Cl$	$<6.0 \times 10^{-12}(351)$	Slow at 5 eV (356)	$4.0 \times 10^{-11}(357)$
			$4.0 \times 10^{-10}(357)$
$O_3^- + CO_2 \rightarrow CO_3^- + O_2$	$4.0 \times 10^{-11}(308)$		
$CO_3^- + O \rightarrow O_2^- + CO_2$	$8.0 \times 10^{-11}(308)$		
$O_3^- + NO \rightarrow NO_3^- + O$	$1.0 \times 10^{-11}(308)$		
$NO_2^- + O_3 \rightarrow NO_3^- + O_2$	$1.8 \times 10^{-11}(358)$		
$NO^- + O_2 \rightarrow O_2^- + NO$	$9.0 \times 10^{-10}(359)$		
$CO_3^- + NO_2 \rightarrow NO_3^- + CO_2$	$8.0 \times 10^{-11}(355)$		
$CO_3^- + NO \rightarrow NO_2^- + CO_2$	$9.0 \times 10^{-12}(308)$		
$N_2O^- + O_2 \rightarrow O_3^- + N_2$	fast at 80°K(355)		
$O_3^- + N_2 \rightarrow$ products	$<1.0 \times 10^{-15}(355)$		
$O_3^- + SiO \rightarrow SiO_3^- + O$	fast at 300°K (355)		
$O_3^- + CO \rightarrow$ products	slow at 300°K(355)		
$O_2^- + SO_2 \rightarrow SO_2^- + O_2$	$5.4 \times 10^{-10}(355)$		
$O_3^- + SO_2 \diagup {\,SO_3^- + O_2 \atop \,SO_4^- + O}$	$5.1 \times 10^{-10}(355)$		

B. Three-body reactions

Reaction		
$O^- + 2\,CO_2 \rightarrow CO_3^- + CO_2$	$1.5 \times 10^{-28}(355)^a$	$9.0 \times 10^{-29}(360)^a$
$O^- + CO_2 + He \rightarrow CO_3^- + He$		$9.0 \times 10^{-30}(360)^a$
$O_2^- + 2\,CO_2 \rightarrow CO_4^- + CO_2$		$2.0 \times 10^{-29}(360)^a$
$O_2^- + CO_2 + O_2 \rightarrow CO_4^- + O_2$		$9.0 \times 10^{-31}(361)^a$
$O^- + 2\,O_2 \rightarrow O_3^- + O_2$		$7.5 \times 10^{-31}(362)^a$
$O^- + N_2 + He \rightarrow N_2O^- + He$	$\sim 1.0 \times 10^{-30}(355)^a$ at 80°K	
$O_3^- + 2\,N_2 \rightarrow$ products	$<1.5 \times 10^{-31}(355)^a$	

[a]Rate constant in cm^6 sec^{-1}.

TABLE 14
Rate coefficients for electron attachment and detachment processes

Reaction	Temperature, °K	Rate coefficient, $cm^6 \ sec^{-1}$	References
A. Three-body attachment with neutral third body			
$e^- + O_2 + O_2 \rightarrow O_2^- + O_2$	$195 < T < 600$	$(1.4 \pm 0.2) \times 10^{-29}$	364
$e^- + O_2 + N_2 \rightarrow O_2^- + N_2$	$300 < T < 500$	$(1 + 0.5) \times 10^{-31}$	365–367
$e^- + O_2 + H_2O \rightarrow O_2^- + H_2O^c$	$300 < T < 400$	$(1.4 \pm 0.2) \times 10^{-29}$	368
$e^- + O_2 + CO_2 \rightarrow O_2^- + CO_2$	$300 < T < 525$	$(3.3 \pm 0.7) \times 10^{-30}$	368
$e^- + NO + NO \rightarrow NO^- + NO^c$	300	$(1.3 \pm 0.1) \times 10^{-31}$	369
$e^- + 2 N_2O \rightarrow N_2O^- + N_2O^c$	300	$(6 \pm 1) \times 10^{-33}$ $cm^3 \ sec^{-1}$	370, 371
$e^- + NO_2 + N_2 \rightarrow NO_2^- + N_2{}^c$	300	4×10^{-11b}	372
B. Dissociative attachment			
$e^- + O_3 \rightarrow O^- + O_2$	300	$(1 - 10) \times 10^{-12}$	373
C. Radiative attachment			
$e^- + O \rightarrow O^- + h\nu$	$150 < T < 500$	$(1.3 \pm 0.1) \times 10^{-15}$	374, 375
$e^- + O_2 \rightarrow O_2^- + h\nu$	300	$10^{-19 \pm 1}$	374, 376
$e^- + OH \rightarrow OH^- + h\nu$	300	$10^{-15 \pm 1}$	377
D. Collisional detachment with neutrals			
$O_2^- + O_2 \rightarrow 2 O_2 + e^-$	$375 < T < 600$	$(2.7 \pm 0.3) \times 10^{-10} \times \left(\dfrac{T}{300}\right)^{1/2} \exp\left[- \left(\dfrac{5590}{T}\right)\right]$	364
$O_2^- + N_2 \rightarrow O_2 + N_2 + e^-$	$375 < T < 600$	$(1.9 \pm 0.4) \times 10^{-12} \times \left(\dfrac{T}{300}\right)^{3/2} \exp\left[- \left(\dfrac{4990}{T}\right)\right]$	364
$O^- + O_2 \rightarrow O + O_2 + e^-$	$4000 < T_i{}^a < 20{,}000$	$2.3 \times 10^{-9} \exp\left(\dfrac{-26{,}000}{T_i}\right)$	378
$O^- + N_2 \rightarrow O + N_2 + e^-$	$4000 < T_i{}^a < 20{,}000$	$2.3 \times 10^{-9} \exp\left(\dfrac{-26{,}000}{T_i}\right)$	378
$O_2^- + O_2(^1\Delta_g) \rightarrow O_2 + O_2 + e^-$	300	2×10^{-10}	379
E. Associative detachment			
$O^- + O \rightarrow O_2 + e^-$	300	1.4×10^{-10}	380
$O^- + N \rightarrow NO + e^-$	300	1.6×10^{-10}	380
$O^- + H_2 \rightarrow H_2O + e^-$	300	8.0×10^{-10}	380, 381
$O^- + NO \rightarrow NO_2 + e^-$	300	3.0×10^{-10}	380, 381
$O^- + N_2 \rightarrow N_2O + e^-$	300	$\sim 1 \times 10^{-19}$	370, 381
$O_2^- + O \rightarrow O_3 + e$	300	2.5×10^{-10}	380
$O_2^- + N \rightarrow NO_2 + e$	300	3.0×10^{-10}	380
$O^- + O_2(^1\Delta_g) \rightarrow O_3 + e$	300	3×10^{-10}	379

[a]The ion temperature T_i is a value calculated using the Wannier relation [see L. R. Megill and J. B Hasted, *Planetary Space Sci.*, **13**, 339 (1965)].

[b]In units of $cm^3 \ sec^{-1}$ since it is a saturated three-body process [see B. H. Mahan and I. C. Walker *Chem. Phys.*, **47**, 3780 (1967)].

[c]Product ions not mass spectrometrically identified.

merits and demerits of which have been critically examined in a recent review by Fite (317) to which the reader is referred for further experimental discussion.

Direct rocket-borne mass spectrometer ion measurements (see Vol. 1, Chapter 10), have allowed detailed, quantitative verification of the most important rate constants for the E and F_1 layers.

b. NEGATIVE ION REACTIONS. Most of the work on measurements of the total cross-sections and reaction rates for processes involving negative ions and neutrals in the upper atmosphere has been done during the last five years. Excellent reviews on the subject exist (307,349). Fairly detailed negative ion reaction schemes for the atmospheric plasmas have also been proposed (308,350).

Laboratory data on binary and three body negative ion-neutral reactions are summarized in Table 13; most of the rate constants are for 300°K and only in a few cases for energies $\gtrsim 1$ eV. However, unlike in the case of the positive ion chemistry of the atmosphere, these negative ion reaction rate data have not been subjected to critical test since the negative ion composition of the ionosphere has as yet not been determined experimentally.

c. ELECTRON ATTACHMENT AND DETACHMENT PROCESSES. One of the important negative ion-neutral molecule reaction processes occurring in the D region is the associative-detachment process in which an electron is released from a negative ion. This process has long been expected theoretically, but only discovered experimentally in 1966 (359).

In general, electron attachment and detachment processes of aeronomic interest are: three-body attachment, with a ground state molecule or an electron as the third body, and its inverse, collisional detachment; dissociative attachment and its inverse, associative detachment; and radiative attachment and its inverse, photodetachment. The results of the laboratory experiments for gases and ions of aeronomic interest are given in Table 14. Laboratory techniques used in obtaining the tabulated data include swarm techniques, high-frequency studies of electrons produced by high energy particles and by photo-ionization, low energy electron beam techniques, flowing afterglow techniques, and ion beam techniques; these experimental techniques are discussed by Branscomb (3) and Phelps (363). Rate coefficients for low energy processes such as the three-body attachment to O_2, the radiative attachment to O, and the associative detachment of O^- in collisions with various atmospheric gases are reasonably well known. Other possibly important low energy processes such as dissociative attachment to O_3, radiative attachment to O_2, and the associative detachment of O_2^- are less well known.

d. ELECTRON-ION AND ION-ION RECOMBINATION PROCESSES. Both electron-ion and ion-ion recombination processes which are of importance in upper atmosphere plasmas have been reviewed from time to time (382). The significant electron-ion recombination processes occurring in the ionosphere are (a) radiative recombination: $X^+ + e^- \rightarrow X^* + h\nu$ and (b) dissociative recombination: $XY^+ + e^- \rightleftharpoons (XY^*)_{\text{unstable}} \rightleftharpoons X + Y +$ kinetic energy. These processes involve the capture of the electron by the positive ion without the assistance of a third body. As in the case of electron-ion recombination, ion-ion recombination in the ionosphere is controlled predominantly by two-body rather than three-body processes, perhaps with the possible exception of the lower end of the D region.

(1) *Electron-Ion Recombination.* (a) *Radiative recombination.* Reliable information concerning the rates of radiative recombination comes from theoretical calculations (383,384). The recombination coefficient α is not particularly sensitive to the identity of the positive ion, varying by less than a factor of two in going from H^+ to K^+. The partial recombination coefficient for electron capture into the lower states of the excited atom varies as $T_e^{-0.5}$, while for capture into the highly excited states lying within $\sim kT_e$ of the continuum, it varies as $T_e^{-1.5}$; the total, α, varies as $T_e^{-0.7}$, beginning with a value of $\sim 5 \times 10^{-12}$ cm^3 sec^{-1} at 250°K. Only few experimental studies of recombination have been carried out under conditions where two-body radiative recombination is the predominant process (385); those that have yield α values in reasonable agreement with theory.

(b) *Dissociative recombination.* In ionospheric regions containing molecular ions, dissociative electron-ion recombination is the predominant electron-loss process:

$$XY^+ + e^- \rightleftharpoons (XY^*)_{\text{unstable}} \rightleftharpoons X + Y + \text{kinetic energy}$$

Information concerning the recombination coefficients of molecular ionospheric ions has been obtained from a wide variety of experimental and theoretical studies as well. Laboratory microwave afterglow/mass spectrometer studies of diatomic ionospheric ions show a loss by dissociative recombination with a coefficient substantially in excess of 10^{-7} cm^3 sec^{-1} at 250°K and decreasing with increasing electron and ion temperature. The ions studied are NO^+, O_2^+, and N_2^+; Figure 10 shows the temperature dependence of the dissociative recombination coefficient α for these species under conditions when $T_e = T_i = T_n = T$. Figure 10 also shows what apparently is the variation of $\alpha(N_4^+)$ under the same conditions. The large value of α_{diss} $\geqslant (10^{-7}$ cm^3 sec$^{-1})$ results from the radiationless initial capture step (which involves no energy change) which forms the unstable excited molecule, followed by a high probability of dissociation before self-ionization. Not shown in the figure is the recent experimental work of Mehr and Biondi (393) who used microwave electron heating to study $\alpha(O_2^+)$ under conditions $T_e \geqslant T_i = 300$°K. They found $\alpha = 1.95 \times 10^{-7}$ cm^3 sec^{-1} at $T_e = 300$°K, this value

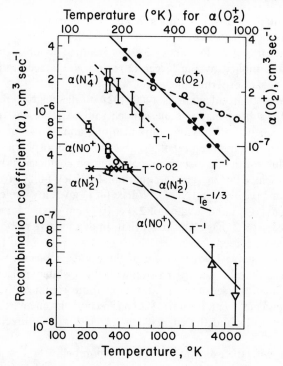

Figure 10 Temperature dependence of the dissociative recombination coefficients $\alpha(NO^+)$, $\alpha(O_2^+)$, and $\alpha(N_2^+)$ under conditions where $T_e = T_i = T_n = T$. (1) Data for $\alpha(NO^+)$: ($\square$), Weller and Biondi (Ref. 386); ($\bigcirc$), Gunton and Shaw (Ref. 387); ($\bullet$), Young and John (Ref. 388); ($\triangle$), Stein et al. (Ref. 389); ($\triangledown$), Lin and Tease (Ref. 390). (2) Data for $\alpha(O_2^+)$: ($\bigcirc$), Mentzoni (Ref. 391); ($\bullet$, $\blacktriangledown$), Kasner and Biondi (Ref. 392). (3) Data for $\alpha(N_2^+)$: ($\bigcirc$), Kasner and Biondi (Ref. 394); ($\times$), Kasner (Ref. 395); the $\times$ symbols indicate conditions where $T_e = T_i = T_n = T$, while the broken line indicates preliminary results obtained when T_e is varied while $T_i = T_n$ is held at 300°K. (4) The curve marked $\alpha(N_4^+)$ apparently applies to the variation of $\alpha(N_4^+)$ under conditions where $T_e = T_i = T_n = T$ and is from data: ($\bigcirc$), Kasner and Biondi (Ref. 394); ($\bullet$), Hackam (Ref. 396).

decreasing as $T_e^{-0.70}$ up to $T_e = 1200°K$ and as $T_e^{-0.56}$ up to $T_e = 5000°K$.

There is practically little information on the recombination coefficients of the D layer ions, H_3O^+ and its hydrated forms (masses 19, 37, 55). Wilson and Evans (397) using microwave techniques to measure the decay of electron density behind shock fronts in argon containing small amounts of oxygen and hydrocarbon, reported that α varies roughly as T^{-2} over the range $2400°K < T < 5600°K$, with a value of 1.5×10^{-7} cm^3 sec^{-1} at 3000°K; a similar value was reported earlier (398) by Green and Sugden from hydrogen-oxygen-acetylene flame studies at 2100°K for $\alpha(H_3O^+)$. If Wilson and Evan's α values refer to H_3O^+ ions and if the inverse temperature dependence observed by them is maintained down to much lower temperatures, the coefficient at $\sim 300°K$ may be in excess of 10^{-6} cm^3 sec^{-1}. Such a large recombination coefficient, according to Donahue (399) is required to offset the enhanced ionization rate implied by the larger D region NO concentrations recently measured in rocket experiments.

Several theoretical calculations (400–402) of dissociative recombination coefficients have been made; none can be said to represent true ab initio calculations, since they employ simplifications and/or use of experimental information concerning the potential curves of the ionospheric ions in order to obtain values of the dissociative recombination coefficients. For the *direct* process represented by the above equation, Bradsley (402) gives a value of 2.6×10^{-7} cm^3 sec^{-1} for $\alpha_d(NO^+)$, Warke (401) gives a value of 1.1×10^{-7} cm^3 sec^{-1} for $\alpha_d(O_2^+)$ and a value of 2.0×10^{-7} cm^3 sec^{-1} for $\alpha_d(N_2^+)$, all at $300°K$. Bradsley (402) has also shown that, in dissociative recombination, an *indirect* process proceeding via resonance electron capture to form a vibrationally excited, stable Rydberg state of the excited molecule which pre-dissociates as a result of a pseudo-crossing with the unstable molecule as indicated in the equation (see above), may contribute significantly to the total recombination coefficient. Biondi (382c) has recently given an excellent discussion of these results and the energy dependencies of the direct and indirect processes.

In general, with the exception of the D region below 80 km, there is satisfactory agreement between ionospheric requirements and laboratory measurements of α (399).

(2) *Ion-Ion Recombination.* With the possible exception of the lower part of the D region, ion-ion recombination in the ionosphere as in the case of electron-ion recombination is controlled predominantly by two-body rather than three-body processes. The simple theory of recombination between positive and negative ions has long been considered to involve a collision of either ion with a neutral specie while within a certain "trapping distance" of the other (403).

$$X^+ + Y^- + M \longrightarrow X + Y + M$$

The process has been theoretically treated by several authors (404–408) using novel techniques such as Monte Carlo calculations to follow the histories of the ion pairs; such treatments have, in general, predicted a variation of the three-body recombination coefficient as $T_i^{-2.5}$, and for the ions in the D region a value $K_{\text{Thomson}} \sim 10^{-25}$ cm^6 sec^{-1} is estimated at $T_i = 350°K$. Recent experimental information (409,410) supports the predicted magnitude. Of particular interest is the study of Mahan and Person (410) without mass analysis of what they considered to be the reaction

$$NO^+ + NO_2^- + N_2 \longrightarrow \text{neutral products}$$

for which they obtained a value $k \simeq 2 \times 10^{-25}$ cm^6 sec^{-1} at 300°K.

On the other hand, a simple two body ion-ion recombination process such as *mutual neutralization* of the form

$$A^+ + B^- \longrightarrow A^* + B$$

in which one or both of the neutrals produced may be in excited states, should also be considered. The two-body ion-ion recombination coefficients that have been calculated theoretically and determined experimentally for ionospheric ions are given in Table 15.

TABLE 15
Two-body ion-ion recombination coefficients at 300°K

Technique	Recombining ions	Recombination Coefficient, α, cm^3 sec^{-1}	References
Afterglow decay measurements in photo-ionized NO–NO$_2$-rare gas mixtures, using pulsed charge collection in a parallel plate ionization chamber, without mass identification	NO$^+$, NO$_2^-$ (assumed)	$(2.0 \pm 0.5) \times 10^{-7}$	410
Afterglow studies in air-like N$_2$–O$_2$ mixtures ionized by a pulse of MeV electrons, using rf impedance probe	NO$^+$, NO$_2^-$, NO$_3^-$ (mass-identified)	$(4.4 \pm 1) \times 10^{-8}$	411
Theoretical calculation	O$^+$, O$^-$⎫ N$^+$, O$^-$⎭	5×10^{-8} (variation as $T_i^{-0.5}$, predicted)	412

Ion-ion neutralization cross sections determined by Aberth et al. (413), using the merging beams technique (414), for $N^+ + O^-$ and $N_2^+ + O_2^-$ at barycentric kinetic energies between 0.5 and 98 eV and for $O_2^+ + O_2^-$ between 0.5 and 50 eV give values in the range $10^{-7} - 10^{-8}$ cm^3 sec^{-1} for the recombination coefficient. Thus, it appears that the two body ion-ion recombination coefficient is of the order of $10^{-7} - 10^{-8}$ cm^3 sec^{-1} at 300°K.

Other two-body ion-ion recombination processes are not expected to play a significant role in charge removal from the ionosphere, as estimates of the rates of such processes are orders of magnitude smaller than the simple mutual neutralization process.

e. MOLECULE-ION CLUSTERS.   Rocket-borne mass spectrometer measurements of the ions of the regions below 82 km have repeatedly shown (302,415) peaks at masses 19 and 37 which have been attributed to H_3O^+ and $H_3O^+ \cdot H_2O$, respectively. The presence of H_3O^+ as one of the dominant ions of the D region and the role of the polar water molecule as an important clustering agent are also substantiated by the similarity of the sharp decrease observed near the mesopause in H_3O^+, $H_5O_2^+$, and neutral water vapor concentrations (416). Further, the heavy ions (> 45 amu) observed below 82 km could also be due to higher hydrates of H_3O^+ or hydrates of other atmospheric ions.

Based on the suggested (417) existence of O_2^+ in the D region presumably due to photo-ionization of $O_2(^1\Delta_g)$, Ferguson and Fehsenfeld (418) have postulated a mechanism for clustering involving $O_2 \cdot O_2^+$ and $O_2^+ \cdot H_2O$ as the intermediates. The agreement between the concentrations of H_3O^+ and $H_3O^+ \cdot H_2O$ observed by Narcisi and those calculated on the basis of $O_2 \cdot O_2^+$ participation is satisfactory (419). The work of Turner and Rutherford (420) in which reaction rates of N^+, O^+, N_2^+, NO^+, O_2^+, and Ar^+ with H_2O and of O_2, NO, and H_2O with H_2O^+ were measured, indicates that the major loss mechanisms for H_3O^+ in the atmosphere are clustering, recombination, and charge transfer with metal vapors. Many of the ions present in the D region may, therefore, be hydrated, especially as a great number of exothermic ion-molecule reactions involving H_2O are fast.

The works of Fite and Rutherford (421) and of Phelps et al. (360,422) show that negative ions such as NO_2^-, O_2^- cluster with water molecules, the rate coefficients of these clustering reactions being very large. Significant concentrations of hydrated negative ions below 82 km cannot therefore be ruled out.

3.   *Airglow.*   The observations of airglow emission has contributed a good deal to our present understanding of the physics and chemistry of the upper atmosphere (311–315). Between 85 and 100 km (D region) the presence of significant amounts of such reactive species as O, H, OH, O_3, and NO leads to the occurrence of a variety of chemiluminescent reactions. The light emission from these reactions is visible from the ground at night (the nightglow) and from rockets in the day (the dayglow). Interesting emission spectra, including resonance scattering from traces of sodium and other metals, are also visible in the twilight glow, which is observed when the sun appears to be below the horizon at ground level but is still in view from an altitude of 50–150 km.

The night airglow is due almost exclusively to chemiluminescent processes utilizing energy stored in photodissociation products created during the day by solar radiation. Since the major effect of the solar radiation on the upper atmosphere of the earth is to dissociate O_2, most night glow emissions are expected to be produced by processes involving atomic oxygen; hence, it is not surprising to observe emission from O and O_2. The strongest features in the night glow are listed in Table 16, together with the processes that are

TABLE 16
Nightglow emission features (301,423)

λ, Å	Emitter	Height of emitting layer, km	Intensity, rayleighs[a]	Probable excitation process
5893	$Na(^2P)$	~ 85	100	$Na + O_2^* \to Na^* + O_2$
6300	$O(^1D)$	Above 200	100	$O_3^+ + e \to O^* + O_2$
5577	$O(^1S)$	~ 85	250	$O + O_2^* \to O^* + O_2$
Continuum 4000–15,000	$NO_2(?)$	~ 85	1000	$NO + O + M \to$ $NO_2^* + M$
Herzberg bands 3000–4000	$O_2(A^3\Sigma_u^+)$	~ 85	1000	Complex, but based on $O + O + M \to O_2^* + M$ (and $H + O_3 \to OH + O_2^*$)
Atmospheric bands 7000–9000	$O_2(b^1\Sigma_u^+)$	~ 85	3×10^4	Complex, but based on $O + O + M \to O_2^* + M$ (also $O(^1D) + O_2 \to$ $O + O_2(^1\Sigma)$)
Infrared atmospheric bands, 1.27μ, 1.58μ	$O_2(a^1\Delta g)$	~ 85	5×10^4	$O + O + M \to O_2^* + M$ $O_2^* + M \to O_2(^1\Delta) + M$ (also from ozone photolysis)
Meinel bands 5000 Å—5μ	$OH(v \leqslant 9)$	~ 85	4.5×10^6	$H + O_3 \to OH^* + O_2$

[a] 1 rayleigh $= 10^6$ photons per sec from a 1-cm^2 column of atmosphere.

considered responsible for the production of the excited species. It may be noted that the largest total photon flux is due to OH vibration-rotation bands from the ground electronic state. A discussion of the specific processes which produce the emissions given in the table may be found in the review by Young (423). Figure 11 shows the theoretical computation of the altitude profiles of [O], [O_2], and [O_2] + [N_2] = [M] normalized to rocket data for [O] at 120 km, together with the rate of O_2 formation by

$$O + O + M \xrightarrow{k_a} O_2 + M$$

and

$$O + O_2 + M \xrightarrow{k_b} O_3 + M$$

$$O + O_3 \longrightarrow 2O_2$$

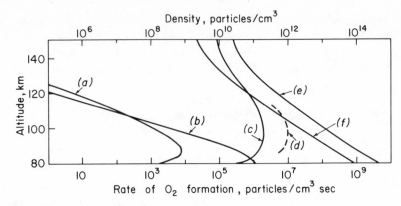

Figure 11 Young's composite diagram of (1) the densities of [O], $[O_2]$, and $[O_2] + [N_2]$ derived from calculations in Ref. 425, normalized to rocket measurements of atomic oxygen at 120 km, and also adjusted so that $[O]/[O_2] = 1$ at this altitude in conformance to rocket measurements; (2) the rate of O_2 formation using the depicted densities and rate coefficients listed in Ref. 423; and (3) the atomic oxygen profile deduced from rocket measurement of 5577 Å emission in the night glow as reported in Ref. 426. (a) Simple recombination $(d[O_2]/dt = k_a[O]^2[M])$; (b) recombination through ozone $(d[O_2]/dt = 2k_b[O][O_2][M])$; (c) atomic oxygen, theory normalized to rocket experiments; (d) atomic oxygen derived from night glow and laboratory data; (e) total density; (f) molecular oxygen. (Taken from Ref. 423.) In a recent private communication to the author, Young has suggested that calculations on the basis of new measurements of the quenching of excited oxygen atoms which radiate the nightglow emission at 5577 Å, require that the curve (d) be modified downward by a factor of between 2 and 3. Such a revision shows better agreement with both theory and rocket measurements.

as given by Young (423) who used the rate coefficients of 3×10^{-33} and 8×10^{-34} cm^6 sec^{-1}, respectively, for k_a and k_b (424), and assumed that O_3 is in a steady state.

Of current interest are the weak emission features arising from long-lived species such as $O(^1D)$ (radiative lifetime 110 sec) or $O_2(^1\Delta_g)$ (radiative lifetime ~ 45 min), since such species would be expected to have a good chance of participating in further reactions before losing their energy. The red emission from $O(^1D)$ is only observed at altitudes of 200 km and above where the pressure is low, because this state is efficiently quenched by O_2 and N_2. The relatively strong green line of atomic oxygen, which has the ^1D level as its lower state, has its maximum intensity near 100 km where the red line is not observed at all. The $^1\Delta_g$ state of O_2 has a lifetime much greater than that of $O(^1D)$, but is only weakly quenched by O_2 and N_2, so that the infrared atmospheric bands are emitted at 100 km and below. The weak nightglow emissions include scattered Lyman-α (1216 Å) radiation of atomic hydrogen. Scattered Lyman-α is observed very strongly in the day glow at altitudes down to about 100 km; solar Lyman-α can be detected down to 70 km, its penetration to this depth being the fortuitous results of the presence of a window at 1216 Å in the absorption spectrum of O_2 (see Section II). During the day, under steady illumination, the usual night glow emission features appear greatly enhanced, and some new features appear.

4. Reactions of Excited Species.   The airglow is the result of light emission by electronically excited atoms, molecules, and ions. Clearly, these excited species influence the chemistry of the upper atmosphere; it is, therefore, necessary to know how the rates of ion-molecule reactions are altered by either the neutral or charged species possessing electronic and/or vibrational energy.

Because of experimental difficulties in obtaining the excited neutral reactant free from other reactive species, very little information has been obtained on ion reaction rates with excited neutral species. Schmeltekopf et al. (427), who measured the ion-atom interchange reaction of O^+ with vibrationally excited N_2

$$O^+ + N_2(v) \longrightarrow NO^+ + N; \quad k = (2 \pm 1) \times 10^{-12} \text{ cm}^3 \text{ sec}^{-1}$$

found that at a vibrational temperature of $4000°K$ the rate increases by a factor of 20 over $N_2(v = 0)$. Vibrationally excited nitrogen is believed to be produced at E region altitudes mainly by the quenching of $O(^1D)$ by N_2, and at higher altitudes by photoelectron impact on N_2; an alternative source is the reaction

$$N + NO \longrightarrow N_2(v \leqslant 12) + N$$

The enhanced reaction rate of O^+ with vibrationally excited N_2 may account for the decrease in electron density in the F region during magnetic storms and auroras (428). Similarly, the enhanced vibrational temperatures of N_2, believed to give rise to the high electron temperatures observed in the E region, should increase the rate of removal of O^+ ions by about a factor of 10 (429).

In view of the observation of the highly forbidden $a^1\Delta_g \rightarrow X^3\Sigma_g^-$ infrared atmospheric bands in the airglow (430), the metastable $O_2(^1\Delta_g)$ is the best choice for an electronically excited neutral reactant for laboratory studies; Fehsenfeld et al. (431) have studied the reactions of $O_2(^1\Delta_g)$ with O_2^- and O^-

$$O_2(^1\Delta_g) + O_2^- \longrightarrow 2O_2 + e^-; \quad k = 2 \times 10^{-10} \text{ cm}^3 \text{ sec}^{-1}$$

$$O_2(^1\Delta_g) + O^- \longrightarrow O_3 + e^-; \quad k = 3 \times 10^{-10} \text{ cm}^3 \text{ sec}^{-1}$$

The rates suggest that these reactions are fast enough to be important in the D region.

Electronically excited species that are considered to be important in the upper atmosphere are listed in Table 17; all of these species except $N_2(^3\Delta_u)$

TABLE 17
Electronically excited species of importance in the upper atmosphere (301)

Ground state	Excited species	Excitation energy, eV	Lifetime, sec	References lifetime
$O(^3P)$	^1D	1.96	110	315
	^1S	4.17	0.74	315
$O_2(^3\Sigma_g^-)$	$a^1\Delta_g$	0.98	2.7×10^3	432
	$b^1\Sigma_g^+$	1.63	12	433
	$A^3\Sigma_u^+$	4.53	Metastable	
$N(^4S)$	^2D	2.37	9×10^4	315
$N_2(^1\Sigma_g^+)$	$A^3\Sigma_u^+$	6.17	$10, 1.4(v = 0)$	434, 435
	$^3\Delta_u$	7.1	Metastable	
	$^5\Sigma_g^+$	9.63	Metastable	
	$C^3\Pi_u$	11.03	4.7×10^{-8}	434, 436
$N_2^+(^2\Sigma_g^+)$	$A^2\Pi_u$	1.12	3×10^{-6}	437
	$B^2\Sigma_u^+$	3.17	6×10^{-8}	434, 436
$H(^2P)$	^2P	10.20	1.6×10^{-9}	438

have been reported in emission in the airglow. Short-lived or highly excited states which contribute to the airglow, for example, $O(^3S)$ at 9.52 eV, $\tau = 1.7 \times 10^{-9}$ sec (439,440) are not included in the table, since only relatively long-lived species, with lifetimes greater than 10^{-3} sec, are likely to involve in chemical reactions. However, the possibility of radiation trapping may alter this view slightly for $H(^2P)$.

Although nitrogen is the most abundant constituent of the atmosphere except at very high altitudes, neutral nitrogen compounds play a relatively minor role in upper atmosphere chemistry since N_2, unlike O_2, is not readily dissociated by light in any spectral region. Apart from a weak predissociation in the $a^1\Pi_g \rightarrow X^1\Sigma_g^+$ (Lyman-Birge-Hopfield) system below 1250 Å, and possibly stronger predissociations in the 800–1000 Å region (441), the production of N atoms depends on a primary photo-ionization process

$$N_2 + h\nu(\lambda < 800 \text{ Å}) \longrightarrow N_2^+ + e^-$$

followed by dissociative recombination

$$N_2^+ + e^- \longrightarrow N + N$$

or by ion-molecule reactions such as

$$N_2^+ + O \longrightarrow NO^+ + N$$

Bands of N_2 and N_2^+ and lines of N and N^+ are commonly found in auroral spectra, though absent from the normal nightglow. However, the 0,0 band of the first negative system of N_2^+ at 3914 Å is present in the twilightglow and dayglow as a result of fluorescent scattering. It is believed that the aurora arises from bombardment of the outer layers of the atmosphere with energetic particles, mainly protons, emitted by the sun and constrained by the earth's magnetic field to enter near the poles. Spectra comparable to auroral spectra have been obtained in the laboratory by bombarding air with ions.

5. Reactions of Neutral Species. Numerous studies of the reactions of neutral species with some relevance to the upper atmosphere have been published. Comprehensive reviews of work on hydrogen, nitrogen, and oxygen species, atomic and molecular as well, may be found in Refs. 424 and 442–447. Studies on the relaxation behavior of systems containing a mixture of electronically and vibrationally excited molecules with ground-state atoms have also been reviewed recently (301,448).

C. Atmospheres of the Other Planets

The foregoing discussions concerned chiefly the upper atmosphere of the Earth. Atmospheres of the other planets may involve other ions. The importance of CO_2^+ on Venus and Mars is known and the possibility exists that HCO_2^+ is formed at high rates on Venus (449–455). The outer planets have atmospheres containing copious quantities of H_2; in their ionospheres H_3^+ should appear prominently, and at temperatures perhaps as low as $100°K$.

Studies of the reaction of $O(^1D)$ with CO_2 may help to explain why the atmospheres of Venus and Mars consist mainly of CO_2, with almost no CO or O_2, despite photolysis of the CO_2 by solar radiation. It has been suggested (456) that the existence of a long-lived CO_3 radical, formed by reaction of $O(^1D)$ with CO_2, would help account for the stability of the atmospheres of Mars and Venus, since except at very short wavelengths the photolysis of CO_2 gives $O(^1D)$ as a product. Because of the low densities prevailing in the Martian atmosphere, two-body collision processes assume a greater importance than in the terrestrial atmosphere, and radiative association may be the major recombination mechanism (457).

Of the other planets, there has been some discussion of the upper atmospheres of Jupiter (458) and of Mercury (459). Whereas reactions involving the dissociation and ionization products of CO_2 and N_2 are significant in Venutian atmospheres (460), the reactions of H_2 and He^+

$$He^+ + H_2 \longrightarrow HeH^+ + H \longrightarrow He + H_2^+$$

have been predicted to explain the composition of the ionosphere on Jupiter (457). The results of space probes scheduled for the 1970s should certainly enhance our knowledge of the upper atmospheres of the many planets in our solar system.

REFERENCES

1. G. L. Weissler, "Photoionization in Gases and Photoelectric Emission from Solids." In *Handbuch der Physik*, Vol. 21, edited by E. Flügge. Berlin: Springer, 1956.
2. R. W. Ditchburn and U. Öpik, "Photoionization Processes." In *Atomic and Molecular Processes*, edited by D. R. Bates. New York: Academic Press, 1962.
3. L. M. Branscomb, "Photodetachment." In *Atomic and Molecular Processes*, edited by D. R. Bates. New York: Academic Press, 1962; *Ann. Geophys.*, **20**, 88 (1964).
4. E. W. McDaniel, *Collision Phenomena in Ionized Gases*. New York: Wiley, 1964.
5. J. A. R. Samson, *Advan. Atomic Mol. Phys.*, **2**, 177 (1966).
6. A. L. Stewart, *Advan. Atomic Mol. Phys.*, **3**, 1 (1967).
7. P. G. Burke, *AERE Harwell Rept. T. P.*, **183** (1965).
8. G. V. Marr, *Photoionization Processes in Gases*. New York: Academic Press, 1967.
9. J. A. R. Samson, *Techniques of Vacuum Ultraviolet Spectroscopy*. New York: Wiley, 1967.
10. J. A. R. Samson, *J. Opt. Soc. Am.*, **54**, 6 (1964).
11. R. I. Schoen, *Canadian J. Chem.*, **47**, 1879 (1969).
12. For example, see H. Hurzeler, M. G. Inghram, and J. D. Morrison, *J. Chem. Phys.*, **27**, 313 (1957); **28**, 76 (1958); E. Schönheit, *Z. Physik*, **149**, 153 (1957); R. F. Herzog and F. F. Marmo, *J. Chem. Phys.*, **27**, 1202 (1957); G. L. Weissler, J. A. R. Samson, M. Ogawa, and G. R. Cook, *J. Opt. Soc. Am.*, **49**, 338 (1959); F. I. Vilesov, *Usp. Fiz. Nauk.*, **81**, 669 (1963).
13. R. I. Schoen, D. L. Judge, and G. L. Weissler, *Proceedings of the Fifth International Conference on Ionization Phenomena in Gases*, Vol. I, p. 25. Munich, 1969, North-Holland, Amsterdam, 1962.
14. R. E. Huffman, Y. Tanaka, and J. C. Larrabee, *J. Chem. Phys.*, **38**, 1920 (1963).
15. D. R. Bates, *Monthly Notices Roy. Astron. Soc.*, **106**, 423, 432 (1946); M. J. Seaton, *Proc. Roy. Soc. (London)*, **A208**, 408, 418 (1951); *Proc. Phys. Soc.*, **67**, 927 (1954); *Monthly Notices Roy. Astron. Soc.*, **118**, 504 (1958).
16. T. Y. Wu and T. Ohmura, *The Quantum Theory of Scattering*. Englewood Cliffs, N.J.: Prentice Hall, 1962.
17. D. R. Bates, *Proc. Roy. Soc. (London)*, **A188**, 350 (1947).
18. A. Burgess and M. J. Seaton, *Monthly Notices Roy. Astron. Soc.*, **120**, 121 (1961).
19. D. R. Bates and A. Damgaard, *Phil. Trans. Roy. Soc. (London)*, **A242**, 101 (1949).
20. B. L. Moiseiwitsch, *Proc. Phys. Soc. (London)*, **79**, 1166 (1962); **81**, 35 (1963).
21. D. Schlüter, *J. Quant. Spectrosc. Radiat. Transfer*, **5**, 87 (1965).
22. G. Peach, *Monthly Notices Roy. Astron. Soc.*, **130**, 361 (1965); *Proc. Phys. Soc. (London)*, **87**, 375, 381 (1966).
23. M. J. Seaton, *Proc. Phys. Soc. (London)*, **88**, 815 (1966).
24. M. J. Seaton, *Proc. Phys. Soc. (London)*, **88**, 801 (1966); O. Bely, D. Moores, and M. J. Seaton, in *Atomic Collision Processes*, edited by M. R. C. McDowell. Amsterdam: North-Holland Publ., 1963.
25. O. Bely, *Proc. Phys. Soc. (London)*, **88**, 833 (1966).
26. D. Moores, *Proc. Phys. Soc. (London)*, **88**, 843 (1966).
27. *Photoionization of Atoms and Molecules*. Washington, D.C.: National Bureau of Standards, 1962.
28. N. Wainfan, W. C. Walker, and G. L. Weissler, *Phys. Rev.*, **99**, 542 (1955).
29. P. Lee and G. L. Weissler, *Astrophys. J.*, **115**, 570 (1952).
30. P. Lee, *J. Opt. Soc. Am.*, **45**, 703 (1955).

31. N. Wainfan, W. C. Walker, and G. L. Weissler, *J. Appl. Phys.*, **24**, 1318 (1953).
32. K. Watanabe and F. F. Marmo, *J. Chem. Phys.*, **25**, 965 (1956).
33. G. L. Weissler and P. Lee, *J. Opt. Soc. Am.*, **42**, 200 (1952).
34. G. L. Weissler, P. Lee, and E. I. Mohr, *J. Opt. Soc. Am.*, **42**, 84 (1952).
35. C. D. Maunsell, *Phys. Rev.*, **98**, 1831 (1955).
36. N. Astoin and J. Granier, *C. R. Acad. Sci. (Paris)*, **244**, 1350 (1957).
37. N. Astoin, A. Johannin-Gilles, and B. Vodar, *C. R. Acad. Sci. (Paris)*, **237**, 558 (1953).
38. N. Astoin, *C. R. Acad. Sci. (Paris)*, **242**, 2327 (1956).
39. W. C. Walker and G. L. Weissler, *J. Chem. Phys.*, **23**, 1962 (1955).
40. N. Astoin and J. Granier, *C. R. Acad. Sci. (Paris)*, **241**, 1736 (1955).
41. K. Watanabe, *J. Chem. Phys.*, **22**, 1564 (1954).
42. K. Watanabe, F. F. Marmo, and E. C. Y. Inn, *Phys. Rev.*, **91**, 1155 (1953).
43. H. Sun and G. L. Weissler, *J. Chem. Phys.*, **23**, 1372 (1955).
44. J. Granier and N. Astoin, *C. R. Acad. Sci. (Paris)*, **242**, 1431 (1956).
45. H. Sun and G. L. Weissler, *J. Chem. Phys.*, **23**, 1625 (1955).
46. H. Sun and G. L. Weissler, *J. Chem. Phys.*, **23**, 1160 (1955).
47. W. C. Walker and G. L. Weissler, *J. Chem. Phys.*, **23**, 1540 (1955).
48. R. W. Ditchburn, *Proc. Roy. Soc. (London)*, **A229**, 44 (1955).
49. D. Golomb, K. Watanabe, and F. F. Marmo, *J. Chem. Phys.*, **36**, 958 (1962).
50. G. Moe and A. B. F. Duncan, *J. Am. Chem. Soc.*, **74**, 3136, 3140 (1952).
51. W. C. Walker and G. L. Weissler, *J. Chem. Phys.*, **23**, 1547 (1955).
52. R. E. Huffman, *Canadian J. Chem.*, **47**, 1823 (1969).
53. J. A. R. Samson and R. B. Cairns, *J. Geophys. Res.*, **69**, 4583 (1964).
54. F. M. Matsunaga and K. Watanabe, *Sci. of Light*, **16**, 31 (1967).
55. G. R. Cook and P. H. Metzger, *J. Chem. Phys.*, **41**, 321 (1964).
56. G. R. Cook, B. H. Ching, and R. A. Becker, *Discussions Faraday Soc.*, **37**, 149 (1964).
57. G. R. Cook and M. Ogawa, *Canadian J. Phys.*, **43**, 256 (1965).
58. K. Watanabe, *J. Chem. Phys.*, **22**, 1564 (1954).
59. K. Watanabe, F. M. Matsunaga, and H. Sakai, *Appl. Optics*, **6**, 391 (1967).
60. P. H. Metzger, G. R. Cook, and M. Ogawa, *Canadian J. Phys.*, **45**, 203 (1967).
61. R. B. Cairns and J. A. R. Samson, *J. Geophys. Res.*, **70**, 99 (1965).
62. R. S. Nakata, K. Watanabe, and F. M. Matsunaga, *Sci. of Light*, **14**, 54 (1965).
63. G. R. Cook, P. H. Metzger, and M. Ogawa, *J. Chem. Phys.*, **44**, 2935 (1966).
64. T. Nakayama, M. Y. Kitamura, and K. Watanabe, *J. Chem. Phys.*, **30**, 1180 (1959).
65. P. H. Metzger and G. R. Cook, *J. Chem. Phys.*, **41**, 642 (1964).
66. R. E. Huffman, Y. Tanaka, and J. C. Larrabee, *Discussions Faraday Soc.*, **37**, 154 (1964).
67. R. E. Huffman, J. C. Larrabee, and Y. Tanaka, *J. Chem. Phys.*, **40**, 356 (1964).
68. R. E. Huffman, Y. Tanaka, and J. C. Larrabee, *J. Chem. Phys.*, **39**, 910 (1963).
69. K. Watanabe, in *Advances in Geophysics*, Vol. 5, edited by H. E. Landsberg. New York: Academic Press, 1958.
70. R. E. Huffman, J. C. Larrabee, and Y. Tanaka, *J. Chem. Phys.*, **46**, 2213 (1967).
71. R. E. Huffman, J. C. Larrabee, and Y. Tanaka, *J. Chem. Phys.*, **47**, 4462 (1967).
72. A. Dalgarno, R. J. W. Henry and A. L. Stewart, *Planet. Space Sci.*, **12**, 235 (1964).
73. J. A. R. Samson and R. B. Cairns, *J. Opt. Soc. Amer.*, **55**, 1035 (1965).
74. R. B. Cairns and J. A. R. Samson, *Phys. Rev.*, **139**, A1403 (1965).
75. R. E. Huffman, J. C. Larrabee, and Y. Tanaka, *Phys. Rev. Lett.*, **16**, 1033 (1966).
76. L. A. Hall, W. Schweizer, and H. E. Hinteregger, *J. Geophys. Res.*, **70**, 105 (1965).
77. K. Watanabe and M. Zelikoff, *J. Opt. Soc. Amer.*, **43**, 753 (1953).
78. N. Astoin, A. Johannin-Gilles, J. Granier-Mayence, and J. Romand, *C. R. Acad. Sci., Paris*, **242**, 2327 (1956).

79. E. C. Y. Inn and Y. Tanaka, *J. Opt. Soc. Amer.*, **43**, 870 (1953).
80. E. Vigroux, *Ann. Phys.*, **8**, 709 (1953).
81. P. A. Leighton, *Photochemistry of Air Pollution.* New York: Academic Press, 1961.
82. E. Vigroux, *Ann. Phys.*, **22**, 209 (1967).
83. J. R. McNesby and H. Okabe, *Advances in Photochemistry*, **3**, 157 (1964).
84. W. B. DeMore and O. Raper, *J. Chem. Phys.*, **44**, 1780 (1966).
85. R. P. Wayne, *Quant. J. Roy. Meteorological Soc.*, **93**, 69 (1967).
86. P. Lee and G. L. Weissler, *Phys. Rev.*, **99**, 540 (1955).
87. N. N. Axelrod and M. P. Givens, *Phys. Rev.*, **115**, 97 (1959).
88. P. Lee and G. L. Weissler, *Proc. Roy. Soc. (London)*, **A220**, 71 (1953).
89. R. W. Ditchburn, *Proc. Phys. Soc. (London)*, **75**, 461 (1960).
90. N. Waifan, W. C. Walker, and G. L. Weissler, *Phys. Rev.*, **99**, 542 (1955).
91. A. Pery-Thorne and W. R. S. Garton, *Proc. Phys. Soc. (London)*, **76**, 833 (1960).
92. D. J. Baker, D. E. Bedo and D. H. Tomboulian, *Phys. Rev.*, **124**, 1471 (1961).
93. R. E. Huffman, Y. Tanaka, and J. C. Larrabee, *Appl. Optics*, **2**, 947 (1963); *J. Chem. Phys.*, **39**, 902 (1963).
94. J. A. R. Samson, *J. Opt. Soc. Am.*, **54**, 420, 842, 876 (1964).
95. J. F. Lowry, D. H. Tomboulian, and D. L. Ederer, *Phys. Rev.*, **137**, A1054 (1965).
96. P. Lee and G. L. Weissler, *J. Opt. Soc. Amer.*, **42**, 214 (1952).
97. R. P. Madden and K. Codling, *Phys. Rev. Lett.*, **10**, 516 (1963); *J. Opt. Soc. Amer.*, **54**, 268 (1964); *Astrophys. J.*, **141**, 364 (1965).
98. D. Ederer and D. H. Tamboulian, *Phys. Rev.*, **133**, A1525 (1964).
99. F. Comes and A. Elzer, *Z. Naturforsch.*, **19a**, 721 (1964).
100. O. P. Rustgi, *J. Opt. Soc. Amer.*, **54**, 464 (1964).
101. A. P. Lukirskii and T. M. Zimkina, *Bull. Acad. Sci. USSR, Phys. Ser.* (English Translation), **27**, 808 (1963).
102. E. Schönheit, *Z. Naturforsch.*, **16a**, 1094 (1961).
103. F. Comes and W. Lessman, *Z. Naturforsch.*, **16a**, 1396 (1961).
104. J. A. R. Samson, *Phys. Lett.*, **8**, 107 (1964).
105. O. P. Rustgi, E. I. Fisher and C. H. Fuller, *J. Opt. Soc. Amer.*, **54**, 745 (1964).
106. R. B. Cairns and G. L. Weissler, *Bull. Am. Phys. Soc.*, **7**, 129 (1962).
107. G. L. Weissler, *J. Quant. Spectry and Radiative Transfer*, **2**, 383 (1962).
108. H. E. Blackwell, G. S. Bajwa, G. S. Shipp, and G. L. Weissler, *J. Quant. Spectry. and Radiative Transfer*, **4**, 249 (1964).
109. D. L. Ederrer, *Phys. Rev. Lett.*, **13**, 760 (1964).
110. A. P. Lukirskii, I. A. Brytov, and T. M. Zimkina, *Opt. Spectry. USSR* (English translation), **17**, 234 (1964).
111. K. Watanabe, *Phys. Rev.*, **137**, A1380 (1965).
112. N. Astoin and M. A. Kastler, *C. R. Acad. Sci., Paris*, **259**, 1493 (1964).
113. A. L. Stewart and T. G. Webb, *Proc. Phys. Soc., (London)*, **82**, 532 (1963).
114. A. L. Stewart and W. J. Wilkinson, *Proc. Phys. Soc. (London)*, **75**, 796 (1960).
115. E. E. Salpeter and M. H. Zaidi, *Phys. Rev.*, **125**, 248 (1962).
116. J. W. Cooper, *Phys. Rev.*, **128**, 681 (1962).
117. A. Dalgarno and A. L. Stewart, *Proc. Phys. Soc. (London)*, **76**, 49 (1960).
118. A. Dalgarno and N. Lynn, *Proc. Phys. Soc. (London)*, **70**, 802 (1957).
119. K. G. Sewell, *Phys. Rev.*, **137**, A418 (1965).
120. U. Fano and J. W. Cooper, *Phys. Rev.*, **137**, A1364 (1965).
121. A. Dalgarno, *Proc. Phys. Soc. (London)*, **65**, 663 (1952).
122. J. W. Cooper, *Phys. Rev. Lett.*, **13**, 762 (1964).
123. F. J. Comes, F. Speier, and A. Elzer, *Z. Naturforsch.*, **23a**, 114 (1968).
124. R. J. W. Henry, *Planet Space Sci.*, **15**, 1747 (1967).

125. A. W. Ehler and G. L. Weissler, *J. Opt. Soc. Amer.*, **45**, 1035 (1955).
126. D. R. Bates and M. J. Seaton, *Monthly Notices Roy. Astron. Soc.*, **109**, 698 (1949).
127. A. Dalgarno and D. Parkinson, *J. Atmospheric Terrest. Phys.*, **18**, 335 (1960).
128. R. J. W. Henry, *J. Chem. Phys.*, **44**, 4357 (1966).
129. W. J. Karzas and R. Latter, *Astrophys. J. Suppl. Soc.*, **6**, 167 (1961).
130. J. D. E. Beynon and R. B. Cairns, *Proc. Phys. Soc.* (*London*), **86**, 1343 (1965); Nature, **207**, 405 (1965).
131. R. W. Ditchburn, J. Tunstead, and J. G. Yates, *Proc. Roy. Soc.* (*London*), **A181**, 386 (1943).
132. R. W. Ditchburn, P. J. Jutsum, and G. V. Marr, *Proc. Roy. Soc.* (*London*), **A219**, 89 (1953).
133. G. V. Marr, *Proc. Phys. Soc.* (*London*), **81**, 9 (1963).
134. R. D. Hudson and V. L. Carter, *Phys. Rev.*, **137**, A1648 (1965).
135. R. D. Hudson, *Phys. Rev.*, **135**, A1212 (1964).
136. R. D. Hudson and V. L. Carter, *Phys. Rev.*, **139**, A1426 (1965).
137. K. J. Ross and G. V. Marr, *Proc. Phys. Soc.* (*London*), **85**, 193 (1965).
138. P. J. Jutsum, *Proc. Phys. Soc.* (*London*), **67**, 190 (1954).
139. R. W. Ditchburn and R. D. Hudson, *Proc. Roy. Soc.* (*London*), **A256**, 53 (1960).
140. R. W. Ditchburn and G. V. Marr, *Proc. Phys. Soc.* (*London*), **66**, 655 (1953).
141. G. V. Marr, *Proc. Phys. Soc.* (*London*), **A67**, 196 (1954).
142. A. Burgess and M. J. Seaton, *Monthly Notices Roy. Astron. Soc.*, **120**, 121 (1960).
143. J. W. Cooper, *Phys. Rev.*, **128**, 681 (1962).
144. J. H. Tait, in *Atomic Collision Processes*, edited by M. R. C. McDowell. Amsterdam: North-Holland Publ., 1964.
145. A. E. Boyd, *Planet. Space Sci.*, **12**, 729 (1964).
146. F. F. Marmo, J. Pressman, and L. M. Aschenbrand, *Planet. Space Sci.*, **1**, 291 (1959).
147. R. D. Hudson, "The Absorption Coefficients of the Alkali Metals and the Alkali Earths." *University of Southern California, Report No. AFCRL-TN-60-680*, June 28, 1960.
148. P. J. Nawrocki and R. Papa, *Atmospheric Processes*. Englewood Cliffs, N.J.: Prentice-Hall, 1962.
149. H. A. Kramers, *Phil. Mag.*, **46**, 836 (1923).
150. D. H. Menzel and C. L. Pekeris, *Monthly Notices Roy. Astron. Soc.*, **96**, 77 (1935).
151. P. O. M. Olsson, *Ark. Fys.*, **15**, 131, 159, 289 (1959).
152. B. H. Armstrong and H. P. Kelly, *J. Opt. Soc. Amer.*, **49**, 949 (1959).
153. D. R. Bates, U. Öpik, and G. Poots, *Proc. Phys. Soc.* (*London*), **66**, 1113 (1953).
154. G. H. Dunn, in *Atomic Collision Processes*, edited by M. R. C. McDowell. Amsterdam: North-Holland Publ., 1964.
155. G. H. Dunn, *Phys. Rev.*, **172**, 1 (1968).
156. S. Chandrasekhar, *Astrophys. J.*, **128**, 114 (1958).
157. S. Geltman, *Astrophys. J.*, **136**, 935 (1962).
158. A. Dalgarno and R. W. Ewart, *Proc. Phys. Soc.* (*London*), **80**, 616 (1962).
159. J. W. Cooper and J. B. Martin, *Phys. Rev.*, **126**, 1482 (1962).
160. V. P. Myerscough and M. R. C. McDowell, *Monthly Notices Roy. Astron. Soc.*, **128**, 288 (1964).
161. R. S. Berry, C. W. Reimann, and G. N. Spokes, *J. Chem. Phys.*, **35**, 2237 (1961); **37**, 2278 (1962).
162. R. S. Berry and C. W. Reimann, *J. Chem. Phys.*, **38**, 1540 (1963).
163. R. S. Berry and C. W. David, in *Atomic Collision Processes*, edited by M. R. C. McDowell. Amsterdam: North-Holland Publ., 1964.
164. R. S. Berry, C. W. David, and J. C. Mackie, *J. Chem. Phys.*, **42**, 1541 (1965).

165. L. M. Branscomb, S. J. Smith, and G. Tisone, *J. Chem. Phys.*, **43**, 2906 (1965).
166. L. M. Branscomb, *Phys. Rev.*, **148**, 11 (1966).
167. S. B. Woo, E. C. Beaty, and L. M. Branscomb, *Bull. Am. Phys. Soc.*, **12**, 237 (1967).
168. M. W. Siegel and J. L. Hall, *J. Chem. Phys.*, **48**, 943 (1968).
169. J. Cooper and R. N. Zare, *J. Chem. Phys.*, **48**, 942 (1968).
170. F. C. Fehsenfeld, A. L. Schmeltekopf, H. I. Schiff, and E. E. Ferguson, *Planet. Space Sci.*, **15**, 373 (1967).
171. F. J. Comes and W. Lessman, *Z. Naturforsch.*, **19a**, 65 (1964).
172. F. J. Comes, F. Speier, and A. Elzer, *Z. Naturforsch.*, **23a**, 125 (1968).
173. V. H. Dibeler and J. A. Walker, *J. Opt. Soc. Amer.*, **57**, 1007 (1967).
174. F. A. Elder, D. Villario, and M. O. Inghram, *J. Chem. Phys.*, **43**, 758 (1965).
175. V. H. Dibeler, J. A. Walker, and S. K. Liston, *J. Res. Nat. Bur. Stand. (U.S.)*, **71A**, 371 (1967).
176. V. H. Dibeler, J. A. Walker, and H. M. Rosenstock, *J. Res. Nat. Bur. Stand. (U.S.)*, **70A**, 459 (1966).
177. B. L. Karbatov, F. I. Vilesov, and A. N. Terenin, *Soviet Phys. Doklady*, **6**, 490 (1961); **6**, 883 (1962).
178. D. W. Turner and M. I. Al-Joboury, *J. Chem. Phys.*, **37**, 3007 (1962).
179. R. I. Schoen, *J. Chem. Phys.*, 40, 1830 (1964).
180. D. W. Turner and D. P. May, *J. Chem. Phys.*, **45**, 471 (1966); **46**, 1156 (1967).
181. A. J. Blake and J. W. Carver, *J. Chem. Phys.*, **47**, 1038 (1967).
182. D. C. Frost, C. A. McDowell, and D. A. S. Vroom, *Proc. Roy. Soc. (London)*, **196**, 566 (1967). See also D. A. S. Vroom, thesis, University of British Columbia, 1966.
183. J. A. R. Samson, *J. Opt. Soc. Amer.*, **56**, 552 (1966).
184. R. Spohr and E. van Puttkamer, *Z. Naturforsch.*, **22a**, 705 (1967).
185. J. Berkowitz, H. Ehrhardt, and T. Tekaat, *Z. Physik.*, **200**, 69 (1967).
186. D. W. Turner, paper presented at the 15th annual conference on Mass Spectrometry and Allied Topics, Denver, Colorado, May 1967.
187. P. H. Doolittle, R. I. Schoen, and K. E. Schubert, *J. Chem. Phys.*, **49**, 5108 (1968).
188. R. W. Nicholls, *J. Quant. Spectr. Radiative Transfer*, **2**, 433 (1962).
189. M. E. Wacks, *J. Chem. Phys.*, **41**, 930 (1964).
190. F. R. Gilmore, *J. Quant. Spectr. Radiative Transfer*, **5**, 369 (1965).
191. H. D. Cohen and U. Fano, *Phys. Rev.*, **150**, 30 (1966).
192. P. J. Chantry and G. J. Schulz, *Phys. Rev. Lett.*, **12**, 449 (1964).
193. D. L. Judge and G. L. Weissler, *J. Chem. Phys.*, **48**, 4590 (1968).
194. R. A. Young, G. Black, and A. Y. M. Ung, *J. Chem. Phys.*, **45**, 2702 (1966).
195. K. D. Beyer and K. H. Welge, *Z. Naturforsch.*, **19a**, 19 (1964).
196. E. Archbold and T. P. Hughes, *Nature*, **204**, 670 (1964).
197. M. M. Litvak and D. F. Edwards, *I.E.E.E.*, *J. Quantum Elect.*, **2**, 486 (1966).
198. R. G. Tomlinson, *Phys. Rev. Lett.*, **14**, 489 (1965).
199. M. Young, M. Hercher, and C-Y. Wu, *J. Appl. Phys.*, **37**, 4938 (1966).
200. M. Berry, *Compt. Rend.*, **262B**, 1395 (1966).
201. R. W. Minck and W. G. Rado, *J. Appl. Phys.*, **37**, 355 (1966).
202. M. M. Litvak and D. F. Edwards, *J. Appl. Phys.*, **37**, 4462 (1966); *Bull. Am. Phys. Soc.*, **10**, 388 (1965).
203. E. Hantzsche, R. Rompe, and H. Wolff, *Monatsber. Deutschen Akad. Wiss. Berlin*, **8**, 111 (1966).
204. W. B. Tiffany, H. W. Moos, and A. L. Schawlow, *Science*, **157**, 40 (1967).
205. L. M. Epstein and K. H. Sun, *Nature*, **211**, 1173 (1966).
206. For a short review, see W. J. Jones, *Quarterly Rev.*, **23**, 73 (1969).
207. J. T. Yardley and C. B. Moore, *J. Chem. Phys.*, **45**, 1066 (1966).

208. A. M. Ronn, *J. Chem. Phys.*, **48**, 511 (1968).
209. S. Ezekiel and R. Weiss, *Phys. Rev. Lett.*, **20**, 91 (1968).
210. J. H. Kiefer and R. W. Lutz, *J. Chem. Phys.*, **44**, 658, 668 (1966); *Phys. Fluids*, **9**, 1638 (1966).
211. H. B. Bebb and A. Gold, in *Physics of Quantum Electronics*. New York: McGraw-Hill, 1966.
212. J. W. Gardner, *Electronics Letters*, **2**, 297 (1966).
213. A. V. Phelps, in *Physics of Quantum Electronics*. New York: McGraw-Hill, 1966.
214. B. C. Fawcett and N. J. Peacock, *Proc. Phys. Soc. (London)*, **91**, 973 (1967).
215. S. Namba, P. H. Kim, and A. Mitsuyama, *J. Appl. Phys.*, **37**, 3330 (1966).
216. J. F. Ready, E. Bernal, and L. P. Levine, *Proc. Natl. Elect. Conf.*, **22**, 993 (1966).
217. H. Sonnenberg, H. Heffner, and W. Spicer, *Appl. Phys. Lett.*, **5**, 95 (1965).
218. C. M. Verber and A. H. Adelman, *J. Appl. Phys.*, **36**, 1522 (1965).
219. W. L. Knecht, *I.E.E.E.,J. Quantum Elect.*, **2**, 103 (1966).
220. D. W. Gregg and S. J. Thomas, *J. Appl. Phys.*, **37**, 4313 (1966).
221. A. F. Haught and D. H. Polk, *Phys. Fluids*, **9**, 2047 (1966).
222. C. David, P. V. Avizonis, H. Weichel, C. Bruce, and K. D. Pyatt, *I.E.E.E.,J. Quantum Electron.*, **2** (9), 493 (1966).
223. J. M. Dawson, *AEC Accession No.* 3396, *Rept. No. MATT-222*, 1963. [In *Nucl. Sci. Abstr.*, **19**, 388 (1965).]
224. P. Ausloos, *Ann. Rev. Phys. Chem.*, **17**, 205 (1966).
225. A. H. Laufer and J. R. McNesby, *J. Chem. Phys.*, **42**, 3329 (1965).
226. P. Ausloos, S. G. Lias, and A. A. Scala, *Advan. Chem. Ser.*, **58**, 264 (1966).
227. H. Essex, *J. Phys. Chem.*, **58**, 42 (1954).
228. P. Ausloos and R. Gordon, Jr., *J. Chem. Phys.*, **40**, 3599 (1964).
229. G. G. Meisels and T. J. Sworski, *J. Phys. Chem.*, **69**, 2867 (1965).
230. H. H. Carmichael, R. Gordon, Jr., and P. Ausloos, *J. Chem. Phys.*, **42**, 343 (1965).
231. S. G. Lias and P. Ausloos, *J. Chem. Phys.*, **43**, 2748 (1965).
232. F. Llewellyn-Jones, in *Handbuch der Physik*, Vol. 22, edited by S. Fluegge. Berlin: Springer, 1956.
233. L. B. Loeb, in *Handbuch der Physik*, Vol. 22, edited by S. Fluegge. Berlin: Springer, 1956.
234. W. Bemerl and H. Fetz, *Z. Angew. Phys.*, **8**, 424 (1956).
235. A. Przybylski, *Z. Physik*, **151**, 264 (1958).
236. A. Przybylski, *Z. Physik*, **168**, 504 (1962).
237. W. Sroka, *Phys. Lett.*, **14**, 301 (1965).
238. T. Teich, *Z. Naturforsch.*, **19a**, 1420 (1964).
239. J. A. R. Samson and G. L. Weissler, *Phys. Rev.*, **137**, A381 (1965).
240. L. B. Loeb, *Electrical Coronas*, Ch. 7, pp. 586–608. Berkeley, Calif.: University of California Press, 1965.
241. M. Venugopalan, *J. Appl. Phys.*, **37**, 4286 (1966); *Nature*, **206**, 286 (1965).
242. J. M. El-Bakkal and L. B. Loeb, *J. Appl. Phys.*, **33**, 1567 (1962); T. Nakaya, *J. Phys. Soc. Japan*, **11**, 1264 (1956); H. J. Arnikar, R. L. Mosher, F. Dale, and J. F. Paulson, *J. Appl. Phys.*, **36**, 327 (1965).
243. For example, see S. C. Lind, *Radiation Chemistry of Gases*. New York: Reinhold, 1961; J. W. T. Spinks and R. J. Wood, *An Introduction to Radiation Chemistry*. New York: Wiley, 1964; P. Ausloos and S. G. Lias, *The Chemistry of Ionization and Excitation*. London: Taylor and Francis, 1967; *Fundamental Processes in Radiation Chemistry*, edited by P. Ausloos. New York: Wiley, 1968; L. M. Dorfman and M. S. Matheson, *Progr. Reaction Kinetics*, **3**, 237 (1965).

244. For short reviews, see Ref. 224; also J. L. Franklin, P. K. Ghosh, and S. Studniarz, *Advan. Chem. Ser.*, **80**, 59 (1969).

245. G. A. W. Derwish, A. Galli, A. Giardini-Guidoni, and G. G. Volpi, *J. Chem. Phys.*, **41**, 2998 (1964); R. D. Doepker and P. Ausloos, *J. Chem. Phys.*, **42**, 3746 (1965); M. S. B. Munson, J. L. Franklin, and F. H. Field, *J. Phys. Chem.*, **68**, 3098 (1964); J. Milhaud and J. Durup, *Compt. Rend.*, **260**, 6363 (1965).

246. P. Ausloos and S. G. Lias, *J. Chem. Phys.*, **43**, 127 (1965).

247. A. M. Hogg and P. Kebarle, *J. Chem. Phys.*, **43**, 449 (1965); P. Kebarle and A. M. Hogg, *J. Chem. Phys.*, **42**, 668 (1965); P. Kebarle and R. M. Haynes, *J. Chem. Phys.*, **47**, 1676 (1967); P. Kebarle, R. M. Haynes, and S. K. Searles, *Advan. Chem. Ser.*, **58**, 210 (1966); *J. Chem. Phys.*, **47**, 1684 (1967).

248. S. Wexler, A. Lifschitz, and A. Quattrochi, *Advan. Chem. Ser.*, **58**, 193 (1966).

249. A. M. Hogg and P. Kebarle, *J. Chem. Phys.*, **43**, 498 (1965); P. Kebarle and A. M. Hogg, *J. Chem. Phys.*, **42**, 798 (1965).

250. M. S. B. Munson and F. H. Field, *J. Am. Chem. Soc.*, **88**, 2621 (1966); F. H. Field, M. S. B. Munson, and D. A. Becker, *Advan. Chem. Ser.*, **58**, 167 (1966).

251. G. G. Meisels, *J. Chem. Phys.*, **42**, 3237 (1965).

252. R. L. Platzman, *Vortex*, **23**, 372–89 (1962).

253. E. W. McDaniel, *Collision Phenomena in Ionized Gases*. New York: Wiley, 1964.

254. L. J. Kieffer and G. H. Dunn, *Rev. Mod. Phys.*, **38**, 1 (1966).

255. R. M. St. John and C. C. Lin. *J. Chem. Phys.*, **41**, 195 (1964).

256. S. Hayakawa and N. Nishimura, *J. Geomagnetism and Geoelectricity (Japan)*, **16**, 72 (1964).

257. P. Kebarle and E. W. Godbole, *J. Chem. Phys.*, **36**, 302 (1962).

258. A. Dalgarno, M. B. McElroy, and R. J. Moffett, *Planetary Space Sci.*, **11**, 463 (1963).

259. A. Dalgarno, *Can. J. Chem.*, **47**, 1723 (1969).

260. E. N. Lassettre, *Can. J. Chem.*, **47**, 1733 (1969).

261. L. R. Peterson, S. S. Prasad, and A. E. S. Green, *Can. J. Chem.*, **47**, 1774 (1969).

262. For earlier reviews on the subject, see J. B. Hasted, *Advan. Electron. Electron Phys.*, **13**, 31 (1960); J. B. Hasted, *Physics of Atomic Collisions*. London: Butterworths, 1964; E. W. McDaniel, *Collision Phenomena in Ionized Gases*. New York: Wiley, 1964.

263. M. J. Seaton, *Proc. Phys. Soc. (London)*, **A68**, 457 (1955); A. Dalgarno, *Rev. Mod. Phys.*, **39**, 850 (1967).

264. T. J. M. Boyd and A. Dalgarno, *Proc. Phys. Soc. (London)*, **A72**, 694 (1958).

265. G. B. Field and J. L. Hitchcock, *Phys. Rev. Lett.*, **16**, 817 (1966); R. Thaddeus and J. F. Clauser, *Phys. Rev. Lett.*, **16**, 819 (1966).

266. H. Bethe, *Ann. Phys.*, **5**, 325 (1930).

267. R. F. Stebbings, *Advan. Chem. Phys.*, **10**, 195 (1966).

268. J. M. Peek. *Phys. Rev.*, **143**, 33 (1966).

269. D. Rapp, *J. Geophys. Res.*, **68**, 1773 (1963).

270. W. B. Hanson, T. L. N. Patterson, and S. J. Degaonkar, *J. Geophys. Res.*, **68**, 6213 (1963).

271. For example, see G. Peach, *Proc. Phys. Soc. (London)*, **A85**, 709 (1965).

272. H. B. Gilbody and J. V. Ireland, *Proc. Roy. Soc. (London)*, **A277**, 137 (1964).

273. J. W. Hooper, D. S. Harmer, D. W. Martin, and E. W. McDaniel, *Phys. Rev.*, **125**, 2000 (1962); **121**, 1123 (1961).

274. J. G. Collins and P. Kebarle, *J. Chem. Phys.*, **46**, 1082 (1967); S. Wexler, A. Lifshitz, and A. Quattrochi, *Advan. Chem. Ser.*, **58**, 193 (1966), and references therein.

275. A. M. Arthurs and J. Hyslop, *Proc. Phys. Soc. (London)*, **A70**, 849 (1957).

276. D. C. Allison and A. Dalgarno, *Proc. Phys. Soc. (London)*, **85**, 845 (1965).

277. R. McCarroll and M. B. McElroy, *Proc. Roy. Soc. (London)*, **A226**, 422 (1962).

278. M. B. McElroy, *Proc. Roy. Soc. (London)*, **A272**, 542 (1963).
279. W. L. Fite, A. C. H. Smith, and R. F. Stebbings, *Proc. Roy. Soc. (London)*, **A268**, 527 (1962).
280. D. McNally, *Advan. Astr. Astrophys.*, **6**, 173 (1968).
281. S. Weinreb, A. H. Barrett, M. L. Meeks, and J. C. Henry, *Nature*, **200**, 829 (1963).
282. J. G. Bolton, K. J. Van Damme, F. F. Gardner, and B. J. Robinson, *Nature*, **201**, 279 (1964).
283. N. H. Dieter and H. I. Ewen, *Nature*, **201**, 279 (1964).
284. B. J. Robinson, F. F. Gardener, K. J. Van Damme, and J. G. Bolton, *Nature*, **202**, 989 (1964).
285. N. H. Kieter, H. Weaver, and D. R. W. Williams, *Sky Telescope*, **31**, 132 (1966).
286. C. Arpigny, *Ann. Rev. Astr. Astrophys.*, **3**, 351 (1965).
287. G. Münch, *Astrophys. J.*, **140**, 107 (1964).
288. D. R. Bates and L. Spitzer, *Astrophys. J.*, **113**, 441 (1951).
289. G. B. Field, W. B. Sommerville, and K. Dressler, *Ann. Rev. Astr. Astrophys.*, **4**, 207 (1966).
290. D. R. Bates, *Monthly Notices Roy. Astr. Soc.*, **111**, 303 (1951).
291. K. Takayanagi and S. Nishimura, *Rept. Ionosp. Sp. Res. Japan*, **15**, 81 (1961).
292. T. O. Carroll and E. E. Salpeter, *Astrophys. J.*, **143**, 609 (1966).
293. J. Sayers, *Observatory*, **82**, 241 (1962).
294. W. H. McCrea and D. McNally, *Monthly Notices Roy. Astr. Soc.*, **121**, 238 (1960).
295. D. McNally, *Monthly Notices Roy. Astr. Soc.*, **124**, 155 (1962).
296. R. J. Gould and E. E. Salpeter, *Astrophys. J.*, **138**, 393 (1963).
297. M. R. C. McDowell, *Observatory*, **81**, 240 (1961).
298. T. Tsugi, *Ann. Tokyo Astr. Obs.*, **9**, 1 (1964).
299. T. P. Stecher and D. A. Williams, *Astrophys. J.*, **146**, 88 (1966).
300. M. A. Biondi, *Can. J. Chem.*, **47**, 1711 (1969).
301. M. J. McEwan and L. F. Phillips, *Accounts Chem. Res.*, **3**, 9 (1970).
302. R. S. Narcisi, *Space Res.*, **8**, 360 (1967).
303. J. M. Young, C. Y. Johnson, and J. C. Holmes, *J. Geophys. Res.*, **72**, 1473 (1967).
304. M. B. McElroy, *Planet. Space Sci.*, **15**, 457 (1966).
305. T. M. Donahue, *Planet. Space Sci.*, **14**, 33 (1966).
306. E. E. Ferguson, F. C. Fehsenfeld, P. D. Goldan, and A. L. Schmeltekopf, *J. Geophys. Res.*, **70**, 4323 (1965).
307. E. E. Ferguson, *Can. J. Chem.*, **47**, 1815 (1969).
308. F. C. Fehsenfeld, A. L. Schmeltekopf, H. I. Schiff, and E. E. Ferguson, *Planet. Space Sci.*, **15**, 373 (1967).
309. *Ann. Geophys.*, **20**, 47 (1964).
310. *Can. J. Chem.*, **47**, 1703 (1969).
311. J. A. Ratcliffe, ed., *Physics of the Upper Atmosphere*. New York: Academic Press, 1960.
312. B. M. McCormac, ed., *Aurora and Airglow*. New York: Reinhold, 1967.
313. P. J. Nawrocki and R. Papa, *Atmospheric Processes*. Englewood Cliffs, N.J.: Prentice-Hall, 1962.
314. H. S. W. Massey and R. L. F. Boyd, *The Upper Atmosphere*. London: Hutchinson, 1960.
315. J. W. Chamberlain, *Physics of the Aurora and Airglow*. New York: Academic Press, 1961.
316. F. C. Fehsenfeld, A. L. Schmeltekopf, P. D. Goldan, H. I. Schiff, and E. E. Ferguson, *J. Chem. Phys.*, **44**, 4087 (1965).
317. W. L. Fite, *Ann. Geophys.*, **20**, 31 (1964); *Can. J. Chem.*, **47**, 1797 (1969).

318. J. F. Paulson, *Ann. Geophys.*, **20**, 18 (1964).
319. W. L. Fite, J. A. Rutherford, W. R. Snow, and V. A. J. van Lint, *Discussions Faraday Soc.*, **33**, 264 (1962).
320. J. Sayers and D. Smith, *Discussions Faraday Soc.*, **37**, 167 (1964).
321. E. E. Ferguson, F. C. Fehsenfeld, D. B. Dunkin, A. L. Schmeltekopf, and H. I. Schiff, *Planet. Space Sci.*, **12**, 1169 (1964).
322. F. C. Fehsenfeld, A. L. Schmeltekopf, P. D. Goldan, H. I. Schiff, and E. E. Ferguson, *J. Chem. Phys.*, **44**, 4087 (1966).
323. V. Aquilanti and G. G. Volpi, *Ric. Sci.*, **36**, 359 (1966).
324. J. Heimerl, R. Johnsen, and M. A. Biondi, *Bull. Am. Phys. Soc.*, **13**, 205 (1968).
325. P. Warneck, *Planet. Space Sci.*, **15**, 1349 (1967); *J. Geophys., Res.*, **72**, 1651 (1967).
326. T. F. Moran and L. Friedman, *J. Chem. Phys.*, **45**, 3837 (1966).
327. D. B. Dunkin, F. C. Fehsenfeld, A. L. Schmeltekopf, and E. E. Ferguson, *J. Chem. Phys.*, **49**, 1365 (1968).
328. G. F. O. Langstroth and J. B. Hasted, *Discussions Faraday Soc.*, **33**, 298 (1962).
329. F. C. Fehsenfeld, A. L. Schmeltkopf, and E. E. Ferguson, *Planet. Space Sci.*, **13**, 219 (1965).
330. M. J. Copsey, D. Smith, and J. Sayers, *Planet. Space Sci.*, **14**, 1047 (1966).
331. A. L. Schmeltekopf, F. C. Fehsenfeld, G. I. Gilman, and E. E. Ferguson, *Planet. Space Sci.*, **15**, 401 (1967).
332. D. Smith and R. A. Fouracre, *Planet. Space Sci.*, **16**, 243 (1968).
333. D. E. Golden, G. Sinnott, and R. N. Varney, *Phys. Rev. Lett.*, **20**, 239 (1968).
334. E. E. Ferguson, F. C. Fehsenfeld, P. D. Goldan, A. L. Schmeltekopf, and H. I. Schiff, *Planet. Space Sci.*, **13**, 823 (1965).
335. M. M. Nakshbandi and J. B. Hasted, *Planet. Space Sci.*, **15**, 1781 (1967).
336. D. K. Bohme, P. P. Ong, J. B. Hasted, and L. R. Megill, *Planet. Space Sci.*, **15**, 1777 (1967).
337. A. L. Farragher, W. L. Fite, and J. A. Peden, *J. Chem. Phys.*, **50**, 287 (1969).
338. E. A. Entemann and P. K. Rol, quoted in Ref. 317 (*Can. J. Chem.*).
339. E. E. Ferguson, D. B. Dunkin, F. C. Fehsenfeld, and A. L. Schmeltekopf, *Bull. Am. Phys. Soc.*, **13**, 212 (1968).
340. E. E. Ferguson, quoted in Ref. 317 (*Can. J. Chem.*).
341. V. L. Tal'rose and E. L. Frankevich, *Zh. Fiz. Khim.*, **34**, 2709 (1960).
342. F. C. Fehsenfeld, A. L. Schmeltekopf, and E. E. Ferguson, *J. Chem. Phys.*, **46**, 2802 (1967).
343. F. C. Fehsenfeld, A. L. Schmeltekopf, and E. E. Ferguson, *J. Chem. Phys.*, **44**, 3022 (1966).
344. F. C. Fehsenfeld, A. L. Schmeltekopf, and E. E. Ferguson, *J. Chem. Phys.*, **44**, 4537 (1966); **46**, 2019 (1967).
345. F. C. Fehsenfeld, A. L. Schmeltekopf, and E. E. Ferguson, *J. Chem. Phys.*, **45**, 23 (1966).
346. J. L. Franklin and M. S. B. Munson, 10*th Combustion Symposium*, Pittsburgh: Combustion Institute, 1965.
347. E. E. Ferguson, *Space Res.*, **7**, 135 (1967).
348. F. C. Fehsenfeld, *Can. J. Chem.*, **47**, 1808 (1969).
349. E. E. Ferguson, *Rev. Geophys.*, **5**, 305 (1967); *Advan. Electron. Electron Phys.*, **24**, 1 (1968).
350. R. E. LeLevier and L. M. Branscomb, *J. Geophys. Res.*, **73**, 27 (1968).
351. E. E. Ferguson, F. C. Fehsenfeld, and A. L. Schmeltekopf, *Advan. Chem. Ser.*, **80**, 83 (1968).
352. J. A. Rutherford and B. R. Turner, *J. Geophys. Res.*, **72**, 3795 (1967).

353. A. Henglein and G. A. Muccini, *J. Chem. Phys.*, **31**, 1426 (1959).
354. J. F. Paulson, *Advan. Chem. Series.*, **58**, 28 (1966).
355. F. C. Fehsenfeld, see Ref. 307.
356. B. R. Turner, D. M. J. Compton, and J. W. McGowan, *General Atomic Rept. No.* 7419, November 14, 1966.
357. R. K. Curran, *Phys. Rev.*, **125**, 910 (1962).
358. F. C. Fehsenfeld and E. E. Ferguson, *Planet. Space Sci.*, **16**, 701 (1968).
359. F. C. Fehsenfeld, E. E. Ferguson, and A. L. Schmeltekopf, *J. Chem. Phys.*, **45**, 1844 (1966).
360. J. L. Moruzzi and A. V. Phelps, *J. Chem. Phys.*, **45**, 4617 (1966).
361. D. S. Burch and R. Geballe, *Phys. Rev.*, **106**, 183, 188 (1967).
362. E. C. Beaty, L. M. Branscomb, and P. L. Patterson, *Bull. Am. Phys. Soc.*, **9**, 535 (1964).
363. A. V. Phelps, *Can. J. Chem.*, **47**, 1783 (1969).
364. J. L. Pack and A. V. Phelps, *J. Chem. Phys.*, **44**, 1870 (1966).
365. L. M. Chanin, A. V. Phelps, and M. A. Biondi, *Phys. Rev.*, **128**, 219 (1962).
366. V. A. J. van Lint, E. G. Wikner, and D. Trueblood, *Bull. Am. Phys. Soc.*, **5**, 122 (1960); V. A. J. van Lint, J. Parez, D. Trueblood, and M. E. Wyatt, *Rev. Sci. Instrum.*, **36**, 521 (1965).
367. M. Hirsh, P. Eisner, J. Slevin, and G. Halpern, *Bull. Am. Phys. Soc.*, **11**, 495 (1966).
368. J. L. Pack and A. V. Phelps, *J. Chem. Phys.*, **45**, 4316 (1966).
369. C. S. Weller and M. A. Biondi, *Bull. Am. Phys. Soc.*, **11**, 495 (1966); *Phys. Rev.*, **172**, 198 (1968).
370. J. M. Warman and R. W. Fessenden, *J. Chem. Phys.*, **49**, 4718 (1968).
371. A. V. Phelps and R. E. Voshall, *J. Chem. Phys.*, **49**, 3246 (1968).
372. B. H. Mahan and E. C. Walker, *J. Chem. Phys.*, **47**, 3780 (1967).
373. J. L. Moruzzi and A. V. Phelps, *Bull. Am. Phys. Soc.*, **13**, 209 (1968).
374. L. M. Branscomb, in *Atomic and Molecular Processes*, edited by D. R. Bates. New York: Academic Press, 1962.
375. L. M. Branscomb, D. S. Burch, S. J. Smith, and S. Geltman, *Phys. Rev.*, **111**, 504 (1958).
376. D. S. Burch, S. J. Smith, and L. M. Branscomb, *Phys. Rev.*, **112**, 171 (1958); **114**, 1652 (1959).
377. L. M. Branscomb, *Phys. Rev.*, **148**, 11 (1966).
378. L. Frommhold, *Fortschr. Physik*, **12**, 597 (1964).
379. F. C. Fehsenfeld, D. L. Albritton, J. A. Burt, and H. I. Schiff, *Can. J. Chem.*, **47**, 173 (1969).
380. E. E. Ferguson, *Rev. Geophysics*, **5**, 305 (1967).
381. J. L. Moruzzi, J. W. Ekin, Jr., and A. V. Phelps, *J. Chem. Phys.*, **48**, 3070 (1968).
382. M. A. Biondi, *Ann. Geophys.*, **20**, 34 (1964); *Space Res.*, **7** (1967); *Can. J. Chem.*, **47**, 1711 (1969).
383. M. J. Seaton, *Monthly Notices Roy. Astron. Soc.*, **119**, 81 (1959).
384. D. R. Bates and A. Dalgarno, "Electronic Recombination." In *Atomic and Molecular Processes*, edited by D. R. Bates. New York: Academic Press, 1962.
385. R. G. Fowler and W. R. Atkinson, *Phys. Rev.*, **113**, 1268 (1959).
386. C. S. Weller and M. A. Biondi, *Bull. Am. Phys. Soc.*, **13**, 199 (1968); *Phys. Rev.*, **172**, 198 (1968).
387. R. C. Gunton and T. M. Shaw, *Phys. Rev.*, **140**, A756 (1965).
388. R. A. Young and G. St. John, *Phys. Rev.*, **152**, 25 (1966).
389. R. P. Stein, M. Schiebe, M. W. Syverson, T. M. Shaw, and R. C. Gunton, *Phys. Fluids*, **7**, 1641 (1964).

390. S. C. Lin and J. D. Tease, *Phys. Fluids*, **6**, 355 (1963).

391. M. H. Mentzoni, *J. Appl. Phys.*, **36**, 57 (1965).

392. W. H. Kasner and M. A. Biondi, *Bull. Am. Phys. Soc.*, **12**, 218 (1967); *Phys. Rev.*, **174**, 139 (1968).

393. F. J. Mehr and M. A. Biondi, *Bull. Am. Phys. Soc.*, **13**, 189 (1968).

394. W. H. Kasner and M. A. Biondi, *Phys. Rev.*, **137**, A317 (1965).

395. W. H. Kasner, *Phys. Rev.*, **164**, 194 (1967).

396. R. Hackam, *Planet. Space Sci.*, **13**, 667 (1965).

397. L. N. Wilson and E. W. Evans, *J. Chem. Phys.*, **46**, 859 (1967).

398. J. A. Green and T. M. Sugden, *Ninth Symposium on Combustion*, Pittsburgh: The Combustion Institute, 1963.

399. T. M. Donahue, *Can. J. Chem.*, **47**, 1721 (1969).

400. R. L. Wilkins, *J. Chem. Phys.*, **44**, 1884 (1966).

401. C. S. Warke, *Phys. Rev.*, **144**, 120 (1966).

402. J. N. Bradsley, *J. Phys.*, **B1**, 365 (1968).

403. J. J. Thomson, *Phil. Mag.* [6], **47**, 337 (1924).

404. G. L. Natason, *Zh. Tekhn. Fiz.*, **29**, 1373 (1959).

405. K. A. Brueckner, *J. Chem. Phys.*, **40**, 439 (1964).

406. P. J. Feibelman, *J. Chem. Phys.*, **42**, 2462 (1965).

407. D. R. Bates and R. J. Moffett, *Proc. Roy. Soc. (London)*, **A291**, 1 (1966).

408. I. S. Veselovskii, *J. Exptl. Theoret. Phys. USSR*, **52**, 1034 (1967); *Sov. Phys. JETP*, **25**, 687 (1967).

409. S. McGowan, *Can. J. Phys.*, **45**, 439 (1967).

410. B. H. Mahan and J. C. Person, *J. Chem. Phys.*, **40**, 392, 3683 (1964).

411. M. N. Hirsch, G. M. Halpern, and N. S. Wolf, *Bull. Am. Phys.*, *Soc.* **13**, 199 (1968).

412. C. W. Baulknight and M. H. Bortner, *Report No. AFCRL-64-142*, Air Force Cambridge Research Laboratories, Bedford, Mass., January 1964, unpublished.

413. W. Aberth, J. R. Peterson, D. C. Lorents, and C. J. Cook, *Phys. Rev. Lett.*, **20**, 979 (1968).

414. S. M. Trujillo, R. H. Neynaber, and E. W. Rothe, *Rev. Sci. Instr.*, **37**, 1655 (1966).

415. R. S. Narcisi, *Space Res.*, **7**, 186 (1967).

416. R. S. Narcisi, *Ann. Geophys.*, **22**, 224 (1966).

417. D. M. Hunten, and M. B. McElroy, *J. Geophys. Res.*, **73**, 2421 (1968).

418. F. C. Fehsenfeld and E. E. Ferguson, *J. Geophys. Res.*, **74**, 2217 (1969).

419. E. E. Ferguson and F. C. Fehsenfeld, *J. Geophys. Res.*, **74**, 5743 (1969).

420. B. R. Turner and J. A. Rutherford, *J. Geophys. Res.*, **73**, 6751 (1968).

421. W. L. Fite and J. A. Rutherford, *Discussions Faraday Soc.*, **37**, 192 (1964).

422. J. L. Pack and A. V. Phelps, *J. Chem. Phys.*, **45**, 4316 (1966).

423. R. A. Young, *Can. J. Chem.*, **47**, 1927 (1969).

424. K. Schofield, *Planetary Space Sci.*, **15**, 643 (1967).

425. F. D. Colegrove, F. S. Johnson, and N. B. Hanson, *J. Geophys. Res.*, **71**, 2227 (1966).

426. I. S. Gulledge, D. M. Packer, S. G. Tilford, and J. T. Vanderslice, *J. Geophys. Res.*, **73**, 5535 (1968).

427. A. L. Schmeltekopf, F. C. Fehsenfeld, G. I. Gilman, and E. E. Ferguson, *Planet. Space Sci.*, **15**, 401 (1967).

428. J. C. G. Walker, *Planet. Space Sci.*, **16**, 321 (1968).

429. L. Thomas and R. B. Norton, *J. Geophys. Res.*, **71**, 227 (1966).

430. W. F. J. Evans, D. M. Hunten, E. J. Llewellyn, and A. V. Jones, *J. Geophys. Res.*, **73**, 2885 (1968).

431. F. C. Fehsenfeld, D. L. Albritton, J. A. Burt, and H. I. Schiff, *Can. J. Chem.*, **47**, 1793 (1969).

432. R. M. Badger, A. C. Wright, and R. F. Whitlock, *J. Chem. Phys.*, **43**, 4345 (1965).
433. E. C. Zipf, *Can. J. Chem.*, **47**, 1863 (1969).
434. R. W. Nicholls, *Can. J. Chem.*, **47**, 1847 (1969).
435. D. E. Shemansky and N. P. Carleton, *J. Chem. Phys.*, **51**, 682 (1969).
436. J. E. Hesser, *J. Chem. Phys.*, **48**, 2519 (1968).
437. R. W. Nicholls, *Ann. Geophys.*, **20**, 144 (1964).
438. H. A. Bethe and E. E. Salpeter, *Handbuch der Physik*, **35**, 352 (1957).
439. G. M. Lawrence, *Bull. Am. Phys. Soc.*, **13**, 424 (1968).
440. M. Gaillard and J. E. Hessler, *Astrophys. J.*, **152**, 695 (1968).
441. R. D. Hudson and V. L. Carter, *J. Geophys. Res.*, **74**, 393 (1969).
442. F. Kaufman, *Ann. Geophys.*, **20**, 106 (1964); *Can. J. Chem.*, **47**, 1917 (1969).
443. M. Venugopalan and R. A. Jones, *Chemistry of Dissociated Water Vapor and Related Systems*. New York: Wiley, 1968.
444. A. N. Wright and C. A. Winkler, *Active Nitrogen*. New York: Academic Press, 1968.
445. H. I. Schiff, *Ann. Geophys.*, **20**, 86 (1964); *Can. J. Chem.*, **47**, 1903 (1969).
446. J. F. Noxon, *Space Sci. Rev.*, **8**, 92 (1968).
447. W. F. Evans, D. M. Hunten, E. J. Llewelyn, and A. Vallance-Jones, *J. Geophys. Res.*, **73**, 2885 (1968).
448. G. V. Karachevtsev and V. L. Tal'rose, this volume, Chapter 12.
449. J. C. Brandt and M. B. McElroy, eds., *The Atmospheres of Mars and Venus*. New York: Gordon and Breach, 1968.
450. M. B. McElroy, *J. Geophys. Res.*, **73**, 1513 (1968).
451. T. M. Donahue, *J. Atmospheric Sci.*, **25**, 568 (1968).
452. M. B. McElroy, *J. Atmospheric Sci.*, **25**, 574 (1968).
453. M. B. McElroy and D. F. Strobel, *J. Geophys. Res.*, **74**, 1118 (1969).
454. M. B. McElroy and D. M. Hunten, *J. Geophys. Res.*, **75**, 1188, 5989 (1970).
455. M. B. McElroy, *J. Geophys. Res.*, **74**, 29 (1969).
456. D. M. Hunten, *Can. J. Chem.*, **47**, 1875 (1969).
457. A. Dalgarno, *Rev. Mod. Phys.*, **39**, 858 (1967).
458. S. H. Gross and S. I. Rasool, *Icarus*, **3**, 311 (1964).
459. S. I. Rasool, S. H. Gross, and W. E. McGovern, *Space Sci. Rev.*, **5**, 566 (1966).
460. M. Shimizu, *Planet. Space Sci.*, **11**, 269 (1963).

CHAPTER TWENTY

Nuclear Reactions in Fully Ionized Plasmas at High Temperatures

G. LEHNER

I. INTRODUCTION

There are two types of nuclear energy. This is due to the fact that the binding energy per nucleon of the different nuclei has a maximum for iron. This is demonstrated by Fig. 1. It is thus possible to gain energy either by

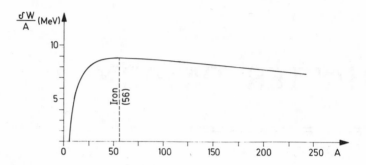

Figure 1 Binding energy per nucleon ($\delta W/A$) as a function of the atomic weight (A).

breaking heavy atoms into lighter ones ("fission") or by combining light ones to yield heavier ones ("fusion"). Both processes have been intensively investigated both for their scientific interest and their practical importance. Several authors have estimated our future energy needs and compared them with available energy resources. The figures quoted by different authors are not exactly the same since the extrapolations are always based on assumptions open to discussion. In any case, however, fossil fuels will be exhausted after a time of the order of several decades or perhaps 100 years or so. Furthermore, even complete exploitation of hydroelectricity will not be sufficient to fulfill mankind's ever increasing demand for energy. Another source of power is the enormous amount of radiation energy which the sun affords. Solar energy can, in principle, be exploited, but only by covering wide areas with sails to absorb it. "The conflict could be resolved if future billions lived (if you could call it that) in the shade of their power supplies," as Tuck says. All these problems of future energy will not be discussed here. Let it suffice to refer the reader to some of the literature on this subject (1–3). It is at any rate clear that we have to make use of nuclear energy either by fission or by fusion, or as Weinberg (4) puts it: we have to burn either the rocks or the sea. While the problem of fission energy has been solved already, the problem of fusion is still at a stage which does not yet allow safe predictions of its future. There are many power producing fission reactors all over the world, though some problems concerning breeder reactors, which would enable us "to burn the rocks," are as yet unsolved. On the other hand, many physicists all over the world are trying to find out what a fusion reactor should look like. The answer to this question is still unknown. There is, however, reason to believe that the answer will be found. The aim is certainly rewarding. We already know two devices relying on fusion energy. Just as fission energy was first used in atomic bombs, fusion energy was unfortunately first produced by the uncontrolled explosions of hydrogen bombs. The stars, which are much older and not man-made, are also sustained by fusion, at least during certain stages of their evolution. There are also stages during which they use gravitational energy. The sun, for instance, is at present in a fusion-driven phase. Thus, all the energy sources on which we depend themselves ultimately rely on fusion.

Fission reactions and fusion reactions show a very fundamental difference. Fission is triggered by slow neutrons penetrating into the nucleus which is to be broken up. The neutrons, electrically neutral, have no difficulty in doing so. Fusion reactions occur between two light nuclei. Take, for instance, the best known example, the d–d reaction which occurs in two branches with about equal probability:

$$d + d \rightarrow \begin{cases} \text{He}^3 + n + 3.27\text{MeV} \\ t + p + 4.04\text{MeV} \end{cases}$$

Some more reactions are listed in Table 1. The deuterons are separated from one another by their Coulomb wall. Tunnelling through it becomes sufficiently

TABLE 1
Some fusion reactions

Reaction	Energy, MeV
$d + d \rightarrow t + p$	4.04
$d + d \rightarrow \text{He}^3 + n$	3.27
$t + d \rightarrow \text{He}^4 + n$	17.58
$\text{He}^3 + d \rightarrow \text{He}^4 + p$	18.34
$t + t \rightarrow \text{He}^4 + 2n$	11.32
$t + \text{He}^3 \rightarrow \text{He}^4 + d$	14.31
$t + \text{He}^3 \rightarrow \text{He}^4 + p + n$	12.08
$\text{Li}^6 + d \rightarrow 2\text{He}^4$	22.4
$\text{Li}^7 + p \rightarrow 2\text{He}^4$	17.3
$\text{Li}^6 + n \rightarrow t + \text{He}^4$	4.79

probable only if the relative energy of the two particles is not too small. The cross-sections for fusion reactions are thus steep functions of the relative energy. This fact is the source of all the difficulties in fusion research. We do have enough deuterons to burn in a reactor. A certain fraction of all the hydrogen atoms in the sea are deuterons (one m³ sea water contains about 20 g of deuterium), that is, the sea provides us with an almost inexhaustible source of fuel. The problem is how to ignite it—how to produce sufficient relative energy among all the colliding deuterons to get so many reactions that the energy output is economically interesting. Another condition is that the apparatus should produce this energy in a controlled manner and not in an explosion like an H-bomb.

It can be shown that using accelerated beams of deuterons colliding with another beam of deuterons or with a target saturated with deuterons fails to meet our requirements (5). Accelerating a beam against a target allows the construction of useful neutron sources. Energy is not gained, however, but lost.

To our present knowledge, the only feasible method is to heat deuterium gas to very high temperatures so that the kinetic energies corresponding to this temperature may trigger the desired reaction to a sufficient degree. The temperatures necessary are formidable, however. The d–d reaction for instance requires about 10^9 °K. At such temperatures any matter takes the form of a fully ionized gas (plasma). It is also obvious that there are no material vessels to confine such a gas. Fortunately, the fact that all particles (deuterons and electrons) are electrically charged as a result of ionization makes it possible to confine them by walls made of magnetic fields. The Lorentz force thus produced bends the particles back into the region of confinement and prevents them from escaping. This looks quite simple, and when intensive fusion research started about 20 years ago physicists engaged in this field hoped to solve the problem within a relatively short time. It turned out, however, that it is extremely difficult to confine a plasma in a closed configuration. Unfortunately, plasmas tend to develop lots of instabilities which may destroy magnetohydrodynamic equilibrium configurations. They are of two different types. First, there are the "magnetohydrodynamic" or "macroscopic" instabilities, such as the instabilities of the Z-pinch, first discussed by Kruskal and Schwarzschild in 1954 (6). Their name derives from the fact that they can be described and discussed within the frame-work of macroscopic plasma theory, that is, by the hydrodynamic equations in conjunction with Maxwell's equations to include the coupling with electrodynamic phenomena. Secondly, there are "microinstabilities," which are not contained in the macroscopic theory. Their appearance depends strongly on the detailed microscopic properties of the plasma as described by its distribution function, which has to be treated by an appropriate kinetic theory. The interaction between particles in a plasma (Coulomb interaction) is of long range and this has two consequences. Firstly, it makes the kinetic theory much more involved than it is for short-range forces. Secondly, it leads to new effects (sometimes called collective effects or "cooperative phenomena"). Thus, an electrostatic wave may be either damped ("Landau damping") or excited to higher and higher amplitudes ("microinstability"), depending on certain peculiarities of the distribution function. In the latter case, one may get a "turbulent" plasma with highly increased fluctuating fields causing enhanced diffusion of the plasma across the magnetic field, that is, confinement may be destroyed within too short a time. These then are the reasons, expressed in extremely simplified terms, why we have not yet succeeded in building a fusion reactor.

The purpose here is not to give a survey of fusion research. This is a wide field that would exceed the scope of the present chapter. We shall just discuss a limited number of experiments in which a plasma actually involving nuclear reactions is produced, in which the plasma is both sufficiently hot and dense (a precise definition of the term "sufficiently" being given later). We thus discuss nuclear reactions in high temperature plasmas. The results described should, however, be viewed in terms of the problems and difficulties mentioned above. The existence of d–d reactions in a plasma is demonstrated experimentally by the neutrons emitted from the plasma region. In the early days of fusion research 10–15 years ago, we were eagerly looking for neutrons because it was felt that any increase of neutron output would take us a step closer to the desired reactor. It is now clear that these experiments are certainly very important. They show that plasmas can really be heated to very high temperatures by the appropriate methods. They also show that magnetohydrodynamic theory can be applied since instabilities, for instance, can be observed in accordance with theoretical predictions. It is not sufficient, however, just to scale up these experiments to get a reactor. It is clear that a better basic understanding of the plasma state is necessary for further progress. Accurate predictions are thus impossible at the present stage. It is the author's opinion that the difficulties can be overcome and that the problem of fusion will finally be solved, but perhaps not very soon. The results discussed in the following sections, however, are not chosen for their relevance to a final fusion reactor; they are a piece of plasma physics which is interesting in itself. In any case, nobody knows as yet which type of experiment comes closest to a future reactor.

Stars are in a happier position—they do not have difficulties because they have plenty of space and may therefore rely on gravitational confinement. They also make use of reactions quite different from those in laboratory plasmas. This is especially true of their later stages, when they have already burnt the very light elements.

II. NUCLEAR REACTIONS IN LABORATORY PLASMAS

A plasma confined by magnetic fields is never in a state of thermodynamic equilibrium. Collisions of any type (collisions in the normal sense of the word or collective effects as mentioned in the introduction) cause a diffusion of the plasma and magnetic field into one another so that the final equilibrium state always constitutes a spatially homogeneous plasma. This may, however, take so long that the plasma can relax to local thermal equilibrium while still confined. Depending on how the plasma is produced, its initial velocity distribution may be far from Maxwellian and then gradually relax to a Maxwellian distribution of its velocities. The terms relaxation and equilibrium are used in this restricted sense. We shall discuss the neutron emission of thermal (Maxwellian) plasmas as well as that of plasmas not yet in equilibrium.

Nuclear reactions are almost exclusively observed in connection with deuterium plasmas, and the d-d reaction leads to neutron emission which is then investigated. The other branch of the reaction only leads to charged particles which cannot freely leave the plasma volume, hence they are only very seldom observed. Sometimes the emission of neutrons is just considered as an indication that d-d reaction did occur, this being qualitative proof that the plasma was hot. One can go a step further and evaluate the plasma temperature from the neutron output. This, however, is sometimes a dangerous procedure. The plasma may or may not be Maxwellian, and the neutron output depends on the velocity distribution of the plasma. On the other hand, more detailed investigation of the emitted neutrons may serve as a valuable tool in obtaining information about the emitting plasma. Neutron measurements may therefore be used as an additional plasma diagnostic technique.

A. Neutrons from Hot Deuterium Plasmas

The neutrons emitted by hot deuterium plasmas carry with them a lot of information on the velocity distribution of the deuterons. After their emission the neutrons may undergo interactions with the surroundings of the plasma. It is sometimes very difficult to take these into account and it may thus be very difficult in many cases to extract such information from the observations. Being interested in general conclusions, we do not discuss these effects, which are different from experiment to experiment. We are looking at the properties of the neutron radiation as emitted by the plasma itself without further disturbing interactions. A more detailed account of what follows has been given elsewhere by Lehner (7).

The two d-d reactions

$$d + d \longrightarrow n + \text{He}^3 + 3.27 \text{ MeV} \qquad [1]$$

$$d + d \longrightarrow p + \text{H}^3 + 4.04 \text{ MeV} \qquad [2]$$

are about equally probable. Some values of the branching ratio and cross-sections as a function of energy have been given by Tuck (8). According to Booth (9) the neutron reaction [1] shows relatively strong anisotropy. This point is somewhat controversial. It seems justified, however, to adopt the values given by the previously mentioned authors. Thus the differential cross-section is

$$\sigma(g, \theta) = A(g)[1 + B(g)\cos^2 \theta] \qquad [3]$$

with g being the modulus of the relative velocity g and θ the angle between g and the direction of neutron emission in the centre-of-mass system. According to Booth (9) we have

$$B(g) = 0.31 + 0.0058 \, E_d \qquad [4]$$

for the reaction [1] and

$$B(g) = 0.13 + 0.0047 \, E_d \qquad [5]$$

for the reaction [2]. E_d is the relative energy in keV (m the mass of the deuteron)

$$E_d = \tfrac{1}{2}mg^2 \qquad [6]$$

The total cross-section follows from eq. [3] by integration. It is

$$\sigma(g) = 4\pi A(g)\left[1 + \frac{1}{3} B(g)\right] \qquad [7]$$

$\sigma(g)$ may be taken, for instance, in the form given by Goldman (10), namely

$$\sigma(g) = \sigma^*(g^*) = \frac{1.79 \times 10^{-23}}{g^{*2}} \exp\left(-\frac{14.578}{g^*}\right) \qquad [8]$$

$$\sigma(g) = \sigma^*(g^*) = 10^{-27} \exp(-9.082 + 8.9606g^* - 2.59541g^{*2}$$
$$+ 0.386918g^{*3} - 0.0287342g^{*4} + 0.00084047g^{*5}) \qquad [9]$$

where eq. [8] is to be used for relative energies below 80 keV and eq. [9] for energies between 80keV and 1000 keV. g^* is the relative velocity measured in units of 10^8 cm sec^{-1}.

Consider now a deuterium plasma with an arbitrary velocity distribution $f(\mathbf{u})$ of the deuterons. $f(\mathbf{u})$ is not necessarily a Maxwellian. Nothing is said about the electrons. They may have (and in many plasmas they actually do) a distribution quite different from the ions. Let the ion distribution be normalized to unity:

$$\int f(\mathbf{u}) \, d\mathbf{u} = 1 \qquad [10]$$

The number of reactions among deuterons in volume elements $d\mathbf{u}_1$ and $d\mathbf{u}_2$ (in velocity space) around $\mathbf{u}_1$ and $\mathbf{u}_2$ is

$$dR = \frac{n^2}{2} f(\mathbf{u}_1)f(\mathbf{u}_2)g\sigma(g) \, d\mathbf{u}_1 \, d\mathbf{u}_2 \qquad [11]$$

where n is the density of the deuterons. We have to transform to relative and centre-of-mass velocities:

$$\mathbf{u}_{1,2} = \mathbf{s} \pm \frac{1}{2}\mathbf{g} \tag{12}$$

Thus we can write the neutron output per unit volume and unit time in its usual form

$$R = \frac{n^2}{2}\langle g\sigma(g)\rangle \tag{13}$$

where the mean value

$$\langle g\sigma(g)\rangle = \iint f\left(\mathbf{s} + \frac{1}{2}\mathbf{g}\right)f\left(\mathbf{s} - \frac{1}{2}\mathbf{g}\right)g\sigma(g)\,d\mathbf{g}\,d\mathbf{s} \tag{14}$$

depends on the distribution f considered.

1. **Total Neutron Output.** We shall now apply eq. [14] to several distribution functions which may serve as examples.

A distribution often used in plasma physics is the so-called elliptic one, that is, a pseudo-Maxwellian distribution with different perpendicular and parallel temperatures $(T_\perp, T_\parallel)$. We shall in later sections use it in connection with pinch plasmas. In this case

$$f(\mathbf{u}) = \frac{\beta_\perp \beta_\parallel^{1/2}}{\pi^{3/2}}\exp\left(-\beta_\perp u_\perp^2 + \beta_\parallel u_\parallel^2\right) \tag{15}$$

where

$$\beta_\perp = \frac{m}{2kT_\perp} \qquad \beta_\parallel = \frac{m}{2kT_\parallel} \tag{16}$$

It is a simple but remarkable property of such a distribution that the product $f(\mathbf{u}_1)\cdot f(\mathbf{u}_2)$ separates also if written in terms of relative and center-of-mass velocities:

$$f(\mathbf{u}_1)\cdot f(\mathbf{u}_2) = S(\mathbf{s})\cdot G(\mathbf{g}) \tag{17}$$

where

$$S(\mathbf{s}) = \left(\frac{2}{\pi}\right)^{3/2}\beta_\perp \beta_\parallel^{1/2}\exp\left[-2(\beta_\perp s_\perp^2 + \beta_\parallel s_\parallel^2)\right] \tag{18}$$

and

$$G(\mathbf{g}) = \frac{\beta_\perp \beta_\parallel^{1/2}}{(2\pi)^{3/2}}\exp\left[-\frac{1}{2}(\beta_\perp g_\perp^2 + \beta_\parallel g_\parallel^2)\right] \tag{19}$$

S may be described as a Maxwellian for particles of mass $2m$ (the total mass) and G as a Maxwellian for particles of mass $m/2$ (which is actually the reduced mass). Both S and G are normalized to unity. Thus the integral [14] simplifies considerably and is now

$$\langle g\sigma \rangle = \frac{\beta_\perp \beta_\parallel^{1/2}}{(2\pi)^{3/2}} \int g\sigma(g) \exp \left[-\frac{1}{2} (g_\perp^2 \beta_\perp + g_\parallel^2 \beta_\parallel) \right] d\mathbf{g}$$

$$= \beta_\perp \left(\frac{\beta_\parallel}{\beta_\parallel - \beta_\perp} \right)^{1/2} \int_0^\infty g^2 \sigma(g) \exp \left(-\frac{1}{2} \beta_\perp g^2 \right) \operatorname{erf} \left(g \sqrt{\frac{\beta_\parallel - \beta_\perp}{2}} \right) dg$$

$$= \beta_\perp \left(\frac{\beta_\parallel}{\beta_\perp - \beta_\parallel} \right)^{1/2} \int_0^\infty g^2 \sigma(g) \exp \left(-\frac{1}{2} \beta_\perp g^2 \right) \operatorname{erf} \left(g \sqrt{\frac{\beta_\perp - \beta_\parallel}{2}} \right) dg$$

[20]

Here

$$\operatorname{erf}(x) = \frac{2}{\sqrt{\pi}} \int_0^x e^{-z^2} dZ \qquad [21]$$

and

$$\operatorname{erf} i(x) = -i \operatorname{erf}(ix) \qquad [22]$$

These integrals may be evaluated numerically. Special cases are:

(a)   the normal three-dimensional Maxwellian $(\beta_\perp = \beta_\parallel = \beta)$, which yields

$$\langle g\sigma \rangle_{3\text{max}} = \left(\frac{2}{\pi} \right)^{1/2} \beta^{-3/2} \int_0^\infty g^3 \sigma(g) \exp \left[-\frac{1}{2} \beta g^2 \right] dg \qquad [23]$$

(b)   the two-dimensional Maxwellian $(\beta_\parallel \to \infty)$

$$\langle g\sigma \rangle_{2\text{max}} = \beta_\perp \int_0^\infty g^2 \sigma(g) \exp \left[-\frac{1}{2} \beta_\perp g^2 \right] dg \qquad [24]$$

(c)   the one-dimensional Maxwellian $(\beta_\perp \to \infty)$

$$\langle g\sigma \rangle_{1\text{max}} = \left(\frac{2\beta_\parallel}{\pi} \right)^{1/2} \int_0^\infty g\sigma(g) \exp \left[-\frac{1}{2} \beta_\parallel g^2 \right] dg \qquad [25]$$

Monoenergetic distributions are also sometimes used. They are not very realistic usually. There are situations, however, for which they are useful approximations. Starting from the three-dimensional monoenergetic distribution

$$f(\mathbf{u}) = \frac{\delta(u^2 - u_0^2)}{2\pi u_0} \qquad [26]$$

we get

$$\langle g\sigma \rangle_{3 \text{ mono}} = \frac{1}{2\pi u_0^2} \int_0^{2u_0} g^2 \sigma(g) \, dg \qquad [27]$$

while the two-dimensional monoenergetic distribution

$$f(\mathbf{u}) = \frac{\delta(u_\perp^2 - u_0^2) \, \delta(u_\|)}{2\pi u_0} \qquad [28]$$

yields

$$\langle g\sigma \rangle_{2 \text{ mono}} = \frac{2}{\pi} \int_0^{2u_0} \frac{g\sigma(g)}{\sqrt{4u_0^2 - g^2}} \, dg \qquad [29]$$

We may add the trivial one-dimensional monoenergetic case, which gives

$$\langle g\sigma \rangle_{1 \text{ mono}} = u_0 \sigma(2u_0) \qquad [30]$$

Figures 2, 3, and 4 show the numerical results for the distributions discussed.

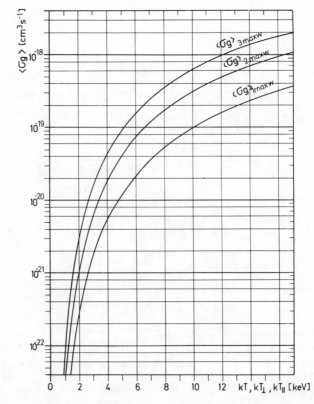

Figure 2 Neutron output for plasmas with 3, 2, and 1-dimensional Maxwellians as functions of T, $T_\perp$, $T_\|$, respectively.

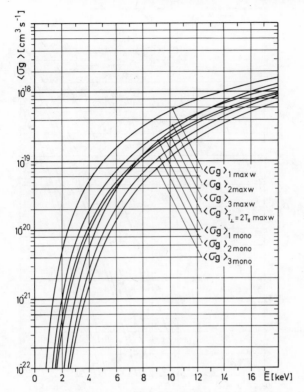

Figure 3 Neutron output for several velocity distributions as a function of mean deuteron energy $\bar{E}$. $\bar{E} = \dfrac{m}{2} u_0^2$ for monoenergetic distributions and $\bar{E} = kT_\perp + \frac{1}{2}kT_\parallel$ for elliptic ones.

Figure 2 shows $\langle g\sigma \rangle_{3,\,21\max}$ as a function of kT, $kT_\perp$, $kT_\parallel$ in keV. Figures 3 and 4 also contain other cases. The variable used is the mean energy $\bar{E}$ because temperatures are not appropriate for monoenergetic distributions. For pseudo-Maxwellians

$$\bar{E} = kT_\perp + \frac{1}{3}kT_\parallel \qquad\qquad [31]$$

Tuck and Hesselberg-Jensen (8,11) have computed $\langle \sigma g \rangle_{3\max}$ and Goldman (10,12) has computed both $\langle \sigma g \rangle_{3\max}$ and $\langle \sigma g \rangle_{3\mono}$, the agreement with our results as contained in Figs. 2, 3, and 4 being good.

With the help of these results it is possible to get some information on the plasma by measuring the total number of neutrons. To make use of eq. [13], however, one has to know the volume and the density of the plasma, too. Yet, the main problem is to know which distribution is to be used. If we know that the distribution is Maxwellian, we can evaluate the temperature; if it is

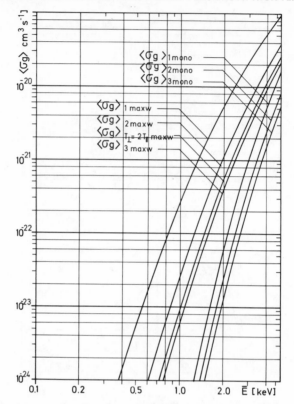

Figure 4   As Figure 3, but for small mean energies $\bar{E}$.

monoenergetic, we get the energy $E = \frac{1}{2}mu_0^2$. But the correct distribution can be found just by looking at the energy spectrum of the neutrons, which we discuss in the following subsection.

2. ***Neutron Energy Spectrum.***   Taking into account the energy spectrum of the neutrons may appreciably increase our knowledge of the plasma, at least in principle. Experimentally, there are difficulties in obtaining the necessary precision, both because the neutrons are subject to interactions after the emission by the plasma and because it is often not possible to get enough events to make the statistics sufficiently reliable.

Let us return to eq. [14] again. We now want to perform the integration, but with the side condition that the energy of the neutron in the laboratory system should have a given value. Such a condition is usually and most easily taken into account by the use of δ-functions, which are clever enough to do the job for us. If we approximate the neutron mass by half the deuteron mass m, the energy of the neutron in the center-of-mass system is

$$E_s = \frac{3}{4}\left(Q + \frac{m}{4}g^2\right) = \frac{m}{4}\,\mathbf{w}^2 \qquad [32]$$

Q is the energy of the reaction (3.27 MeV) and $\mathbf{w}$ the center-of-mass velocity of the neutron. In the laboratory system its velocity is

$$\mathbf{v} = \mathbf{w} + \mathbf{s} \qquad [33]$$

Equation [14] can then be shown to yield the energy spectrum in the following form:

$$\frac{d^2R}{d\Omega\,dE_n} = \frac{2n^2v}{m}\iint f\left(\mathbf{v} - \mathbf{w} + \frac{1}{2}\mathbf{g}\right)f\left(\mathbf{v} - \mathbf{w} - \frac{1}{2}\mathbf{g}\right)$$

$$\times g\sigma(g,\theta)\,\frac{\delta\left(\mathbf{w}^2 - \dfrac{4E_s}{m}\right)}{\sqrt{\dfrac{4E_s}{m}}}\,d\mathbf{w}\,d\mathbf{g} \qquad [34]$$

$d\Omega$ is the element of solid angle and E_n is the neutron energy in the laboratory system,

$$E_n = \frac{1}{4}mv^2 \qquad [35]$$

and m is the deuteron mass. Actually eq. [34] is written in an incomplete form. The limits of integration are not given. They have to be handled with some care in each individual case. With this provision (34) can be integrated numerically. More details are given in Ref. 7. If the distribution f is isotropic the neutron spectrum is also anisotropic.

Let us now discuss some examples. Let us take first the normal isotropic three-dimensional Maxwellian. Numerical results are plotted in Fig. 5. The spectra look very much like Gaussian profiles. Indeed an approximate treatment of our integral shows that for $kT \ll Q$

$$\frac{dR}{dE_n} \approx \frac{n^2}{mv_0}\left(\frac{2\beta}{\pi}\right)^{1/2}\langle g\sigma\rangle_{3\,\mathrm{max}}\exp\left[-2\beta(v - v_0)^2\right] \qquad [36]$$

where

$$v_0 = \sqrt{\frac{3Q}{m}} \qquad [37]$$

is the velocity of the neutron if two deuterons at rest react with one another. Thus the half-width of the " neutron line " is

$$\Delta E_n \approx \sqrt{3\ln2}\,\sqrt{QkT} \qquad [38]$$

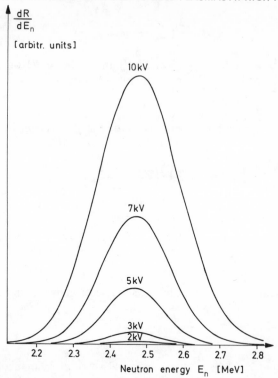

Figure 5   Neutron energy spectra for three-dimensional Maxwellian deuteron plasmas with different temperatures from 2 to 10 keV.

Measuring both E_n and kT in keV we have

$$\Delta E_n \approx 82.5\sqrt{kT} \qquad [39]$$

This is in rather good agreement with the numerical values given in Table 2. Besides the increasing half-width, the center of the line is shifted to higher

TABLE 2

Numerically computed halfwidths of neutron spectra (for Maxwellian deuterons)

kT, keV	1	2	3	5	7	10	15	20	50
ΔE_n, keV	82.7	117	143	186	220	264	324	376	609

energies with increasing temperature. This effect is relatively small, however, and is not discussed here. The interested reader is again referred to Ref. 7.

Next we consider the two-dimensional Maxwellian

$$f(\mathbf{u}) = \frac{\beta_\perp}{\pi} \exp\left(-\beta_\perp u_\perp^2\right) \delta(u_\parallel) \qquad [40]$$

In this case the spectrum depends on the angle of observation. Qualitatively, one can say that the width of the spectrum decreases with decreasing angle of observation. In the perpendicular direction the spectrum is practically the same as for the three-dimensional Maxwellian discussed. If the angle with the axis (α) decreases, the spectrum remains approximately Gaussian and its width goes like $\sin \alpha$ as long as α is not too small. This is demonstrated in Figs. 6 and 7 and by Table 3. It is seen that in the parallel direction ($\alpha = 0°$) the spectrum is no longer Gaussian and not even symmetric.

In the case of a general elliptic distribution the width of the spectrum may be shown to be approximately

$$\Delta E_n \approx \sqrt{Q(kT_\perp \sin^2 \alpha + kT_\parallel \cos^2 \alpha)} \qquad [41]$$

if observed at the angle α (provided that α is not too small as before). For monoenergetic distributions the spectra are quite different.

The three-dimensional monoenergetic case is represented by Fig. 8 and Table 4 and the two-dimensional case by Fig. 9. In the three-dimensional case

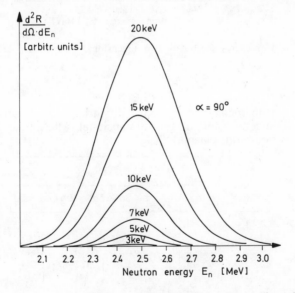

Figure 6 Neutron energy spectra for two dimensional Maxwellians. Perpendicular temperatures from 3 to 20 keV. Angle of observation $\alpha = 90°$.

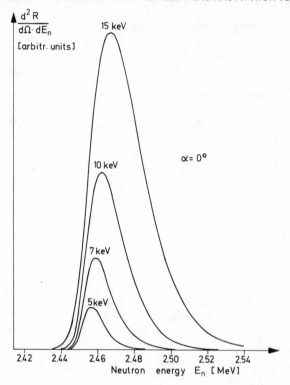

Figure 7 Neutron energy spectra for two dimensional Maxwellians. Angle of observation $\alpha = 0°$.

TABLE 3

Numerically computed halfwidths of neutron spectra (for a two-dimensional Maxwellian deuteron plasma)

kT, keV	ΔE_n, keV			
	$\alpha = 0°$	$\alpha = 30°$	$\alpha = 60°$	$\alpha = 90°$
1	3.38	41.4	71.5	82.5
2	6.55	58.8	101	117
3	8.90	72.2	124	143
5	13.5	93.7	161	184
7	17.9	111	191	216
10	24.9	134	229	264
15	34.1	165	281	324
20	42.8	192	326	376

TABLE 4

Halfwidths for the spectra of Fig. 8

$\frac{1}{2}m\,u_0^2$, keV	3	4.5	7.5	10.5	15
ΔE_n, keV	43	57	82	105	135

the spectrum lies between certain maximum and minimum energies. Expressed in terms of neutron velocities, the limits are

$$v = \sqrt{\frac{3Q}{m}} \pm u_0 \qquad [42]$$

The maximum output occurs at

$$v = \sqrt{\frac{3Q}{m} + 3u_0^2} \qquad [43]$$

At this maximum the derivative of the spectrum makes a jump while the spectrum itself stays continuous.

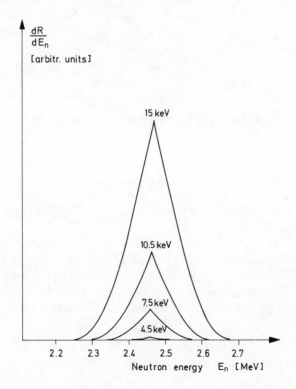

Figure 8   Neutron energy spectra for three-dimensional monoenergetic deuteron plasmas.

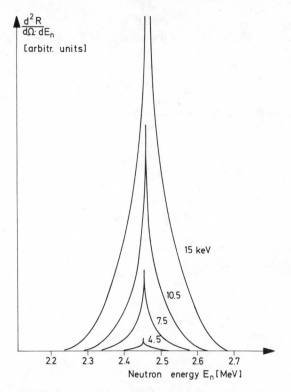

Figure 9 Neutron energy spectra for two-dimensional monoenergetic deuteron plasmas. Angle of observation $\alpha = 90°$.

In the two-dimensional case the above statements [especially eqs. (42) and (43)] remain true for the perpendicular spectrum, except that the spectrum diverges at the maximum (but remains integrable as it has to). Seen from an angle α, the spectrum becomes smaller approximately like $\sin \alpha$, again if α is not too small.

The cases discussed up to now refer to plasmas at rest, that is, the plasmas do not have a directed velocity. If there is also an ordered motion, the neutron lines are shifted to higher or lower energies, depending on the direction of observation. The energy shift is easily calculated and need not be discussed right now. This point will be taken up again in connection with experiments described later.

3. *Neutron Flux.* The neutron flux of an anisotropic plasma is anisotropic itself. There are two different reasons for this. First, the anisotropy of the plasma causes anisotropy of the flux by the transition from the center-of-mass system to the laboratory system even if the reaction is isotropic. If $kT \ll$

Q, an assumption which is always fulfilled for plasmas produced hitherto, this is an extremely small effect which can be neglected. Second, the anisotropy of the cross-section causes anisotropy of the neutron flux already in the center-of-mass system and, consequently, almost the same anisotropy in the laboratory system (on the given assumption).

For a two-dimensional Maxwellian it is thus found that the flux in the direction α is larger than the flux in the parallel direction by a factor

$$V_\alpha \approx 1 + (0.155 + 0.038(kT_\perp)^{2/3}) \sin^2 \alpha \qquad [44]$$

if kT is given in keV. Numerical results for $\alpha = 90°$ that agree well with this approximate formula are shown in Fig. 10 (the curve labelled by $T_\parallel = 0$).

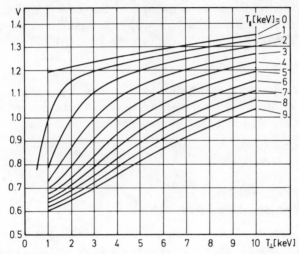

Figure 10   Ratio of neutron flux side-on to neutron flux, end-on as a function of $T_\perp$ and $T_\parallel$ (elliptic distributions).

Figure 10 also contains numerical results for a variety of elliptic distributions.

In the case of a two-dimensional monoenergetic distribution the approximate ratio V_α is

$$V_\alpha \approx 1 + \left(0.155 + 0.0116\frac{mu_0^2}{2}\right) \sin^2 \alpha \qquad [45]$$

where the deuteron energy $mu_0/2$ is to be given in keV. Some numerical values are presented in Table 5.

If a plasma has a macroscopic velocity, the flux depends on the direction. Obviously, it has a maximum value in the forward direction and a minimum value in the backward direction. The observation of this difference is another possibility of demonstrating ordered motion besides the line shift mentioned

TABLE 5

Ratio of neutron flux end-on to neutron flux side-on for two-dimensional monoenergetic deuteron plasmas

$\dfrac{m\,u_0^2}{2}$, keV	1	3	5	7	10
V, 90°	1.17	1.19	1.21	1.23	1.26

above. Detailed discussion is not necessary. The flux anisotropy simply follows from the usual relations connecting the differential cross sections in the center-of-mass and laboratory systems.

A more detailed discussion of the neutron flux anisotropy for anisotropic high temperature plasmas can be found in a report by Lehner and Pohl (*IPP* 1/103, 1969).

B. Experiments

The literature on experiments in which the plasma has been demonstrated to produce neutrons from *d–d* reactions is vast. All these experiments, however, can be classed under the following headings.

1.   Z-pinches (linear or toroidal)
2.   Plasma focuses
3.   θ-pinches
4.   Mirror magnetic wells
5.   Laser produced plasmas

1.   *The Z-pinch.* The Z-pinch provides us with one of the simplest examples of magnetohydrodynamic equilibria. In general such an equilibrium is described by the following equation:

$$\text{grad}\,p = \mathbf{j} \times \mathbf{B} \qquad [46]$$

where p is the plasma pressure, $\mathbf{j}$ the current density and $\mathbf{B}$ the magnetic field. We have to take into account Maxwell's equations as well (electromagnetic units are used throughout)

$$\text{div}\,\mathbf{B} = 0 \qquad \text{rot}\,\mathbf{B} = 4\Pi\mathbf{j} \qquad [47]$$

In the Z-pinch the plasma is confined by the azimuthal magnetic field, which in turn is produced by a longitudinal current in the plasma. Neglecting end effects (considering the pinch as infinitely long), assuming rotational symmetry and no Z-dependence, we get from the above equations

$$4\pi\,\frac{dp(r)}{dr} + \frac{1}{2}\frac{d}{dr}\,B_\varphi^2(r) + \frac{1}{r}\,B_\varphi^2(r) = 0 \qquad [48]$$

Thus $p(r)$ can be computed from $B_\varphi(r)$ and vice versa. If the plasma is considered as an ideal gas (this is a very good approximation at sufficiently low densities), we have

$$p = nkT \qquad [49]$$

In that case we can from our equations derive a relation between the total number of particles N and the total current I through the plasma, the Bennett relation (13)

$$2NkT = I^2 \qquad N = N_i + N_e \qquad [50]$$

where N_i and N_e are the total numbers of ions and electrons per unit length, respectively. Equation [50] is correct for any $p(r)$. A proof is given by Fünfer (14).

Equation [48] may be called the equation of a diffuse pinch (Fig. 11). Very

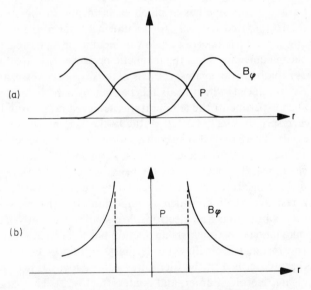

Figure 11 Diffuse (a) and sharp (b) Z-pinch.

often the pinch is viewed in a simplified manner. It is assumed that the plasma and field regions are completely separated by an infinitely thin (sharp) surface which carries the surface current producing the confining field. In this case we are left with the first two terms in eq. [48] (if δ is the thickness of the surface sheath, they diverge like δ^{-1}, and so they dominate if $\delta \to 0$). The equilibrium is described by

$$p = \begin{cases} p_0 & \text{for } 0 < r < r_0 \\ 0 & \text{for } r_0 < r < \infty \end{cases}$$

$$B_\varphi = \begin{cases} 0 & \text{for } 0 < r < r_0 \\ B_{\varphi 0} \dfrac{r_0}{r} & \text{for } r_0 < r < \infty \end{cases} \qquad [51]$$

$$p_0 = \frac{B_{\varphi 0}^2}{8\pi}$$

It is a general feature of magnetohydrodynamics that at a surface of discontinuity the equilibrium can simply be described in terms of the so-called magnetic pressure $B^2/8\pi$. For continuous equilibria this is only true if the magnetic lines of force have no curvature, while in general one gets an equation like [48] containing curvature terms (B_φ^2/r).

Thus far we have described the stationary Z-pinch equilibrium. This, however, is not exactly what one has in pinch experiments. In these experiments the magnetic field is used not only for confinement but also for heating the plasma. Using capacitor banks of very low inductance it is possible to produce fast rising plasma currents. Thus the magnetic pressure rises equally fast, and the plasma is rapidly driven against the axis of the discharge vessel and a radial shock wave is produced, which heats the plasma to a high temperature. In typical Z-pinch experiments the temperatures achieved range from 100 to 1000 eV (1 eV corresponds to 11,600°K). Actually the heating is not due to the shock wave only. There may also be contributions from adiabatic heating and, especially at the lower initial temperatures, from resistive (ohmic) heating. Owing to the large difference in mass the heating mechanism is very different for ions and electrons. Ions are mainly heated by the shock wave and are little affected by resistive heating, which is important for electrons. Adiabatic heating concerns both ions and electrons. We shall not go into details here.

In discussing pinch experiments a distinction has to be made between linear Z-pinches and toroidal Z-pinches. Let us start with linear devices. Many of these have been described in the literature: Andrianov, Curran, Komelkov, Mather, Colgate, Herold, Fünfer, and Anderson (15–23). The papers quoted represent only a small fraction of the available literature.

A typical arrangement is shown in Fig. 12. When the discharge is switched on (by spark gaps usually) the current rises fast $((dJ/dt)_{t=0} \approx 10^{11}$ to 10^{12} amp sec^{-1}), reaching values from 10^5 to 10^6 amp after a quarter-cycle of several microseconds. (A typical current trace is given in Fig. 13a) It shows characteristic kinks at early times. They correspond to minima of the pinch radius because these are related to the maxima of the inductance of the total discharge circuit. Thus the pinch equilibrium is dynamic in the initial phases,

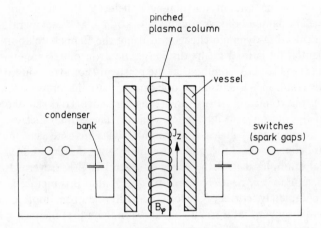

Figure 12 Schematic diagram of a Z-pinch discharge.

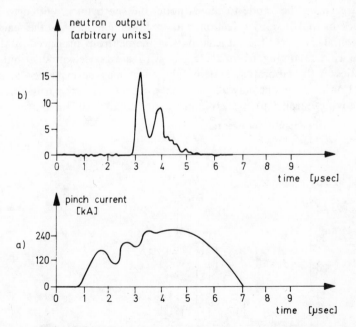

Figure 13 Typical traces of (a) current and (b) neutron pulse of a linear Z-pinch without stabilizing B_z-field (21).

that is, the pinch column oscillates radially due to the kinetic energy of the oscillating mass of the plasma and the potential energy stored both in the compressed plasma and in the magnetic field. With increasing time the oscillations are damped out. A rough guess at the plasma temperature can be made by neglecting dynamic effects and using the Bennett relation equation [50]. If deuterium is used in the discharge, neutron pulses are emitted from the plasma (Fig. 13b). Assuming that the plasma is homogeneous and that its velocity distribution is Maxwellian, one can evaluate the temperature from the neutron output (typically 10^5–10^7 neutrons per shot). To do so one needs the volume of the plasma and its particle density. These quantities can be measured by several means, at least approximately. Thus one gets the quantity $\langle g\sigma(g)\rangle$ as defined by eq. [13], and Fig. 2 finally gives the required temperature. For typical examples it is of the order of several 10^6 °K (several 100 eV).

This all sounds very neat. The only trouble is that this picture is not, or at least not completely, correct. On looking at the neutrons more closely, it is annoying to discover that the neutron emission from the pinch is not isotropic. This has been realized by several authors: Andrianov, Curran, Komelkov, Mather, Colgate, Fünfer, and Anderson (15–19,21,23) who measured the neutron energy spectra usually by means of nuclear plates. The result was that the spectra depend on the direction of observation. Relative to the axis of the discharge from the anode to the cathode, the spectrum is shifted to higher energies in the forward direction and to lower energies in the backward direction. This shows that at least part of the neutrons produced by the discharge is not coming from deuterons with a Maxwellian distribution of velocities in the laboratory system. The effect may be explained in several ways. For instance, one may imagine that the deuterons are partly accelerated and moving parallel to the axis and finally collide with deuterons at rest.

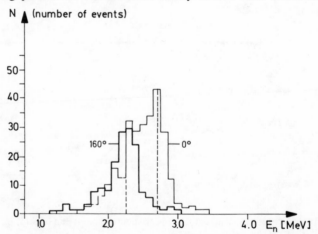

Figure 14 Energy spectra of neutrons from a Z-pinch for two directions (21).

Another possibility is that all the deuterons move parallel to the axis. Their velocity distribution could, for instance, be a shifted Maxwellian. An example discussed by Fünfer (21) is shown in Fig. 14. The unshifted maximum should appear at about 2.45 MeV. Instead, the forward maximum is at about 2.7 MeV, the backward maximum at about 2.26 MeV. If collisions between particles in motion and particles at rest are assumed, this shift would correspond to about 40 keV energy of the moving particles.

This is a disappointing feature of the Z-pinch. But what is the reason? A possible explanation has been given by Anderson (23). It is connected with the instabilities of the Z-pinch equilibrium, which we shall now discuss.

As in "classical" hydrodynamics, where several types of instabilities are well known (Kelvin-Helmholtz instabilities, Rayleigh-Taylor instabilities, etc.), there are also magnetohydrodynamic instabilities, which tend to destroy an equilibrium configuration if it is not stable. In general, the problem of magnetohydrodynamic instabilities is mathematically very involved. For toroidal configurations, for example, the equilibria themselves are usually only approximately known, because eqs. [46] and [47] are difficult to solve except for degenerate geometries of high symmetry. To get information about instabilities one considers small perturbations of a given equilibrium configuration (so small that the equations can be linearized with respect to the perturbations) and calculates a dispersion formula, which allows a distinction to be made between stable and unstable perturbing modes. The Z-pinch is one of the few examples where such a calculation can really be performed without formidable mathematical difficulties. This was first done by Kruskal (6). Many papers on this subject followed: Shafranov, Tayler, Kruskal, Rosenbluth, Braginsky, and Suydam (24–30). In most of them the pinch was assumed to be bounded by a sharp surface as already discussed above, though this is really not a very satisfactory procedure. As Rosenbluth and Newcomb (31,32) have shown, one has in principle to start from a diffuse pinch because the detailed properties of a sharp pinch depend on the structure of the surface sheath even if its thickness becomes smaller and smaller and finally approaches zero. For our present purposes, however, it is sufficient to discuss some features of the simple sharp pinch instabilities. For reasons which will become apparent during the following discussion, we consider an equilibrium which is somewhat more general than the one considered above, eq. [51], that is, we take into account superimposed longitudinal magnetic fields in the plasma (B_{zp}) and in the vacuum region (B_{zv}). The equilibrium equation is then

$$8\pi p + B_{zp}^2 = B_{\varphi 0}^2 + B_{zv}^2 \qquad [52]$$

This equilibrium is disturbed, and the disturbed quantities are assumed to take the following form:

$$q(r, \varphi, z, t) = q(r) \exp(ikz + im\varphi + \omega t) \qquad [53]$$

In ideal magnetohydrodynamics (not taking into account any dissipation) ω^2 can be shown to be real (33). Thus the perturbations are either oscillatory ($\omega^2 < 0$) or they grow exponentially ($\omega^2 > 0$). k is the longitudinal wave number ($k = 2\pi/\lambda$, where λ is the wavelength along z) and m is the azimuthal wave number (the number of waves around the circumference; for reasons of periodicity m has to be an integer). This procedure is called normal mode analysis. The dispersion formula gives ω^2 as a function of the mode considered,

$$\omega^2 = \omega^2(m, k) \tag{54}$$

Except for limiting cases it is not possible, however, to evaluate ω^2 in closed form, because the dispersion formula is

$$\frac{I_m(\sigma)}{I'_m(\sigma)} \cdot \frac{B_{zp}^2 r_0 \eta \zeta}{B_{\varphi 0}^2 \xi} = 1 + \left(\frac{B_{zv}}{B_{\varphi 0}} kr_0 + m\right)^2 \frac{K'_m(kr_0)}{kr_0 K_m(kr_0)} \tag{55}$$

where

$$\xi^2 = k^2 + \frac{\omega^2}{s^2} = k^2 + \frac{\omega^2 \rho_0}{\gamma p_0} \tag{56}$$

$$\eta^2 = k^2 + \frac{\omega^2}{v_A^2} = k^2 + \frac{\omega^2 4\pi \rho_0}{B_{zp}^2} \tag{57}$$

$$\zeta^2 = k^2 + \frac{\omega^2}{s^2} + \frac{\omega^2}{v_A^2} \tag{58}$$

$$\sigma = \frac{\xi \eta r_0}{\zeta} \tag{59}$$

I_m and K_m are modified Bessel functions. ρ_0 is the plasma density. s is the sound velocity, v_A the Alfven velocity and γ the usual ratio of specific heats. To simplify the discussion we have not included the stabilizing effect of an infinitely conducting wall somewhere outside the pinch column (31). We have also neglected terms of the order $1/c^2$ which appear in the dispersion formula if one takes into account the displacement current in Maxwell's equations. A detailed discussion of eq. [55] would exceed the present scope. By expanding the modified Bessel functions I_m, K_m for either very large or very small arguments one can easily get results for these limiting cases (27,34). Let us consider first the simple Z-pinch without superimposed B_z-fields. In this case

$$\frac{\gamma}{2} \frac{\left(\frac{r_0 \omega}{s}\right)^2}{\sqrt{(r_0 k)^2 + \left(\frac{r_0 \omega}{s}\right)^2}} \frac{I_m\left(\sqrt{(r_0 k)^2 + \left(\frac{r_0 \omega}{s}\right)^2}\right)}{I'_m\left(\sqrt{(r_0 k)^2 + \left(\frac{r_0 \omega}{s}\right)^2}\right)} = 1 + \frac{m^2}{kr_0} \frac{K_m(kr_0)}{K'_m(kr_0)} \tag{60}$$

Numerical evaluation of this equation yields (27) the dimensionless growth rates $\omega r_0/s$ as functions of the dimensionless wave number $r_0 k$ (see Fig. 15).

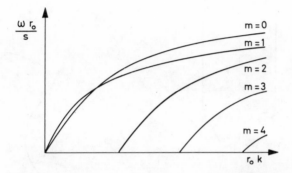

Figure 15 Qualitative sketch of the growth rates of Z-pinch instabilities for several values of m (no stabilizing B_z-fields).

It is seen that there are instabilities for all m and that the largest growth rates belong to $m = 0$ and large k. A discussion of eq. [55] shows that $m = 0$ modes can easily be avoided by superimposing B_z-fields. Actually B_{zp}-fields are more efficient than B_{zv}-fields in stabilizing $m = 0$. The point is that B_{zp} has a strong influence on all wave numbers while B_{zv} has little effect on small k. The condition for stability of all $m = 0$ modes is

$$\frac{B_{zp}^2}{B_{\varphi 0}^2} > \frac{1}{2} \tag{61}$$

If this condition is fulfilled, $m = 0$ modes are suppressed and $m = 1$ modes appear instead. It is easily understood that the pinch should be unstable with respect to these disturbances. In Fig. 16 we see an $m = 0$ and an $m = 1$ instability. In both cases the forces exerted on the disturbed surface are such as to increase the disturbance.

Experiments show exactly what theory claims. A simple pinch is destroyed by $m = 0$ modes after a short time. If sufficiently high B_z-fields are superimposed the $m = 0$ modes disappear and the pinch column shows growing $m = 1$ instabilities (also called corkscrew instabilities). The Kerr cell technique can be used to take pictures of the perturbed plasma column which clearly show the predicted behavior (see, for instance Ref. 14).

Having looked at instabilities, let us now return to our neutrons. As we saw above, they are due, at least partly, to accelerated deuterons. Anderson (23) advanced the hypothesis that the acceleration mechanism is provided by the $m = 0$ instabilities. These grow very fast and thus cause rapid changes of magnetic flux, which induce large voltages across the gaps of instabilities. Anderson (23) shows that the voltages may easily be large enough to explain the observed anisotropy. The process is schematically represented by Fig. 17. Superimposed B_z-fields stabilize the $m = 0$ instabilities and at the same time

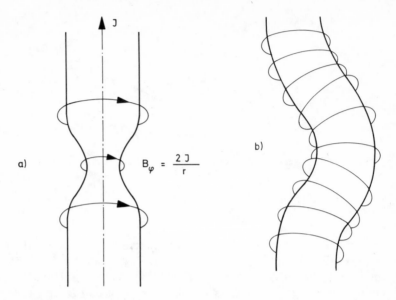

Figure 16 $m = 0$ (a) and $m = 1$ (b) instabilities of a Z-pinch plasma column.

they reduce the neutron output strongly. This shows quite conclusively that the above discussed hypothesis should be correct. This has been verified by several of the authors quoted above.

But even if the $m = 0$ instabilities are completely stabilized, neutrons are still produced, though at a much smaller rate now. This has been discussed, for instance, by Fünfer (21). The situation is thus a complicated one. It seems justified to attribute part of the neutron output to deuterons, which have been accelerated by $m = 0$ instabilities. Another part of the output cannot be explained in this way, however. Its origin has never really been clarified. It may well be due to the plasma temperature and thus be of real "thermonuclear origin." It is also possible, however, that it is connected with other instabilities (perhaps $m = 1$). The most probable explanation is a combination of all these.

Besides the linear Z-pinch the toroidal Z-pinch has also been investigated (35–42). In this case the discharge is bent to form a torus and the discharge current is produced by induction. The largest machine of this type is the British ZETA torus (35–38). This is a torus of 100 cm bore and 1160 cm circumference with currents up to 200 kAmp in pulses of about 2 msec.

Neutrons have also been observed in these toroidal pinches (typically 10^6–10^7 neutrons per shot). Investigations of their energy spectrum again reveals that they are produced by deuterons accelerated along the pinched column in the toroidal vessel. The dependence on a superimposed magnetic field is, however, essentially different from what we have discussed for linear pinches (36,39,

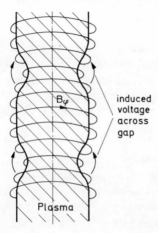

Figure 17 Voltages induced across the gaps of $m = 0$ instabilities.

40,42). A rapid decrease of neutron output is never found with small B_z-fields. On the contrary, in many cases there is an optimum B_z-field for which the output has its maximum. Take, for instance, the case of the so-called "Perhapsatron" torus described by Conner (42). One measures about 4×10^6 neutrons per shot. The output depends on pressure (maximum output is obtained for a filling pressure of 15 μ) and on B_z (maximum is obtained for $B_z = 1200$ G). The energy distribution was measured with a cloud chamber and gave a shift of the maximum up to 2.59 MeV in the forward direction and down to 2.37 MeV in the backward direction. The authors suggest two causes: (a) deuterons of 10 keV reacting with deuterons at rest and (b) the whole plasma moving at 5×10^7 cm sec^{-1}. Both explanations run into difficulties. Probably the truth is somewhere in between. Or consider the ZETA case (35–38). Here one also observes neutrons with anisotropic energy spectrum, which would correspond to 17 keV deuterons. Their number can be calculated from the neutron output, and one thus arrives at 1 amp of 17 keV deuterons along the pinch column. At the same time hard X-rays observed are attributed to run-away electrons representing a current of 25 amp. Thus the neutrons cannot be of thermonuclear origin. The output is also in contradiction with such an origin. The ion temperature as measured from the Doppler widths of spectral lines is about 2 to 3×10^6 °K, while the neutron output would give a much higher temperature.

It is concluded that the neutrons are produced by runaway ions accelerated by the applied voltage. If there is no B_z the discharge is unstable and no (or fewer) neutrons are produced. Some B_z-field stabilizes the discharge and leads to higher neutron output because stability supports the runaway effect. On the other hand, the B_z-field should not be too large because the discharge cannot readily detach from the walls in this case. This seems to be the qualitative explanation of the B_z-dependence.

Usually the reaction neutrons, which freely leave the discharge region, are used for diagnostic purposes. Allibone (41) has (in the so-called sceptre torus) made use of the protons as well (which are produced by the other branch of the d-d reaction and which carry about 3 MeV). The proton spectra (measured by the nuclear emulsion technique) depend also on the direction of observation and thus lead to the same conclusions as the neutron measurements.

Let us briefly summarize the main results of this section. Both linear and toroidal Z-pinches are capable of producing d-d reactions. In both cases they are however, mainly due to acceleration mechanisms (instabilities for the linear case and runaway ions in the applied electric field for the toroidal case). Thus the initially most welcome neutrons turn out to be very disappointing. Other more promising configurations were therefore considered. Z-pinches have more or less been abandoned since then and in many cases have been replaced by θ-pinches. These will be discussed in a later section.

On the other hand, Z-pinches have many interesting features and they should perhaps not be judged from the reactor point of view only. They provide a good means of producing hot plasmas, which may be studied for many reasons (shock waves and their structure, stability problems, heating mechanisms, etc.). The Z-pinch was recently revived in Los Alamos (43). It also has been able to flourish in the guise of the plasma focus, which is discussed in the next section.

Neutrons emitted by hot deuterium plasmas as they have been produced in the Tokamak experiment T-3 at the Kurchatov Institute in Moscow, have been reported (*International Symposium on Closed Confinement Systems*, Dubna, 1969). Ion temperatures up to about 400 eV are calculated from the neutron production rate. They agree well with independent measurements (Doppler width of the D_2-line and temperatures derived from charge exchange measurements).

2.   *The Plasma Focus.*   One may ask how to increase the neutron yield of a Z-pinch. This was previously attempted by increasing the total current in the pinch. This method fails, however. The pinch is formed initially when the current starts to flow, and after a short time the pinch column is destroyed by instabilities. The current increases further, but it is useless now. The time necessary for the radial plasma compression is much smaller than the period of the usual discharges. If the total electric energy initially stored in the bank is to be exploited, things would have to be arranged such that these two times are about equal. This would require enormously high voltages and make the experiment very difficult. The (Mather) plasma focus (44–47) represents a

surprising way out of this predicament. It may be described as a device in which the pinch compression can be started at any time during the cycle of the discharge. Proper timing can, in particular, ensure that the compression coincides with the current maximum. The magnetic fields and magnetic pressure have their maximum at the same time, too, and the resulting plasma compression is extremely powerful.

Historically the plasma focus has been developed not from the Z-pinch, but from the Marshall gun (48–50). This is a coaxial plasma gun as shown in Fig. 18 in which the plasma is driven along a tubular chamber between the

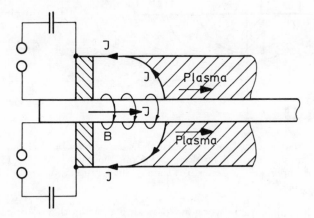

Figure 18 Marshall plasma gun (schematic).

center and the outside electrodes. Radial plasma currents and azimuthal magnetic fields accelerate the plasma. If in this plasma gun the center electrode is cut, the plasma collapses radially after passing the cut. It is compressed towards the axis very much as in a Z-pinch. The difference to the Z-pinch is that no column of appreciable length is formed. The plasma collapses more or less into a small spherical region called the focus, thus giving the device its name. It is an experimental fact that the neutron yield is a maximum if the length of the center electrode is chosen such that the plasma arrives at its end exactly when the current has its maximum. Thus the timing mentioned previously is accomplished by a proper choice of the acceleration distance which is identical with the length of the center electrode. The radial collapse is then driven by the maximum magnetic pressure possible. Figure 19 shows schematically the plasma focus of Mather and co-workers. In the plasma focus the particle density ranges from 10^{19} to 10^{20} cm^{-3}. It emits some 10^{10} neutrons within a fraction of a microsecond. This corresponds to a flux of about 10^{17} neutrons per second. Electron temperatures in the focus reach values up to 5 to 8 keV.

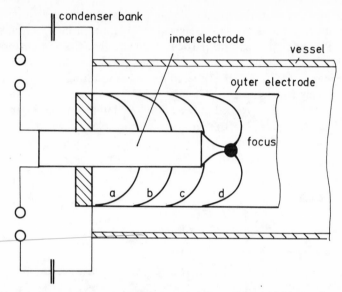

Figure 19   Mather plasma focus (schematic). Data: diameter of inner electrode 5 cm, its length 22 cm; diameter of outer electrode 9.6 cm; condenser bank: $C = 135\ \mu F$, $U = 20$ kV, $I = 10^6$ amp. $\tau/4 = 2.2\ \mu sec$. a, b, c, d are qualitative successive stages of the acceleration.

Mather has also used two guns opposing one another ("opposing gun operation") in the hope of improving performance. The experiment showed, however, that it was worse (46).

There are other focus experiments (15,51–63), which are more or less different from Mather's device. The prototype of some of them is the Filippov focus (Fig. 20), which is essentially a metal-walled Z-pinch. In its latest version (53), it is characterized by the following data: anode diameter 66 cm; capacity of the capacitor bank 576 μF; voltage 18 kV; total currents 1-2 Mamp; initial pressure, for instance, 1 torr D_2; compression velocities of several 10^7 cm sec^{-1}; radius of the focus less than 0.5 mm; focal densities 1 to 3 $\times$ 10^{20} cm^{-3}; focal temperatures 1 to 3 keV; neutron output about 10^{10} per discharge.

In all the quoted papers detailed measurements concerning the location and duration of the focus, the properties of the radiation emitted (neutrons, x-rays, visible light, etc.) are reported. These measurements, however, do not yet give a coherent picture of the plasma focus and its behavior. A lot of neutron diagnostics making use of detailed properties of the neutron anisotropy and the neutron energy spectra are discussed in Section II, have been done. The difficulties are considerable, however, and the authors do not yet agree which mechanism produces the neutrons. Mather and co-workers (44) for instance, have measured the neutron energy spectra for 0°, 90°, and 180°

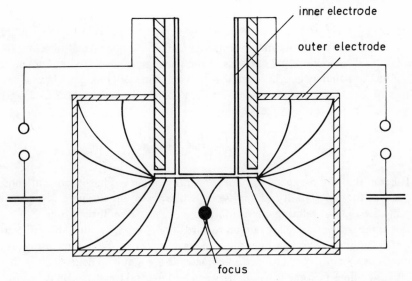

Figure 20 Filippov plasma focus with several qualitative stages of compression.

and found average energies of 2.77 MeV, 2.59 MeV, and 2.22 MeV respectively. This corresponds to a center-of-mass velocity of the plasma source of 1.2×10^8 cm sec^{-1}. Such a result may be explained (as in the case of Z-pinches discussed in the preceding section) by two limiting models: Moving deuterons colliding with deuterons at rest ("target model") or a thermal plasma in fast motion ("moving boiler model"). Detailed neutron diagnostics yields results which are consistent with the moving boiler model and inconsistent with the target model. The assumed velocity of the plasma, on the other hand, is not consistent with the dimensions of the focus and the duration of the neutron pulse (80 to 150 msec in this case).

Compared with this, Maisonnier (56) claims that his neutrons are consistent with the target model only. Agafonov (53), on the other hand, uses the moving boiler model to explain the results as Mather does. Thus this problem is perhaps not yet settled.

In any case the plasma focus provides us with a means of producing highly energetic high density plasmas. It is very interesting to clarify the processes acting in such a device and to find out how the neutrons are produced in it (i.e., what the velocity distribution of the deuterons is). The plasma focus is thus of great interest in itself. In improved and more powerful form, it may become an extremely important source of radiation (both neutrons and electromagnetic radiation) for investigations where pulses of short duration are required. It does not seem very likely, however, that it will be of relevance to the future of fusion reactors.

3. **The θ-Pinch.** The θ-pinch is similar, in principle, to a Z-pinch. While the plasma in a Z-pinch is confined by azimuthal fields of a longitudinal current, the θ-pinch plasma is confined by longitudinal fields of azimuthal currents. These azimuthal currents in the plasma are produced by induction. Thus a θ-pinch may be compared to a 1 : 1 transformer (Fig. 21). The magnetic lines of force have no curvature as in the Z-pinch. Thus the equation describing the θ-pinch equilibrium is simply

$$p(r) + \frac{B_z^2(r)}{8\pi} = \text{constant} \qquad [62]$$

The fact that the magnetic lines of force are not curved has important consequences for the stability of the θ-pinch plasma column. There is a general principle (33,64) relating curvature and stability. Equilibria as the Z-pinch, where the lines of force are curved towards the plasma, are unstable (Fig. 20), while equilibria where the lines of force are curved away from the plasma (as in the "cusp" and "picket fence" geometries) are stable. The θ-pinch with its uncurved lines of force is just in between and neutral (or "marginal" to use a

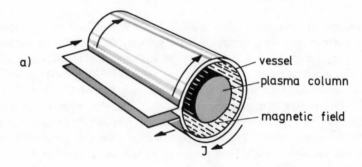

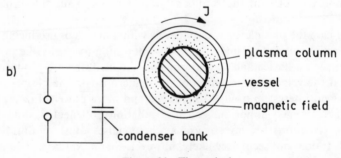

Figure 21 Theta-pinch.

fancier word). This principle has a very plausible reason. Consider the single particles of the plasma, which gyrate around the magnetic lines of force, but at the same time have to follow their lines of force. If these lines of force are curved. the centrifugal forces may produce instabilities, when directed out of the plasma. These instabilities are thus very similar to the Rayleigh-Taylor instabilities of classical hydrodynamics (if gravity is simply replaced by inertia). The neutrality of the θ-pinch can also be derived in a purely formal way from eq. [55] by considering the limit $B_{\varphi 0} \Rightarrow 0$. From the point of view of stability, the θ-pinch is thus much more interesting than the Z-pinch, and consequently a large amount of work has been done on θ-pinches. It would, however, be an oversimplification to say that θ-pinches are never unstable. There may be resistive instabilities in θ-pinches with trapped antiparallel magnetic fields. There may be rotational instabilities due to centrifugal forces if the column starts to rotate, as sometimes happens for reasons which have not been properly clarified. There may be inertial instabilities during the dynamical phase. We shall not discuss any of these problems. But it should be emphasized that the θ-pinch, simple as it looks, is not yet completely understood, though many groups in various laboratories have done quite a lot of work on it. The following represents only a small fraction of the work published (65–101).

As already discussed in connection with the Z-pinch, heating and confinement are accomplished by the same fast rising field. This leads to radial oscillations at the beginning, and later on these oscillations damp out. The magnetic field increases further, and thus the dynamic phase, during which shock heating is dominant, is followed by an "adiabatic" phase. The temperature (we shall see later that this word is not really justified here) still increases until the maximum of the current is reached. Later on it decreases again together with the current. Sometimes the discharge is crowbarred both to avoid the rapid decrease of current and plasma temperature and also to increase the lifetime of the capacitor bank. If deuterium is used as filling gas neutron pulses can be observed which last appreciably longer than in the case of Z-pinches. As far as we know, they are not related to any instabilities or other strange effects. In this sense one may say that these neutrons really are of thermonuclear origin, with the restriction, however, that the velocity distribution function of the deuterons is not necessarily a Maxwellian.

The lifetime of a (linear) θ-pinch plasma is not limited by instabilities but by its finite length, that is, the order of magnitude of the lifetime is simply given by

$$\tau \approx \frac{l}{u_{\parallel}} \qquad [63]$$

where l is the length of the coil and $u_{\parallel}$ the mean parallel velocity of the ions. The electrons have a larger velocity. Owing to space charges, however, the electrons cannot escape faster than the ions. In all that follows the terms parallel and perpendicular refer to the direction of the axis of the pinch, that is, to the direction of the magnetic field. Equation [63] describes the lifetime of a simple straight θ-pinch. One can try to increase τ by applying "magnetic mirror fields" at both the ends of the θ-pinch coil. Doing this actually leads to a reduction of the plasma end losses and thus to an increase of τ, as predicted by theory. The order of magnitude of τ cannot be changed in this way, however. It can be increased by increasing l, which is the reason why several relatively long θ-pinches have been built (up to 8 m length of the coil (65)).

The main difference between θ-pinches and Z-pinches is thus that the lifetime is limited by different effects: end-effects for θ-pinches and instabilities for Z-pinches.

Let us now discuss a more special problem already mentioned above—the question of velocity distribution, which is related both to the heating mechanism and the relaxation of non-Maxwellian distributions due to collisions. The heating is produced by radial compression, and so it is primarily perpendicular energy that is transferred to the plasma. This is true of both shock heating and adiabatic compression. If, for instance, we describe the ions by an elliptic distribution (as discussed in Section II), the heating primarily increases $T_\perp$ only and not $T_\parallel$, so that $T_\perp > T_\parallel$. Collisions between the particles then lead to an exchange of energy between the perpendicular and parallel degrees of freedom. Thus what actually happens is a question of competition between two different time scales, namely the compression time and the collision time. If the first one is small enough (as it is in the case of really fast and powerful θ-pinches), one should expect a strongly anisotropic plasma with $T_\perp \gg T_\parallel$ at least during the early stages. Later on $T_\perp$ and $T_\parallel$ approach one another. The process of complete relaxation cannot be observed, however, because the plasma is lost faster and faster as the relaxation goes on (see eq. [63] with $u_\parallel \sim \sqrt{T_\parallel}$). It is quite possible that the ion distribution function is not an elliptic one. In this case $T_\perp$ and $T_\parallel$ should be replaced by perpendicular and parallel mean energies $E_\perp$ and $E_\parallel$ in the preceding arguments. Thus the behavior of a real θ-pinch is more or less governed by the transfer of energy into the parallel direction due to collisional relaxation. This is a problem of kinetic plasma theory, which cannot be completely solved. Simplifying assumptions, however, yield a tractable theory, and one can try to predict the time history of $T_\perp$ and $T_\parallel$ in a θ-pinch on the basis of such a simplified model. A detailed discussion of these problems has been given elsewhere (82,84,102,103).

In the present article the problem is of interest because it has consequences for the properties of the emitted neutron radiation. At least in principle (not taking into account experimental difficulties at the moment), $T_\perp$ and $T_\parallel$ can be measured as functions of time (by investigating neutron output, energy spectrum, and flux as discussed in Section II) and compared with theoretical predictions. We shall come back to this point later in this Section.

After these generalities concerning the θ-pinch, let us now discuss some of the experiments which have been performed. It seems that the θ-pinch was invented in Los Alamos. The first experimental results were reported in reference (86). This first and now famous θ-pinch was called "Scylla" (as a response to that a θ-pinch built by the Frascati group was baptized "Cariddi" in reference (95)). Scylla (coil length 10 cm, tube diameter 5 cm) produced neutrons during the second and third half-cycle of the discharge (the duration of the half-cycle was several μsec). These neutrons were found to emerge from a central region of 1.5 cm diameter and 3 cm in length. The neutron pulses were bell-shaped and symmetric within the half-cycles (quite different from the Z-pinch results). The total number of neutrons was 10^5 and 10^6 per shot, sometimes up to 10^7. It depends on the initial filling pressure (which ranged from about 10 to 1000 μHg) and had a maximum at about 100 μHg. All the measurements were consistent with the assumption that the plasma has a density of 6×10^{16} cm^{-3} and a temperature of about 1.3 keV. Neutron energy spectra (from nuclear emulsions) have also been obtained. They seemed to indicate a rotation of the deuterons in the sense of the induced azimuthal electric field. This is similar in principle to the effects observed with toroidal Z-pinches. The difference, however, is that with Scylla the energy in this rotation is much too small to have any effect on the neutron output. There was also no indication that the neutrons were connected with instabilities. The symmetric bell-shaped form of the neutron pulse would in any case not suggest such a connection because for instabilities producing the neutrons one should expect spiked pulses such as appear in Z-pinches. The fact that the neutrons do not appear in the first half-cycle is explained by preionization processes which take some time. Summarizing, the Scylla was a very successful experiment and was probably the first experiment to produce mainly real thermonuclear neutrons.

It is thus clear why many θ-pinch experiments followed. In these experiments θ-pinches were investigated over a wide range of parameters (various regimes of initial pressure, temperature and particle density; superimposed parallel and antiparallel bias magnetic fields; various dimensions of the coil, etc.). We shall restrict the following discussion to only a few examples concerning measurements on the nuclear reactions in θ-pinch plasmas, that is, to experiments where the reaction products are used for diagnostic purposes. Most measurements are based on neutrons.

An experment involving both reaction protons (≈ 3 MeV) and tritons (≈ 1 MeV) in Scylla was performed by Nagle (100). The protons and tritons leaving the coil end-on through a slit were recorded with nuclear plates after a discrimination with respect to their energy by a magnetic field. Side-on observations would be very difficult for several reasons. If we assume Maxwellian deuterons, the energy spectra should not depend, however, on the direction of observation. Their shape should be approximately Gaussian (see the corresponding discussion of neutron spectra in Section II2). This in fact is exactly what was found, and both protons and tritons led to the same temperature 1.3 keV, in good agreement with earlier Scylla results.

Goldman and co-workers also made measurements on the deuteron energies in a θ-pinch (10,12). If He^3 is added to the deuterium, one gets the reaction

$$d + \text{He}^3 \quad \longrightarrow \quad \text{He}^4 + p + 18.3 \text{ MeV} \qquad [64]$$

where the α-particles carry away 3.6 MeV and the protons 14.7 MeV. Goldman and co-workers compared the neutron output from the d–d reaction with the 14.7 MeV proton output from the reaction for deuterium plasmas containing various fractions of He^3. They considered both three-dimensional Maxwellian and three-dimensional monoenergetic distributions and computed the corresponding mean values of $\langle \sigma g \rangle$. For the $d(d, n)$ reaction their values agree with the ones given in Figs. 2, 3, and 4 of Section II. For the He^3 (d, p) reaction their results are given in Table 6. Comparing the He^3 (d, p) reaction rates with the $d(d, n)$ reaction rates one finds that their ratio (the ratio of 14.7 MeV protons and 2.45 MeV neutrons produced) is a function of the mean energy for a given distribution function. This is shown (according to Goldman et al.) in Fig. 22. Having measured the ratio of proton and neutron output, Goldman et al. conclude for reasons of consistency between all measurements that the plasma in their pinch may be best described by a monoenergetic distribution of about 10 keV.

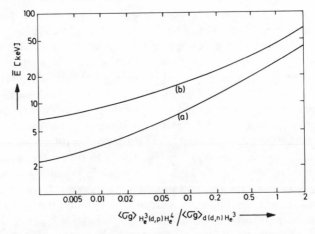

Figure 22 Ratio of reaction rates for the H$_e^3$ (d, p) H$_e^4$ and $d(d, n)$ H$_e^3$ reactions assuming (a) three-dimensional Maxwellian and (b) three-dimensional monoenergetic distribution (12).

TABLE 6

Values of $\langle \sigma g \rangle$ for the $He^3(d, p)$-reaction
as a function of mean energy $\bar{E}(10, 11)$

	$\langle \sigma g \rangle$, cm^3 sec^{-1}	
$\bar{E}$, keV	Maxwellian	Monoenergetic
2	5.12E–25	—
3	1.59E–23	3.18E–27
4	1.37E–22	1.52E–25
5	6.25E–22	2.12E–24
6	1.97E–21	1.48E–23
7	4.91E–21	6.70E–23
8	1.03E–20	2.26E–22
9	1.93E–20	6.19E–22
10	3.30E–20	1.45E–21
15	2.15E–19	2.60E–20
20	7.05E–19	1.44E–19
30	3.23E–18	1.03E–18
40	8.45E–18	3.25E–18
50	1.65E–17	7.69E–18
75	4.57E–17	3.27E–17
100	8.04E–17	7.60E–17

As a last example, let us discuss some experiments done with the ISAR I megajoule θ-pinch (82,84). These experiments represent an effort to make full use of the information contained in the neutron radiation as discussed in Section II. The neutron measurements performed thus concerned the total production rate, energy spectra side-on and end-on, and also the neutron flux side-on and end-on. In addition, other diagnostic techniques were used to obtain as much information as possible so that conclusions could be drawn on the basis of consistency arguments. The main object was the problem of relaxation, which we have mentioned already: primarily perpendicular energy is transferred to the plasma, while parallel energy is produced by relaxation only. ISAR I is a very fast bank, and one would therefore expect an anisotropic plasma. The problem then is how the anisotropy decays and how the decay compares with theoretical predictions. Theoretical discussion shows that ion-ion collisions are not very efficient at the temperatures involved, at least not within the small times (several μsec) available. On the other hand, the experimental results indicate an efficient mechanism of relaxation. Without relaxation the adiabatic heating processes dominant in the later stage of the discharge would require that $T_\perp$ follow the magnetic field; one would expect

$$T_\perp \sim B \tag{65}$$

A look at Fig. 23 shows that this is not the case.

At this point we have to discuss the extremely important influence the electron temperature T_e exerts on the discharge. In an isothermal plasma the relaxation of the ions is mainly due to ion-ion collisions, while electron-ion collisions are practically negligible. This is a consequence of their small mass. If the electron temperature is very small relative to the ion temperature, the main relaxation mechanism is, however, provided by the ion-electron collisions. For a detailed discussion see Refs. 102 and 103.

Now it is a typical feature of fast θ-pinches that the electron temperatures are indeed much smaller than the ion temperatures by an order of magnitude and more. Two competing theories have been put forward to explain this fact (bremsstrahlung due to high Z-impurities and heat conduction to the ends). In the case of ISAR I the ion temperatures range from 3 to 5 keV, depending on the parameters, while the electron temperatures are not more than a few 100 eV. The electron temperatures are measured by the scattering of laser light. This effect can be used to explain the behavior of the ISAR I plasma. This is indicated by Fig. 23. It shows the magnetic field B in units of B_{max} ($B_{max} \approx 180$ kG is reached after a quarter-cycle of about 10 μsec), the mean electron density on the axis $\bar{n}_{ea}$ (as measured by means of a Mach-Zehnder interferometer), the β-value of the plasma (where β is as usual defined as the ratio of plasma pressure to total magnetic pressure), and the experimental values $T_\perp$ (from the neutron production rate on the assumption of a two-dimensional Maxwellian as discussed in Section II). Furthermore, it shows four theoretical curves for $T_\perp$ and four curves for $T_\parallel$. These are computed with experimentally verified initial data and for different assumptions regarding the electrons because the detailed time history of the electron temperature was not measured for these discharges. Three curves correspond to $T_e = 200, 300,$ and 400 eV respectively, while the fourth one is computed without allowance for ion-electron collisions. It is seen that this last curve gives $T_\perp$ almost proportional to B except for the relatively small effect from ion-ion collisions. The electrons, however, lead to strong deviations from this behavior, and electron temperatures in the 300–400 eV range fit very well with the experimental results.

The observations can best be explained by the assumption of an elliptic distribution for deuterons with $T_\perp$ essentially larger than $T_\parallel$ (so that for the neutron rate it is sufficient to consider it as a two-dimensional Maxwellian). Nuclear plate measurements of the neutron energy spectrum made both side-on and end-on support this conclusion. The side-on spectrum yields perpendicular temperatures of about 4 ± 1 keV while the end-on spectrum is not compatible with parallel temperatures above 1 keV. Another indication is the behavior of the neutron flux ratio side-on to end-on. It seems that it increases initially and decreases again at later times. At least at the present

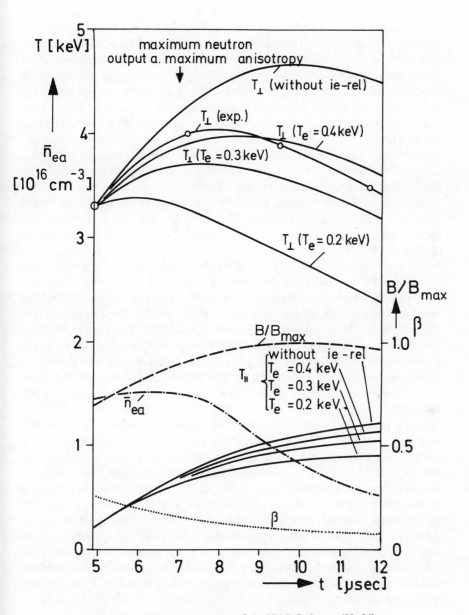

Figure 23 Relaxation process of the ISAR I plasma (82, 84).

stage it is not possible, however, to draw quantitative conclusions from the experimental flux ratios (which would make use of the theoretical values presented in Fig. 10 of Section II). The neutrons coming from the plasma are scattered in the coil and the other matter surrounding the plasma, and it is difficult to estimate the influence of such effects on the flux ratio (which is measured by plastic scintillators mounted side-on and end-on). On the other hand, the flux ratio has to be measured with a precision of several percent if reasonable resolution with respect to temperatures is required as can be seen from Fig. 10. It should be possible, however, to develop this flux ratio method further into a useful diagnostic tool which would tell at once whether a hot plasma is anisotropic or not and how the anisotropy changes with time, at least qualitatively. This would require some more knowledge about the effects (scattering, etc.) disturbing the signals.

During certain (both early and late) phases of the θ-pinch additional relaxation mechanisms due to so-called anomalous effects (due to micro-instabilities) also seem to be of importance. These, however, will not be discussed here.

The experiments treated in this section show that θ-pinches are well suited for producing hot thermonuclear plasmas There is little doubt that even higher temperatures can be obtained by still faster and larger devices. We use the word thermonuclear here in a sense which includes anisotropic plasmas produced by fast pinches The main point is that the nuclear reactions are not produced by exotic acceleration and runaway mechanisms as in the Z-pinches. Initial anisotropy is not dangerous. It would just take some time for the plasma to become Maxwellian. The only trouble with linear θ-pinches is that the plasma escapes at the open ends with increasing speed during relaxation.

The θ-pinch experiments have reached a stage now where an essentially new step is necessary. In principle, there are two possibilities of increasing the confinement time of hot plasmas. One could build large banks for very long coils. In a later section we shall discuss the confinement times necessary for pulsed fusion reactors (Lawson criterion). It thus turns out that these requirements could only be met by θ-pinches several kilometers long. Such an approach, therefore does not look very encouraging. The second possibility would be to bend the θ-pinch into a torus. Now a toroidal θ-pinch is not in equilibrium because the field lines along the inside are shorter than along the outside of the torus, that is, the field is stronger inside than outside, and the plasma is driven to the outside. A simple estimate shows that the time required for the plasma column to reach the walls is

$$\tau \approx \frac{\sqrt{Rr}}{v_{\text{th}}} \qquad [66]$$

R is the large radius and r the small radius of the torus. v_{th} is the thermal velocity of the plasma. For a more detailed discussion of this problem see Refs. (104,105). This time τ does also not look very promising. If a linear pinch is compared with such a torus, the linear pinch looks even better. We thus have to look for real toroidal equilibrium configurations, that is, we have to use additional fields which produce equilibrium. There are several possibilities of doing this, at least as far as equilibrium is concerned. It is not clear, however, whether there is any toroidal equilibrium of high β—of large plasma pressure relative to magnetic pressure (we are not talking about low β configurations here)—which is stable. The future of the θ-pinch is thus called in question because nobody knows as yet if the fight against instabilities can be won.

The energy sources of all the θ-pinch experiments described in this section are usual types of capacitor banks. Magnetic fields obtained by flux compression can also be used. The initial field at any rate is produced by a capacitor bank. Explosions are then used to concentrate the initial flux into a smaller region so that (if it is done fast enough) the flux is nearly constant and the magnetic field increased (up to 10^7 G have been obtained in that way). Some authors, (106,107), have applied this method to θ-pinches. The trouble with this approach is that the high fields cannot be generated as fast as necessary for really fast compressions. Another trouble is that it is extremely difficult to obtain enough shots (to eliminate statistical errors, etc.) because each shot destroys at least part of the device. Thomson thus describes the results of five discharges, and so does Hamm. Neutrons are observed in both cases. The discharges are not reproducible. The neutron yield changes by orders of magnitude from shot to shot. Conclusions as to the mechanism of neutron production are therefore not yet possible. As to the flux concentration method itself, the reader may be referred to Herlach's recent paper (108) which covers the present stage of the art at length. A discussion of the theoretical limits of this method was given by the author (109). Further literature can be found in these references.

New experimental results concerning the neutrons produced in θ-pinch plasmas have been obtained by Neuhauser (*Report IPP* 1/109, 1970).

4. *Mirror Magnetic Wells.* Neutrons have also been produced by plasmas trapped in mirror magnetic wells (110,111). These experiments are different from the ones discussed in the preceding sections. The plasma parameters differ by orders of magnitude, and the plasma is also produced by another method. Cosensgen's (110,111) so-called 2X-device is a large mirror machine with a superimposed quadrupole field produced by four bars parallel to the axis of the mirror. The pure mirror field is unstable with respect to exchange instabilities, which are caused by the curvature of the magnetic

lines of force. The instabilities can, however, be avoided by additional fields so that one gets a minimum B configuration in which the modulus of the magnetic field increases away from the plasma. It was first shown by Ioffe and co-workers (112) that this procedure really leads to an improvement of plasma confinement because the exchange instabilities are eliminated. They applied a hexapole field produced by six Ioffe bars (Fig. 24). As mentioned above, four bars are used instead in 2X.

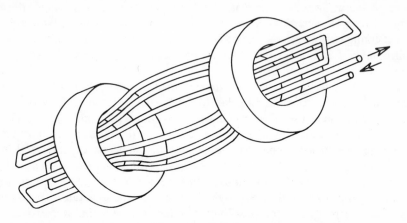

Figure 24   Ioffe bars.

The 2X plasma is produced by guns which inject the plasma along the axis of the mirror. The plasma injected has an initial temperature of 2.5 keV. After the injection it is heated to higher temperatures by adiabatic compression in the rising mirror field. The plasma produced forms a column of 6 cm diameter and 160 cm length (its volume is 4.5 liters). The energy of the deuterons is supposed to range from 1.5 to 50 keV with a mean value of about 6 to 8 keV. Owing to the mirror the plasma is strongly anisotropic. Its velocity space is filled only for angles between 60° and 90° to the axis. The maximum density is about 5×10^{13} cm^{-3}, and the lifetime of the plasma is about 1 msec (smaller densities but larger times than with pinches). This density corresponds to a β of 5%. As in fast θ-pinches, the electron temperature is much smaller than the ion temperature (or the mean ion energy, to be more cautious), namely 150–250 eV. The reasons for that are probably the same as in the θ-pinch (113). The long confinement time is (among other methods) also demonstrated by a neutron flux signal which extends over more than 500 μsec. More details of the neutron radiation are not given. The main subject of the investigations are microinstabilities which define the confinement time. We shall not discuss these problems here, but refer the reader to the relevant literature [(114–120) to mention just a few papers].

5. *Laser Produced Plasmas.*   During recent years increasing efforts have been devoted to the production of plasmas by lasers. If the beam of a powerful laser is focused on matter the energy density is sufficient to produce a small volume of hot plasma. In this article we want to mention just one of these experiments which is related to our subject. Quite recently Basov and co-workers have reported on laser produced plasmas which are hot enough to produce a few neutrons (123,124). They used a mode locked neodymium doped laser with five stages of amplification emitting 10 to 30 joules in less than 10^{-11} sec. The beam was focused on solid lithium deuteride. In several, but not all, shots a neutron was observed by means of a scintillation counter. Considering the solid angle covered and the efficiency of registration, it is concluded that about 10 neutrons are produced per shot. This is supposed to correspond to a plasma of approximately 2 keV deuteron temperature. More information is not yet available. Future experiments are planned with a target of lithium deuteride and tritide. This would enhance the neutron output and make the measurements easier.

The field of laser produced plasmas is developing rather fast. Neutrons from laser produced plasmas have in the meantime been found also in the Limeil laboratories (F. Floux and co-workers, *Phys, Rev.*, **A1**, 821, 1970) and in the Sandia laboratories (G. W. Gobeli and co-workers, *Phys. Rev.*, **188**, 300, 1969).

C. The $d\,(t,\,n)$ Reaction

As we have seen, most investigations concern neutrons produced by $d(d, n)$ reactions in a hot plasma. Sometimes the protons from the $d(d, p)$ reaction are considered. Goldman and co-workers (10,12,71), on the other hand, added He^3 to their plasma to make use of the protons from the He^3 (d, p) reaction. These reactions are included in Table 1. Another very important reaction is the $d(t, n)$ reaction

$$t + d \quad \longrightarrow \quad He^4 + n + 17.58 \text{ MeV} \qquad [67]$$

The neutron gets 14.1 MeV, the α-particle 3.5 MeV of this energy. This is actually the most easily achieved fusion reaction. At lower energies its cross-section is much larger than that of any other reaction (8). At 15 keV, for instance,

$$\sigma_{d(d, n)} = \sigma_{d(d, p)} = 0.065 \text{ millibarns} \qquad [68]$$

while

$$\sigma_{d(t, n)} = 15 \text{ millibarns.} \qquad [69]$$

Here we are not interested in the cross-sections themselves but in the reaction rates. Introducing $\langle \sigma g \rangle$ as in Section II the reaction rate is

$$R = n_1 \, n_2 \, \langle \sigma g \rangle \qquad [70]$$

if n_1 and n_2 are the densities of the (different) particles involved. $\langle \sigma g \rangle$ has been computed. (8,11). Table 7 is based on these results. It contains for

TABLE 7
$\langle \sigma g \rangle$ for Maxwellian plasmas

T, keV	$d(d, p)$	$d(d, n)$	$d(t, n)$	$d(\mathrm{He}^3, p)$
1	7.9E–23	8.0E–23	6.5E–21	—
2	2.7E–21	2.8E–21	2.8E–19	1.6E–23
5	8.6E–20	9.0E–20	1.4E–17	7.3E–21
10	5.8E–19	6.2E–19	1.2E–16	2.2E–19
50	1.0E–17	1.2E–17	8.3E–16	6.0E–17
100	2.3E–17	2.8E–17	8.2E–16	1.8E–16

comparison $\langle \sigma g \rangle$ for $d(d, n)$, $d(d, p)$, and (He^3, p) reactions also, where some values are taken from Goldman (10,12,71) and from Section II of the present article. It is noted that the $d(t, n)$ reaction rates in the 1–10 keV range are roughly a hundred times larger than the $d(d, p)$ or the $d(d, n)$ reaction rates. Thus a plasma containing both deuterons and tritons would produce much more neutrons than a pure deuterium plasma (a maximum for a 1:1 mixture of deuterons and tritons). This would make neutron diagnostics much easier. The only reason that it has not been done already is that tritium is β-active (its half-life is 12.4 years and it emits electrons up to 0.18 MeV). Tritium is therefore not pleasant to work with.

Detailed computations on the production rate and the energy spectra of neutrons from the $d(t, n)$ reaction such as are given for the $d(d, n)$ reaction in Section II are not yet available. The author is, however, preparing a report on these problems (121).

Much useful information on reactions among light nuclei such as the reactions discussed previously can be found in the compilation of Meyerhof (122). This reference is also very useful for its large bibliography.

The problem of neutron energy spectra for the different velocity distributions of the ions involved has been discussed in some detail (G. Lehner, *Z. Physik*, **232**, 174, 1970). Numerical computations of neutron energy spectra from the d-t reaction have also been performed in the meantime (Lehner and Pohl, *Report IPP* 1/107, 1970).

D. Remarks on the Reactor Problem

It is quite tempting to speculate on fusion reactors in an article like this. The author has tried, however, to keep to the known facts about nuclear reactions in experimentally produced plasmas. On the other hand, a few words on the problem do seem appropriate here because the experiments discussed in the preceding sections (and many others not discussed) have been conducted with the ultimate aim of achieving a fusion reactor. To avoid any misunderstanding, it should be emphasized that the choice of experiments described in the present article is by no means governed by the relevance they may have for a future reactor. There are many experiments in which low-temperature and low-density plasmas are investigated with respect to fundamentally important problems. It may or may not turn out that some of them come closer to a future reactor than those producing high-density, high-temperature plasmas and, therefore, nuclear reactions now. A Z-pinch, for instance, produces neutrons, but is certainly very far from being a reactor candidate.

Though nobody knows yet how to realise a reactor, it is possible to discuss some reactor problems on the basis of reasonable assumptions and estimates. This has been done, for instance, by Mills in a series of reports and papers (125). Ribe et al. (126) discussed the chances of θ-pinches. Post (127), Fowler and Rankin (128), and Sivukhin (129) did the same for mirror machines. Carruthers et al. (130) consider the problem of competition between fusion and fission reactors (breeders). Taking an estimate of the probable cost of both fusion and fission power as a basis, they conclude that fusion should be able to compete. In view of the present state of fusion research, such considerations may appear a bit premature. On the other hand, "these economic studies are used to identify technological problems requiring investigation."

One has to distinguish two types of fusion reactors, d–d reactors and d–t reactors. In the d–d reactor the plasma contains deuterons only (initially at least). In the d–t reactor one has a 1:1 mixture of tritons and deuterons.

There are several reasons for preferring a d–d reactor. Deuterium is abundantly available and much cheaper than tritium. It is also less dangerous because it is a stable isotope, while tritium is β-active. The disadvantage of the d–d reactor is that it is more difficult to realise. It needs higher temperatures, higher densities, and larger confinement times than a d–t reactor (we shall give a precise meaning of this statement below). On the other hand, tritium is not readily available in the quantities necessary for d–t reactors. It has been proposed, therefore, that tritium be bred in the reactor itself. Actually, in a d–d reactor half of the deuterons burnt yields tritons, while the other half yields He^3. This is not sufficient, however. Efficient breeding can, at least in principle, be achieved by surrounding the hot plasma core of the reactor with a lithium blanket (131–133) that is, a blanket containing Li^6 in any convenient form. The reaction neutrons leaving the plasma would enter the blanket and produce tritium via the reaction

$$Li^6 + n \longrightarrow t + He^4 + 4.79 \text{ MeV} \qquad [71]$$

Many technological problems associated with this approach are unsolved as yet. It is certainly difficult to extract the tritium from the blanket and to inject it into the hot plasma core. It has also been proposed (134), that reactor blankets containing fissile materials be used to enhance the energy output, but at the expense of increased radiation damage problems. Another proposal is to surround d–d reactors with sodium blankets. The neutrons coming from the plasma would be captured in such a blanket and release an energy of 12.6 MeV, which is very welcome. Again, the technological problems connected with the sodium blanket are as yet unsolved. On top of all this, there are the problems of producing the necessary magnetic fields by superconducting coils and so on. For details and further literature on the subject the reader is referred to the papers quoted.

A very basic problem is the power balance in a reactor. In such a balance one has to compare the fusion power output with the losses of energy. The fusion power depends on the temperature and density of the plasma and its composition. In computing this power one has to take into account the secondary reactions due to the reaction products. From Table 1 it can be seen that in a d–d reactor, for instance, t and He^3 are produced and undergo further reactions, and so on. One would thus have to consider an almost endless chain of reactions (as one has to do in stellar plasmas). Under reactor conditions the cross-sections for most secondary reactions are so small, however, that they can safely be neglected. The problem is still complicated because assumptions concerning the fate of the energetic particles produced have to be made. Take the two branches of the d–d reaction as an example:

$$(t + 1.01 \text{ MeV}) + (p + 3.03 \text{ MeV})$$

$$d + d \qquad\qquad\qquad\qquad\qquad\qquad [72]$$

$$(He^3 + 0.82 \text{ MeV}) + (n + 2.45 \text{ MeV})$$

Because both reactions occur with almost equal probability, it can be seen that approximately two-thirds of the energy released goes to charged particles primarily (p, t, He^3), while about one-third goes to neutrons. The plasma is kept in equilibrium by strong magnetic fields so that the charged particles cannot escape. The neutrons, however, may escape. If there is a sufficiently thick blanket, their energy may be thermalized and at least be partly re-covered by a heat engine with its usual thermodynamic limitations. In a sodium blanket the energy may be enhanced as mentioned above. In a d–t reactor 80% of the energy released is carried away by the neutrons. The fate of the neutrons is thus extremely important here.

The power density of a reactor is given by

$$P = \frac{1}{2} n_d^2 \langle \sigma g \rangle_{dd} W_{dd} \qquad [73]$$

for a d–d reactor and by

$$P = n_d n_t \langle \sigma g \rangle_{dt} W_{dt} \qquad [74]$$

for a d–t reactor, where W is the energy released per reaction. The choice of W depends on the problem considered, that is, one may take the total energy of the energy going to the charged particles only and include the energy released by secondary reactions among the reaction products. The plasma has to be confined by a magnetic field. With the usual definition of β we have

$$\frac{B^2}{8\pi} \beta = nkT \qquad [75]$$

so that the power density is

$$P \sim \beta^2 B^4 \frac{\langle \sigma g \rangle}{T^2} \qquad [76]$$

$\langle \sigma g \rangle / T^2$ is a function of T only. For dd it has a maximum at $T \approx 20$ keV and for dt at $T \approx 10$ keV, that is, at these temperatures P is a maximum for given B and β. This provides us with a first estimate of the temperatures at which a reactor should work. Equation [76] has to be interpreted with some care, however. As pointed out by several authors, the problem is not to make P as large as possible. P is limited by technological considerations, mainly by the maximum power which the walls can stand (130). Thus, with P regarded as fixed the temperatures mentioned allow us to work with minimum magnetic fields. Obviously, it is desirable to have β as close to 1 as possible (not to have large fields in the plasma). It is possible that instabilities are going to prevent us from attaining higher β-values.

Hot plasmas lose appreciable amounts of energy by electro-magnetic radiation. First there is the usual bremsstrahlung. Under reactor conditions the main contribution comes from ion-electron collisions, while at very high temperatures the electron-electron contribution becomes dominant. Without going into details let us just mention that

$$P_{ei} \sim n_e n_i Z^2 \sqrt{T} \qquad [77]$$

In a pure deuterium or deuterium-tritium plasma $n_e = n_i$ and $Z = 1$. Comparison of P_{ei} and P shows that $P < P_{ei}$ at low temperatures and $P > P_{ei}$

at sufficiently high temperatures because (in the range of interest) $\langle \sigma g \rangle$ is a much steeper function of T than $P_{ei} \sim \sqrt{T}$. The temperatures for which P_{ei} just cancels with P are sometimes called critical temperatures. Taking into account just charged particle energies we get

$$T_{\text{crit}} \approx 35 \text{ keV (for } dd) \tag{78}$$

and

$$T_{\text{crit}} \approx 4 \text{ keV (for } dt). \tag{79}$$

Below T_{crit} the plasma is radiation cooled. It is very important to have the plasma as pure as possible. High Z impurities would considerably increase the bremsstrahlung losses.

Lawson (135) has considered a pulsed reactor. He assumes a plasma injected into the reactor with its thermal energy and staying there for a time τ. A simple energy balance taking into account fusion power and bremsstrahlung losses leads to the conclusion that τ must be larger than a certain minimum value. The problem has been reconsidered by Carruthers et al. (130). If the total energy is recovered with an overall efficiency η, the condition for power balance (which represents a lower limit) is

$$3nkT + P_{ei}\tau = \eta\left(\frac{n^2}{2}\langle \sigma g \rangle W\tau + 3nkT + P_{ei}\tau\right) \tag{80}$$

which can be rewritten as follows

$$n\tau = \frac{3kT}{[\eta/(1-\eta)]\langle \sigma g \rangle W - \dfrac{P_{ei}}{n^2}} \tag{81}$$

Thus $n\tau$ is a function of T only. For a d–d reactor with a sodium blanket and with allowance for secondary reactions with tritium and He^3 (see Table 1) one gets

$$W_{dd} = \frac{1}{2}(4.04 + 3.27 + 17.58 + 18.34) + 12.6 = 34.2 \text{ MeV} \tag{82}$$

where 12.6 MeV is generated by neutron capture in the blanket. For a d–t reactor $n^2/2$ has to be replaced by $n^2/4$ if $n_d = n_t = n/2$, (n is the total density) and for a lithium walled reactor

$$W_{dt} = 17.58 + 4.79 = 22.4 \text{ MeV} \tag{83}$$

For these values Carruthers et al. give $n\tau$ as functions of T (Fig. 25). Lawson originally took $\eta = \frac{1}{3}$. Carruthers et al. claim that this value is too optimistic and propose $\eta = 1/30$. Actually for the d–d case there is no balance below

$\eta = 1/14$ and so they take $\eta = 1/10$. With the Lawson value $\eta = \frac{1}{3}$ (see Fig. 25) the minimum values and the corresponding temperatures are

$$n\tau \approx 10^{15} \qquad T \approx 100 \text{ keV} \qquad \text{(for } d\text{–}d\text{)} \qquad [84]$$

$$n\tau \approx 5 \times 10^{13} \qquad T \approx 30 \text{ keV} \qquad \text{(for } d\text{–}t\text{)} \qquad [85]$$

For the revised η values $n\tau$ has to be larger by more than a factor 10. $n\tau$ is often taken as a number of merit characterising experimentally produced plasmas. Take θ-pinches, for instance. Their densities of some 10^{16}cm^{-3} and confinement times of some 10^{-6} sec give $n\tau$ values from 10^{10} to 10^{11}, still many orders of magnitude too low. Nor have the temperatures necessary yet been achieved. Assume that you would like to transform a θ-pinch into a d–t reactor. At $n = 10^{+16}$ one would need $\tau \approx 10^{-2}$ sec or more and a length of many kilometers, which is certainly very discouraging. This demonstrates that endless toroidal machines are necessary. One has to add that the Lawson

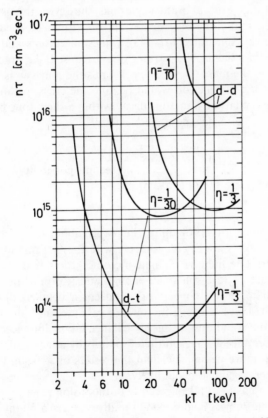

Figure 25 Lawson criterion for d-d and d-t reactions (130).

criterion is not yet sufficient. If the plasma contains a magnetic field (if $\beta < 1$), the electron cyclotron radiation (the bremsstrahlung due to the gyration of the electrons around the magnetic lines of force) may become very important (136–140). Because of their large mass the ion radiation is negligible. From this point of view it is very important to make β as large as possible.

The question coming up with the Lawson criterion is how to realize the required $n\tau$ values. Is it easier to have n large and τ small or n small and τ large? The answer to this question actually divides plasma physicists in two schools. The future will have to decide between them.

The main difficulty comes from the fact that charged particles cannot freely penetrate the Coulomb wall. Thus one could increase, at least in principle, the cross sections at low energies by shielding the positive charges of the nuclei with negative charges. Actually, stars make use of this effect. They work at very high densities. Electrons come so close to the nuclei that the Coulomb barrier is more or less lowered, depending on the conditions (see next section). For laboratory plasmas, however, this is not so. It has been proposed that μ-mesonic deuterium or tritium be used to obtain enhanced fusion by shielding (141–143). μ-mesonic atoms and molecules are much smaller than the usual electronic ones because Bohr's radius is inversely proportional to the mass ($m_\mu \approx 200\ m_e$). Thus the μ meson is much closer to the nucleons than an electron would be, and the cross sections are reduced. The only snag is that the μ mesons decay within a short time by either of two modes. There is the usual spontaneous decay

$$\mu^{\pm} \longrightarrow e^{\pm} + v + \bar{v} \qquad [86]$$

with a half-life of 2.15×10^{-6} sec. The second possibility is to be captured by the nucleons (in a mesonic atom)

$$\mu^- + p \longrightarrow n + v \qquad [87]$$

The second mode (its probability increases about proportionally to Z^4, which is "Wheeler's law") can compete with the first one for high Z atoms only, however. The lifetime of light mesonic atoms is thus defined by the spontaneous decay. It is still small enough and it is difficult to imagine that this approach to fusion could work. Indeed, a detailed discussion of the problem (144) shows that a μ meson can catalyse only one fusion reaction during its lifetime, and that an energy balance taking into account the energy necessary to produce a μ meson therefore fails by a factor of about 10^8. This result is much more pessimistic than the results of Jackson (145), who also found that energy gain seems unlikely.

Much notice has been taken recently of the fusion reactor problem and the literature on the subject is increasing rapidly. A large amount of information can be found in the "Proceedings of the British Nuclear Energy Society

Conference on Nuclear Fusion Reactors" (Culham 1969, published by the UKAEA Culham Laboratory for the British Nuclear Energy Society).

III. NUCLEAR REACTIONS IN STELLAR PLASMAS

A. Stellar Evolution and Nuclear Reactions

The problem of nuclear reactions in stellar plasmas would require much space for a full discussion. We shall have to restrict ourselves to a very short account of some of the basic facts. The principles are the same in both laboratory and stellar plasmas. There are, however, typical differences between them owing to the fact that certain parameters (as densities and temperatures) and composition are quite different.

How stellar energy is produced is an old question. Before the discovery of nuclear energy the problem could not be solved. All explanations on the basis of gravitational energy only ran into difficulties. Another source of energy was necessary, and gradually it became clear that this must be fusion energy. Already in 1929 Atkinson and Houtermans tried to give a theory of nuclear energy in stars (146). Time was not yet ripe for a solution, however, because nuclear physics was not yet sufficiently developed. But about a decade later, in 1938, Bethe (147) and v. Weizsäcker (148) discovered the carbon-nitrogen cycle. This was the beginning of the modern theory of stellar energy and stellar evolution, which rapidly developed and is still developing further. Its present stage has been described by several authors (149–153).

Any discussion of stellar evolution starts from the famous Hertzsprung-Russel diagram. It may be given in several forms (154,155). Figure 26 gives

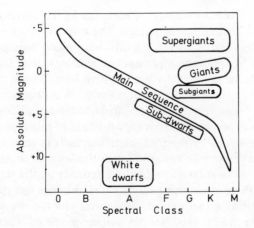

Figure 26   Sketch of the Hertzsprung-Russel diagram.

a rough sketch in which the visual absolute magnitude of stars is plotted against their spectral class. The picture obtained in this way is very characteristic. Most stars are close to a somewhat curved region, which is called the main sequence. In addition there are other regions with typical stars, mainly the giants and white dwarfs. Actually, stars are not so different. It is a generally accepted theory today that the Hertzsprung-Russel diagram does not represent a universe with many different types of stars, but rather a universe in which all stars are more or less similar in principle. The position of a star in the diagram is connected with its age, and different stars follow more or less typical paths through the diagram during their evolution.

During its evolution a star passes through different regimes of density and temperature and its composition changes. The evolution is driven both by nuclear and gravitational energy sources. A very young star appears to be composed of hydrogen atoms only at relatively low density and temperature. Nuclear reactions are of little influence. Thus, the star contracts and gains energy from gravitation. Density and temperature increase so that nuclear reactions become possible. These stop the contraction, and the star is sustained by nuclear energy until the fuel (hydrogen being burnt to helium at this stage) is exhausted. The contraction begins again until new nuclear reactions become possible at higher density and higher temperature and stop the contraction. Gravitational and nuclear stages thus follow one another with increasing density and temperature. Nuclei with increasingly high Z are burnt up to the iron peak of binding energy. In still later stages nuclear reactions consume energy. Fusion is no longer possible and high densities and high temperatures due to further contraction lead now to endothermic reactions so that, roughly speaking iron is again split up into helium for instance.

The problem of the abundance of elements in the universe is obviously closely related to that of stellar energy. The nuclear composition of a star depends on its age, that is, on the elements which have been produced in the preceding stages by fusion or other nuclear reactions. It is also necessary to explain the existence of elements heavier than iron. This is the problem of nucleosynthesis. It is assumed that nucleosynthesis is due to neutron capture processes (152). Measurements done with H-bomb explosions may in some cases provide an experimental basis for problems of this type (156).

The energy produced by thermonuclear reactions in stars is lost either in the form of electromagnetic radiation or in the form of neutrinos. Whether and to what degree neutrinos are involved depends on the stage considered. As we shall see, there are burning stages which produce neutrinos and others which do not. Neutrinos are extremely important for the late stages of stellar evolution, during which they are no longer produced by thermonuclear reactions. There are, for instance, the URCA processes proposed by Gamow and Schoenberg (157). There are also several typical "weak interaction" processes producing neutrinos such as are familiar from β-decay and other processes. For a plasma physicist it may be very interesting and perhaps surprising that his familiar plasmons—quasiparticles of plasma waves— may according to present theory, also decay into neutrinos (158):

$$\text{plasmon} \longrightarrow v + \bar{v} \qquad [88]$$

So besides the usual visible light astrophysics the new field of neutrino astrophysics has been created, see for instance Chiu (159). Right now people are looking for neutrinos coming from the sun (160–162).

It has to be said, however, that the later stages of stellar evolution are quite hypothetical at the present time. Only the first stages are relatively well established.

If we compare thermonuclear reactions in stellar and laboratory plasmas, there are some peculiar differences.

The velocity distribution of ions in a stellar plasma may always be assumed to be Maxwellian (in laboratory plasmas this is very often not the case), at least if we do not consider exceptional cases of extremely high densities, at which we would have to take into account the effects of degeneracy even for nuclei.

The reaction rate can be calculated (see Section II, where we considered the d–d reaction). By introducing center-of-mass and relative velocities we obtain

$$R = n_1 n_2 \left(\frac{\mu}{2\pi kT}\right)^{3/2} 4\pi \int g^3 \sigma(g) \exp\left(-\frac{\mu g^2}{2kT}\right) dg \qquad [89]$$

where μ is the reduced mass,

$$\frac{1}{\mu} = \frac{1}{m_1} + \frac{1}{m_2} \qquad [90]$$

and $n_{1,2}$ are the particle densities. The energy production rate is obtained by multiplication of R by the energy produced per reaction.

The problem is to take into account all reactions possible in a star of given composition. This is not difficult in principle, but it is very difficult in practice because the cross sections $\sigma(g)$ are not well known for many reactions. They cannot be derived purely theoretically. They have to be taken from measurements, and measurements are often not available for the energies of interest in astrophysics. One thus has to rely on extrapolations and interpolations of measured cross-section curves, with due allowance for resonances, etc. Fortunately, the formidable work of compiling and extrapolating what is known today has been done by several authors (150,151). Thus, the problem is both simpler and more difficult than for a laboratory plasma; simpler with respect to the distribution function, which is clearly given; more difficult with respect to the choice of reactions and their cross sections.

Another difference has been mentioned already in the preceding section. Stellar plasmas are usually much denser than laboratory plasmas. This leads to an enhanced reaction rate because the cross-section is increased by shielding effects. $\sigma(g)$ in eq. [89] above contains a factor (larger than one) which distinguishes $\sigma(g)$ from the measured values and which describes the effects of shielding. Actually, this is itself a difficult problem. It has been discussed by several authors (163–165). Salpeter, for instance, has given a detailed treatment (166). He uses methods very similar to those usual in plasma physics, which in turn go back to the theory of electrolytes as originally discussed by Debye and Hückel (167). The Poisson equation of electrostatics is used to define the shielding potential, where the potential enters the charge density in the form of Boltzmann factor. This procedure yields the Poisson-Boltzmann equation, which has to be solved (for nondegenerate electrons, in the case of degeneracy one gets an analogous equation). This is the weak screening case only. Strong screening needs separate treatment, also given by Salpeter at least approximately. Cameron (168) has discussed the problem of "extremely strong screening" at extremely high densities, where the Coulomb barrier is more or less completely shielded. In this case nuclear reactions no longer require high energy (high temperature). Generally speaking, nuclear reactions may be produced by high temperature or by high density. In the first case one speaks about "thermonuclear reactions." In the second case one may use the term coined by Cameron, "pycnonuclear reactions." Cameron regards these as the cause of nova explosions. The problem has also been discussed by Wolf (163), who uses the methods of solid state physics to evaluate the shielding effects and finds reaction rates much lower than Cameron.

B. Thermonuclear Burning Stages in Stars

As mentioned already, the early burning stages (the hydrogen and helium burning stages) seem to be well established. Later stages are more or less hypothetical. We shall only give an extremely condensed survey on the burning stages in this section (149–153).

1. *Hydrogen Burning.* In the early stages of stellar evolution hydrogen is burnt to helium by two different mechanisms: (a) the proton–proton chain and (b) the carbon-nitrogen cycle. In both cases protons are burnt to He^4. The proton–proton chain actually has three branches. For two of them He^4 is needed as a catalyst. This is shown in Table 8. The carbon-nitrogen cycle has two branches, both starting from C^{12}, which is needed as a catalyst

TABLE 8
The three proton–proton chains

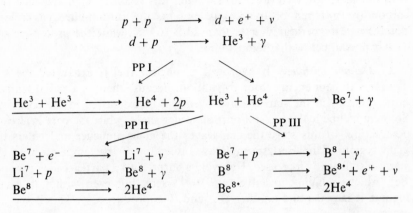

only because it is reproduced. One branch reproduces N^{14} which is injected into the cycle again (see Table 9). Without going into any details let us just

TABLE 9
The two CNO cycles (PP IV)

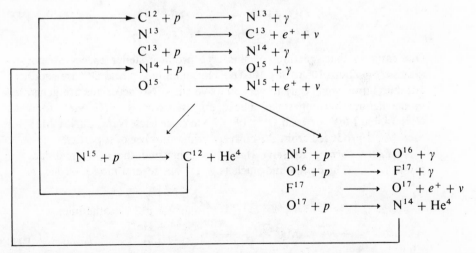

say that hydrogen burning is the energy source of the main sequence stars in the Hertzsprung-Russel diagram. The temperatures range from 10 to 30×10^6 °K. The reactions may be summarized by

$$4p \longrightarrow He^4 + 26.73 \text{ MeV} \qquad [90]$$

so that 6.68 MeV is produced per proton burnt. Tables 8 and 9 show that neutrinos are produced with these reactions, that is, part of the energy escapes with the neutrinos. (Reeves (150) estimates this at about 5%). Provided that carbon (or nitrogen or oxygen) is present, the carbon-nitrogen cycle is dominant at temperatures larger than 20×10^6 °K, while the proton–proton chains prevail below that temperature.

2. **Helium Burning.** If hydrogen as nuclear fuel is exhausted the star contracts to gain energy from gravitation. Because there is a radial temperature gradient in the star, the hydrogen will be exhausted in the core first. So there will be hydrogen still burnt in outer shells, while the core is already contracting. In this stage the star leaves the main sequence and enters the giant region of the Hertzsprung-Russel diagram. If the temperature in the star has sufficiently increased, He^4 will be burnt. Two α particles may produce Be^8, which is highly unstable ($\tau \approx 10^{-16}$ sec), but even within its small lifetime it may capture another He^4 and thus produce C^{12}. This is the 3 α reaction

$$3 He^4 \longrightarrow C^{12} + \gamma \qquad [91]$$

If a sufficient quantity of C^{12} has been produced in this way further reactions can produce higher Z atoms:

$$
\begin{aligned}
C^{12} + He^4 &\longrightarrow O^{16} + \gamma \\
O^{16} + He^4 &\longrightarrow Ne^{20} + \gamma \\
Ne^{20} + He^4 &\longrightarrow Mg^{24} + \gamma \dots
\end{aligned}
\qquad [92]
$$

One assumes that reactions of this type produce stellar energy at temperatures from about 10^8 to 3×10^8 °K. Thus mainly C^{12} and O^{16} are produced and Ne^{20} and Mg^{24} only in very massive stars. No neutrinos are generated in the helium burning stage. The energy released is 7.275 MeV for each C^{12}; 14.436 MeV for each O^{16}; 19.167 MeV for each Ne^{20}; 28.481 MeV for each Mg^{24} produced from the corresponding number of α particles.

3. **Later Burning Stages.** If He^4 is exhausted the next candidate for fusion is C^{12}. The compound nucleus Mg^{24} has several modes of decay:

$$
2C^{12} \longrightarrow Mg^{24*} \longrightarrow
\begin{cases}
\left.\begin{array}{l}
Mg^{24} + \gamma \\
Na^{23} + p \\
Ne^{20} + He^4
\end{array}\right\} \text{exothermic} \\
\left.\begin{array}{l}
Mg^{23} + n \\
O^{16} + 2He^4 \\
O^{16} + Be^8
\end{array}\right\} \text{endothermic}
\end{cases}
\qquad [93]
$$

The first three reactions are exothermic and the others are endothermic. The branching ratios are not well known. The reactions $Na^{23} + p$ and $Ne^{20} +$

He^4 seem to be about equally probable. The branching ratio to $Mg^{23} + n$ is negligible. The energy released is about 13 MeV per $C^{12} - C^{12}$ reaction if secondary reactions (leading to isotopes in the range $20 \leqslant A \leqslant 28$) are included. The temperatures necessary are about 6×10^8 to 10^9 °K.

After carbon is exhausted oxygen may be burnt. Two O^{16} nuclei form a compound nucleus S^{32} which again has several modes of decay:

$$2O^{16} \longrightarrow S^{32*} \longrightarrow \left.\begin{cases} S^{31} + n \\ P^{31} + p \\ Si^{28} + He^4 \\ S^{32} + \gamma \end{cases}\right\} \text{exothermic} \\ Mg^{24} + 2He^4 \text{ endothermic} \qquad [94]$$

The two modes $P^{31} + p$ and $Si^{28} + He^4$ are most (and about equally) probable. The mean energy release per reaction is about 19 MeV. Another process competing with oxygen burning is the photodisintegration of Ne^{20}:

$$Ne^{20} + \gamma \longrightarrow O^{16} + He^4 \qquad [95]$$

The He^4 produced may itself be captured by another atom, for instance, Ne^{20}, so that the total reaction would be

$$2Ne^{20} \longrightarrow O^{16} + Mg^{24} + 4.58 \text{ MeV} \qquad [96]$$

These processes occur at about 1.3 to 2×10^9 °K. Oxygen burning and neon disintegration may overlap or precede one another, depending on the conditions. Secondary reactions produce lots of neutrinos, and an increasingly large fraction of the total energy produced is carried away by them.

Similar processes at still higher temperatures (2–4×10^9 °K) may produce all the elements up to iron. The energy release, however, is not sufficient to stop gravitational contraction, which is merely slowed down. Finally, the reactions are reversed and high Z nuclei may be destroyed again to form He^4 and neutrons. The energy is taken from further gravitational contraction, and stars of very high density are formed in the white dwarf region of the Hertzsprung-Russel diagram.

We see that lots of nuclear reactions occur in stellar plasmas at temperatures from about 10^7 °K up to several 10^9 °K. Hydrogen burning, for instance, takes place at 1 to 3×10^7 °K (≈ 1 to 3 KeV) that is, at temperatures similar to those obtained experimentally in laboratory plasmas. For a d–t reactor we would need about 3×10^8 °K—a temperature at which stars burning helium work. For a d–d reaction we would need about 10^9 °K, which would correspond to a star burning carbon or even oxygen. Stars and reactors thus work at similar temperatures. One should not forget, however, that the densities of stellar plasmas are higher than those of laboratory plasmas by many orders of magnitude.

REFERENCES

1. P. Putnam, *Energy in the Future*. New York: D. van Nostrand, 1953.
2. H. Thirring, *Energy for Man*. Bloomington: Indiana University Press, 1958.
3. H. Brown, *The Challenge of Man's Future*. New York: The Viking Press, 1953.
4. A. M. Weinberg, "Burning the Rocks," Conf. on the Physics of Breeding, 1959, ANL-6122, p. 10.
5. R. F. Post, *Rev. Mod. Phys.*, **28**, 338 (1956).
6. M. D. Kruskal and M. Schwarzschild, *Proc. Roy. Soc.*, **A223**, 348 (1954).
7. G. Lehner and F. Pohl, *Z. Phys.*, **207**, 83 (1967).
8. J. L. Tuck, *Nuclear Fusion*, **1**, 201 (1961).
9. D. L. Booth, G. Preston, and P. F. D. Shaw, *Proc. Phys. Soc.*, **69A**, 265 (1969).
10. L. M. Goldman, R. W. Kilb, and H. C. Pollock, General Electric Res. Lab., Rep. 64-RL-(3600E), 1964.
11. T. Hesselberg-Jensen, T. O. Kofoed-Hansen, A. H. Sillesen, and C. F. Wandel, Risö-Report No. 2, 1958.
12. L. M. Goldman, R. W. Kilb, and H. C. Pollock, *Phys. Fluids*, **7**, 1005 (1964).
13. W. M. Bennett, *Phys. Rev.*, **45**, 890 (1934).
14. E. Fünfer and G. Lehner, "Plasmaphysik." In *Ergebnisse der exakten Naturwissenschaften*, vol. 34, edited by S. Flügge and F. Trendelenburg. Berlin: Springer-Verlag, 1962.
15. A. M. Andrianov, O. A. Bazilevskaia, S. I. Braginskii, B. G. Brezhnev, S Khvaschevski, V. A. Khrabrov, N. G. Kovalski, N. V. Filippov, T. I. Filippova, V. E. Palchikov, I. M. Podgorny, Yu. G. Prokhorov, and M. M. Sulkovskaya, *Proc. Second UN Intern. Conf. Peaceful Uses of Atomic Energy*, **31**, 348. Geneva, 1958.
16. S. C. Curran, K. W. Allen, H. A. B. Bodin, R. A. Fitch, N. J. Peacock, and J. A. Reynolds, *Proc. Second UN Intern. Conf. Peaceful Uses of Atomic Energy*, **31**, 365. Geneva, 1958.
17. V. S. Komelkov, U. V. Skvortsov, and S. S. Tserevitinov, *Proc. Second UN Intern. Conf. Peaceful Uses of Atomic Energy*, **31**, 375. Geneva, 1958.
18. J. W. Mather and A. H. Williams, *Proc. Second UN Intern. Conf. Peaceful Uses of Atomic Energy*, **32**, 26. Geneva, 1958.
19. S. A. Colgate, *Proc. Second UN Intern. Conf. Peaceful Uses of Atomic Energy*, **32**, 123. Geneva, 1958.
20. H. Herold, E. Fünfer, G. Lehner, H. Tuczek and C. Andelfinger, *Z. Naturforsch.*, **14a**, 323 (1959).
21. E. Fünfer, H. Herold, G. Lehner, H. Tuczek, and C. Andelfinger, *Z. Naturforsch.*, **14a**, 329 (1959).
22. E. Fünfer, H. Herold, G. Lehner, H. Tuczek, and C. Andelfinger, *Z. Naturforsch.*, **13a**, 524 (1958).
23. O. A. Anderson, W. R. Baker, S. A. Colgate, J. Ise, Jr., and R. V. Pyle, *Phys. Rev.*, **110**, 1375 (1958).
24. V. D. Shafranov, *Nuclear Fusion*, **5**, 86 (1957).
25. R. J. Tayler, *Proc. Phys. Soc.*, **B70**, 31 (1957).
26. R. J. Tayler, *Proc. Phys. Soc.*, **B70**, 1049 (1957).
27. M. D. Kruskal and J. L. Tuck, *Proc. Roy. Soc.*, **A245**, 222 (1958).
28. M. N. Rosenbluth, *Proc. Int. Conf. on Ionization Phenomena in Gases*, 903. Venice, 1957.
29. S. I. Braginsky and V. D. Shafranov, *Proc. Second UN Int. Conf. Peaceful Uses of Atomic Energy*, **31**, 348. Geneva, 1958.

30. B. R. Suydam, *Proc. Second UN Int. Conf. Peaceful Uses of Atomic Energy.* **31**, 157. Geneva, 1958.

31. M. N. Rosenbluth, *Proc. Second UN Int. Conf. Peaceful Uses of Atomic Energy*, **31**, 85. Geneva, 1958.

32. W. A. Newcomb, *Ann. Phys.*, **10**, 232 (1960).

33. I. B. Bernstein, E. A. Frieman, M. D. Kruskal, and R. M. Kulsrud, *Proc. Phys. Soc.*, **A244**, 17 (1958).

34. G. Lehner, *Z. Naturforsch.*, **16a**, 700 (1961).

35. E. P. Butt, R. Carruthers, J. T. D. Mitchell, R. S. Pease, P. C. Thonemann, M. A. Bird, J. Blears, and E. R. Hartill, *Proc. Second UN Int. Conf. Peaceful Uses of Atomic Energy*, **32**, 348. Geneva, 1958.

36. G. N. Harding, A. N. Dellis, A. Gibson, B. Jones, D. J. Lees, R. W. P. McWhirter, S. A. Ramsden, and S. Ward, *Proc. Second UN. Int. Conf. Peaceful Uses of Atomic Energy*, **32**, 365. Geneva, 1958.

37. B. Rose, A. E. Taylor and E. Wood, *Nature*, **181**, 1630 (1958).

38. W. B. Thompson, S. F. Edwards, J. Hubbard, and S. J. Roberts, *Proc. Second UN Int. Conf. Peaceful Uses of Atomic Energy*, **32**, 65. Geneva, 1958.

39. K. Siegbahn and P. Ohlin, *Proc. Second UN Int. Conf. Peaceful Uses of Atomic Energy*, **32**, 113. Geneva, 1958.

40. S. A. Colgate, J. P. Ferguson, and H. P. Furth, *Proc. Second UN Int. Conf. Peaceful Uses of Atomic Energy*, **32**, 129. Geneva, 1958.

41. T. E. Allibone, D. R. Chick, G. P. Thomson and A. A. Ware, *Proc. Second UN Int. Conf. Peaceful Uses of Atomic Energy*, **32**, 169. Geneva, 1958.

42. J. P. Conner, D. C. Hagerman, J. L. Honsaker, H. J. Karr, J. P. Mize, J. E. Osher, J. A. Phillips, and E. J. Stovall, Jr., *Proc. Second UN Int. Conf. Peaceful Uses of Atomic Energy*, **32**, 297. Geneva, 1958.

43. J. A. Phillips, A. E. Schoffield, and J. L. Tuck, *Proc. APS Topical Conf. on Pulsed High-Density Plasmas*, Los Alamos Report LA-3770, G-3. Los Alamos, 1967.

44. P. J. Bottoms, J. P. Carpenter, J. W. Mather, K. D. Ware, and A. H. Williams, *Proc. Plasma Physics and Controlled Nuclear Research*, CN-24, G-5. Novosibirsk, 1968.

45. J. W. Mather, P. J. Bottoms, and A. H. Williams, *Proc. APS Topical Conf. on Pulsed High-Density Plasmas*, Los Alamos Report LA-3770, C-1. Los Alamos, 1967.

46. J. W. Mather, *Phys. Fluids*, **8**, 366 (1965).

47. J. W. Mather, *Proc. Plasma Physics and Controlled Nuclear Fusion Research*, **2**, 389. Culham, 1965, 1966.

48. J. Marshall, *Phys. Fluids*, **3**, 134 (1960).

49. J. Marshall, "Plasma Acceleration," *Proc. 4th Lockheed Symp. on Magnetohydrodynamics*, p. 60. Stanford: Stanford University Press, 1960.

50. J. Marshall and T. F. Stratton, *Proc. Plasma Physics and Controlled Nuclear Fusion Research*, Part 2, 663. Salzburg, 1961.

51. J. W. Long, N. J. Peacock, P. D. Wilcock, and R. J. Speer, *Proc. APS Topical Conf. on Pulsed High-Density Plasmas*, Los Alamos Report LA-3770, C-5. Los Alamos, 1967.

52. D. A. Meskan, H. L. van Paassen, and G. G. Comisar, *Proc. APS Topical Conf. on Pulsed High-Density Plasmas*, Los Alamos Report LA-3770, C-6. Los Alamos, 1967.

53. W. I. Agafonov, G. V. Golub, L. G. Golubchikov, V. F. Dyachenko, V. D. Ivanov, V. S. Imshennik, Yu. A. Kolesnikov, E. B. Svirsky, N. V. Filippov, T. I. Filippova, *Conf. Plasma Physics and Controlled Nuclear Fusion Research*, CN-24, G-2. Novosibirsk, 1968.

54. R. P. Vasilyeva, M. I. Pergament, and A. P. Yaroslavsky, *Proc. Plasma Physics and Controlled Nuclear Fusion Research*, CN-24, G-3. Novosibirsk, 1968.

55. N. J. Peacock, P. D. Wilcock, R. J. Speer, and P. D. Morgan, *Proc. Plasma Physics and Controlled Nuclear Fusion Research*, CN-24, G-4. Novosibirsk, 1968.

56. Ch. Maisonnier, M. Samuelli, J. G. Linhart, and C. Gourlan, *Proc. Plasma Physics and Controlled Nuclear Fusion Research*, CN-24, G-6. Novosibirsk, 1968.

57. N. V. Filippov and T. I. Filippova, *Proc. Plasma Physics and Controlled Nuclear Fusion Research*, **2**, 405. Culham, 1965, 1966.

58. N. V. Filippov, T. I. Filippova, V. P. Vinogralov, *Proc. Plasma Physics and Controlled Nuclear Fusion Research*, Part 2, 577. Salzburg, 1961.

59. C. Patou, A. Simonnet, and J. P. Watteau, *Proc. APS Topical Conf. on Pulsed High-Density Plasmas*, Los Alamos Report LA-3770, C-2. Los Alamos, 1967.

60. A. Coudeville, A. Jolas, and J. P. Watteau, *Proc. APS Topical Conf. on Pulsed High-Density Plasmas*, Los Alamos Report LA-3770, C-3. Los Alamos, 1967.

61. E. H. Beckner, *Proc. APS Topical Conf. on Pulsed High-Density Plasmas*, Los Alamos Report LA-3770, C-4. Los Alamos, 1967.

62. E. H. Beckner, *J. Appl. Phys.*, **37**, 4944 (1967).

63. E. H. Beckner, *Rev. Sci. Instr.*, **38**, 507 (1967).

64. K. Hain, R. Lüst, and A. Schlüter, *Z. Naturforsch.*, **12a**, 833 (1957).

65. H. A. B. Bodin, J. McCartan, A. A. Newton and G. H. Wolf, *Proc. Plasma Physics and Controlled Nuclear Fusion Research*, CN-24, K-1. Novosibirsk, 1968.

66. E. M. Little, A. A. Newton, W. E. Quinn, F. L. Ribe, G. A. Sawyer, and K. S. Thomas, *Proc. Plasma Physics and Controlled Nuclear Fusion Research*, CN-24, K-2. Novosibirsk, 1968.

67. A. C. Kolb, R. H. Dixon, D. Düchs, R. C. Elton, and M. P. Young, *Proc. Plasma Physics and Controlled Nuclear Fusion Research*, CN-24, K-3. Novosibirsk, 1968.

68. L. Könen, P. Noll, K. Sugita, F. Waelbroeck, K. Watanabe, and H. Witulski, *Proc. Plasma Physics and Controlled Nuclear Fusion Research*, CN-24, K-4. Novosibirsk, 1968.

69. J. L. Tuck, *Proc. Plasma Physics and Controlled Nuclear Fusion Research*, CN-24, K-5. Novosibirsk, 1968.

70. R. L. Bingham, L. M. Goldman, and R. W. Kilb, *Proc. Plasma Physics and Controlled Nuclear Fusion Research*, CN-24, K-12. Novosibirsk, 1968.

71. L. M. Goldman, *Phys. Rev. Lett.*, **9**, 361 (1962).

72. W. E. Quinn, E. M. Little, F. L. Ribe, and G. A. Sawyer, *Proc. Plasma Physics and Controlled Nuclear Fusion Research*, **1**, 237. Culham, 1965.

73. H. A. B. Bodin, T. S. Green, A. A. Newton, G. B. F. Niblett, and J. A. Reynolds, *Proc. Plasma Physics and Controlled Nuclear Fusion Research*, **1**, 193. Culham, 1965, 1966.

74. C. Andelfinger, G. Decker, E. Fünfer, A. Heiss, M. Keilhacker, J. Sommer, and M. Ulrich, *Proc. Plasma Physics and Controlled Nuclear Fusion Research*, **1**, 249. Culham, 1965.

75. E. Fünfer, *Proc. APS Topical Conf. on Pulsed High-Density Plasmas*, Los Alamos Report LA-3770, A-1. Los Alamos, 1967.

76. H. A. B. Bodin, and A. A. Newton, *Proc. APS Topical Conf. on Pulsed High-Density Plasmas*, Los Alamos Report LA-3770, A-2. Los Alamos, 1967.

77. A. Kaleck, H. Kever, L. Könen, P. Noll, K. Sugita, F. Waelbroeck, and H. Witulski, *Proc. APS Topical Conf. on Pulsed High-Density Plasmas*, Los Alamos Report LA-3770, A-4. Los Alamos, 1967.

78. E. A. McLean, A. D. Anderson, and H. R. Griem, *Proc. APS Topical Conf. on Pulsed High-Density Plasmas*, Los Alamos Report LA-3770, A-5. Los Alamos, 1967.

79. U. Schumacher, R. Wilhelm, and H. Zwicker, *Proc. APS Topical Conf. on Pulsed High-Density Plasmas*, Los Alamos Report LA-3770, D-1. Los Alamos, 1967.

80. A. Heiss, H. Herold, and E. Unsöld, *Proc. APS Topical Conf. on Pulsed High-Density Plasmas*, Los Alamos Report LA-3770, D-7. Los Alamos, 1967.

81. E. L. Kemp, W. E. Quinn, F. L. Ribe, and G. A. Sawyer, *Proc. APS Topical Conf. on Pulsed High-Density Plasmas*, Los Alamos Report LA-3770, G-1. Los Alamos, 1967.

82. C. Andelfinger, E. Fünfer, G. Lehner, F. Pohl, U. Seidel, J. Sommer, and M. Ulrich, *Proc. APS Topical Conf. on Pulsed High-Density Plasmas*, Los Alamos Report LA-3770, G-2. Los Alamos, 1967.

83. A. C. Kolb, M. P. Young, and E. A. McLean, *Proc. APS Topical Conf. on Pulsed High-Density Plasmas*, Los Alamos Report LA-3770, G-5. Los Alamos, 1967.

84. C. Andelfinger, E. Fünfer, G. Lehner, H. Paretzke, F. Pohl, U. Seidel, J. Sommer, and U. Ulrich, Report IPP 1/67. Garching bei München: Institut für Plasmaphysik, 1967.

85. A. C. Kolb, *Proc. Second UN Int. Conf. Peaceful Uses of Atomic Energy*, **31**, 328. Geneva, 1958.

86. W. C. Elmore, E. M. Little, and W. E. Quinn, *Proc. Second UN Int. Conf. Peaceful Uses of Atomic Energy*, **32**, 337. Geneva, 1958.

87. E. M. Little, W. E. Quinn, F. L. Ribe and G. A. Sawyer, *Proc. Plasma Physics and Controlled Nuclear Fusion Research*, **2**, 497. Salzburg, 1961.

88. E. M. Little, W. E. Quinn, and F. L. Ribe, *Phys. Fluids*, **4**, 711 (1959).

89. H. A. B. Bodin, T. S. Green, G. B. F. Niblett, N. J. Peacock, J. M. P. Quinn, J. A. Reynolds, and J. B. Taylor, *Proc. Plasma Physics and Controlled Nuclear Fusion Research*, **2**, 511. Salzburg, 1961.

90. H. A. B. Bodin, T. S. Green, G. B. F. Niblett, N. J. Peacock, J. M. P. Quinn, and J. A. Reynolds, *Proc. Plasma Physics and Controlled Nuclear Fusion Research*, **2**, 521. Salzburg, 1961.

91. H. R. Griem, A. C. Kolb, W. H. Lupton, and D. T. Phillips, *Proc. Plasma Physics and Controlled Nuclear Fusion Research*, **2**, 543. Salzburg, 1961.

92. A. C. Kolb, H. R. Griem, W. H. Lupton, D. T. Phillips, S. A. Ramsden, E. A. McLean, W. R. Faust, and M. Swartz, *Proc. Plasma Physics and Controlled Nuclear Fusion Research*, **2**, 553. Salzburg, 1961.

93. H. L. Jordan, *Proc. Plasma Physics and Controlled Nuclear Fusion Research*, **2**, 589. Salzburg, 1961.

94. J. E. Allen, M. U. Martone, and S. E. Segre, *Proc. Plasma Physics and Controlled Nuclear Fusion Research*, **2**, 617. Salzburg, 1961.

95. J. E. Allen, C. Bartoli, B. Brunelli, J. A. Nation, B. Rumi, and R. Toschi, *Proc. Plasma Physics and Controlled Nuclear Fusion Research*, **2**, 621. Salzburg, 1961.

96. A. C. Kolb, W. H. Lupton, R. C. Elton, E. A. McLean, M. Swartz, and M. P. Young, *Proc. Plasma Physics and Controlled Nuclear Fusion Research*, **1**, 261. Culham, 1965.

97. U. Ascoli-Bartoli, S. Martellucci, and M. Martone, *Proc. Plasma Physics and Controlled Nuclear Fusion Research*, **1**, 275. Culham, 1965.

98. R. L. Bingham, L. M. Goldman, and R. W. Kilb, *Proc. Plasma Physics and Controlled Nuclear Fusion Research*, **1**, 301. Culham, 1965.

99. M. Keilhacker and H. Herold, *Proc. Plasma Physics and Controlled Nuclear Fusion Research*, **1**, 315. Culham, 1965.

100. D. E. Nagle, W. E. Quinn, F. L. Ribe, and W. B. Riesenfeld, *Phys. Rev.*, **119**, 857 (1960).

101. K. Boyer, W. C. Elmore, E. M. Little, W. E. Quinn, and J. L. Tuck, *Phys. Rev.*, **119**, 831 (1960).

102. G. Lehner, Z. Phys., **206**, 284 (1967).
103. G. Lehner and F. Pohl, Z. Phys., **216**, 488 (1968).
104. A. Schlüter, Report IPP 6/38. Garching bei München: Institut für Plasmaphysik, 1965.
105. J. Junker, Phys. Fluids, **11**, 646 (1968).
106. J. J. Hamm, H. Knoepfel, H. Krögler, J. G. Linhart, and R. Verbeek, Proc. Plasma Physics and Controlled Nuclear Fusion Research, CN-24, K-8. Novosibirsk, 1968.
107. D. B. Thomson, R. S. Caird, K. J. Ewing, C. M. Fowler, and W. B. Garn, Proc. APS Topical Conf. on Pulsed High-Density Plasmas, Los Alamos Report LA-3770, H-3. Los Alamos, 1967.
108. F. Herlach. J. Appl. Phys., **39**, 5191 (1968).
109. G. Lehner, Springer Tracts in Modern Physics, **47**, 67 (1968).
110. F. H. Coensgen, W. F. Cummins, R. E. Ellis, F. R. Kovar, and W. E. Nexsen, Jr., Proc. APS Topical Conf. on Pulsed High-Density Plasmas, Los Alamos Report LA-3770, H-1. Los Alamos, 1967.
111. F. H. Coensgen, W. F. Cummins, R. E. Ellis and W. E. Nexsen, Jr., Proc. Plasma Physics and Controlled Nuclear Fusion Research, H-2. Novosibirsk, 1968.
112. Yu. V. Gott, M. S. Ioffe, and V. G. Telkovsky, Proc. Plasma Physics and Controlled Nuclear Fusion Research, **3**, 1045. Salzburg, 1961.
113. G. Francis, J. W. Hill, and D. W. Mason, Proc. Plasma Physics and Controlled Nuclear Fusion Research, **1**, 53. Culham, 1965.
114. Yu. V. Gott, M. S. Ioffe, and E. E. Yushmanov, Proc. Plasma Physics and Controlled Nuclear Fusion Research, **1**, 35. Culham, 1965.
115. Yu. T. Baiborodov, M. S. Ioffe, R. I. Sobolev, and E. E. Yushmanov, Soviet Phys. JETP, **26**, 336 (1968).
116. F. H. Coensgen, W. F. Cummins, W. E. Nexsen, Jr., and A. E. Shermon, Phys. Fluids, **9**, 187 (1966).
117. Yu. T. Baiborodov, Yu. V. Gott, M. S. Ioffe, and R. I. Sobolev, Proc. Plasma Physics and Controlled Nuclear Fusion Research, H-1, Novosibirsk, 1968.
118. G. Francis, J. W. Hill, B. McNamara, and D. W. Mason, Proc. Plasma Physics and Controlled Nuclear Fusion Research, H-3. Novosibirsk, 1968.
119. R. Lecoustey and C. Renaud, Plasma Phys., **9**, 527 (1967).
120. P. Brossier, P. Lecoustey, C. Renaud, and J. Tachon, Proc. Plasma Physics and Controlled Nuclear Fusion Research, H-7. Novosibirsk, 1968.
121. G. Lehner and F. Pohl, to be published.
122. W. E. Meyerhof and T. A. Tombrello, Nuclear Phys., **A109**, 1 (1968).
123. N. G. Basov, S. D. Zakharov, P. G. Kryukow, Yu. V. Senatskii, and S. V. Chekalin, JETP Lett., **8**, 14 (1968).
124. Physics Today, **21**, No. 11, 57 (1968).
125. R. G. Mills, Reports MATT 15 (1959), 34 (1960), 60 (1961), 145 (1962), 437 (1966), 548 (1967); Nucl. Fusion, **7**, 223 (1967).
126. F. L. Ribe, T. A. Oliphant, and W. E. Quinn, Los Alamos Report LA-3294-MS. Los Alamos, 1965.
127. R. F. Post, "Nuclear Fusion," Suppl. Part 1, in Proc. Plasma Physics and Controlled Nuclear Fusion Research, 99. Salzburg, 1961.
128. T. K. Fowler and M. Rankin, "Plasma Physics," in J. Nucl. Energy, Part C, **8**, 121 (1966).
129. D. V. Sivukhin, "Plasma Physics," in J. Nucl. Energy, Part C, **8**, 607 (1966).
130. R. Carruthers, P. A. Davenport, and J. T. D. Mitchell, Culham Report, CLM-R-85, 1967.
131. K. O. Hintermann and R. Wideröe, Proc. Second UN Int. Conf. Peaceful Uses of Atomic Energy, **32**, 440. Geneva, 1958.

132. A. J. Impink, Report MIT Research Lab. of Electronics TR-434 (1965).
133. W. G. Homeyer, Report, TR-435. MIT Research Lab. of Electronics, 1965.
134. L. N. Lontai, Report, TR-436. MIT Research Lab. of Electronics, 1965.
135. J. D. Lawson, *Proc. Phys. Soc.*, **B70**, 6 (1957).
136. J. Schwinger, *Phys. Rev.*, **75**, 1912 (1949).
137. B. A. Trubnikov and V. S. Kudryatsev, *Proc. Second UN Int. Conf. Peaceful Uses of Atomic Energy*, **31**, 93. Geneva, 1958.
138. W. E. Drummond, in "Plasma Physics." Vienna: Int. Atomic Energy Agency, 1965.
139. W. E. Drummond and M. N. Rosenbluth, *Phys. Fluids*, **3**, 45 (1960).
140. W. B. Riesenfeld, *Plasma Physics and Thermonuclear Research*, Vol. 2, edited by E. L. Longmire, J. L. Tuck and W. B. Thompson. Oxford: Pergamon Press, 1963.
141. L. W. Alvarez, H. Bradner, F. S. Crawford, Jr., J. A. Crawford, P. Falk-Vairant, M. L. Good, J. D. Gow, A. H. Rosenfeld, F. Solmitz, M. L. Stevenson, H. K. Ticko, and R. D. Tripp, *Phys. Rev.*, **105**, 1127 (1957).
142. F. C. Frank, *Nature*, **160**, 525 (1947).
143. Y. B. Zeldovich, *Soviet Physics Doklady*, **95**, 493 (1954).
144. S. O. Dean, Meeting of the APS Division of Plasma Physics. Boston, 1966.
145. J. D. Jackson, *Phys. Rev.*, **106**, 330 (1957).
146. R. d'E. Atkinson and F. G. Houtermans, *Z. Phys.*, **54**, 656 (1929).
147. H. A. Bethe, *Phys. Rev.*, **55**, 434 (1939).
148. C. F. von Weizsäcker, *Z. Phys.*, **39**, 633 (1938).
149. G. Burbidge, "Nuclear Astrophysics." in *Evoluzione delle Stelle* (Proc. of the 28th Varenna Course, 1962), edited by L. Gratton. New York and London: Academic Press, 1963.
150. H. Reeves, "Stellar Structure." In *Stars and Stellar Systems*, Vol. VIII, edited by L. H. Aller and D. B. McLaughlin. Chicago and London: University of Chicago Press, 1965.
151. W. A. Fowler, G. R. Caughlan, and B. A. Zimmerman, *Ann. Rev. of Astronomy and Astrophysics*, **5**, 525 (1967).
152. E. M. Burbidge and G. Burbidge, "Stellar Evolution." In *Encyclopedia of Physics*, **51**, 134 (1958), edited by S. Flügge. Springer Verlag, 1958.
153. M. H. Wrubel, "Stellar Interiors." In *Encyclopedia of Physics*, **51**, 1 (1958), edited by S. Flügge. Springer Verlag, 1958.
154. H. C. Arp, "The Hertzsprung-Russel Diagram." In *Encyclopedia of Physics*, **51**, 75 (1958), edited by S. Flügge. Springer Verlag, 1958.
155. A. R. Sandage and L. Gratton, "Observational Approach to Stellar Evolution." In *Evoluzione delle Stelle* (Proc. of the 28th Varenna Course, 1962), edited by L. Gratton. New York and London: Academic Press, 1963.
156. G. I. Bell, *Rev. Mod. Phys.*, **39**, 59 (1967).
157. G. Gamow and M. Schoenberg, *Phys. Rev.*, **59**, 539 (1941).
158. J. B. Adams, M. A. Ruderman, and G. H. Woo, *Phys. Rev.*, **129**, 1383 (1963).
159. H. Y. Chiu, *Neutrino Astrophysics*. New York: Gordon and Breach Science Publishers, 1965.
160. F. Reines, *Proc. Roy. Soc.*, **A301**, 159 (1967).
161. R. Davis, D. S. Harmer, and K. C. Hofman, *Phys. Rev. Lett.*, **20**, 1205 (1968).
162. J. N. Bahcall, N. A. Bahcall, and G. Shaviv, *Phys. Rev. Lett.*, **20**, 1209 (1968).
163. R. A. Wolf, *Phys. Rev.*, **137**, B1634 (1965).
164. E. Schatzman, *J. de Phys. et Radium*, **9**, 46 (1948).
165. G. Keller, *Astrophys. J.*, **118**, 142 (1953).
166. F. E. Salpeter, *Aust. J. Phys.*, **7**, 373 (1954).
167. P. Debye and E. Hückel, *Phys. Z.*, **24**, 185 (1923).
168. A. G. W. Cameron, *Astrophys. J.*, **130**, 916 (1959).

Author Index

Numbers in *italics* indicate the pages on which the full references appear.

Subject Index